WITHDRAWN

Restoration Forestry

**An International Guide
To Sustainable
Forestry Practices**

D1616763

Restoration Forestry

An International Guide To Sustainable Forestry Practices

Michael Pilarski, Editor

KIVAKÍ
PRESS

585 East 31st Street
Durango, Colorado 81301
(303) 385-1767

Publisher's Cataloging in Publication Data

Restoration forestry : an international guide to sustainable forestry practices / Michael Pilarski, editor

    p. cm.
    Includes bibliographical references.
    Preassigned LCCN: 94-076630.
    ISBN 1-882308-51-4

    1. Sustainable forestry.   I. Pilarski, Michael

SD387.S87R47 1994   634.9
                       QB194-1212

Book and cover design by Olive Charles
Title illustrations by Olive Charles
All other illustrations as credited
Indexing by Sarah Colligan and P. S. Thomas

Printed on recycled paper.

First Edition, First Printing 1994
Printed in the United States of America
5 4 3 2 1   98 97 96 95 94

This book is dedicated to the forests
and the children of the world.

Gus diZerega

Acknowledgments

THANKS TO ALL THOSE who reviewed portions of the manuscript and made suggestions for improvement: Andrew Bodlovich, John Bergenske, Dianne Brause, Orville Camp, Jim Cooperman, Steve Erickson, Marianne Edain, Larry Geno, Kathy Glass, Dervilla Gowan, Jason Greenlee, Herb and Susan Hammond, Arthur Lee Jacobson, Dianne Lindsay, Mike Maki, Denise de Marie, Andy Moldenke, Suzanne Pardee, Jude Rubin, Jean Stam, and David Wertz.

Thanks to all those who aided the book through typesetting, proofreading and production details, including: Lev Alexander, Sierpa Alälaäkkalla, Troy Brower, Fyre, Arthur Lee Jacobson, Eric Miller, Chris Murphy, Princess, Bronwyn Smith, and Michael G. Smith.

Thanks to Michelle and J. T. Thompson and the staff at Lost Valley Center for co-hosting and co-organizing the 1990 Restoration Forestry Conference which started this whole book project rolling.

Thanks to Carol Lanigan, Friends of the Trees office manager, whose counsel, typesetting, layout and attending to numerous details made it all possible.

Thanks to all the authors who contributed to *Restoration Forestry*.

Thanks to Greg Cumberford and Olive Charles at Kivakí Press for their support and belief in this book and for producing the book for all of us.

Contents

Contents

Contents

Preface

Artist: Rod Kline, Friends of the Trees

The Pacific Northwest, U.S.A.
The states of Washington, Oregon, Idaho, and western Montana. Asterisk marks the location of Lost Valley Center. Star marks location of Friends of the Trees Society's office.

THE BOOK *RESTORATION FORESTRY* was first conceived of in the summer of 1990 when Friends of the Trees Society teamed up with Lost Valley Center to organize the Restoration Forestry Conference. It was held November 11-12, 1990 at the Lost Valley Center near Eugene, Oregon. Preparing for the conference led us on a search for the best sustainable forestry practitioners and scientists in the Pacific Northwest. The conference was successful in bringing together many of the Pacific Northwest's leading foresters, forest ecologists and forest activists. The original intention was to publish a Conference Proceedings, but it grew and grew—until over the next three years, thousands of books, articles and manuscripts were compiled and sifted through to provide this book. *Restoration Forestry* includes excerpts from, or reviews the best information sources we found.

While preparing this book, I talked to hundreds of foresters and environmentalists. I asked each of them "What are the best examples of ecologically-sound forestry you know of? Who are the best practitioners? Where are the best models?" They answered that existing models are few and far between. I followed up the leads they did give me and asked the same questions. The trail is never ending, but *Restoration Forestry* reports on what I've found so far. You can pick up the trail where I left off. The explosion of knowledge and experience is growing faster than any one person or network can follow.

A Permaculture Perspective

The editor of *Restoration Forestry* brings a permaculture perspective to forestry. Permaculture is an integrated design methodology for sustainable human settlements where people live in harmony with nature. Permaculture advocates the preservation of existing wildlands and the rehabilitation of degraded ecosystems. Permaculture creates productive agro-ecosystems, homes and cities which are largely self-reliant and minimize outside inputs of energy or resources. Permaculture forests close to habitations are intensively managed, high yielding, and use a mix of native and non-native species. Forests further out become less intensively managed and rely on native species. Stability and diversity are the keynotes.

The Editor's Roots

The roots of this book go back to the 4th grade (1958), when I decided I was going to be a naturalist. I kept this vision firmly in front of me as I grew up, and after high school entered a university to get a degree in forestry or natural history. Dissatisfied with the education offered me, I dropped out in my third year and moved to the mountains of the Pacific Northwest. Since then, most of my life has been spent in back-country forests around the Pacific Northwest. My extensive hands-on education in natural history has centered on homesteading, wildcrafting, seed collecting, nursery work, tree planting, orcharding, organic farming, gardening and many other rural occupations. My hands-on experience is combined with extensive reading and writing on plants and trees. In 1978, I founded Friends of the Trees Society and have devoted my life to helping heal the Earth. Friends of the Trees Society's goal is to double the world's forest cover. *Restoration Forestry* is a contribution to further this goal.

Similarities Between the Organic Agriculture and Restoration Forestry Movements

Since 1972, I have been active in the organic agriculture movement as a farmer, organizer, and networker. In 1974, I co-organized the first conference on sustainable agriculture in the Pacific Northwest. Public awareness and acceptance of organic farming and gardening has grown considerably in the two decades since then.

Restoration forestry today is in an analogous position to that of organic agriculture 20 years ago. Restoration forestry is poised for a period of rapid growth, both in public consciousness and in practice. This book, *Restoration Forestry*, is one of the first books to chronicle the growth and evolution of the worldwide movement for ecologically-sound forestry.

—Michael Pilarski, January 8, 1994

Unless stated otherwise, all reviews and text are by Michael Pilarski.

Disclaimer and Request for Information:

Restoration Forestry may be the most complete international directory in its field; yet it is but the tip of a rather large iceberg. *Restoration Forestry* is certainly not a complete guide. Coverage is short for parts of the globe and there is little interface with French and Spanish-speaking sources or other languages. We hope to improve the situation in future editions.

Prices of books, subscriptions and memberships are listed where information was available. Although these change over time, they do give the reader some indication of what prices to expect. There will inevitably be some out-of-date addresses and/or phone numbers. We would appreciate notice of any inaccuracies or changes.

We would like to publish a 2nd edition of *Restoration Forestry*. You are encouraged to send material for a future edition to: Friends of the Trees Society, PO Box 1064, Tonasket, Washington 98855 USA.

Friends of the Trees' office is located in Okanogan County, Washington state.

Miguel Guizar

1   Introduction

Introduction

Michael Pilarski

WHAT IS RESTORATION FORESTRY? Restoration forestry is working with nature to restore the world's forests to their former grandeur and function. The forests are the world's humidifiers, lungs, oxygen producers, soil producers, biomass producers and carbon cyclers. Forests are the basis for much of life on earth. Assuring humanity of a steady supply of wood products is only part of the goal of restoration forestry.

The history of forests throughout the "civilized world" has been largely of destruction and degradation. Present-day, industrial forest management practices are largely contributing to this destruction of life on earth. The world's forests are on a downward spiral. It is time to reverse this trend and begin to build up forest resources.

Terminology

Restoration forestry is the term I chose as best portraying the concepts I wished to communicate in this book. There are many other terms which could have been used. Terminology is not that important; it is the underlying concepts which are important. Some of the terms used in this book to describe ecologically-sound forestry practices include:

> Restoration Forestry
> Sustainable Forestry
> New Forestry
> Ecological Forestry
> Ecoforestry
> Natural Selection Forestry
> Natural Selection Ecoforestry
> Holistic Forestry
> Bioforestry
> Old-growth Forestry
> Stewardship Forestry
> Public Forestry
> Community Forestry
> Social Forestry

Are these all the same? No, but there is much common ground.

Restoration Forestry—A Thousand Definitions

Restoration Forestry, as a book, represents more than one view. It represents as many views as there are authors. If you were to consider the entire group of people whose work is mentioned or reviewed in *Restoration Forestry*, you would have thousands of unique viewpoints. There are many points of agreement, however, as you will discover as you read through this book and put your own synthesis together. Restoration forestry, as a discipline, is not set in stone. It draws on old traditions and new insights to illumine an evolving path.

Forest ecosystems are not simple. They are extremely complex and always changing. Each forest is unique. Restoration forestry is not a set of simple rules. It is an art as well as a science. It must come from a place of awe, wonder and humility. The forest is the best forester. Left to herself, nature increases the forests' richness of biomass, biodiversity, complexity, and soil. We must listen to the forest. This means we must spend much time in observation. It means getting to know a forest personally. It means having fewer acres per forester, locally-based forestry, and resident forest stewardship.

I believe we will only have true restoration forestry when foresters and forest workers love their forests somewhat akin to how we love our mothers. Restoration forestry calls for management based on science and love. Heart and mind working together.

Some Attributes of Restoration Forestry

Restoration forestry enables a strong web of functional symbiotic relationships within the ecosystem. All the parts are there. A forest without its bird component, without its insects, or mycorrhiza or mammals is not a whole being. Expecting a forest to function productively without all of its components is like expecting the human body to perform well without kidneys, thyroid, adrenals, white corpuscles, etc. Forests, like bodies, are self-healing to a certain extent. Trees die, forests seldom do, although they might have to move to a new location if growing conditions change radically.

Restoration forestry assists nature to heal degraded forests and bring them back to a state of biological productivity, biodiversity, ecological stability and resilience. Restoration forestry means increasing the area under forest cover and increasing the age classes, the standing volume and the diversity of forest ecosystems. It means careful harvesting methods that minimize disturbance of soil and plant communities. It means that many more people will have to be employed in the woods, not less; using smaller machines and more reliance on draft animals. It means smaller mills and more value-added processing close to the wood source. It means minimal waste, maximum recycling, and the development of non-tree paper pulp and alternative building materials. It means more people caring for the forest and researching its complex processes, so that we can ever refine our management/dance with the forest.

Restoration forestry leads to a steady yield of high value timber. Clearcut/short rotation forestry leads to a periodic return of low-quality timber. Restoration forestry makes much better ecological sense and it makes better economic sense.

The Promise of Restoration Forestry

Dismal scenarios of the future abound in today's world full of crises, wars, hungry people, alienation, and desperation. Every year the severity of the environmental crisis becomes more apparent. Restoration forestry offers positive visions of an abundant future. Restoration forestry leads to healthy forests across the world producing an abundance of high-quality timber and myriad other forest products. Restoration forestry practiced on the broad scale would lead to a landscape containing old-growth forests and big trees. Restoration forestry promises self-reliant communities with healthy, diverse economies based on self-employed individuals, small companies, and worker-owned enterprises. Wide scale tree plantings in cities, towns, villages and homesteads provide more agreeable, healthful and beautiful places to live.

Restoration forestry can aid agriculture in many ways. Maximal use of trees, agroforestry, shelterbelts, windbreaks and hedgerows can increase world food production, significantly increasing fruit and nut crops. Large amounts of marginal farm and grazing land can be retired from agriculture for restoration and reforestation. Over the course of several centuries, more of the world can be allowed to revert towards wilderness. The world's forest cover could be doubled and the natural productivity of the world's ecosystems restored in large part.

This is a lot for restoration forestry to promise; however, the synthesis of restoration forestry, permaculture, organic agriculture, restoration ecology, bioregionalism, participatory democracy and decentralization might make it possible. There is enough experience, knowledge and technical know-how to attain this vision. We certainly don't know it all, but collectively we know enough to head in the right direction.

Who Is Steering?

This positive scenario is possible, but it isn't where the world is heading right now. Barring the miraculous, it will take time to turn society's path from destruction towards restoration. Think of earth as a car and we are all passengers together. Who is steering? Toward what destination? It is as if some drunk, rich multi-national is at the wheel following greed and power, and driving straight for a precipice. Perhaps the life-affirming occupants will take control of the wheel before we go over the precipice—perhaps not. Will civilization crash, or steer its way to a positive future? On-the-ground examples of restoration forestry are badly needed in either case.

Restoration forestry offers methods to restore the forests, but it will only become a reality if society commits the resources to do it. Restoration forestry can only happen as part of a greater paradigm shift away from the path of exploitation, war and death, and towards a path based on love, caring, and stewardship. Restoration forestry is part of a life-affirmative worldview which is manifesting world-wide. The numbers of individuals and organizations consciously working toward peace on earth and goodwill towards trees increases daily. Our combined small daily efforts hold the promise of a peaceful, forested future.

Top Ten Books On Restoration Forestry

Michael Pilarski

*R*ESTORATION FORESTRY reviews hundreds of books. So many, in fact, that readers may wonder where to start. Here are ten books I consider to be among the most essential publications on restoration forestry thus far (from a cold temperate zone bias). See the Book Index to find what page they are reviewed on.

1. *Seeing the Forest Among the Trees: The Case for Wholistic Forest Use*. Herb Hammond. 1992.

2. *Community Guide to the Forest: Ecology, Planning and Use*. Susan Hammond and Herb Hammond. 1992.

3. *Wildwood*. 1990. Merv Wilkinson and Ruth Loomis.

4. *Forest Farmer's Handbook*. Orville Camp. 1984.

5. *Clearcut: The Tragedy of Industrial Forestry*. Bill Devall, Editor. 1993.

6. *The Forest and the Trees: A Guide To Excellent Forestry*. Gordon Robinson. 1988.

7. *Ancient Forests of the Pacific Northwest: Protecting a Vanishing Ecosystem, A Source Book for Activists*. Heather Diefenderfer, Editor. 1992.

8. *The Redesigned Forest*. Chris Maser. 1988.

9. *Defining Sustainable Forestry*. Greg Aplet, Nels Johnson, Jeffrey T. Olson and V. Alaric Sample, Editors. 1993.

10. *Restoration Forestry*. Michael Pilarski, Editor. 1994.

Definitions of "Restoration Forestry" from the Restoration Forestry Conference

At the Restoration Forestry Conference held in November, 1990, at Lost Valley Center, near Dexter, Oregon, the participants were asked to write a short definition of sustainable forestry. Here are the definitions of some participants. Writer's names are given where known.

"Restoration Forestry Is..." by Bobcat

RESTORATION: as in the restoration of a work of art, is not the re-creation of the original masterpiece. Rather, attempts are made to return the work of art to conditions more closely resembling its original state.

Primary goal: maintain or restore forest ecosystems.

Secondary goal: extract material "products" from the forest, e.g., wood, herbs, mushrooms.

What it takes to accomplish this goal: sustainability with minimum interference/disturbance of natural ecosystem processes.

"Restoration Forestry Is..." by John Phillips:

Sustainable forestry subdivides into two headings: maintenance and restoration, the former working in forests that have not been badly treated and the latter working with heavily or recently heavily cut forests. Both employ the same concepts, relying on biodiversity as being crucial to sustaining forest health.

Healthy forests are the basis for sustainability, which means we can have forests forever.

"Restoration Forestry Is..."

Forest resource management which mimics natural cycles, systems, and species composition. Maintenance of overall forest health must be the criterion which drives all management decisions. Volume of commercial harvests would never exceed volume growth over a specified period of time (10 years, 20 years). Biological components of the forest community would be maintained in perpetuity giving consideration to natural successional cycles.

"Restoration Forestry Is..." by Meca Wewona

Sustainable Forestry must be multi-aged, multi-height and multi-species. Harvest only what you can grow of all species.

Economics must fit the forest—not the forest fitting economics.

Designated areas will have to be re-planted, then managed over time to achieve multi-height, multi-age, and multi-species status.

Governments and other agencies must be pressured to realize the needs of the forest.

Some financial assistance will have to be provided for the people, co-ops, or communities interested in sustainable forestry.

In all cases, natural rather than chemical controls for insect or disease problems should be used.

"Restoration Forestry Is..." by Ned Fritz

Restoration forestry is managing each stand changed by humans so that the stand returns toward the species richness and composition it had before substantial human impact. We do this best by logging those individual trees that nature has selected.

"Restoration Forestry Is..." A Working Definition of a Sustainable Forest:

1. A primarily mixed evergreen forest which maintains a healthy, natural diversity and mixture of trees and understory plants native to the area.

2. Trees should be grown to an age that produces the maximum amount of high-quality sawlogs rather than fiber.

3. That the forest provide community stability, employment, fish and wildlife habitat, clean water, clean air, healthy soils and a moderate climate, as well as aesthetic, recreational, and other important beneficial uses associated with healthy forests.

"Restoration Forestry Is..."

To transcend current economic world view to one based on a utility and relationship that is centered in site specific understanding of spirit of place—and each plant or animal's expression—visible or invisible to the whole. Forestry is not the economic utilization of timber. Forestry is understanding the relationship between fungus and fish, field and fire. Take the money lender out of the church. Take the corporations out of the forest, then the people—the foresters, grounded and aware will sustain what they love.

"Restoration Forestry Is..."
by Steve Erickson

1. Provides sufficient habitat for a diverse array of species and communities, including those dependent on nature and late successional forests, so all species naturally occurring in that ecosystem will persist over time;

2. Provides hydrological stability in the landscape, so habitat for aquatic organisms, including those economically important to humans, is not degraded, eliminated or destroyed, and clean and healthful water is provided to all who require it, including humans;

3. Harvest trees and other forest products no faster than they grow and are replenished, assuring as well a continued supply of finer grained quality wood from older trees; or considering quality as well as quantity;

4. Provides a sustainable flow of forest commodities, so human communities economically dependent on extraction and processing of forest products are not subject to the erratic boom and bust cycles that historically have, and are currently occurring;

5. Protects the productivity of forest soils, so they're not degraded or lost, but retained, conserved and enhanced by use of, and imitation of processes that occur naturally;

6. Is conducted in a manner that does not pollute soil, air or water.

"Restoration Forestry Is..."
Sustainable Forest: By the Man Who Walks in the Woods

Must account not only for all uses of the forests (e.g., production of clean air, wildlife) but also those of which we are as yet completely unaware (thus large areas with viable connective corridors must be left). But more, we must revise our economic and especially our spiritual worlds if we are to sustain. We should disassemble much of what we call society or cultures. Sustained yield of wood products (a very narrow aspect of sustainable forestry) must be tied to a sustainable component of trees which have achieved culmination of mean annual increment.

"Restoration Forestry Is..."
by Michael Pilarski

Sustainable forestry is regenerative; forests grow larger, productivity and biomass increase over time.

Sustainable forestry is socially-equitable and user-friendly; improves habitat for wildlife and people; and is site-specific, client-specific and culture-specific.

"Restoration Forestry Is..."

The art, science, and practice of utilizing of forests to provide for human needs while simultaneously maintaining and enhancing the integrity/diversity/productivity of the forest ecosystem.

"Restoration Forestry Is..."
by Brett KenKairn

Forestry which recognizes site-specific ecologic conditions as well as local economic considerations in developing a management technique for sustained health and production of a biologically diverse multi-age forest system.

"Restoration Forestry Is..."

* Building from the biological capacity of the landscape.

* Maintaining the hydrological behavior by paying heed to the riparian floral needs when constructing accesses.

* Keeping the production of final product as close to the source as possible, e.g., small co-op value-added activities. The buck stays in the communities which will maintain/enhance and thus reverse the source.

"Restoration Forestry Is..."
by Thyson Banighen

Sustainable forestry fosters the social, economic well-being of communities and the environmental well-being of the forest, strengthens local decision making in self-reliant forestry practices, cooperative endeavors, and general community economic development at the local level, involves citizens' nurtured stewardship of the forest while in trust for this and future generations of all life.

"Restoration Forestry Is..."
by Dale Thornburgh

Is a forest managed under a system so some commodity products can be extracted and still allow the total biodiversity of the forest community to exist in its natural dynamic state. Over time, the forest has the ability to change its gene and species biodiversity under natural selection pressures. Human directed changes should not alter the dynamic state of the system, but mimic natural changes as much as possible.

"Restoration Forestry Is..."
by Marianne Edain

Goal: To return cut-over, degraded land to ecologically productive forests. Methods: Mimic natural succession of the site as it is, not as it was, by providing (as much as is humanly possible) the catalysts/conditions for moving the site into the next stage of succession.

"Restoration Forestry Is..."

A system whereby humans can manage or not manage land and forested land to maintain a sustained benefit to themselves, to wildlife and to the soil.

A system that regards the non-timber aspects of the forest as equally important as the timber products.

That restores degraded land in a gentle fashion.

That regards the forest as a place to encourage diversity of species.

That regards natural forest systems as reserves of species, habitat and knowledge.

That seeks to restore fragmented old growth ecosystems with corridors and rights of way for wildlife.

"Restoration Forestry Is..."

- Natural forestry based on "nature's ways."
- An holistic approach to the ways we manage our forests.
- Activity that provides resources for humans but maintains the health of forest ecosystems.
- Forest practices that ensure the "old forests" diversity but a selective aid to our population.

"Restoration Forestry Is..."
by Mark Goddard

- Sustained with nature's ground rules.
- Biodiversity—species without prejudice.
- Putting back what we have taken from the earth.
- A partnership with Nature.
- A respectful investment in tomorrow.

"Restoration Forestry Is..."
by Craig Patterson

Maintaining reverence for the natural cycles and diversity of Nature's time tested ecosystems, and living within the limits of those comprehensive and diversified ecosystems.

It is not arbitrarily creating a man-based standard which defines environmentally, economically, politically or socially what's good for "profit taking" is good for the planet. Gandhi's statement, "There is enough for every man's need, but not for every man's greed," should be our sustainable foundation.

"Restoration Forestry Is..."
by Ken Carloni

1. Mimics native ecosystems.
2. Is labor and information intensive. (Not energy and capital intensive.)
3. Is flexible.
4. Is resilient.
5. Accumulates nutrients in the system.
6. Is self-perpetuating.

"Restoration Forestry Is..."
Stewardship
by Mike Dubrasich

Sustaining the production of an optimal mix of forest resources, providing for present and future resource needs, while protecting and enhancing the intrinsic ability of the forest to produce resources.

Resources: timber, water, wildlife, esthetics, etc.

Intrinsic ability: ecosystem balance and diversity, soil, air and water system health.

Steward: human relationship and interaction with the forest.

"Restoration Forestry Is..."
by Gabriel Petlin

Sustainable forestry allows economic utilization of the forest for humans while maintaining the forest structure, species composition, wildlife habitat, biodiversity, scenic and recreational values, and watershed protection.

Forests should be managed in the public trust doctrine, and therefore big industry should have no role.

"Restoration Forestry Is..."
by Orville Camp

"A harvesting program which addresses forest ecosystem needs first and in so doing also serves our needs."

Nature has the only time-tested and proven management program, therefore, we need to learn how to use nature. A key ingredient of nature's management program is the natural selection process. Let's use it.

"Restoration Forestry Is..."
by Jeff Mecham

Ecological Forestry = the care and management of our forests as if they were home and family—which, of course, they are.

1

Restoration Forestry: An International Guide to Sustainable Forestry Practices

Introduction To the Conference

Michael Pilarski

ON NOVEMBER 9-11, 1990, around eighty people gathered at the Lost Valley Center to discuss restoration forestry. The Lost Valley Center is located in the Willamette Valley near Eugene, Oregon. The Conference was sponsored and organized by Lost Valley Center and Friends of the Trees Society.

The Restoration Forestry Conference was the first conference of its kind on the West Coast. A grass-roots conference on ecologically sound forestry. Conference participants looked at forestry issues in the Pacific Northwest with an eye to solutions. The participants included a cross section of the Pacific Northwest's leading restoration foresters, forest scientists and forest activists. We were especially pleased to have Orville Camp and Merv Wilkinson share their years of experience. The conference benefitted from the participation of Oregon State University forest ecologists David Perry, Miles Hemstrom, Michael Amaranthus, and a number of Forest Service employees, including several District Rangers.

There were some points of disagreement and many points of agreement. Nobody thought present forest practices were sustainable, and we all wanted to see less clearcutting. We explored options of forestry management and different harvesting methods.The conference included keynote speakers, plenary sessions, panel discussions, workshops, and participatory planning groups. Steve Erickson in the next article gives a more in-depth report.

Orville Camp and Merv Wilkinson were honored with the "Restoration Forester of the Year Award" for their outstanding contributions to the planet and to restoration forestry. Between the two of them they have close to a century of hands-on experience. Orville's Camp Forest Farm near Selma, Oregon and Merv's Wildwood Forest on Vancouver Island are two of the best models of restoration forestry.

What came out of the conference?

The most important thing that came out of the conference was that the people working in similar lines of work were able to strategize ways to reach common objectives for healthier forest ecosystems and healthier economies in the Pacific Northwest. It is impossible to know all the future ramifications of an event such as this. Connections and friendships made or renewed have led to further collaboration and cooperation. On the visible spectrum, we can point to three developments:

1. The book *Restoration Forestry* obtained its initial impetus at the conference.

2. Papers were prepared for the conference for inclusion in the Proceedings by Matthew Hall, Jefferson Mecham, Ken Carloni, Tim Foss, and Michael Dubrasich.

3. Several of the California participants who attended the conference were inspired to found the Institute for Sustainable Forestry (ISF) on the ride home from the conference. Notably, Jan and Peggy Iris, Walter Smith, and Seth Zuckerman. ISF has grown into one of the best restoration forestry organizations on the West Coast.

Other Restoration Forestry Conferences

When will the next Restoration Forestry Conference be? The closest events to it since have been the two Pacific Cascadia Ecoforesters meetings in 1993. They were smaller (invitation only) gatherings of eco-foresters, some of whom were at the Restoration Forestry Conference. (See "Ecoforesters' Recommendations to Clinton.") The next full-scale public conference on restoration forestry that I am aware of, as this book goes to press, is the international conference on sustainable forestry, the Vision 2020 Conference, May 1995 on the North Coast of California. It is being organized by the Trees Foundation in Redway, California.

Lost Valley Center
  81868 Lost Valley Lane
  Dexter, Oregon 97431
  Tel: (503) 937-3351

If you are looking for a Pacific Northwest venue for a seminar, gathering or conference, consider the Lost Valley Center. Their facilities can handle up to 200 people and includes large dining hall, meeting rooms, dormitories, cabins, gardens, and forestland in a quiet, rural setting.

Think of the Forest as a Waterbed

I think you can manage for some level of commodity production and still maintain amenity use of environmental protection, and biological diversity, if you understand that forests are truly a web. They are really incredibly connected. Dave Perry likes to use the example of forests as a waterbed... in a waterbed you have billions of water molecules floating around and if you sit on one edge of the waterbed it comes up in the other, and even though many of these molecules never actually bump into each other, there is a connectedness of flow in the forest ecosystem. Like throwing a rock into a pond, it sends out a ripple whch really transcends the whole pond. We need to realize that any action in the forest has an effect throughout the forest and in a lot of cases, forests are a delicate web as well and so understanding that, I think, is the key to sustainable forestry.

—Michael Amaranthus

Whither Restoration Forestry?

A poem of sorts by Michael Pilarski

Presented at the 1990 Restoration Forestry Conference.

Whither restoration forestry?
What meaning in your mind?
Shall we restore? Implore? Abhor? Ask what for?
Before it's too late or in the nick of time.
When is too little forest not enough?
Shall we gamble again? and again?
Whither sustainable forestry?
Lip service? Revolution? Or evolution?
New perspectives on new forestry?
Or the same old forestry dressed up in new
  clothes?
A wolf in sheep's clothing?
Or a new hope for old forests?
Ecological forestry, eco-forestry.
Ecologically sound and socially equitable forestry.
Natural selection forestry,
individual tree selection,
or clearcut them all?
Words come tumbling from mouths and papers.
What do they mean to each person?
One word, a thousand definitions.
Fragmented forests.
Fragments and threads of human decency.
Will the forests grow large again?
Or shrink ever smaller?
What about human souls?
Will the old growth survive, revive, flourish?
Or will they become memories
like barren rocky hillsides under a hot Mediterra-
  nean sun?
Biological diversity, human diversity, or mono-
  cultures coast to coast?
Genetically uniform supertrees like television
  heroes.
Work with nature or triumph over nature?
Shall we boast long as we stand over the bleeding
  earth?
Adaptive forestry, or combative forestry?
Restoration or desolation?

Restoration Forestry:
Echoes of the Past, Visions of the Future

Steve Erickson

LONG-TIME ACTIVIST MICHAEL PILARSKI, of Friends of the Trees Society, organized a three-day conference at Lost Valley Conference Center outside of Eugene, Oregon, November 1990.

The subject was "Restoration Forestry," but conference participants considered a broader range of issues. This was inevitable, considering the varied backgrounds and focus of the people attending: academics and researchers, land management agency personnel, ecological activists, land owners, and consultants trying to practice on-the-ground, real-world restorative and sustainable forestry.

Because of this yeasty mix, emphasis was on communication between groups and individuals rather than overused, stupefying scientific jargon.

Both Dave Perry, Oregon State University researcher, and Mike Amaranthus of the U.S. Forest Service, emphasized the importance of a healthy soil biota for successful forest regeneration and tree planting.

Over 80% of all plant species worldwide are known to form symbiotic relationships between their roots and different fungi—the conifers of the Pacific Northwest are no exception.

These micorrhizal relationships (from the Greek—literally "fungus root") extend the effective area of the tree's roots over a thousandfold.

The fungus-root symbiosis helps the trees gather nutrients, such as calcium and phosphorus, that are usually scarce in Pacific Northwest forest soils and allows the roots to take up far greater amounts of water.

In return, the fungus receives a stable, sheltered environment below ground and nutrients from the host tree.

Industrial forestry frequently impacts these critical below-ground processes and functions. Large windrow slash burns literally sterilize the soil. Large clear-cuts can remove all fungus host trees, eliminating sources of fungus to colonize the roots of newly planted or naturally regenerated seedlings.

The fungi rapidly die off once their host tree is dead.

Erosion can also impact this vital ecosystem process by removing the upper portion of the topsoil. Compaction from machinery can destroy the soil pores, literally preventing the soil from breathing.

Several strategies are useful for preventing these disastrous effects: not damaging the soil via burning, compaction, and erosion; providing refugia for the micorrhizal fungus, such as retained trees within the clearcut; and prompt regeneration, either natural or by artificial planting, are chief among these.

Agency people were in attendance, including several USFS district rangers and assorted lower-level personnel. The cracks within the USFS' "timber beast" mind set gaped wide open at this conference.

In conversation, a district ranger from the Nez Perce National Forest in Idaho reported that they haven't made their "allowable cut" for two years running now, and expect next year's shortfall to be truly major. The reasons are being documented in excruciating detail to cover their posteriors.

This is apparently happening throughout the Montana and Idaho national forests. Conscientious district rangers and forest supervisors are refusing to "get out" the impossibly high cuts mandated in the forest plans.

Whether they will survive retribution from state congressmen dominated by the timber industry and by Forest Service higher-ups in Washington, D.C., remains to be seen.

It was reported that the district ranger from the Clackamas District, Siuslaw National Forest, went on a field trip to Collins Pine and Fir, a privately-owned corporation based near Mt. Lassen, California, and "got religion."

He returned and announced there will be no more clearcutting in the Clackamas District. Period. *Not* "no more clearcutting this year or next," but "no more clearcutting ever"—as long as he's district ranger.

Collins Pine and Fir was the largest example presented of sustainable forestry currently being practiced.

Their selection logging system was set up in the late

1940's by foresters from the U.S. Forest Service. The cycle has now come around full circle, with today's Forest Service foresters rediscovering their work.

Collins does not clearcut on its 90,000 acres, which are open to the public. There are four nesting pairs of Spotted Owls on their forest and the company is reportedly proud of it.

The company mill has a stable work force that has enjoyed immunity from the erratic boom-and-bust cycles and lack of security that plague workers of other large, industrial forest land owners.

More timber is growing on Collins' Forest now than when they started in the 1940's and more timber has been harvested than was present then.

While the largest, Collins Pine and Fir was by no means the only on-the-ground example of people trying to practice forestry sustainably.

Merve Wilkinson has been practicing single tree selection on several hundred acres of mature forest on Vancouver Island since the late 1930's. His experience refutes industry claims that individual tree selection logging is not practical in the Douglas-fir region.

In southwestern Oregon, Orville Camp's Forest Farm Association works primarily with small landowners on land that is recovering from previous industrial logging operations.

His sensitive, single tree selection logging methods and discriminating road layout seem to be a viable way for people to help heal these forests, even while exploiting them economically.

Jan Iris, founder of Wild Iris Forestry in northern California, has developed uses and markets for early successional tree species that industrial loggers spend vast amounts of energy and poison trying to kill, such as Tan Oak. Wild Iris logs, mills and dries the Tan Oak, in a small kiln, producing beautiful, durable flooring.

Wild Iris is demonstrating a useful model for decentralized, community based forestry.

These examples of people trying to practice forest sensitively and sustainably—in different forest types, in different situations and at different scales—were eye openers for many of the activists present.

With few exceptions, activists working on forestry issues rarely know, or are able to articulate, what they see as the future of forestry in the Pacific Northwest; all too often, their focus is only on not cutting the last fragments of natural (never logged) forest, while ignoring the millions of already cut-over land.

When environmentalists negotiate with the timber industry, such as the Timber-Fish-Wildlife agreement and the recent Sustainable Forestry Roundtable debacle, the results are ineffectual stop-gap measures and political manipulation of the environmental community.

This manipulation will continue until the environmental community, particularly the leaders and negotiators for the large organizations, have a clear, coherent vision of sustainable forestry that includes the nitty-gritty details of on-the-ground implementation.

One such vision was presented at the Restoration Forestry Conference in the form of the Forests Forever! initiative, which a minority 48% of California voters approved in November's election.

Chief author of the initiative, Robert Sutherlund of the Environmental Protection Information Center, Garberville, was obviously disappointed at the narrow loss, but the results stand out like a green thumb in an election where virtually all other environmental initiatives lost heavily.

One statement by Sutherlund seems key to determining the future strategy of forest activists in Washington:

"We must confront the economics directly. Trees that grow at 2.5 to 3 percent a year will never be as profitable as other investments. The forest cannot be everything to everybody. Maximizing short-term profit is incompatible with long term sustainability."

This is a lesson that "leaders" of Washington's environmental community need to learn.

Participants in the Restoration Forestry Conference

November 8-11, 1990
Lost Valley Center, Dexter, Oregon

The organization, agency or company the participant worked for at the time of attending the conference is noted, where known.

*Denotes speaker/presenter at the conference.

Mike Amaranthus*
U.S. Forest Service
Grants Pass, Oregon

Tyhson Banighen*
Turtle Island Earth Stewards
Vancouver, B.C.

Doug Barber
KEZI Radio
Eugene, Oregon

Robert "Bobcat" Brothers*
Headwaters
Ashland, Oregon

Ed Brown
U.S. Forest Service
Chemult, Oregon

Faith Brown
U.S. Forest Service (USFS)
Chemult, Oregon

Lynn Burditt*
Blue River District Ranger, USFS
Willamette National Forest
Eugene, Oregon

Pamela Burnette*
Weyerhaeuser Paper Co.
Secondary Fiber Div.
Eugene, Oregon

Bill Burwell*
Springfield, Oregon

Brett Ken Cairn
Rogue Institute for
Ecology & Economy
Eugene, Oregon

Orville Camp*
Camp Forest Farm
Selma, Oregon

Mary Camp
Camp Forest Farm
Selma, Oregon

Henry Carey
Forest Trust
Santa Fe, New Mexico

Ken Carloni
Wild Plant Nursery
Roseburg, Oregon

Charlotte Corkman
Portland, Oregon

Mike Dubrasich*
Sylvan Systems
Hood River, Oregon

Marianne Edain
Whidbey Environmental Action Network
Langley, Washington

Steve Erickson
Whidbey Environmental Action Network
Langley, Washington

Ianto Evans
Aprovecho Institute
Cottage Grove, Oregon

Tim Foss*
U.S. Forest Service
Cle Elum, Washington

Mitch Friedman*
Greater Ecosystems Alliance
Bellingham, Washington

Edward C. Fritz
Forest Reform Network
Dallas, Texas

Paige Giberson
Eugene, Oregon

Mark Goddard
The Goddard Land

Sisters, Oregon

Diana Gordon
Washougal, Washington

Kirsten Green
Portland, Oregon

Matthew Hall
Aprovecho Institute
Cottage Grove, Oregon

Miles Hemstrom*
Willamette National Forest, USFS
Eugene, Oregon

Lynn Huntsinger*
Dept. of Forestry and Natural Resources
University of California
Berkeley, California

Jan Iris*
Wild Iris Forestry
Redway, California

Peggy Iris*
Wild Iris Forestry
Redway, California

Patti Keene
Public Forest Foundation
Cottage Grove, Oregon

Roy Keene*
Public Forest Foundation
Eugene, Oregon

Gene Lawhorn
Sutherlin, Oregon

Jeff Mecham
Aprovecho Institute
Cottage Grove, Oregon

Curtin Mitchell*
Ecological Forestry
Loraine, Oregon

Jay Noyes
Light Hawk Pilot
Hood River, Oregon

Craig Patterson
Salem, Oregon

David A. Perry*
Oregon State University,
Department of Forestry
Corvallis, Oregon

Gabriel Petlin
Berkeley, California

John Phillips
Willits, California

Michael Pilarski*
Friends of the Trees Society
Tonasket, Washington

Colette Rush
Seattle, Washington

Robert S. Russell
Sierra Club
Marcola, Oregon

Don Shawe
Rahane Forest Farm
Hood River, Oregon

Linda Smiley
Aprovecho Institute
Cottage Grove, Oregon

Pete Sorenson
Eugene, Oregon

Jeffrey St.Clair*
Forest Watch Editor
Oregon City, Oregon

Greg Schroer*
Wildlife Society
Kirkland, Washington

Walter Smith
Institute for Sustainable Forestry
Willits, California

Robert Sutherland*
Environmental Protection Information Center
Garberville, California

Sharon Teague*
Eugene, Oregon

Chris Tebbett
Boonville, California

J. T. Thompson
Lost Valley Center
Dexter, Oregon

Michelle Thompson
Lost Valley Center
Dexter, Oregon

Dale Thornburgh
Forestry Department
Humboldt State University
Arcata, California

Rick Valley
Northern Groves Bamboo Nursery
Portland, Oregon

Roy Wagner
Redmond, Washington

Meca Wawona
New Growth Forestry
Ukiah, California

Jim Wiebush*
Elk City District Ranger, USFS
Elk City, Idaho

Mark Wigg*
Pacific Forest Consultants
Portland, Oregon

Merv Wilkinson*
Wildwood
Ladysmith, British Columbia

Bill Woodrich
KBOO Radio
Portland, Oregon

Seth Zuckerman
Sierra Magazine
Berkeley, California

Lost Valley Center residents
Dexter, Oregon

A number of the Lost Valley residents participated to some degree. Lost Valley Center has a keen interest in forestry since their 60-acre land base includes a 40-acre recent clearcut, as well as some sizable second-growth Douglas-fir.

Restoration Forestry Consultants

2

AT ONE POINT during the Restoration Forestry Conference, we asked the professional foresters attending who would like to be listed in the Proceedings as consulting foresters in restoration forestry. A few people signed up, and here are their addresses with descriptions of their services. These are just a few of the qualified people at the Restoration Forestry Conference. (The asterisk indicates people who attended the Conference.)

Also included are several additional people who did not attend the Conference, but who were contacted during the course of compiling this book and agreed to be listed.

See also the British Columbia Selection Logging Speakers Bureau in the British Columbia, Canada section for names and addresses of other restoration foresters.

There are hundreds of people mentioned in *Restoration Forestry*, who would be qualified for listing here; as well as hundreds we are not aware of. In other words, this list is just the tip of the iceberg. If you would like to nominate yourself, or a forester you know, for future editions of this list contact Friends of the Trees Society.

Tyhson Banighen, M.A.*
   Turtle Island Earth Stewards
   Box 39077, Point Grey RPO
   Vancouver, British Columbia, V6R 4P1, CANADA
   Tel: (604) 736-9221/Fax: (604) 736-9218

   Forest Trust Consultant. Protect your forests, place them in Trust. [See Banighen's article on land trusts in the British Columbia section.]

Rudolf W. Becking
   1415 Virginia Way
   Arcata , California 95521
   Tel: (707) 822-1649

   Forest Research consultant. Specializing in Redwood, Douglas Fir, Dipterocarp and Teak. Ecology, mensuration, photogrammetry.

Robert "Bobcat" Brothers*
   Box 212
   Williams, Oregon 97544
   Tel: (503) 482-3917

   Contact person for implementing restoration forestry through administrative and legal enforcement of federal agency regulations: Siskiyou NF; Rogue River NF; Medford District, Bureau of Land Management. Also: measuring tree growth after clearcutting, forest fragmentation mapping.

Dieter Deumling
   4550 Oak Grove Road
   Rickreall, Oregon 97371

Mike Dubrasich*
   3535 Lippman Road
   Hood River, Oregon 97031
   Tel: (503) 354-2499

   Professional consulting forester.

Marianne Edain* and Steve Erickson*
   Frosty Hollow Native Seeds
   Box 53
   Langley, Washington 98260
   Tel: (206) 221-2332

   Services for ecological restoration. Provides design, consultation, troubleshooting, seed collection, etc. [See Erickson's article "Forest Vision" in Definitions section. Also Frosty Hollow entry in sources of seeds.]

Scott Ferguson
   Individual Tree Selection Management Inc.
   American Bank Bldg, Stuite 204
   Portland, Oregon 97205
   Tel: (503) 222-9772

   Years of experience with Individual Tree Selection. One of the best known forestry consultants for sustainable forestry in the Douglas fir region. [See article by Marie Reeder in the Pacific Northwest section.]

Tim Foss*

HC60 Box 10160

Cle Elum, Washington 98922

Tel: (509) 674-2017

I can be a contact for people/groups who want some forestry advice/opinions or who want help understanding the Forest Service workings, including timber sales, EA's, Forest Plans, etc. I am a professional forester with the Wenatachee National Forest and an environmentalist. [See Foss' article "New Forestry—A State of Mind" in the definitions section.

Grant Gibbs

Lite Logging

11632 Hwy 209

Leavenworth, Washington 98826

Forestland managers, including thinning and logging, in the Wenatchee River Valley in the East Cascades.

Mark Goddard*

The Goddard Land

P.O. Box 1032

Sisters, Oregon 97759

Tel: (503) 549-3614

Fire-safe landscape maintenance & native plants of Central Oregon.

Richard D. Goodenough Associates

Black River Road

Pottersville, New Jersey 07979

Matthew Hall*

28068 Ham Road

Eugene, Oregon 97405

Tel: (503) 344-0647

An English forester experienced in management of small and farm woodlands and arboriculture. Interested in promoting woodlands in agriculture worldwide. Doing horse-logging and selection logging. Restoration of deforested land. Teaches courses in environmental forestry. (See Hall's article on hedgerows.)

Curtin Mitchell*

Forestcare Company

P.O. Box 38

Loraine, Oregon 97451

Tel: (503) 942-5424

Consultant in putting forest land in Trust; and in non-timber products. [See Forestcare Company entry in the Pacific Northwest Restoration Forestry Organizations section.]

Walton R. Smith

221 Huckleberry Road

Franklin, North Carolina 28734

Selection forest harvesting. (See Smith's article "The Voice of Experience—Sustaining Hardwood Forests" in the section on North America's Eastern Forests.)

Global Resource Consultants

Rt. 1, Box 246 B

Rixeyville, Virginia 22737

Tel: (703) 330-3889

Richard Fox, Director. A consortium of natural resource professionals with backgrounds in government, environmental organizations and private business who have joined together to market their skills to environmental NGOs, sustainable forestry programs, etc. Areas of expertise: reforestation; nurseries; agroforestry; wildlife management; biodiversity; soil conservation; sustainable forestry certification; environmental education; international networking; and proposal writing.

List of Foresters Using Selection Management

Forest Reform Network

Attn: Edward C. Fritz

5934 Royal Lane, Suite 223

Dallas, Texas 75230

Tel: (214) 352-8370

Ned Fritz has compiled a list of several dozen foresters using selection management, which can be requested from him at the above address.

3 What Is Restoration Forestry?

3

A Synopsis of Some Restoration Forestry Practices and Principles

3

Michael Pilarski

Restoration forestry restores the health of the forest as well as the health of rural communities.

Restoration forestry puts people to work building up the forest resource base.

Introduction

NO ONE PERSON HAS ALL THE ANSWERS when it comes to restoration forestry. There are many viewpoints on the subject, as demonstrated by the numerous authors in *Restoration Forestry*. The following are brief comments on a number of forestry practices and policies from my personal viewpoint. These are not meant to be dogmatic statements. There are exceptions to every rule. Most of these points are addressed in greater detail in *Restoration Forestry*.

Note the different definitions of "restoration" and "restoration forestry" in regard to the following article. Restoration, as used here, is the set of techniques and strategies for repairing damaged ecosystems. Restoration forestry, on the other hand, includes restoration as well as all other aspects of forestry practices and policy.

This article was not written from an international perspective. It is adapted from a 1993 proposal sent to President Clinton's forestry team. Although this article is aimed at the U.S. forest situation, it should provide some useful insights to people in other countries.

Restoration Forestry Goals

At the start, let us take a look at what I consider the goals of restoration forestry. These are: to double the world's forest cover, create more wilderness, grow bigger trees, allow longer rotations, create healthy ecosystems and more jobs. The types of jobs would change over time to some extent. Less restoration work would need to be done after a century of catch-up work. Over time there would be increased flows of products from the forests. Timber, over time, will be of increasingly larger diameter and higher quality as more of the forests once again reach old-growth dimensions.

Fifty-Year Moratorium on Logging in Any Old-Growth Forests (Ancient Forests)

Create a system of core reserves in the landscape and link them with biological corridors. Core reserves (no logging allowed) can include old-growth forests as well as the best second growth stands and young natural forests. Surround the core reserves with buffer zones. Remove high elevation forests, as well as steep sites and unstable slopes at all elevations, from the timber base. Reserve forests are currently located mostly on high-elevation, low-productivity sites. Work also towards a network of reserves of the best lowland forests.

No new roads or helicopter logging in roadless areas. Thinning or salvage should not be used as a pretext to log in unroaded areas. Although helicopter logging causes less damage to a forest than ground skidding, helicopter logging is energy and technology intensive and is seldom justified. The danger of helicopter logging is it enables the logging of sites that were previously protected by their sheer inaccessibility.

California national forests in 1993 declared a ban on cutting trees larger then 30" dbh (diameter breast height). (They also banned clear-cutting.) Large trees are an important component of healthy forest ecosystems and are increasingly rare in most forests. Diameter limits would vary with region, site, and species. It has been recommended that Washington and Oregon eastside national forests ban cutting trees larger than 21" dbh. Diameter limits are especially needed in forest areas where few big trees are left. These would be temporary moratoriums. Thirty to fifty years would give us some time to think about it.

Timber Harvest Methods

Greatly reduce clear-cutting as a timber harvest method. Clear-cutting is clearly a major cause of forest and watershed degradation, fragmentation and devaluation. Some restoration foresters would like to ban clear-cutting completely, but most would agree that there are situations when clear-cutting is an appropriate harvesting method. Where clearcuts are used they should be small in size and utilize New Forestry techniques such as dispersed green tree retention for snag recruitment, leave clumps, and irregular edges. Trashy clearcuts are ecologically preferable to broadcast burning the site or piling and burning the slash since we want to maintain biomass to feed the forest.

With restoration forestry, most harvesting would be done using natural selection harvesting, a single tree selection system developed by Orville Camp. Only a small part of the volume is taken out any one year and the best is always left. The forest is thinned from below, rather than from above. Careful observation of nature enables foresters to discern which trees nature has selected to take out. Natural Selection Ecoforestry as developed by Orville Camp leads to uneven aged, multi-species, natural, mature forests.

Single-tree selection, in and of itself, is not necessarily good forestry, depending on who is doing the selecting. Some people consider single-tree selection to be selecting all the biggest and best trees. Or all the individuals of the most valuable species. Timber flows from the forests should be the result of improvement practices. No more high-grading. Most timber should come from low elevation, easily accessible forests.

Other harvesting methods in order of severity range from small group selection to commercial thinning to shelterwood cuts, New Forestry, seed-tree cuts and clearcuts. Small-group selection fits in well with restoration forestry, if it adhers to natural selection guidelines. Shelterwood and seed tree cuts, are sometimes appropriate but presently they are overutilized as a practice since they are essentially two-stage clearcuts. Most of the volume is removed on the first entry. After regeneration has occurred the remaining large trees are cut. This is even-aged management. Restoration forestry would replace even-aged forestry with uneven-aged forestry on most sites.

Various "New Forestry" harvesting methods such as dispersed or clumped leave-trees and minimal retention cuts (leaving less than 15 percent of the original forest stand volume), constitute forms of clear-cutting. New Forestry practices are useful but as a form of clear-cutting should only be used on a small part of the production forests.

Manage for long-lived, high quality timber. In many parts of the world, and for most species, this means letting trees live to 200 or more years. Thinning and natural selection supplies other sizes of timber. There are exceptions to every rule. Some species are short-lived.

Multiple-Species Forestry Replaces Monoculture Forestry

Forests should be encouraged which reflect the natural mix of species, age classes and levels of succession in the greater landscape mosaic. There are very few instances where mo-noculture stands can be justified. Deciduous species should be allowed to play their natural role in succession instead of being sprayed with herbicides or cut to favor planted conifers.

Retain and Create Biological Legacies in Forests

Forests need snags of all decomposition levels and sizes as well as large down logs, large woody debris and humus. Forests need the structure and function provided by dead and dying trees. We can take some, but what percentage can be safely removed is site specific.

Reforestation

The number of people planting trees can be greatly increased. Many forestlands are unstocked or understocked. Do not plant where natural regeneration is proceeding adequately. Where planting is deemed beneficial, most areas should be planted with native trees and plants from local seed sources. The so-called genetically-superior "Super" trees are not the way to go. In the long run, they prove less adapted than local seed stock. Relying on local seed keeps genetic diversity high.

Reforestation involves more than planting trees. There is often need to do follow up work to insure survival. Follow-up care can include bud-caps (for browsing protection), shading, mulching, hand release of seedlings (hoeing) and irrigation. Many expensive tree planting efforts fail due to lack of follow-up care. Restoration forestry relies primarily on local networks of seed collectors, small-scale nurseries, and tree planting cooperatives. In the long run, ecological forest management relies almost totally on natural regeneration. Healthy forests reseed themselves just fine.

Restoration of Streams, Rivers and Riparian Areas

Preserving endangered fishing stocks and rehabilitating fisheries is very important. All fish and aquatic species must be considered as well as salmon. We need to stop logging practices which cause accelerated erosion, sedimentation and flooding. Broadscale spraying of herbicides and insecticides are not acceptable, as aquatic organisms are very susceptible to biocides. It will take a lot of restoration work to restore aquatic ecosystems and riparian corridors along streams, rivers and estuaries.

Protect all riparian corridors with wide no-cut zones. At least double present minimum widths. There are exceptions, such as single-tree or small patch cutting to speed conifer recruitment or provide logs for beneficial structures in streams. Nature usually provides adequate down logs and canopy gaps in riparian areas through floods, blowdowns, earth slumps, root rots, etc.

Erosion control is needed on many forested lands,

3

especially in mountainous areas. The focus should be on restoring healthy habitats and functions. Major flood events can flush stream systems in a beneficial way if there are healthy watersheds. If the watershed is unhealthy, major flood events can increase sediment load and reduce pools. There is a time lag between when the ecosystem is damaged and when heavy damage becomes apparent. Small cumulative impacts add up over years until a large storm triggers major erosion. "A stitch in time saves nine" is an appropriate adage in the case of erosion control. Nipping erosion in the bud is more cost effective than repairs after major damage is done to the watershed.

Stream restoration on a large scale would create thousands of jobs. The Mattole Restoration Council offers a model of citizens planning and carrying out watershed-level stream restoration and erosion control.

Roads

Roads are major causes of erosion. Remedies include decommissioning many roads, better design, and erosion proofing the roads which are retained. Audit all forest roads for erosion problems and do erosion-proofing and restoration where needed. An ambitious, ten-year program could decommission a lot of roads, with priority given to steep terrain, eroding areas and buffer areas around core reserves. Putting roads to bed requires technologies such as ripping roadbeds, recontouring, armoring channels, bio-engineering, and planting with native trees and plants. Besides dealing with the roadway itself, there sometimes needs to be erosion control on adjacent slopes.

There is a need to identify the most ecologically-benign road layouts. It will be cost effective in some instances to downsize roads or move roads out of riparian areas. Smaller equipment requires smaller roads which have less impact. There are new ideas in road layout that complement restoration forestry, such as: narrower roads, erosion proofed and designed to avoid concentrating overland water flow. Orville Camp, P.A. Yeoman, and others have worked out low-impact, contour road systems.

Sticking to carefully planned skid trails when logging minimizes damage. Cut and haul at times when damage will be minimal to soil. Make more use of skylines and balloons.

Decommissioning and erosion-proofing roads is largely a one-time investment which would greatly reduce sedimentation into streams, rivers and estuaries. A steady supply of clean water supports fisheries, as well as other aquatic life forms and webs of life. Clean water is one of the critical elements for human survival. The costs of flood damage if road stabilization is not addressed will more than outweigh the costs of fixing it.

Thinning

Everyone agrees that outside of the preserves, some level of thinning is okay, but there is a lot of debate on what to thin, when to thin, how much to thin and how much biomass can be removed from the site. What is the difference between thinning and partial cuts? Thinning can be used by unscrupulous people to high-grade the forest. Watch out for timber sales disguised as restoration thinning that are glorified shelterwood cuts.

It is hypothecized that thinning may help some forests reach old-growth characteristics and function earlier. Some forests are subject to increased disease/pest levels without thinning. We can choose to do the thinning or let nature do the thinning through fire, insects, root-rots and diseases. In pre-commercial thinning the felled trees are not taken out of the forest. In commercial thinning the trees are extracted for human use. In restoration forestry, the emphasis is on what is left, not what is taken out. Always leave the best. Thinning releases superior trees to put on increased growth rates. Most thinning cuts should leave 75% to 90% of the original volume and canopy or more.

Ecologically beneficial thinning is a highly developed skill. You can't send just anyone out there with a spray can or a chainsaw. Training centers are needed to teach restoration thinning. Some of the most advanced thinking on thinning from the bottom up comes from Orville Camp's Natural Selection Ecoforestry. See also the article on Headwaters Alliance's guidelines for restoration thinning.

How much volume can be removed from a forest without harming productivity? Forests need biomass. It is the living flywheel which keeps the momentum of the forest going. Continually bleed a forest of its biomass and it will weaken and become more susceptible to a host of problems, such as windthrow, insects, diseases, rots, climate change, drought, and fire. Tropical forests are especially prone to damage since most of the biomass is in living plants. Healthy temperate forests have a lot more of their biological heritage tied up in humus, litter, snags and down logs. Thus, they are more resilient to disturbances. How much biomass can be removed, and how often will vary from site to site. Rich sites can handle more removal compared to poor sites.

Greatly reduce slash-burning

Pacific Northwest forests after clear-cutting look like battlefields. For decades it was conventional forest practice to broadcast burn the site after clear-cutting. Broadcast burns in the Pacific Northwest can be so hot they consume all biomass including the litter and humus layers of the soil. This is a great blow to forest fertility.

In 1992, I had the opportunity to work with some

Mopan Mayan traditional farmers in Belize. Some of the farmers were switching to a "slash and mulch" system of land clearance instead of the traditional "slash and burn". This was because fallow times were shortening and they obtained better yields, and less erosion using the slow nutrient release of the mulch system as contrasted to the quick, but shorter-lived, flush of nutrients from burning. In a sense, we need to make a similar conversion in our broad-scale forestry practices here in the Pacific Northwest. Mulch logging residue, don't burn it.

Prescribed Burning

Prescribed burning is another controversial subject. The importance of fire in ecosystem functioning is just beginning to be understood. Fires perform benefical roles in ecosystem processes. Fire plays many roles in forest ecology: reducing insect and disease infestations, and affecting species composition, stocking density and nutrient cycling. Frequent light fires can reduce the incidence of large stand-destroying fires. Natural fire periodicity varies from region to region. Native Americans burned extensively before white settlement and knew more about prescribed burning than anyone alive today. *Restoration Forestry* contains a section on Native American traditional fire management and a section on fire ecology and management.

Because of today's high fuel loads in much of the forests, prescribed burning needs to be approached cautiously as a management tool. I automatically distrust the Forest Service will use prescribed burning wisely. Small-scale experiments, close monitoring, and citizen involvement are warranted.

Creating a network of fire breaks within the forests should be explored as a way to help control catastrophic wildfires. This does not conflict with a policy of increased use of prescribed burns. In fact, a good network of fuelbreaks is necessary to control prescribed burns.

Grazing on Public Forestlands

Restoration forestry encompasses livestock management in forests and restoration of degraded grazing lands. Unless carefully managed, livestock have negative impacts on forest ecosystems through: eating or stepping on regeneration; selective browsing/grazing with a reduction or elimination of preferred species; soil compaction; fouling of water sources; and streambank erosion. The seeding of logged-over, eastside forests with non-native range grasses is commonly practiced. This practice should be stopped as the non-native grasses crowd out native plants, delay or forestall tree regeneration, cause loss of replanted stock and disrupt ecosystem function. Use native plants for reseeding.

The need for restoration work to heal grazing damage is extensive throughout the western United States. This calls for a large labor force to do erosion control, riparian restoration, seeding of native plants, and fencing to protect riparian areas and water sources.

Audit all public land grazing allotments for levels of ecosystem impact. Standards should be set which prohibit overgrazing. In some areas, livestock numbers should be reduced in combination with longer rotations and rest years with no grazing and in other areas livestock should be taken off altogether.

Pest Control

Restoration foresters almost universally agree on no use of synthetically produced biocides (insecticides, fungicides, mammalicides, herbicides, etc). Restoration forestry allows naturally occuring diseases and insects to perform their function in maintaining a healthy forest. Pest control, when desired, is achieved by cultural methods, such as thinning, control of species composition, and predator habitat enhancement.

Currently, herbicides are used in forest plantations around the world to control competing vegetation. Competing vegetation would seldom be a problem under restoration forestry since most regeneration would be natural. Where reforestation does have problems with weeds, grass or brush, than mulching, hand-hoeing or cutting can be successfully used. Domestic livestock (sheep, goats, hogs and others) can sometimes be used to advantage in weed or brush control. Permaculture teaches us to choose biological resources over technological resources to get a job done.

Non-Timber Products

There are many non-timber, forest products: ornamentals, medicinals, seeds, berries, nuts, fruits, mushrooms, basketry materials, resins, waxes, spices, and others. These can provide myriad sustainable livelihoods if managed wisely. The resource can be increased by improving existing stands of desired species, establishing new stands and management activities. Overharvesting of these products can harm ecosystem biodiversity and health. Collection of forest products needs regulation and close scrutiny by biologists and the public.

Assessment and Monitoring

Implementing restoration forestry will require more people employed in assessing and auditing plant communities, old-growth, roadless areas, stand composition and health, roads, erosion, stream damage, thinning needs, firebreak routes, and grazing allotment impacts. Where are the least impacted, healthiest forest ecosystems? Where are the most degraded? Prioritize areas to treat first.

Quality-control monitoring of logging, thinning, planting, restoration, etc., will call for a larger labor force than presently. The Public Forestry Foundation recommends that public forest monitoring must be: funded up-front according to acres to be treated or disturbed; fully integrated with citizen foresters who will not benefit from the resource's exploitation; and, be supported by workable legal provisions for citizen enforcement.

Restore Damaged Ecosystems and Forests

After centuries of take, take, take, it is time for humanity to give back to the forests. Large amounts of labor and resources need to be allocated to restoration in the decades ahead. Government funding of restoration at present is a drop in the bucket compared to the need. There have been some notable programs in the past such as the Civilian Conservation Corps (CCC). Three big questions are:

1. What kinds of restoration work?
2. Who will do the restoration work?
3. Where will the funding come from?

What Kinds of Restoration Work?

Restoration involves many kinds of work, including: tree planting, revegetation, stream restoration, erosion control, erosion-proofing and decommissioning roads, seed collecting, direct seeding, nursery production, wildlife habitat improvement, fencing, trail building/maintenance, fire breaks, fuel reduction, prescribed burning, noxious weed control, ecosystem inventory and monitoring.

We need to identify the most successful restoration projects to date. There is a large body of knowledge on restoration from local, regional and international sources. Restoration ecology has much to contribute in cataloging the experiences to date and making the information available. Failures should also be identified and analyzed so lessons can be learned.

Restoration can be used as a smokescreen for continued forest degradation. One Forest Service tactic to watch out for on national forests is putting restoration dollars into the worst areas while continuing to cut and degrade the best forests. Restoration should start at the least damaged areas and work towards the most degraded areas.

Who Will Do the Restoration Work?

Priority should be given to displaced timber workers, local contractors using local labor, and local environmentalists. Fair wages should be paid for the type of work involved. We do not want to see restoration work done by exploitive contractors who employ non-local labor. As a case in point, during the 1980's, tree planting in the Pacific Northwest was largely taken over by contractors employing non-local Hispanics (legal and illegal). There needs to be accountability mechanisms which, at the same time, do not discourage small contractors. Current performance bonds are so high that many small, local contractors and individuals cannot afford to bid on jobs.

Encourage Grass-Roots Organizations of Restoration Volunteers

There is a large and growing demand for meaningful outdoor programs for young adults, teens, children and the public at large. There are already many models of volunteer citizens groups doing restoration work, such as adopt-a-highway, adopt-a-stream, volunteer trail maintenance, the Tree-People of Los Angeles and others. Australia has developed a large network of tree planting volunteers over the past decade in their efforts to re-green Australia.

Funds allocated to volunteer groups will have greater affect than equivalent amounts directed through government agencies such as the U.S. Forest Service. Restoration work camps, hostels and voluntary programs can proliferate if given seed money and people's creative energy is unleashed. Internships can lead to skill-gaining and eventual paid employment.

International Restoration Camps

There are millions of youth and other age groups around the world who would be thrilled to go to international workcamps for restoration and tree planting. In fact, there are already hundreds of thousands of people doing this. It is debatable if jetting people around the world for restoration is worth the ecologic and economic costs. With more training and more ecological means of travel, these objections can be largely satisfied. Such camps could be centers of education in restoration. People would go back to their countries and towns with new ideas and techniques to share. Rapid proliferation and exchange of knowledge will be essential for a successful worldwide restoration effort.

Youth Restoration Communities

In the U.S.A., I envision youth restoration communities near the edges of federal lands needing restoration. Purchasing run-down ranching properties in our rural areas is not very expensive. Part of the contract would be that community residents do an agreed amount of restoration work on public land. Small villages would be created where young people could stay and live. Many young people have no jobs, no land base, no productive work. Young people could come out to the country and learn how to live productive lives. These villages could take many forms, including permanent land bases with buildings largely constructed by participants using local materials. Vegetable gardens, orchards, berry patches, greenhouses and other food production systems can enable them to meet much of their food needs. The restoration communities would have experienced, permanent staff and visiting trainers to teach and help give direction.

Fund Small-Scale Restoration Forestry Experiments

Models of good forestry are few and far between. We need a lot more experimentation to yield the knowledge and experience to draw on for future management decisions. Through tax-incentives and cost-sharing many more small projects can be supported than by putting the money through present bureaucratic research institutions. Increase funding to the vibrant grass-roots. We need small-scale answers.

Restoration Forestry Training

Putting restoration forestry into affect on a broad scale would call for greatly increased numbers of skilled people. There is a need to identify the best people on the ground in restoration forestry practices as well as forest and watershed restoration. They are needed to set new standards and to train others. In the interests of rapid expansion and decentralized initiative, the formation of many alternative teaching facilities throughout our forest regions should be encouraged. These can take many forms. Current models should be cataloged and analyzed to give restoration forestry people a variety of models to choose from.

Some training can be supplied by current institutions such as universities, colleges and vocational training programs with some modification of curriculum. Conservation biology and restoration ecology departments in particular should get more funding. However, many existing institutions have a great deal invested in the status quo. We cannot expect a change to restoration forestry overnight.

Restoration forestry conferences can be held at local, regional, national and international levels. Funding can assist low-income people to attend. Conferences and seminars enable the sharing of ideas and fast dissemination of successes. This particularly needs to happen at the grass-roots level.

Encourage Restoration Forestry Networks

Provide funding to grass-roots initiatives. Building networks from the bottom up, as well as undertaking efforts from the top down. Regional networks can link up into larger coalitions. Government agencies, academia and special interest groups have their own networks of progressive thinktanks and practitioners. These people need to be encouraged to link up, share information, and cooperate with the grassroots.

Where Will the Funding Come From?

Use local tax money for local restoration. Presently most restoration work is funded by the federal government. Divert part of the tax stream going to the federal government to local restoration projects. This eliminates expensive levels of bureaucracy.

Do you use forest products? Consider tithing to a tree planting fund. Environmental tithing grew substantially in the 1980's, and is now many millions of dollars annually. Billions of dollars could be raised if just half of the companies and organizations using wood products would donate small tithes into tree planting funds. There could be many tree tithing programs of all sizes with minimal bureaucracy. The funds can go directly to grass-roots tree-planting efforts. Confederacies of such programs could cooperate in various ways including networking, research, education, and international transfer of resources to areas of greatest need.

Earth restoration can only be done on the local level. Mostly what is needed is labor. Much of the materials needed can be produced locally. Earth-moving machinery is useful where available and affordable. Reforestation and restoration work have been accomplished in many countries with hand-tools alone. The ideal is locally funded, planned and implemented reforestation and restoration.

Restoration Forestry Centers

Timber towns could have facilities which provide a common meeting ground for agency personnel, timber workers, environmentalists, ranchers, wildcrafters, guide outfitters, etc. Facilities could include libraries, reading rooms, meeting spaces, offices, maps, displays. There are few examples of "neutral" forest resource centers in the U.S.A. Neutral, in the sense of not being in the pockets of the timber industry or environmentalists. One such model is the Forest Resource Center in Minnesota.

Another type of useful service center for timber towns would be local marketing centers for wood products and secondary products to help small entrepreneurs research new products, identify markets, and market their products. These centers could also assist people/groups doing non-extractive endeavors, such as eco-tourism, camps, training centers, research centers, etc. Such centers can also help with regulations, financing, accounting, legalities, graphic design, brochure production, and other assistance. A regional logo and a common catalog of products and services would assist marketing.

Replace Tree Pulp for Paper With Herbaceous Fiber Crops

When it comes to making paper, trees have many ecological disadvantages compared to herbaceous farm crops such as kenaf, flax, straw, hemp and many more. Wood pulp is more energy demanding, causes more pollution and depletes forests. *Restoration Forestry* has a section on this subject.

Stop Export of Raw Logs

Value-added exports only. Log export bans can apply not only to countries, but also to states or even at the county level. The number of jobs in any forest community which is shipping raw logs can be greatly increased by milling them into lumber. Jobs can be increased even further by manufacturing finished products. There are literally thousands of products made from wood. What uses are there for each tree species found locally? Artisan crafts offer much potential for increasing jobs: furniture, cabinetry, wood carving, turnery, basketry, wicker, etc.

Timber Industry Workers and Jobs

> Foresters are needed to study and interpret the more complex features of a forest, but only the logger in his day-to-day decisions on what trees can be harvested, and how they can be felled and yarded out, can really practice the logging-phase of forestry.
>
> —D. M. Trew

Restoration forestry needs restoration loggers. The distinction between foresters and loggers is a blurred one. Some foresters are loggers. Some loggers know as much, or more, about forestry as professional foresters. Careful logging is a skill. Loggers can fell trees and yard out logs in a way that minimizes damage to the surrounding forest; however, they are seldom rewarded for doing so. They are presently rewarded for maximum board feet cut and loaded a day. In restoration forestry, loggers will vie with one another to see who can do the most careful job and leave the best forest. The emphasis is on what is left, rather than what is taken out. This is logging with a soft touch. Many loggers pride themselves on this already. Everyone knows there is lots of room for improvement in the industry.

Reinstating existing technologies or devising new techniques for timber harvesting which does least damage to forest ecology will require more workers and, generally, less expensive equipment. Smaller scale equipment, slower speed and more careful logging will take more workers per volume moved. This does not necessarily mean decreased income for the workers. More money is spent on people and less on machines. Restoration forestry advocates safer workplaces, profit sharing, and worker-owned, worker-managed, small-scale forest enterprises. The skills and knowledge of timber workers need to be respected by environmentalists and by industry.

All in all, between restoration, reforestation, improved management and more careful logging; restoration forestry leads to many more jobs in the forest industry, not less. All of these jobs would pay off in the long run with increased, sustainable production of forest products.

Local Control

Decentralize decision making. What kind of restoration work gets done should be largely determined locally. Community forest boards are becoming more common on national forests. These citizen forest boards and the lessons learned from them are laying the groundwork for more local control. Forestry boards, community roundtables, whatever their names, can be comprised of government agencies, timber industry, forest workers, environmentalists, ranchers, farmers, landowners, other stakeholders, as well as the general public. Environmentalists in some rural, timber communities are afraid of having forest decisions made locally due to the power of the industry/labor coalition. There are examples of successful concensus building but there remains a great need for skills in consensus, decision making, negotiation, mediation and fence mending.

Summary

If put into practice, these outlined practices and policies would substantially increase jobs in the forest sector. A large supply of timber would still come out of the forests. Initially, expect some reduction in quantity and no more old-growth trees. After 30 years of restoration forestry the health and productivity of our forestlands will be much higher than today. Over the space of several generations we can help the forests grow towards the magnificent stature that existed before Europeans arrived on the scene.

These proposals are cost-effective. Society can make no better investment than healthy productive forests, clean water and soil. Some people may ask if we can afford restoration forestry. I ask, can we afford not to?

Forest Vision: The Search for Sustainable Forestry

Steve Erickson

Standard Clear-cut Logging

INDUSTRIAL FORESTRY ATTEMPTS to emulate modern industrial agri-business (not agriculture). This is reflected in the language used (*harvest*, *crop tree*, *weed*, *rotation*, etc.), land tenure (large, politically powerful corporations owning the bulk of the productive land) and control of production, distribution, and marketing. This industrial mind-set quite logically leads to clearcut plantation forestry, with disastrous social and environmental effects. The result is establishment of even-age conifer monocultures, shortening of the initial grass/forb/shrub successional stage and elimination of the mature and old growth stages entirely.

New Forestry

Reproducing naturally-occurring ecosystem patterns, processes, and functions, while allowing logging, is a professed goal of many proponents of "New Forestry." For this reason, vehement opposition to classic "selective" logging is voiced by some. The claim is that selective logging will prove as much a disaster as the industrial clear-cutting model that now dominates the landscape. These people look to modifying clear-cutting instead.

Dr. Jerry Franklin, inventor of the term, adamantly maintains that New Forestry is not a set of rigid prescriptions. This can make it rather slippery, hard to pin down, and subject to obvious abuse. But as articulated by its more honest advocates, some general guidelines have emerged: Preserve future options; plan on a landscape level so connectivity is preserved between "reserves;" minimize fragmentation by grouping cuts together; minimize the frequency of disturbance by "hitting an area hard" and then leaving it alone; retain or create biological legacies, such as large, green trees, snags, and down logs; retain or create structural diversity; delay canopy closure in plantations by doing more frequent and less intense thinnings.

Classic Selective Logging

There are two basic kinds of "classic" selective logging: individual tree and group selection.

In individual tree selection, only single trees are cut according to forest conditions and goals of the forester. Canopy openings are created in specific locations for specific purposes. Orville Camp, for example, working on cutover former industrial forest lands in the mixed conifer region of southwestern Oregon, attempts to develop closed-canopy, species-diverse stands, while encouraging reproduction of the remaining genetically superior individuals. Merve Wilkinson, in old growth Douglas-fir on Vancouver Island, removes selected canopy dominants to encourage both understory growth and reproduction.

Both of the above examples are in sharp contrast to what usually passes as selective logging—removing the biggest trees (high-grading), or "thinning" the stand so only one age class remains, a preliminary step before clear-cutting.

Industrial foresters claim that individual tree selection is not practical. Felling individual trees will damage the remaining trees and Douglas-fir requires large openings to reproduce successfully. Skill and experience are the keys to avoid damaging surrounding trees, as Wilkinson and Camp demonstrate.

Group selection creates small (generally less than 2.5 acres) openings. These can be large enough for both planted Douglas-fir and natural regeneration so that over time, properly done, group selection will result in stands composed of patches of diverse ages.

A number of proposals have been put forward that provide for alternatives to conventional clear-cut logging. Here, we review what's been tabled.

Sustainable Forestry Roundtable (SFR) Proposal

The SFR proposal came out of "negotiations" involving Washington state agencies led by the Department of Natural Resources (DNR), counties, large industrial timber companies, some small forest landowners, some Native American tribes, and several environmental groups. It was inherently political and not ecologically based. Considered here are the main provisions of the "final" SFR proposal.

1. A mandatory "green up" between adjacent clear-cuts comprised of either 5-year-old trees or 6-foot seedlings. These are aesthetic, not ecological considerations;

2. Two green trees, two snags, and three down logs per acre to be left after clear-cutting. Whether this will provide sufficient replacement snags and down woody debris is questionable;

3. Ten percent of each landowner's land managed as "late successional" forest, as defined by the Washington Department of Wildlife. Loopholes reduced the strength of this provision considerably. The oldest stands would not necessarily be set aside and logging would be allowed in the "late successional" areas.

There was no limit on the rate of harvest, no minimum "rotation age," and the proposal assumed that even-age management (clearcutting) would continue to be the dominant logging method.

Forests Forever

The Forests Forever initiative ran on last November's ballot in California and almost passed. It banned clear-cutting, limited entry into stands to once per decade, limited harvest to the amount grown in the previous decade, and required eventual recovery to uneven age stands that could produce the maximum possible sustainable volume of timber. High grading was prevented by limiting cutting of "mature" trees to the volume of mature trees that grew in the previous decade. Maturity was defined as culmination of mean annual increment.

Landowners had to produce "sustained-yield plans" showing how they would achieve "maximum long-term sustained yield;" this required creating the "ideal" distribution of different age classes of trees.

These provisions effectively mandated a sustainable rate of harvest and required the recovery of degraded forest lands and plantations to full productivity.

SUSTAIN Proposal

SUSTAIN is a coalition of groups working to change forest practices on state and private lands and is developing a sustainable forestry proposal to regulate private and state forest land in Washington. It attempts to synthesize New Forestry and Forests Forever, avoiding several perceived problems of these systems, notably New Forestry's lack of any explicit requirement for a sustainable rate of harvest, and Forests Forever's imposition of standardized multi-

age stands everywhere, along with frequent entries and roading required by selective logging.

Even and uneven-age stands are treated differently. The intent is to prevent conversion from structurally diverse uneven-age stands to plantations.

Logging in uneven-age stands is essentially the same as in Forests Forever—selective logging—with the rate of harvest based on the previous decade's growth of the individual stand. Entry is limited to once per decade, with an exception for small landowners. Ten mature trees per acre must be retained for future snag and down log recruitment.

Determining the rate of harvest of even-age stands is more complex. The intent is to develop structural diversity in succeeding stands, while minimizing entries and roadbuilding, and approximating typical distributions of even and uneven-age forest patches.

A decadal "allowable cut" is determined only for stands which have reached maturity (Culmination of Mean Annual Increment–CMAI); immature plantations aren't cut. The area of even-aged stands which have reached the minimum rotation age is divided by 1/10 the minimum rotation age; this determines the decadal "allowable cut."

For example: out of 10,000 acres of plantations which have reached CMAI (say, 80 years old), 1250 acres could be clear-cut in the first decade. Since the allowable cut is figured on a decadal basis, it will change as younger plantations mature.

To develop structural diversity and provide a future supply of large-diameter logs, total clearcutting is prohibited. According to Jerry Franklin, 15% of a stand's volume must be retained for there to be enough variation in tree size to create structural diversity in the succeeding stand. So, 1/3 of the volume of the plantation is deferred from harvest and retained until the next rotation. At the next rotation, 1/2 of the surviving retained trees can be cut.

To copy the patchiness of natural landscape patterns, up to 10 contiguous acres can have less than 15% of the volume retained. In these clearings, at least 25 mature trees must be retained on every 2.5 acres. Other areas must retain at least 15% of the volume, with an overall average of 1/3 of the volume deferred from harvest.

To protect riparian zones, skirt "no cut" buffers are required around all streams.

So, how do these different "sustainable" forestry systems stack up in restoring and sustaining forest ecological functions, processes, and patterns?

Forest Fragmentation/ Habitat Connectivity

Dispersed clear-cutting, as inflicted on the National Forests, is blamed as the villain leading to forest fragmentation. But corporate forest lands are in no better shape: giant, contiguous clear-cuts eliminate fragmentation problems by eliminating the forest.

Most discussions on fragmentation ignore the overall rate of harvest and its effect on the landscape. Plum Creek's "New Forestry" experiments in Kittitas County, Washington illustrate this. Because the goal is still the liquidation of all mature forest within a short time, low fragmentation cutting of the last unlogged forest merely postpones the final liquidation. Low fragmentation is no substitute for an adequate system of preserves.

Since selection logging in the Northwest is currently only practiced on a relatively small scale, landscape fragmentation is not an issue. Insensitively practiced, however, the many small patch cuts created by group selection hold the potential for massive forest fragmentation. However, aerial photographs of Collins Pine and Fir in California give a clue to the likely effects of sensitive selective logging on forest connectivity and fragmentation. Since the late 1940's, Collins has only practiced selective logging (no clear-cutting) and aerial views show a relatively unbroken canopy on their 90,000 acres.

Forests Forever would have essentially the same effects on connectivity as classic selection logging. Much would depend on the individual practitioner.

At first glance, SFR looks promising, with its network of "late successional" reserves and corridors designed by wildlife biologists. However, the "late successional" reserves are simply not large enough because the areas in between will continue to be completely clear-cut. It follows that larger reserves would be required than if more ecologically "friendly" logging occurred in between. Without question, the more ecologically hostile the landscape outside the reserves, the larger the reserves must be.

The SUSTAIN proposal's sustainable rate of harvest provisions should have the effect of limiting the extent and rate of fragmentation. The tree retention requirements should make the logged areas less ecologically hostile, allowing them to function as corridors for mobile species as they recover from logging. The unlogged riparian buffers should also function, to some extent, as corridors.

Forest Stand Structural Diversity

Standard clear-cutting creates even-age stands that are not allowed to mature. This eliminates structural diversity in succeeding stands.

In SFR, logging in the "late successional" areas is intended to enhance structural diversity. However, lax DNR regulation and loopholes almost guarantee abuse.

The SUSTAIN tree retention regime will result in stands with two age classes during the first "rotation." While a vast improvement over current clear-cutting, these stands are nowhere near as structurally diverse as those under a selective logging regime where all age classes are maintained, such as the Forests Forever system's "maximum sustained yield" provisions.

However, not all stands of natural forest in the Pacific Northwest have this kind of "maximized" structural diversity. Windstorms and fires have created a much patchier landscape.

The SUSTAIN proposal attempts to account for this, by producing patchy stands that include both even and uneven-aged components.

Biological Legacies (Snags and Large Down Logs)

Standard industrial clear-cutting eliminates snags and large down logs. SFR provides these at a minimal level. Selective logging systems, including Forests Forever, provide abundant opportunities, but don't mandate future snag and large down log recruitment. The SUSTAIN proposal explicitly provides for this ecological attribute.

Disturbance Pattern/Erosion/Flooding

Standard industrial clear-cutting takes no account of these. SFR would likely not reduce current levels of erosion and flooding caused by clear-cutting while classic selective logging depends on the individual practitioner for its effects on erosion and flooding.

Forests Forever would fare better. In its ultimate application which entails individual tree selection in all-aged stands, erosion-causing disturbance would be minimized and rain-on-snow floods would probably be eliminated, due to retention of an almost total canopy. However, roads present a problem in the Forests Forever system. The potential for erosion caused by poorly designed, built, and maintained roads is high.

The SUSTAIN proposal follows Forests Forever for uneven-aged stands. For even-age stands, the New Forestry dictum of "hitting an area hard" and then leaving it alone is followed. The relatively long time between logging entries and the few roads required (compared to selective logging systems) would hopefully result in less erosion. Clear-cutting in the transitory snow zone is prohibited; combined with the rate-of-harvest provisions, this will hopefully prevent rain-on-snow floods.

Genetic Integrity/Genetic Diversity

Clear-cutting relies on tree planting rather than natural regeneration. SFR also relies on clear-cutting and tree planting. Research indicates that the tree seed zones currently in use are far too large to even approximate the close genetic fit that exists between trees and their immediate environment. Ultimately, to retain existing forest tree genetic diversity, reliance on natural reseeding and regeneration is necessary. All the other forestry systems can provide for this.

Buy the All-New, Sustainable Forestry Today!

Whenever the dominant industrial world view is threatened by a new paradigm, co-optation is the response, whether the threat is changing oppressive relations between humans or viewing nature as having purposes and rights. This trend is well underway in the terminology and "lingo" that has grown up in the forestry reform movement. "New Forestry" has become to the sustainable forestry movement as the term "natural foods" has become to the sustainable agriculture movement—a buzzword to be manipulated to obscure the central issues and "take the heat off." "Natural," "New Forestry," "New Perspectives," "Sustainable Forestry Roundtable," have all been turned into convenient labels for marketing cosmetic changes as all-new commodities.

Should activists reject out of hand any reform packages bearing these or other devalued terms? I think not, but it does mean that we need to look beyond the buzzword titles and read the fine print, and only then decide whether or not a proposal will really produce ecosystem sustainability.

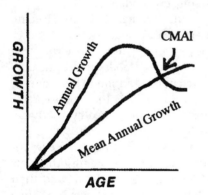

How a Tree Grows

The steeper curve is the amount the tree grows every year. The flatter curve is the average growth per year, the total volume of the tree divided by its age. Mature trees were defined as those which have reached their maximum mean annual growth, or Culmination of Mean Annual Increment (CMAI). This is the point at which the tree produces the most lumber averaged over its lifetime. CMAI always occurs after the tree has passed its maximum annual growth. Harvesting before CMAI, industry's current practice, reduces the total volume of timber available over time.

Reprinted with permission from Northwest Conservation, *Summer 1991.*

New Forestry: A State of Mind

Tim Foss

3

ANYONE EVEN REMOTELY INVOLVED with timber management today knows that all is not well. Timber sales are appealed right and left, often successfully so. Forest Plans are under attack before they even roll off the presses, and the quagmire of lawsuits seems to deepen daily. Before the Hatfield-Adams amendment brought some temporary stability to the situation, most of the timber program in USFS Region 6 wasted up in an injunction, and it's virtually guaranteed to be again after that amendment expires. Most of us can't help but wonder how we ever got into this mess and how are we ever going to get out? This article explores a way out: a new concept in forest management called "New Forestry."

The Problem

The rub, as I see it, involves paradigms — a set of theories and beliefs, accepted as true, by people involved with a given subject. These theories and beliefs, together with the tools used to carry them out, create a paradigm, which is literally the "reality" of the situation for those people who subscribe to the paradigm. This paradigm may or may not be based on truth, but as long as we operate within the paradigm, we'll never know. For example, there was once a paradigm that held that the world was flat. All commerce, all navigation, all religion operated within this paradigm even though the Greeks had proved over a thousand years earlier that the world was round. This evidence was ignored because it did not fit into the paradigm. Only when a few visionary people, most notably Christopher Columbus, poked their heads outside the paradigm and looked around did this begin to change. Why did it take so long? Because, as a rule, people will generally cling to an old paradigm for dear life. Letting go of our "reality," even when a new reality is staring us in the face, is a scary proposition. Chris Maser, in his book *The Redesigned Forest*, says "After 20 years as a research scientist, I know that a paradigm, any paradigm, that has become comfortable has also become self-limiting. New data cannot and will not fit into the old paradigm. It is a carefully constructed, impervious, rigid membrane of tradition that, like concrete, hardens with age and must be periodically broken, like the exoskeleton of an insect, if a new thought-form is to grow, a new vision is to move society forward." (Maser, 1988).

In forestry, we have a long-standing paradigm of wise use, which is based on the notion that "a managed forest provides more benefits than an unmanaged forest and through proper harvest scheduling, we can maximize these benefits." This leads to such truths as:

- Healthy trees—healthy forest.
- We can have a sustainable forest forever by cutting down old trees and planting new ones.
- We know how timber cutting will affect wildlife and those that can't live in managed forests can live in set-aside areas.
- Anything that competes with the trees in our plantations can be suppressed through the use of technology.
- We, as professionals, are best qualified to make forest management decisions since we understand how the forest operates.

This paradigm has served us well for many years, and was certainly an improvement over the previous paradigm which held that the forests were endless and we would never run out of trees. Getting back to the "rub," however, it seems that the owners of the National Forests, the American people, are no longer accepting our professional forestry paradigm (it's questionable if they ever did). They are telling us, as evidenced throughout the media, that they see their forest not simply as a source of "outputs" for human consumption, but as a living biological entity that deserves our respect. In short, they want Forests, not tree farms.

Meanwhile, back at experimental forest...

At the same time, our own researchers have been finding new tidbits of information that chip away at our comfortable paradigm. A group of scientists known as the Andrews Research Group, among others, have been discovering things about forest ecosystems we "sawlog foresters" had never imagined. For instance, the work of Chris Maser and James Trappe is showing that down rotting logs, scientifically labeled "coarse woody debris", are homes to a whole host of organisms, including fungus-eating rodents such as the California Red-backed Vole and the Deer Mouse. These fungus-eaters are an important vector for dispersal of mycorrhizal fungi which form associations with tree roots and facilitate nutrient uptake. No logs = no voles = no mycorrhizae = depressed growth (Maser, 1988; Franklin, 1989).

These scientists have also found an incredible diversity of life in the crowns of old-growth forests. For instance, they identified numerous species of insects that are parasitic on other insects. In young forests, these parasites are absent, and the insect populations are heavily weighted toward plant-eaters, such as aphids. They theorized from this that the multidimensional crowns of the old growth forest must be a crucial factor in maintaining a balance in insect populations for the whole forest (Franklin, 1989).

Other scientists have been studying the interactions of the streamside ecosystems. We now know, for instance, that logs in the creek, once thought of as an evil of logging, create pools, which are an essential component of fish habitat. The value of leaf litter in the stream and the necessity of insect habitat, too are coming to light (Franklin, 1989). Scientists at the University of Montana and elsewhere have even discovered a vast and previously unknown ecosystem in the groundwater beneath streams (Booth, 1989). These are just a few of the thousands and thousands of ecosystem relationships now being discovered. We are realizing that all we thought we knew about the forest represented only the barest fraction, and that the trees are only one component of a huge jigsaw puzzle.

Each ecosystem component, from the fungus to the squirrels to the Douglas-fir to the Spotted Owl, and everything in between interacts in some way with every other component. This diversity or complexity is now understood to be an essential component of a healthy ecosystem. And we are beginning to realize that we are probably still a long way from understanding what really makes the forest tick; we are finally admitting that we don't even know all the questions, let alone all the answers. "Along with uncertainty and change, our woefully inadequate knowledge of forest ecosystems should create humility amongst us because we have only just entered a period of rapid expansion in such knowledge" (Franklin & others, 1988).

In addition, forestry issues have become part of larger global environmental concerns. Our forests are being put under environmental stress as never before from air pollution, acid rain, and perhaps most ominous, global climate change. "The ability of the ecosystem to tolerate or absorb new kinds of stresses or changes is clearly of increasing importance. The key to that resilience is in the maintenance of ecological complexity or diversity" (Franklin and others, 1988).

In light of this expanding ecological knowledge, many scientists have begun joining their voices calling for reform. They are saying that our traditional forestry practices of simplifying ecosystems are reducing the forest's productive capacity, and that we can no longer afford to manage our Forests as tree farms (haven't we heard that somewhere before?). The time has come, they contend, for a fundamental shift in our paradigm.

Out of this was born the idea of "New Forestry." It is a new paradigm based on ecosystems, rather than just trees. The central idea in New Forestry is that the function of all forest organisms is important, and management must maintain habitats for those organisms or at least provide for quickly re-establishing them. Tree cutting becomes appropriate only when we can leave an intact forest ecosystem when we're done.

So what do we do about it? Once we begin to understand the problems, once we've come around to the new way of thinking about the forest, how do we actually put it into practice? Presently, there are many different ideas about the tools, and it's probably that no one concept or technique will be applicable to every ecosystem. The next few sections discuss these tools, but it is critical that the forest manager understand that tools by themselves will not do the job. New Forestry must be underpinned by a new state of mind, a new respect for the life that is the Forest.

The Franklin View

Dr. Jerry Franklin's concept, which has attracted the most attention so far, is primarily oriented toward the western Pacific Northwest and is based on emulating the way the natural forest recovers from a fire. In this area, most stands were periodically replaced by large fires every several hundred years. The snags, down logs, surviving green trees, etc. were all important to the regeneration of the new forest. (For an excellent discussion of these processes, refer to Chris Maser's new book *Forest Primeval*, available from Sierra Club Press). Franklin's concept, then, consists of several parts:

1. A system of interconnected reserved areas. These would provide the necessary habitat for species that cannot tolerate any level of disturbance. (There may not be any in this category, but then

again, there may. Remember, we don't know all the answers). These reserved areas would also provide a base for continued learning about the ecology of old-growth, and would keep our options open should we discover some critical function of old-growth that we don't yet understand. (Remember, we don't know...). These reserved areas would need to be large enough, and contiguous enough to provide a reasonable amount of old-growth habitat. The jury's still out on how much that is, but much research is being directed at answering that question.

2. The retention of large snags and down logs. The snags are important habitat for a variety of cavity-nesting birds, and as a future supply of coarse woody debris. According to Jerry Franklin, a tree has fulfilled only about half its ecological function at the time it dies (Franklin and others, 1988). Leaving snags can be a safety hazard, of course, so they may need to be clumped or strategically located to avoid this. Working with the State agencies responsible for work safety will be essential to find a workable solution.

The down logs would provide the benefits of coarse woody debris including habitat for a variety of vertebrates and invertebrates, erosion protection, nutrient cycling, etc. Some slash disposal is probably still necessary for fire protection and plantability, and much research remains to determine just how much is appropriate to leave.

3. Leaving a variety of green trees (referred to as green tree retention) throughout the harvest area to provide a measure of vertical diversity. How many trees is still an open question, but Franklin (1989) suggests between 8 and 15 trees per acre — about an average shelterwood spacing. These trees would be a variety of ages, sizes, species, and vigors. They would provide habitats for vertebrates and invertebrates that live in the crowns of older trees, and would provide a measure of "multi-layeredness" once the new stand is up and growing. A multi-layered canopy is a feature of old-growth forests that seems to be essential to animals like the spotted owl.

4. Protection of riparian ecosystems. This would entail at most a very light cut in riparian areas, or preferably no cutting at all. The riparian ecosystem is highly complex, and seems to be very key to the overall health of the forest (Mahlein and Hemstrom, 1988). Maintaining the balance between all organisms—fish, birds, aquatic plants, large mammals, small mammals, insects, riparian vegetation, stream nutrients, etc.—is crucial. These riparian areas would also serve as travel corridors between reserved areas, and maintaining cover would be a key to this function (Harris, 1984).

5. Delaying canopy closure. This would mean planting wider, thinning wider, and possibly thinning more frequently. The purpose is to allow sunlight to reach the forest floor for a longer period of time, thereby extending the period of time during which understory vegetation is a component of the stand. This would contribute to that all-important vertical diversity (Franklin, pers. commun.).

6. Minimizing fragmentation. Cutting units would be placed adjacent to existing clearcuts, rather than "pockmarking" uncut areas. The traditional practice of dispersing clearcuts throughout uncut areas creates a great deal of "edge." This is great for deer and elk, but "interior" species that require old-growth will avoid these edge areas for a distance of up to 300 feet (Harris, 1984). A series of dispersed clearcuts, then, may completely degrade the habitat value of several thousand acres of old-growth. The practice of minimizing fragmentation will maintain these old-growth patches, and hence our future options, as long as possible.

As noted, this New Forestry-ala-Franklin (which he refers to as "sloppy clearcuts") is intended to simulate the conditions a natural forest would have when recovering from a fire. By providing the building blocks of diversity, it sets up the site to re-establish the ecosystem as soon as possible. On a landscape scale, having a mosaic of these types of harvest units interspersed with riparian zones and leave areas would, to the best of our current knowledge, maintain a healthy forest ecosystem. According to Franklin, "Maintenance or rapid compositional, functional, and structural diversity, is the objective of alternative silvicultural systems, *not just the re-establishment of trees* (my emphasis) ... The object becomes one of insuring that many forest ecosystem elements are perpetuated, and not just crop trees. Based on these concepts, perhaps the most critical issue is not the size of the area that is logged or how often it is logged (i.e. rotation age). It may, in fact, be what is left behind following logging — the biological legacies." (Franklin, 1989a). He also touches on his reservations about selection harvesting. He writes, "Although selective cutting does allow high levels of biological legacies, the necessity for dense road systems and frequent logging entries has high environmental and economic costs." (Franklin, 1989).

As noted by ecologist Miles Hemstrom and biologist Dieter Mahlein (1988), however, this brand of new forestry "...will not supplant natural ecosystems on reserved lands, nor will it resolve questions regarding whether to enter these and other remaining roadless areas. It is a new forestry strictly for landscapes committed to timber management." This is an important point: to recognize that Franklin's concept of new forestry is not intended to replace present management in visually sensitive areas, big winter range, or other special areas, but rather to introduce a measure of ecosystem consideration in timber management areas.

The Chief of the Forest Service and Congress have both endorsed this concept of new forestry and are putting their money where their mouth is. A major research project, dubbed "New Perspectives in Forestry" is being organized by PNW experiment station in Portland. It will be a long-term study to try out different techniques under controlled conditions and to quantify what the effects on the total ecosystem are. This will help answer many of the unknowns. Many National Forests too, are either implementing or at least considering these tools.

So what other toolboxes are out there?

Not everyone views new forestry exactly like Jerry Franklin. For instance, he doesn't discuss the concept of rotation much, except to say, as noted above, that it may not be as important as biological legacies. Chris Maser, by contrast, asserts that a long rotation is essential to re-establishing site productivity. In his book *The Redesigned Forest*, he calls for no more than three short (50-100 year) rotations, followed by a 300-400 year rotation for any given site. He asserts that it is essential to periodically re-establish the old-growth ecosystem in order to maintain the forest productivity (of all resources).

Larry Harris, author of "The Fragmented Forest," envisions a series of long-rotation islands scattered across the forest. Each island would have a block of untouched old-growth at its center, and then would be divided up like a pizza, each "slice" being managed as an even-age stand, but on a 300-400 year rotation, which would maintain 25% of the island in an old-growth state at any one time. These islands would comprise about 20% of the commercial forest, would range in size from 25 to 500 acres, and would be interconnected by riparian corridors (Harris, 1984).

All these forms of new forestry, however, still envision even-age management and clearcuts (however sloppy they maybe), and this does not sit well with everyone. Gordon Robinson, former forester with Southern Pacific Railroad and later the Sierra Club, lists five components of what he calls "excellent" forestry:

1. long rotations;
2. sustained yield;
3. maintenance of all native habitats;
4. protection of the soil; and
5. uneven-age management.

Robinson contends that all five elements are necessary for proper forest management, and he cites numerous examples to prove his point (Robinson, 1988).

Ned Fritz, coordinator of the Forest Reform Network, labels Franklin's version of new forestry as simply "buttered-up clear-cutting." In a letter to A.F.S.E.E.E., Fritz contends, "For at least 25 years, the Forest Service has been boasting of its snags, wildlife trees, stringers, streamside corridors, scenic areas, research natural areas, and other patches of vegetation, while demolishing the vast bulk of the 80 million acres of available timberland... After calling for alternative silvicultural systems, his (Franklin's) specific proposals are some that the Forest Service has been applying for years as part of dominant even-age management. Even with those amelioratory measures, even-age management devastates natural diversity far more than any form of continuous logging." Fritz goes on to say that "Selection management is the silvicultural system that comes closest to fulfilling all the ecological elements that Franklin wants to protect in his "New Forestry."

Selection Management—Is it practical?

So does selection harvest, or selective cutting, or uneven-age management, or whatever you want to call it, have a place in modern forestry? According to many private landowners and consultants successfully practicing it in nearly every timber type, the answer is an emphatic "yes!" Uneven-age management has long been a standard management system in northern hardwoods, ponderosa pine, and a few other timber types, but has been considered impractical elsewhere, particularly in the western Pacific Northwest. These landowners and consultants seem to be showing, however, that it can be successful in a great many situations.

Merve Wilkinson, of Ladysmith, British Columbia, provides an outstanding example of how selection harvesting can work in old-growth Douglas-fir. He began managing his 137 acres on Vancouver Island in 1945, using techniques he learned from an old Danish Forestry professor. His property at the time was 100% old-growth, mostly Douglas-fir with a smattering of grand fir, western red cedar, and western hemlock. On his first cut, he removed about 15% of the stand—mostly wind-thrown trees and any that were nearly dead. Since that time, he has made eight complete selection harvests — about one every five years. Each time, his harvest has taken those trees that are clearly on the way out, or that are overtopping an obviously-healthier tree, or that may be suppressed beyond recovery. He has no formal marking guides, basing his cutting on seat-of-the-pants experience and common sense. He is always careful to leave enough trees that the ecosystem remains pretty much intact. (This is what I noticed most about his property—that he is getting substantial timber production and yet it still feels like a forest.) His property is currently a mixture of old-growth Douglas-fir and second-growth Douglas-fir, hemlock, grand fir, and cedar. His current harvests likewise consist of some old-growth and some second-growth. In many cases, the old-growth trees are still adding enough wood to make it worth keeping them on the stump. There appears to now be a lower percentage of Douglas-fir than there was in the natural stand, but it still comprises about 75% of the trees in all age classes. This brings up a most interesting point: that all species seem to regenerate readily and grow quickly in the partial shade. This flies in the face of conventional wisdom, particularly regarding Douglas-fir, but at least on his site it works beautifully. Of course, they won't grow in complete shade, but according to Merve, about 50-75% crown closure makes for the best regeneration and growth.

As far as logging goes, Merve has a permanent low-standard road system and a series of designated skid trails. He relies on careful falling and skidding to preserve the residual stand. It seems to work, as even the grand fir shows virtually no sign of mechanical injury. He also does no spraying, fertilizing, planting, burning, or other cultural treatments. Over the years, Merve has figured his annual growth increment is about 500-700 board feet per acre per year. Merve is proving that uneven-age management works as well or better than even-age management, at least in his area. He works with the natural forces, rather than against them, and the result is a beautiful working forest. (Wilkinson, pers. commun.)

Centered in southern Oregon, the Forest Farm Association is a group of private landowners dedicated to continuous production of all the forest values; hence the term "forest farms," as opposed to "tree farms." The stated goal of the organization is "...to work for environmentally sound forest management practices which conserve both forest lands and forests to serve people's needs." The president of this organization, Orville Camp, owns 180 acres of forest near Selma, Ore., which he has nursed back to productive health after the previous owner stripped it of all merchantable timber in the mid 1960's. In the process, he developed his own brand of management called "natural selection ecoforestry." This involves going through his forest each year and looking for those trees that have been genetically selected for removal and then cutting them. In his predominantly young stands, he is cutting those trees that are falling behind in growth and would eventually be shaded out and die. This is not too much

different than a standard thinning, except that he does this over his whole property each year. In this way, he takes a very light cut, which minimizes ecosystem disruptions and he is able to remove the "non-crop" trees before significant growth reductions occur. As a result, he has some even-aged stands, some two-or-three-storied stands, and some all-aged stands. He welcomes this situation and does not try to make it all even-age or uneven-age.

Orville's land, like Merve's, produces a regular supply of forest products, but still feels like a forest. When he bought the land in 1967, the average growth rate was about 15 rings per inch, but currently it is about 6 rings per inch. Orville feels this is a result of re-establishing, at least in part, the natural ecosystem processes that maintain forest fertility. It was interesting to contrast his land to an adjacent BLM clear-cut which had been planted three times, including placing of shade cards, and still didn't look like it was regenerating very well. There was a great deal of brush and probably would have been sprayed if the tool had been available. Orv's land appears to have no regeneration problems because, according to him, every time an opening is created it is small and partially shaded. The key, he says, is to let nature regenerate trees in her own way, rather than trying to force it. (Camp, pers. commun.) For a complete discussion of Natural Selection Forestry, read the *Forest Farmer's Handbook*, by Orville Camp.

Recently a partnership has been formed between the Forest Farm Association and the International Woodworkers of America local 3-436. The Union has recognized that natural selection forestry and similar techniques hold the promise of continued forest management, and therefore employment, on lands that might otherwise be locked up. They have formed a company, Rogue Sustainable Forestry Co., that seeks long-term contracts with public and private landowners to manage their lands thorough natural selection forestry. The logs then go to another joint-venture company, Rogue Forest Products (Sterling, 1989).

These are two of the best examples of selection management that I have seen. There are many, many others throughout the country in virtually every timber type. For an excellent discussion of uneven-age management throughout the country, see "Keepers of the Perpetual Forests" by Edward C. "Ned" Fritz in the August 1988 issue of *Forest Watch*.

Within the Forest Service, too, there is a growing recognition of the benefits of uneven-age silvicultural systems. In California, Regional Forester Paul Barker has called for 80-85% of sales in that region to utilize silvicultural systems other than clear-cutting by 1992. On the

Idaho Panhandle National Forest, Supervisor Bill Morden told his staff to look at alternatives to clear-cutting. Morden says "I want them to look more holistically at the woods." In Region 6, an uneven-age management task force has been formed to monitor and gain experience with selection harvesting.

But what of the problems with selection harvesting articulated by Jerry Franklin and others? If not handled well, these problems can turn well-intended selection harvesting into a biological disaster. The following are my own observations of how successful forest managers throughout the Northwest are dealing with these problems.

Does uneven-age management require a more extensive road network?

This view is valid if management proceeds in a haphazard manner, just as how haphazard clear-cutting has, in some cases, resulted in a high road density. However, there seems to be no evidence that skid distances need to be any shorter with the selection harvesting than with any other silvicultural system. A well-planned road is central to good forestry, and should be essentially the same for any piece of land whether under even-age or uneven-age management.

Is there more soil compaction due to the frequent re-entries under uneven-age management?

Again, unplanned skidding can produce severe soil compaction under any silvicultural system. Most forest landowners now recognize that soil compaction can be minimized by sticking to a system of designated skid trails which would be the same regardless of cutting method. Skidders stay on these trails, which average 100-150 feet apart and winchline is pulled to the logs. This prevents any compaction except on the skid trails themselves, which if carefully planned, amount to no more than 5% of the total area. These skid trails become a permanent part of the transportation system (again regardless of silvicultural system) and are used in all succeeding entries. In selection harvesting especially, it is critical they be located properly on the first entry.

Does uneven-age management result in more residual stand damage?

Selection harvesting does require more careful logging than most other silvicultural systems. Residual stand damage can be minimized, however, by careful falling and skidding. Merve Wilkinson is even able to protect pole-size stems while falling old-growth by jacking the trees to fall where he wants them. Falling costs may be slightly higher than under a clear-cut system.

Is uneven-age management economical?

From what I've observed, on skidder ground, uneven-age management can be practiced profitably almost anywhere that clear-cutting can. The skidding costs are slightly higher, due to the frequent moves, falling may cost more as noted above, and planning seems to be more time consuming, but rarely are the costs high enough to make it prohibitive. True, clear-cutting grosses more money up front than selection, but when you factor in the costs of planting, precommercial thinning, burning, spraying and other cultural treatments, uneven-age management becomes very attractive in the long run.

What about on steep ground?

To my knowledge, true individual tree selection has not been done on skyline ground in this country. It is, however, common practice in Europe. Skyline thinning is fairly common in the Pacific Northwest and there is no technical reason why the same technology couldn't be applied to skyline harvesting. Economics remains a question: Is it worth rigging up a skyline system for the low volumes per acre involved in selection? Much work remains to be done to answer this question. Small, low-tech skyline systems are a possibility, as is the concept of pre-constructing corridors and pre-bunching logs. Even if individual tree selection is still uneconomical, group selection may be the answer.

Will uneven-age management work in all situations?

It may or may not, depending on the objectives. Clear-cutting may be the only option in root-rot pockets, etc., if timber production is our primary goal. We do know, however, that many species, including Douglas-fir, can grow and thrive in partial shade. The key seems to be identifying how much shade the trees in a particular ecotype can tolerate without serious growth reduction.

Does selection harvesting perpetuate insect and disease problems already on the site?

It may, if natural regeneration is planned and if certain species on that site already have serious insect or disease problems. A major concern with uneven-age management is that it fosters a change toward the more tolerant species and these are the ones that seem most prone to insects and disease. A potential solution to this is planting of more resistant species following logging. Planting has not generally been done under uneven-age management, but it can give the land manager more control over species changes and could also shorten regeneration time. We do need to remember, too that insects and disease are components of the natural ecosystem and eliminating them all is probably not wise.

Uneven-age management has been shown to work well in many situations. Those landowners practicing it are producing a steady income and maintaining a forest environment. The common denominator among them is that they really respect the forest. It seems that if the forest manager really cares, the rest falls into place.

Toward Holistic Forestry

As we've seen, New Forestry encompasses a wide array of tools, from simply leaving more slash on the ground all the way to individual tree selection. But New Forestry is more than just tools. It's moving toward a new paradigm —a whole new way of looking at the forest. It's respecting the forest for the living ecosystem that it is; one composed of millions of living individuals. Chief Seattle, in his well-known speech said: "If we sell you our land, you must remember to teach your children that the rivers are our brothers, and yours, and you must henceforth give the rivers the kindness you would give any brother.... Teach your children what we have taught our children—that the Earth is our mother. Whatever befalls the Earth soon befalls the sons of the Earth. If men spit on the ground, they spit on themselves."

Once we come around to this new view, the tools will naturally follow. At this point, debating about the tools only masks the true issues and intent of the emerging view of the forest. Let's recognize that we have an ever-increasing array of tools with which to maintain all parts of the global ecosystem, including humans. The forest is not a factory for goods and services. It is a living entity which we have an ethical obligation to respect and perpetuate, even the parts which seemingly have no present use to human beings. We have an opportunity as never before to be part of this new world view. As leaders in the forestry profession, we in the Forest Service must stop resisting this paradigm shift and start leading it. The time is now for a New Forestry.

Reprinted with permission from Inner Voice, *journal of the Association of Forest Service Employees for Environmental Ethics (AFSEE), P.O. Box 11615, Eugene, OR 97440. Tel: (503) 484-2692.*

Sources of More Information

Orville Camp, 2100 Thompson Cr. Rd., Selma, OR 97538 (503) 597-4313

Merve Wilkinson, R.R. 3, Ladysmith, B.C. VOR 2EO Canada (604) 722-2853

New Perspectives in Forestry Project, contact: Tim Toile or John Henderson, PNW Research Station, P.O. Box 3880, Portland, OR 97208

Woodland Management, Inc. (consultants), Kruse Woods One Building, Suite 282, Lake Oswego, OR 97035 (503) 684-4004

Individual Tree Selection Management (consultants), 621 SW Morrison St., Portland, OR 97205 (503) 222-9772

Literature Cited

Booth, William. 1989. "Beneath Rivers, Another Realm." *Washington Post*, October 26.

Camp, Orville. 1984. *The Forest Farmer's Handbook*. Sky River Press. Ashland, Oregon.

Franklin, Jerry. 1989. Toward a new forestry. *American Forests*. Nov.-Dec. '89: 37-44.

Franklin, Jerry. 1989a. "An ecologist's perspective on northwestern forests in 2010." *Forest Watch*. Aug. 89.10(2):6-9.

Franklin, Jerry, *et al*. 1988. "The importance of ecological diversity in maintaining long-term site productivity." In: *Proceedings of symposium on Maintaining the long-term productivity of Pacific Northwest forest ecosystems*.

Fritz, Edward C. 1988. "Keepers of the perpetual forests." *Forest Watch*. Aug. 88 9(2):10-13.

Harris, Larry D. 1984. *The Fragmented Forest*. University of Chicago Press, Chicago, Ill.

Mahlein, Dieter and Miles Hemstrom. "Ecosystem management—a new forestry." *Forest Watch*. March 88.8(8):8-11.

Maser, Chris. 1988. *The Redesigned Forest*. R & E Miles, San Pedro, California.

Maser, Chris. 1988. *Forest Primeval*. Sierra Club Books, San Francisco, Calif.

Robinson, Gordon. 1988. *The Forest and the Trees—a Guide to Excellent Forestry*. Island Press, Covelo, Calif.

Sterling, Robert. 1989. "Unlikely allies collaborate their future in forests." *Medford Mail Tribune*, Dec. 21-27.

Titone, Julie. 1989. "Supervisor sees forest, not trees." Spokesman Review, *Spokane Chronicle*, Dec. 10.

Excellent Forestry

Gordon Robinson

FORESTS FORM AND THRIVE BEST where there are no people—and hence no forestry, and those are perfectly justified who say:

> Formerly we had no forestry science and enough wood; now we have that science, but no wood... Germany formerly contained immense, perfect, most fertile forests. But the large forests have become small, the fertile have become sterile. Each generation of man has seen a smaller generation of wood. Here and there we admire still the giant oaks and firs, which grew up without any care, while we are perfectly persuaded that we shall never in the same places be able, with any art or care, to reproduce similar trees. The grandsons of those giant trees show the signs of threatening death before they have attained one-quarter of the volume which the old ones contained, and no art nor science can produce on the forest soil which has become less fertile, such forests as are here and there still being cut down.... Without utilization, the forest soil improves constantly; if used in an orderly manner it remains in a natural equilibrium; if used faultily it becomes poorer. The good forester takes the highest yield from the forest without deteriorating the soil, the poor one neither obtains this yield nor preserves the fertility of the soil.

The foregoing was extracted from the Foreword to *Principles of Silviculture* by the late Frederick S. Baker, Professor of Forestry and Dean of the Forestry School of the University of California. It is interesting to note that he was quoting from the preface to *Advice on Silviculture*, 1816, by a famous German forester named Heinrich Cotta, and that the piece was also used by Dr. B. E. Fernow to introduce the American Forestry Quarterly in 1902. Thus, we have it from three great foresters spread over a period of 150 years that the ideal forest is where there are no people.

The quality of forestry in the United States is low and getting lower despite all the encouraging reports we get these days to the contrary. Most industry continues to cut saw timber faster than it grows, and to consume whatever timber it can buy without husbanding its own lands. The quality of management of our national forests is being eroded under pressure from industry. Many people are questioning these matters. I propose therefore to describe excellent forestry together with its justification to provide the layman with a basis for judging the quality of timber management wherever it is encountered, or at least to know what questions to ask.

Forestry is defined as "the scientific management of forests for the continuous production of goods and services." "The practice of forestry with the objective of obtaining the maximum of volume and quality of products per unit area through the application of the best techniques of silviculture and management" defines intensive forestry. But silviculture consists of silvics modified by economics, and silvics is defined as the ecology of trees. To avoid confusion resulting from consideration of shifting economic factors, I am using the phrase "excellent forestry," which might also be referred to as applied silvics.

Excellent forestry has four characteristics, each of which requires considerable elaboration for clear understanding. First of all, cut must be matched with growth—that is to say the amount of timber removed from one's property must not be more than the amount that will grow in the cutting interval. This is generally referred to as sustained yield and where one is working with virgin timber, this means continuous production at an even rate with the aim of achieving at the earliest practicable time an approximate balance between net growth and harvest either by annual or somewhat longer periods.

Excellent forestry also implies growing timber on long rotations, generally speaking I would say from 100 to 200 years. Rotation is the age of trees at the time of cutting plus whatever time is required for re-establishment after logging.

A third characteristic of excellence is selection management in preference to alternative systems such as clearcutting wherever this is consistent with the silvics of the species involved. This implies frequent light cuts, generally not removing more than 10% of the volume at one time. Where clearcutting must be practiced, as in the management of highly intolerant species, the openings should be kept as small as possible, preferably no greater in diameter than half the height of the surrounding timber.

Finally, excellent forestry is characterized by infinite care to avoid damage to the soil, the all-important basic resource.

The advantages of such management are truly overwhelming. The lowest fire hazard of all the cover types found in our western forests is mature old-growth timber. While the highest hazard is dry grass, the second highest is logging slash on cutover land and stands of saplings. This situation results from the fact that in the mature forest air is trapped by the full canopy thus providing a micro-climate kept humid by transpiration of the trees. Also it is cool because of the shade. Fire hazard is primarily a function of fuel moisture content and, in the mature forest, moisture is relatively high and remains so even in the middle of hot summer days.

Furthermore, the mature forest is comprised mostly of trees free of branches close to the ground and their bark tends to be fire resistant. Thus, even when fires do occur, they tend to go along the ground burning merely leaf litter and debris and occasional patches of reproduction. A dramatic illustration of this principle occurred in the Haystack Fire of the Klamath River Country in 1956. At one point the fire roared up the south slope of the Siskiyous, going through three adjacent ownerships situated at about the same elevation and having the same cover type. One was a section of national forest which had been logged a few years before in accordance with the Forest Service Region 5 standard marking rules. This had resulted in the removal of about 60% of the volume comprising primarily the oldest and largest trees. The second piece was virgin timber, and the third was property belonging to a lumber company that had recently removed every thing permitted under the California State Forest Practice rules. That involved cutting about 90% of the volume, and spared only trees under 20 inches or so in diameter. The fire killed about half of the timber on the national forest parcel, killed every living thing on the lumber company's land, but as near as I could tell did not burn any more than a few patches of small reproduction in the virgin forest, although it did burn the decayed heart out of the few standing dead trees which fell, leaving a few hollow logs to become habitat for a variety of friendly little living things. Clearly, the forester who maintains the full canopy and practices light selective logging is least likely to suffer disaster from fire.

While foresters frequently insist upon the felling of all dead trees during logging operations for fire suppression purposes, it is frequently overlooked that these very trees are required habitat for many birds who perform great service in controlling insect enemies of our forests. These birds include woodpeckers, chickadees, titmice, nuthatches, creepers, mountain bluebirds, and the violet-green swallow.

Light selective logging, or clear-cutting in small openings, provides maximum assurance against windthrow. During the great Columbus Day storm of 1963 along the west coast, a tremendous amount of damage occurred in heavily cut stands. Relatively, the damage was much less in virgin timber.

Damage from insects and diseases is far more severe where clear-cutting is practiced than in the selection forest. Where large areas are clear-cut, as in conversion to even age management, certain insects may breed in the slash in great numbers and later attack the young reproduction.

Where clear-cutting is practiced there is always a tendency to establish plantations of one species rather than mixtures without regard as to how the planted species naturally occur. A pure stand forms an ideal situation for a disease to build up to epidemic proportions. Infection is direct and rapid from tree to tree and if one species is destroyed there is nothing left. The most hazardous pure stands are even-aged stands because fungus parasites are often virulent during only one stage of the development of the trees. Pure stands of trees outside their natural range are particularly liable to difficulty. Pure stands, those composed of a single species, are particularly susceptible to disastrous outbreak. For instance, outbreaks of the hemlock looper have been especially destructive only in stands composed of a high percentage of hemlock, where a heavy mixture of other species occurs, infestation soon thins out and loses its destructive power. Attacks of the spruce bud worm also have been most destructive in stands composed of a high percentage of the firs and Douglas fir. It is particularly important that the cuttings in stands that normally grow as mixed types should not favor the leaving of the single species. Since most insects and diseases of forest trees are limited rather sharply to one or a few hostplants, mixed stands offer far fewer opportunities for epidemics than do pure stands. In the case of insects, every tree in a pure stand offers food and breeding ground. In the case of fungi the liberated spores find favorable hosts every where. In both cases destructive concentration can readily be built up in pure stands.

Plantations of young pine in California are being invaded by a variety of little-known insects, some indigenous and some imports. They damage the stand by reducing growth from sap sucking and defoliation. Some insects kill the tops of the leaders causing crooked or forked stems. Dead stubs make easy entry for heart rot and, in a number of cases insects will kill the trees outright. The pine reproduction weavil and the more familiar bark weevils are principal agents of tree killing in young stands.

Fomes annosus, the agent which causes decay in the butt logs of a good many fire-damaged old trees is a minor nuisance in a virgin forest and tends to be eliminated almost entirely in the selection forest. However, where clear-cutting is practiced, the disease spreads through the stumps and roots of the felled timber to become an epidemic, killing young trees.

Forests can and should be managed to produce a continuous even flow of mature timber. Old growth is far superior to young growth, however you look at it. Stumpage prices are much higher for old growth than for young growth timber. Furthermore, it is anticipated that young growth stumpage prices are not likely to increase substantially over the next 25 to 50 years. Prices of higher-grade commodities will increase substantially, but that can't come from young growth. There will be a great increase in the use of pulp, but the great quantities of young growth available will hold prices down. In pulp, furthermore, quality of fiber will become an important factor.

The points made in this report show the advantage of growing timber slowly and on long rotations. In the dense canopy of a selection forest the trees tend to grow slowly. This is not to say that the total timber grown is any less on a volume basis than in even-aged stands. Returning to quality considerations, the suitability of second growth Douglas fir for veneer is greatly diminished because it is not only undesirable for veneer faces but also veneer cuts are rough; the numerous knots tend to chip the knife although lathe settings are no more critical than in old growth. If lumber is produced the yield of high grade material is lower than from old growth trees.

As a tree matures and grows in girth, the cambium produces longer and thicker walled cells. The length of fibres laid down in new growth in conifers increases with the age of the tree. Length generally varies from 1 millimeter at age one to about 4 millimeters at age 70—after which length remains constant with increase in age. This means that where timber is being grown for fibre, the longest fibres occur only in that part of the tree which has grown after age 70. It would seem to be good business, therefore, to grow trees to an age of 100 to 200 years and to use for pulp chips the slabbing from squaring or rounding the logs, and making high quality lumber and plywood from the remainder of the core. This is essentially what is done with our virgin timber today, but not with trees grown on a short rotation.

What has been said about the length of fibres is true also of the density or strength of fibres. That part of the tree which has been lain down by the cambium layer after age 70 contains the strongest fibres as well as the longest ones. There seems to be one slight difference, however, between this and the length of fibre in that as trees grow more slowly they tend to have dense fibre in the crown as well as in the lower bole. Consequently the tops of trees grown on a long rotation are superior for pulp purposes.

That part of the conifer grown below 40 to 50 years of age is inferior in having a high proportion of extractives. The yield of fibre will be small and the amount of dissolved material that must be disposed of is proportionally higher than in pulping slow-growth old wood. This adds to production costs as well as water pollution problems with pulp mills.

We hear much talk these days from both foresters and industry to the effect that they cannot afford to grow trees on long rotation or to great size and that they must clearcut for economic reasons. These appear to be false impressions. A recent study showed that the cost of felling, limbing, and bucking trees from 45 to 48 inches in diameter cost $7.04 per thousand board feet in contrast with $18.36 per thousand board feet for trees between 12 and 16 inches in diameter. Similarly the cost of yarding and loading was twice as much for trees 12 inches in diameter as it was for trees 30 inches in diameter.

The February, 1969, issue of the *Journal of Forestry* reports the findings of a research team studying comparative logging costs under four cutting specifications ranging from single tree selection to clear-cutting. They concluded that logging costs from standing tree to truck do not differ appreciably with cutting method, and the forest manager is therefore free to choose a cutting technique on the basis of management and silvicultural considerations other than costs .

A recent study in the redwood region indicated a logging cost of $11.37 per thousand board feet in a selection forest and $11.45 per thousand board feet where clear-cutting was practiced. This was a study conducted by the U.S. Forest Service in the Redwood Purchase Unit. A similar study made in the pine region showed that where clear-cutting was practiced, involving 17,000 board feet per acre, 133 man minutes per thousand board feet were expended. Heavy selection cutting involving 13,000 board feet per acre required only 118 man minutes per thousand board feet. But, surprisingly, a light, sanitation-salvage cut involving only 3,000 board feet per acre cost only 119 man minutes per thousand, considerably less than clear-cutting.

These rather surprising figures are explained by the fact that where selective cutting is employed we are removing only the largest trees which gives us the greatest handling efficiency during each step of the logging process.

The size of clear cut openings is a slightly different consideration. Here, presumably, we would not have the compensating factor of large trees as in selection cutting, although clear-cut patches may be selected on approximately the same basis as individual trees. An experiment was conducted in 1965 by the Forest Service in the mixed conifer area of the Sierra to determine the relative cost of logging various sized openings. The openings ranged from a diameter of 30' to 90'. Costs for logging were found to range from $7.04 to $7.99 per thousand board feet, and the author observed that the differences were not statistically significant, concluding thereby that the size of the opening is irrelevant to the cost of logging.

Selection management provides us with many advantages in obtaining reproduction. There is no difficulty with seed source. We are assured of reforestation with trees acclimated to the particular site. Collecting seeds in one area for reforestation in another is far more hazardous than most foresters realize. In general, naturally regenerated stands are less susceptible to disease than those artificially reproduced.

Seedlings are preferable to sprouts, because sprout growth is usually more susceptible to disease. At best, trees are more or less injured by planting. Roots are particularly subject to injury thus increasing the incidence of damage or disease. Less obvious are difficulties arising from collecting seed from different life zones than those in which they are sewn. Experience shows, for example, that trees grown in low elevation from seed gathered in a higher elevation are apt to be late in starting their spring growth. This can be serious in localities where we experience long summer droughts as in western United States. Conversely, trees grown in a higher elevation from seed collected in a lower elevation may burst their buds and start to grow at the first signs of spring only to be killed back by heavy frosts.

More subtle difficulties arise when trees are planted outside their natural range. Silviculturists have warned of this since forestry began in the United States, but so far they appear not to have been heard. For example, foresters have been planting Monterey Pine in northern California because of its rapid growth and presumed desirability for pulping. It had generally been assumed that the limited natural range of this species to the Monterey peninsula was the result of the tree failing to migrate back northward following an ice age. Now we are finding, however, that a native rust is killing off the plantations. Evidently there is something about the soil or climate of the Monterey peninsula that permits the tree to grow there despite presence of this rust. Or it could be that some alternate host for the rust itself is unable to grow in the area. Future research will probably give us an explanation. The point is that the general principle of relying upon natural reforestation is a valid one that should not be ignored.

American foresters notoriously disregard the effects of logging practices upon soils. This is particularly true of the post-war era in which logging has become highly mechanized and where much of the remaining timber being logged is on steep ground. The oversized and unwieldy equipment used by logging operators is totally unacceptable in the concept of excellent forestry. Logging should be conducted with light, small equipment, preferably rubber tired, in order to be maneuverable around trees left in selection forests and to function without disturbing the soil. All logging should be planned and supervised to prevent this damage, and no logging should be permitted where complete protection of the soil cannot be assured.

Clear-cutting promotes erosion and compaction of the surface soil, particularly where mineral soil is exposed. Clear-cutting allows organic matter to become desiccated, slowing down decay in dry climates such as characterize much of our western forests. Clear-cutting exposes the forest floor to intense insulation and evaporation and, as a result, the normal soil life of fungi, bacteria, worms, microscopic plants and animals of all kinds are destroyed or at least greatly changed, with fauna and flora of open lands coming in. This is usually undesirable. Clear-cutting invites invasion of vegetation that severely competes with forest tree seedlings. In the northwestern United States, clear-cutting of forests and forest fires have in creased floods from watersheds from both rain-snow melt floods and snow melt floods. Where stocking of the forests has recovered with time the flood peak discharges again decrease.

Conditions in natural stands point strongly to the fact that there is no factor more important in relation to disease than tree vigor. Stands on good sites are generally not damaged significantly by native diseases, but those on poor sites often suffer severely. If a site is allowed to deteriorate by careless logging, particularly by excessively bulldozing the surface, subsequent stands are going to be less vigorous than their predecessors and more subject to loss through insects and diseases.

Something should be said also for maintaining the natural mixture of species that occurs in the forest. This, too, is best done through reliance upon natural reproduction. Some species make excessively heavy demands on soil nutrients when planted in pure stands. They may do well in youth but later slow up and deteriorate. The admixture of species that makes light demand on the soil and whose leaf litter decomposes readily into a mild, rich humus is often necessary. Furthermore, pure stands may fail to utilize the site completely, either because they are composed of an intolerant species and in consequence have thin open crowns which presumably fail to utilize the sunlight completely, or because they are shallow rooted and utilize only part of the soil.

Selection management with careful planning of roads and logging is of great importance in sustaining the quality and productivity of the soil for these many reasons. It tends to maintain soil porosity and its water adsorption qualities thus reducing erosion and flood damage. Care of the soil and maintaining a full canopy also protects the habitat for fish in streams by keeping the water clean and cold and by preserving spawning beds. Silt and slime, the products of erosion, are unsuitable for spawning.

Excellent forestry largely preserves the beauty of the natural forest. I dare say that for most people such well-managed forests will quite adequately serve most of their wildland recreational needs. By maintaining the natural beauty of the forests we therefore take a good deal of pressure off wilderness. In contrast, present practices on the national forests, and to a greater extent on private forest lands, is creating an ever increasing demand for more wilderness.

If national parks and wilderness areas become the only places of natural beauty we have for outdoor experiences, people who do not care for wilderness per se will crowd in with those who do. This would not only increase the use of such places but would add to the clamor for roads and other nonwilderness development. Furthermore, if we should reach the sad state of having no large, old-growth timber except within our national parks, we would surely face a great clamor to log that too. Indeed, the overture to this clamor is already being heard. We had a foretaste in the ridiculous arguments advanced in opposition to the Redwood National Park which will be all too familiar to the reader.

Excellent forestry costs nothing but restraint, and offers the greatest gifts a forest can provide—except in the ideal situation where there are no people, and hence no forestry.

Reprinted with permission from Conifer, Winter 1969.

Social Forestry in New Mexico

Marco Hawk-Lowenstein

People are part of the southwest ecosystem.

NEW MEXICANS HAVE CREATED the landscape that we love. Firewood gathering, small saw mills and cattle are part of the way of life that stretches back 400 years for the Spanish settlers and over ten thousand years for the Pueblo and Apache tribes. The traditional residents became intimately familiar with the cycles and changes in their surroundings through regular use, through storytelling and through customs. These communities are more than the perceived cause of ecosystem degradation; they are an abundant and powerful resource for long term solutions to our environmental problems.

Northern New Mexico's unique and fragile ecosystem supports a variety of human cultures. Over thousands of years, these cultures have adapted to the natural systems to such a degree that the natural and human forces that shape the landscape are no longer separable. In our efforts to protect the forests from the logging industry, the Forest Service, and human ignorance, we must always remember that local people continue to play a crucial role in maintaining local ecosystems. By including people in our thinking about forest management issues, we can avoid many of the personal and environmental tragedies plaguing the Pacific Northwest.

There is more than one kind of environmentalism.

Environmental activists new to any area should respect and call on the local people who have known the land for generations. People who cannot be neatly pigeonholed into the environmental "party line" may still have much to contribute to forest preservation. Though many local people are uninvolved in politics, actively oppose environmental causes, or work for the large timber industry and the Forest Service, they commonly complain that the resource should be managed for local priority, that the wildlife is not as plentiful as it used to be, and that the water does not run as clear and deep any more. This knowledge and memory, tied with modern ecosystem science, can be a strong base for sustainable management of Southwestern natural resources. Local people are natural allies for conservationists if we can accept an environmentalism that includes moderate amounts of forestry, hunting, cows, and agriculture.

Rural environmentalism contrasted with urban environmentalism

The concept of rural and urban environmentalism is helpful in understanding the land based people. Put simply, the rural environmentalist sees the land as a working environment, a place to gain one's livelihood. In contrast, the urban environmentalist sees a place for leisure and recreation, an amenity to an information-age lifestyle. Consequently, rural environmentalists often see themselves as a part of the environment, while the urban environmentalist often sees an external or theological entity to be protected. While the urban environmentalist's problem set is typically global, the rural view tends to be locally centered. While rural people are likely to be vocal and even militant on issues that they perceive as affecting their well-being, they may be oblivious or unconcerned about the bigger picture or even of issues in the next valley. These distinctions lead to different approaches and attitudes toward forestry. By understanding these differences we will be better able to find common ground with land-based communities in working to preserve New Mexico's precious forest resource.

Urban people's past failure to consider local or total interests and viewpoints has created much of the polarization that "People for the West," a lobby group sponsored by the mining industry, is trying to provoke. Public Forestry Foundation will make a concerted effort to support environmentally-sound issues that are important to local people, both out of respect and in the time-honored northern New Mexico tradition of living with the land.

Evaluating forestry activities

Social participation must be included in the current arsenal of environmental evaluation. In addition to forest ecosystem questions, we should ask:

- Have local people been involved in the decision process from the beginning?
- Has the process served as a forum for improving understanding and bringing people together?
- Will the project support the traditional lifestyles of local people?
- Will the action benefit the local ecosystem and people or merely further an industrial, environmental, or bureaucratic agenda?
- Will local people be empowered to participate in future management decisions?
- Does the action expand or reduce future biological and social options?

Subsidies

Most forestry on public lands in New Mexico is not cost effective in terms of dollar returns to the Treasury. Below-cost timber sales can be assailed on their lack of economic merit; however, small, environmentally-sound harvesters of wood products may be the first to get squeezed out if these sales are stopped. The problem is not the fact that subsidies exist, but rather who and what is being subsidized. Destruction or degradation of old-growth habitat for the benefit of multi-national companies like Duke City Lumber is hard to justify. On the other hand, subsidies for sustainable management of forest resources, which benefit the local people, the public at large, and all species are worth the cost.

Creating a long-term conservation strategy

Alienation of local people is part of a larger problem, namely the lack of a long range forest conservation strategy. Strategically we need local people as allies to stop over-logging, mining, and overgrazing by corporate multinationals. Although many Anglo environmentalists are vocal and active today, New Mexico's Hispanic and Native American communities are more likely than any of us to carry the torch for future generations. Without forsaking our covenant to protect the land from exploitation, we must, in the long run, build a broad based forestry-intelligent coalition to protect New Mexico's sacred and fragile ecosystems.

We have opportunities to work with local citizens including ranchers and loggers to develop new forest management strategies. We cannot go on waiting for the Forest Service, universities, or the timber industry to inaugurate sustainable systems. Much of the job of visu-alizing and creating new forestry models falls on us. Specifically, we can begin by encouraging the Forest Service to provide small forest product sales to local people. We can promote locally based economic development initiatives like La Madera Forest Products in Vallecitos.

We should also work together to bolster riparian conservation and restoration projects that improve range conditions. All of these efforts are much more productive and gratifying than making unnecessary war on industry and agency officials.

I hope that these concepts, based on my community experience and research, will provide some food for thought for forest activists in New Mexico and other communities. Make your own contacts with local people, read ethnography and local history, and study rural development and social justice issues. Social forestry can be a useful tool for our efforts to protect and restore forest ecosystems.

Reprinted with permission from the Public Forestry Foundation's newsletter, The Citizen Forester, *February 1993.*

Marco Hawk-Lowenstein can be reached at Public Forestry Foundation Southwest Office, PO Box 701, Santa Fe, NM, 87504. Tel: (505) 471-1633

Ecoforesters' Recommendations to President Clinton for the New Federal Forest Policy

Ecoforester's Conference—The Alternative Forest Summit
May 21-23, 1993

THE PACIFIC CASCADIA ECOFORESTERS' Working Group convened May 21-23, 1993, at a private forest in Rickreall, Oregon, and finalized their recommendations to the Clinton Administration for consideration for new federal forest policy. Most of the sixteen foresters, among the Pacific Northwest's most respected ecoforesters, have extensive on-the-ground knowledge and experience restoring damaged forests back to healthy ones.

Introduction

The Ecoforestry Institute and the Forest Land Management Committee teamed up to bring together a forum of ecoforesters to contribute to Clinton's Forest Plan deliberations. Jean Stam, of Forest Land Management Committee, in searching for solutions to our wood products needs and forest misuse dilemma, has brought to our attention many ecoforesters. She felt they needed to come together and give us one set of Ecoforestry Principles and Practices. At the same time, the Ecoforestry Institute was preparing for a conference to set out guidelines for Jack Ward Thomas on Alternative Forestry. Their combined efforts led to this event near Salem, Oregon.

The group named itself Pacific Cascadia Ecoforestry Working Group. The participants outlined the best forestry models and proposals they were aware of. The recommendations to Clinton list some of these ecoforestry models and proposals. Besides the Recommendations to Clinton, they also produced a set of Principles of Ecologically Responsible Forestry. The Principles and Recommendations are reprinted here.

The Forest Land Management Committee has produced a video of the conference for $22.00.

A follow-up meeting was held to address "Practices of Ecoforestry" September 17-19, 1993, on Vancouver Island.

Pacific Cascadia Ecoforestry Working Group

Standing, from left: Tom Bradley, Walter Smith, Richard Gienger, Tracy Katelman, Ray Travers, Hawk Rosales, Dennis Martinez, Michael Maas. Seated, from left: Dieter Deumling, David Simpson, Michael Evenson, Patti Keene, Orville Camp, Jerry Schaeffer, Chris Maser, Alan Drengson. Not pictured: Don Shawe.

Principles of Ecologically-Responsible Forestry

Human well-being ultimately depends on the well-being of the complex ecosystem that is the forest. We therefore commit ourselves to retain or restore the processes that ensure the integrity, adaptability, diversity and quality of the entire life-system of the forested landscape, in a manner consistent with the traditional, historically beneficial Native American caretaking ethic. To this end, therefore, we affirm the inherent value of the multitude of beings in the forest and work to maintain or rehabilitate the range of ecological functions of forests: their physical structure, composition, function, and quality of habitat.

A socially functional community provides for its long-term economic well-being by planning for perpetual use of forest-related products and the amenities within ecological constraints. We accept that the role of the ecologically responsible forester (ecoforester) is to help identify the ecological constraints and options for the use of those products and amenities within the context of the landscape, respecting the wide range of values inherent in the forces itself, including the spiritual, aesthetic, educational, recreational, and environmental.

Recommendations to the Clinton Administration for the new federal forest policy:

1. We urge the establishment of ancient forest reserves as a biological legacy. The system must include the restoration of surrounding and connecting landscapes.

2. We recognize the role of federal forestlands in the production of forest products and in the economies of forest-related communities and urge the adoption of the principles of ecologically responsible forestry (ecoforestry) across federal forestlands, outside of the ancient forest reserves system.

3. We commend the administration for the Forests for the Future, Forest Stewardship, and International Forestry programs, and urge increased funding for technical assistance and cost-sharing for the Forest Stewardship Program in the western states (to bring spending into proportion regionally) and the inclusion of ecoforestry practitioners in funded projects. Because of the large, unmet need, we urge the implementation of the principles of ecologically responsible forestry (ecoforestry) be adopted immediately on a number of specific federal forestland sites in each of the forest cover types for demonstration, training and research, including:

   * the implementation of Natural Selection Forestry as proposed in the Peak-Stella area of the Rogue River National Forest, Prospect District, Oregon

   * the Vision 2020 Project in the Six Rivers National Forest, Orleans District, CA

More, we recommend support for developing projects and the inclusion of Ecoforestry Institute in the site selection decisions. Possible projects to be considered include:

   * the Applegate River partnerships in southern Oregon, to include community members and groups as full partners in the design and decision making process

   * the Confederated Modoc-Paiute tribes to restore Waneemah National Forest sites on the eastside of the Cascade mountains in Oregon

   * the Mattole/BLM project in Northern California

   * the South Fork Eel BLM partnership project in California

   * the Yakima partnership project in Washington

4. We also urge support for ecologically responsible forestry projects on State and private lands, and across mixed-ownership tenures, including:

   * the Columbia Gorge Landtrust in Oregon

   * the Headwaters Redwood Forest Complex in California

   * the Institute for Sustainable Forestry Watershed Project in California

   * the Intertribal Sinkyone Forest Restoration Project in California

We recommend federal support for state and private project development to include grants, loans, access to federal expertise and studies. The Pacific Cascadia Ecoforestry Working Group, through the Ecoforestry Institute, offers to help identify development of projects such as the following:

   * the Umatilla Tribal Forestry project in Oregon

   * the Indian Creek/Usal Creek Stewardship Project in California

   * the Coldspring Conservancy Inc. project in Oregon

5. We urge the federal government to support and assist the development of small-scale community-based, value-added production capacity providing year-round high-wage, high-skill jobs in forest-related communities.

6. We urge protection and preservation of Native American cultural resources, particularly traditional land uses, culturally important sites, materials, plants, and animals, including sacred sites as designated by traditional communities. We also urge cooperative management of ancestral lands with traditional tribal leaders to ensure continued access to those resources.

7. Because it is vital to the survival and restoration of our salmon and steelhead runs, we urge ecologically responsible forestry practices in whole system approaches to rehabilitation.

8. In order to realize the above goals, watershed and landscape planning over the entire region must include local communities, practitioners, the scientific community, and Native Americans, as well as federal, state, and local agencies. We urge administrative reform so that projects affecting local communities include local community practitioners in their design, development, monitoring, and evaluation.

Adopted by the Pacific Cascadia Ecoforestry Working Group, May 23, 1993.

Participants in the Pacific Cascadia Ecoforesters' Working Group

Orville & Mary Camp, Natural Selection Ecoforestry, Selma, Oregon

Tom Bradley, Silva Ecosystems Consultants, Winlaw, British Columbia, Canada

Chris Maser, forest regeneration consultant and author, Corvallis, Oregon

Walter Smith & Tracy Katelman, Institute for Sustainable Forestry, Redway, California

Michael Evenson, Six Rivers Project, Redway, California

David Simpson, Mattole Restoration Council, Petrolia, California

Patti Keene, Public Forestry Foundation, Eugene, Oregon

Ray Travers, forestry consultant, Victoria, British Columbia

Jerry Schaeffer, natural selection ecoforester, O'Brien, Oregon

Dieter Deumling, forester & forest historian, Rickreall, Oregon

Hawk Rosales, Intertribal Sinkyone Wilderness Council, Ukiah, California

Alan Drengson, Ecoforestry Institute Society, Victoria, B.C.

Don Shawe, he has worked his forest for 50 years, Hood River, Oregon

Dennis Martinez, indigenous forest restorationist, Talent, Oregon.

List of Contacts for Projects listed by Pacific Cascadia Ecoforesters' Working Group

Peak-Stella Demonstration project of the Rogue River National Forest
Prospect Ranger District, Oregon
Contact: Orville Camp
2100 Thompson Creek Road
Selma, Oregon 97538
Tel: (503) 597-4313/Fax: (503) 597-4044

The Vision 2020 project in the Six Rivers National Forest
Orleans District
Contact: Michael Evenson
c/o The Trees Foundation
P.O. Box 2202
Redway, California 95560
Tel: (707) 923-4377

Headwaters Redwood Forest Complex in California
Contacts: Cecelia Lanman, Darryl Cherney, Josh Kaufman and Kurt Newman
P.O. Box 397
Garberville, California 95542
Tel: (707) 923-2931

Intertribal Sinkyone Forest Restoration Project in California
Contact: Hawk Rosales
190 Ford Road, #333
Ukiah, California 95482
Tel: (707) 485-8744 (See article by Dennis Martinez.)

The South Fork Eel BLM Partnership Project
Contact: Institute for Sustainable Forestry
P.O. Box 1580
Redway, California 95560
Tel: (707) 923-4719/Fax: (707) 923-4257

Institute for Sustainable Forestry Watershed Project in California
Contact: Institute for Sustainable Forestry
(address as above)

The Mattole/BLM Project in Northern California
Contact: Mattole Restoration Council
P.O. Box 60
Petrolia, California 95558
Tel: (707) 629-3670
(See entry in "Restoration Ecology Resource Guide.")

The Indian Creek/Usal Creek Stewardship Project in California
Contact: Richard Gienger at EPIC
P.O. Box 397
Garberville, California 95440
Tel: (707) 923-2931

The Applegate River Partnerships in southern Oregon
Contact: Applegate Partnership–Jack Shipley

Ecoforestry Table of Comparisons

Industrial Forestry	Ecoforestry
Trees are viewed as "products"	Forests are viewed as ecological communities
Short-term production goals	Long-term sustainability
Agricultural production model	Forest ecosystem model
Trees are the only cash crop	Diverse forest products
Tree survival dependent on humans	Self-sustaining/self-managing/self-renewing
Chemicals	No chemicals
Clearcuts	Harvesting surplus wood/natural selection
Same age stands of trees	All ages of trees
Monoculture/single or few species	All species of trees
Simplified ecosystem	Biodiversity/complexity
Capital intensive	Labor intensive
Redesigning nature	Accepting nature's design
Life span: 100 years	Life span: millennia
Loss of the sacred	Sense of the sacred

Gus diZerega

4 Certification Programs for Sustainably-Produced Wood Products

4

Sierpa Alalaakkalla

Certification Directory for Sustainably-Produced Wood Products

Good Wood certification inspectors as restoration forestry extension

CERTIFICATION PROGRAMS for sustainably-produced wood products are drawing on the experiences of the organic food certification programs. The organic agriculture movement went through several stages. There were few of us in the early days, but gradually organizations were formed—local, state, regional and finally, national in scope. Eventually thousands of people became involved, and there are hundreds of organizations. Some, such as CCOF (California Certified Organic Farmers), have dozens of chapters.

Organic food certification programs began in the 1980's, after a decade of trust and local marketing. There are now dozens of certification programs, some state-wide, some national and hundreds of people are employed in the USA as organic certification agents. They go out and visit the farms and talk to the farmers. In a sense, these certification agents are organic agriculture's extension agents. They carry advice from farmer to farmer, they are asked advice all the time. Most of them are experienced practitioners themselves.

If we see some of the same patterns emerge in restoration forestry, we will see the certification agents for the "good wood" certification programs act in a capacity as restoration forestry extension agents. They will have to know what constitutes forestry worth certifying. These certification agents should be knowledgeable in forestry, forest ecology, logging, and so forth. It will benefit restoration forestry if a high standard of knowledge and communication skills is maintained for certifying agents.

Directories to Sustainably-Produced Wood Products

The Good Wood Guide

Simon Counsell. A Friends of the Earth-UK Handbook. 75 pp. (Address under organizations.)

An international listing of sources of certified sustainable forestry products (mostly tropical wood). Dozens of listings of organizations and companies in the United Kingdom offering furniture, home interiors, garden furniture, housewares, toys, etc. Lists architects and designers also.

The Good Wood Guide

1993. Institute for Sustainable Forestry, Garberville, California (Address under organizations.)

The Institute for Sustainable Forestry (ISF) has published the most complete certification list for the USA I've seen. A good portion of the directory you see here is taken from ISF's guide. A different publication than the UK guide reviewed above. There is some overlap, but the ISF Guide is much stronger in the USA, while the FOE Guide is stronger in the UK.

The Wood Users Guide

Pamela Wellner and Eugene Dickey. 1991. Rainforest Action Network. 68 pp. $10 ppd., paperback.

"Provides a long list of temperate timbers and a comprehensive list of tropical timber. Contains a list of domestic alternatives to tropical hardwoods and lists addresses of suppliers. Sources of used lumber, alternative woods and related forest products are also mentioned, along with the major corporations on the RAN hit list ('The Bad Guys')."

Certifiers of Sustainably-Produced Wood Products

Forest Stewardship Council
Jamison Ervin
RR1, Box 188
Richmond, Vermont 05477
Tel: (802) 434-3101

The Forest Stewardship Council was formed in 1992 by a gathering of interested organizations and individuals from around the world. The purpose of the council is to develop and promote a set of common principles and guidelines which will be used to evaluate certifying organizations like the Rogue Institute of Ecology and Economy, Green Cross, and The Rainforest Alliance. This will enable wood products users worldwide to know that each certifier has agreed to common standards regarding forest stewardship and community responsibility before affixing its seal to wood products.

The council is composed of forestry activists, technologists, and representatives of forest dwellers. Its goal is to set certification standards and nurture a marketing network between community-based producers and consumers. FSC's forest management principles have gone through numerous drafts.

The Founding Assembly of FSC was held in Toronto in October 1993 with 130 participants from 25 countries. After intensive discussions it was decided that the FSC should be established, and that the organization should incorporate as an association with members. The membership will be divided into two chambers. The first chamber will be made up of social, environmental and indigenous organizations and it will have 75% of the voting power in general assemblies. The second chamber will have 25% of voting power and will be made up of individuals and organizations with an economic interest in the timber trade. The FSC will aim at geographic and North-South balance in its membership.

Following the decision of the assembly to allow representatives with commercial interests to vote at the founding assembly, a group of 11 NGOs decided to withdraw from further voting. These organizations, including Greenpeace, Friends of the Earth, Rainforest Action Network, Swedish Society for Nature Conservation and a few organizations from the South.

FSC's office will be moved to either Switzerland or Mexico in 1994. Inquiries to the Richmond address after that point will be forwarded to the new office.

Ecoforestry Institute
P.O. Box 12543
Portland, Oregon 97212
Tel/Fax: (503) 231-0576

Developing certification systems for raw materials and secondary products. (See review in Pacific Northwest Restoration Forestry organizations.)

Friends of the Earth—UK (FOE-UK)
26-28 Underwood St.
London, N1 7JQ UNITED KINGDOM
Tel: 01 490 1555/Fax: 01 490 0881

Friends of the Earth—UK is one of the most respected, international groups defending the world's rainforests.

They have a certification program.

Green Cross Certification Co.
1611 Telegraph Ave, Suite 1111
Oakland, California 94612
Tel: (415) 832-1415/Fax: (415) 832-0359.
Contact: Debby Hammel.

The Green Cross Certification Company (a division of the Scientific Certification Systems) is undertaking an ambitious wood certification program. Inspection teams will assess a project's degree of sustainability with respect to five major factors: preservation of natural biodiversity, logging and milling operations, soil conservation, silvicultural techniques, and maximum species utilization. Green Cross also recognizes the land-use rights of indigenous populations.

Green Cross will establish two separate panels of experts or "standards boards" to set criteria and review applications and on-site inspections. One panel will be for tropical-forest projects, and one for temperate zone projects. Active in creation of FSC.

Haribon Foundation
Richpelt Tower, Suite 901
17 Annapolis St. Greenhills
San Juan, Metro Manila , PHILIPPINES

Regional Contact for the Forest Stewardship Council.

Institute for Sustainable Forestry
P.O. Box 1580
Redway, California 95560
Tel: (707) 923-4719/Fax: (707) 923-4257

The Institute for Sustainable Forestry (ISF) is one of the leading groups in the U.S. promoting restoration forestry. Their "Good Wood guide" was the source of much of the information in this resource guide printed here. ISF is setting up a program called: Pacific Certified Ecological Forest Products (PCEFP) for certifying forest operations in the Redwood region of California. Active in creation of FSC.

North Shield
Box 385
Ely, Minnesota 55731
Tel: (218) 365-3309

Regional Contact for the Forest Stewardship Council.

Project For Ecological Recovery
77/3 Soi Nomchit, Nares Rd.
Bangkok 10500, THAILAND

Regional Contact for the Forest Stewardship Council.

Rainforest Alliance Smart Wood Certification Program
270 Lafayette St., Suite 512
New York, New York 10012
Tel: (212) 941-1900. Fax: 941-4986

Smart Wood, a program of the Rainforest Alliance, has

implemented a two-step program certifying sources of tropical timber, and the North American importers. Active in creation of FSC.

Red Del Tercer Mundo
> Miquel del Corro 161
> Montevideo 11200, URUGUAY

Regional Contact for the Forest Stewardship Council.

Rogue Institute for Ecology and Economy
> Box 3213
> Ashland, Oregon 97520
> Tel: (503) 482-6031.

Community Forestry Certification Program. Joining forest workers and environmentalists to identify and promote sustainable forestry management alternatives. Active in creation of FSC.

Silva Forest Foundation
> Box 9, Slocan Park
> British Columbia, B0G 2E0, CANADA
> Tel: (604) 226-7222/Fax: (604) 226-7446.

The Silva Forest Foundation (SFF) provides education and research for restoration forestry in Canada. SFF has developed some initial certification standards for ecologically responsible forest uses that maintain fully functioning forests. Eventually SFF hopes to provide a certification system for non-timber forest uses such as eco-tourism and mushroom picking.

Skephi
> Tromolpos 1410
> Jakarta, 13012, INDONESIA

Regional Contact for the Forest Stewardship Council.

Soil Association of the United Kingdom
> 86 Colston Street
> Bristol BS1 5BB, UNITED KINGDOM

Developing certification of tropical and temperate wood. Active in creation of FSC.

Good Wood and Where To Get It

Almquist Lumber
> 100 Taylor Way
> Blue Lake, California 95521
> Tel: (707) 668-5454

Distributor of Wild Iris, "Smartwood" and salvaged native California hardwoods.

Collins Pine Co.
> Box 796
> Chester, California 96020
> Tel: (916) 258-2111

Green Cross evaluation. 90,000 acres in the Sierra. Family owned operation since the 1940's producing soft-

woods. Wholesale only.

Ecological Trading Co., Ltd.
> 659 Newark Road
> Lincoln, LN6 8SA UNITED KINGDOM
> Tel: 44-91-276-5547/Fax: 265-4227
> Director: Chris Cox

One of the first companies established to market tropical wood from sustainably logged forests. It took them several years to find any in the world that qualified, but as a result of their search they know where many of the best examples are located.

EcoTimber International
> 350 Treat Street
> San Francisco, California 94110
> Tel: (415) 864-4900

Committed to supplying only sustainably-harvested tropical hardwoods from many sources.

Edensaw Woods, Ltd.
> 211 Seton Rd.
> Port Townsend, Washington 98368
> Tel: (206) 385-7878

Green Cross and Smartwood certified hardwoods.

Eternal Forest Productions
> Bob Richards and Tim Schmitz;
> P.O. Box 77
> Skamokawa, Washington 98647
> Tel: (206) 795-3316 or -8708

Sustainable, non-clearcut wood products.

Florida Ridge Wood Products Div.
> 414 Bridges Rd.
> Groveland, Florida 34736
> Tel: (904) 787-4251

Forest Trust Wood Products Brokerage
> Box 519
> Santa Fe, New Mexico 87504
> Tel: (505) 983-8992

Providing contractors in New Mexico with a complete line of high quality materials for Southwest-style building and fence construction.

Glimer Wood Company
> 2211 NW Saint Helens Rd.
> Portland, Oregon 87210
> Tel: (503) 274-1271

Handloggers Hardwood Lumber
> 135 E. Francis Drake Blvd.
> Larkspur, California 94939
> Tel: (415) 461-1180

Tropical wood from a 200,000-acre sustainably harvested (uncertified) concession in Belize.

Into the Woods
300 N. Water ST.
Petaluma, California 94952
Tel: (707) 763-0159

Distributing Wild Iris California hardwoods, recycled and salvaged lumber and finished products from soft and hard woods.

The Luther's Mercantile
412 Moore Lane
Healdsburg, California 95448-0774
Tel: (707) 433-1823

La Madera Forest Products Association
Box 30113
Española, New Mexico 87532
Tel: (505) 753-8407

A cooperative of woodcutters from largely Hispanic villages in northern New Mexico.

Menominee Tribal Enterprises
Box 10
Neopit, Wisconsin 54135
Tel: (715) 756-2311

Green Cross certified. Large volume wholesale only. Conducting sustainable-yield forestry on their 218,000 acres of tribal land since 1854.

Mount Storm
7890 Bell Rd.
Windsor, California 95492
Tel: (707) 838-3177

Pittsford Lumber Co.
50 State St.
Pittsford, New York 14534
Tel: (716) 384-3489

Sea Star Trading Co.
Box 513
Newport, Oregon 97365
Tel: (800) 359-7571

Sustained yield tropical woods and veneer and local salvage. Certified source of Smartwood.

Southern Humboldt Builders Supply
690 Thomas Drive
Garberville, California 95442
Tel: (707) 923-2778

Distributing fine-quality Wild Iris hardwoods.

The Timber Source
431 Pine Street
Burlington, Vermont 05401
Tel: (802) 865-1111

Providing sustainable construction lumber and ply-

wood for large-scale projects.

Tosten Brothers
Box 156
Miranda, California 95553
Tel: (707) 943-3093

Producing hardwoods and softwoods for a century on their 5,000-acre ranch in the redwoods.

Warren Fulmer
11750 Hillcrest Rd.
Medford, Oregon 97404
Tel: (503) 772-8577

Certified by the Rogue Institute. Softwoods for secondary producers.

Wild Iris Forestry
Box 1423
Redway, California 95560
Tel: (707) 923-2344

Wild Iris Forestry is a pioneer in restoration forestry. Their mill and kiln turns madrone, tanoak, oaks, and other local hardwoods into beautiful lumber and flooring. The Irises were much of the inspiration behind the Institute for Sustainable Forestry and Pacific Certified Ecological Forest Products. (See Pacific Northwest section).

Wildwoods Company
445 "I" Street
Arcata, California 95521
Tel: (707) 822-9541

Certified source of Smartwood.

Wise Wood
3519 Washington St.
McHenry, Illinois 60050-4456
Tel: (815) 344-4943

Smartwood from Mexico and Belize.

Woodworkers Supply
5402 S. 40th St.
Phoenix, Arizona 85040
Tel: (602) 437-4415

Alternative Building Materials

The forests have been harvested for building materials primarily. Alternative building materials may take some of the pressure off this limited resource. Following are a few references in this very fast growing field.

Building with Nature
Box 369
Gualala, California 95445
Tel: (707) 884-4513
Carol Venolia, Architect

A networking newsletter with information and inspiration about healthful, ecologically-sound, spiritually sensitive design and construction—low-toxic materials, earth building, responsible uses of wood, small houses, place spirit, building profiles, business profiles, psychoneuroimmunology, heating and cooling insulation, lighting, developers, EMFs, etc..

Center for Resourceful Building Technology
Box 3866
Missoula, Montana 59806
Tel: (406) 549-7678

Fostering efficient resource use in building. Publish an 88-page *Guide to Resource Efficient Building Elements*.

Environmental Bamboo Foundation
P.O. Box 245
Denpasar, Bali, INDONESIA

International networking for the promotion of bamboo as a building material. Bamboo enthusiasts take note.

Environmental Building News
RR1, Box 161
Brattleboro, Vermont 05301

Bi-monthly newsletter of design and construction.

The Forest Partnership
Box 426
Burlington, Vermont 05402
Tel: (802) 865-1111

Consulting, marketing and education. "Forest Friendly" guidelines. Newsletter available.

International Institute for Bau-Biologie and Ecology, Inc.
Box 387
Clearwater, Florida 34615
Tel: (813) 461-4371/Fax: (813) 441-4873

Information, home-study courses, and seminars on holistic building techniques and retro-fits. Very informative material.

The Forest Stewardship Council's Principles

Principle #1: Management Plan

A WRITTEN MANAGEMENT PLAN must exist which clearly states management objectives for each forest, the means for achieving those objectives, and provides for responses to changing ecological, social and economic circumstances.

1.1 Prior to harvesting, a written management plan must be produced that contains or otherwise provides for the following:

a) rationale of production activity;

b) management objectives;

c) analysis of inventories of the target species and factors affecting their population;

d) evaluation of affected ecosystems;

e) research activities to improve knowledge of affected species and habitat;

f) quantifiable production objectives based on resource inventories;

g) methods for achieving objectives: planning, road building, harvesting and extraction activities, etc.;

h) maps and detailed work plans;

i) delineation of protected areas and other areas off-limits to production activities;

j) provisions for consultation with affected communities;

k) provisions for training of personnel;

l) provisions to control and enforce limits on production levels;

m) provisions for protection of the forest against unauthorized or unacceptable damage from burning, theft, settlement, grazing;

n) rationale for choice of equipment;

o) monitoring and reporting requirements; and,

p) process for periodic revision of the plan based on new information, at a minimum every five years.

1.2 Management and harvesting activities must operate within all national and international laws, treaties and agreements which apply, including the payment of all legally prescribed fees, royalties, taxes and other charges.

Principle #2: Forest Security

The ownership of the forest must be clearly defined and documented, and the areas dedicated by the owners to permanent forest cover.

2.1 Clear evidence of long-term forest use rights to the land (e.g. legal title, customary rights, or lease agreements) and protection of forest cover must exist.

2.2 Illegal exploitation and encroachment (e.g. in-migration) should be controlled.

Principle #3: Social and Economic Benefits

Participating parties should receive an equitable share of the benefits arising from forestry production activities.

3.1 Participating and affected communities are given first priority in terms of job training, employment, profit-sharing, health services, education, and availability of loans and credits.

3.2 Adequate provisions are given for health and safety of employees and their families in terms of pay, hygiene, living and working conditions, insurance and compensation schemes.

3.3 Suitable mechanisms exist for local consent by, and compensation to, local communities for damage to resources (crops, trees, land, water quality, and other resources), impairment of essential environmental functions and loss of income.

3.4 A formal process for hearing and resolving grievances should be established, documented and distributed amongst affected parties.

Principle #4: Local Rights

The legal and/or customary rights of indigenous peoples and other long-settled forest-dependent communities affected by forestry activities must be protected, and forest management planning and implementation must provide for full and informed consent in relation to activities that affect them.

4.1 Local communities' customary rights to own, manage or use forest resources should be recognized and documented in written legal and binding agreements.

4.2 Management plans should include maps that indicate areas that are bound by agreements in terms of the customary or legal rights of local people.

4.3 A formal process should exist so that all groups of people directly affected by forestry activities can be consulted, or preferably directly participate, in the selection of forest management objectives.

4.4 Management plan should be available for review by directly affected parties.

4.5 Compensation should be provided for in the case of loss or damage in the event of activities that impair the legal and/or customary rights, or livelihoods of local people.

Principle #5: Environmental Impact

Forest management must minimize adverse environmental impacts in terms of wildlife, biodiversity, water resources, soils, and non-timber and timber resources.

5.1 Biological implications of forest activities (e.g. silviculture) must be initially assessed and safeguards incorporated for the protection of the forest resource in terms of ecological structure, protection of threatened plant and animal species and nesting areas, establishment of conservation zones, and control of hunting and trapping.

5.2 Written guidelines must exist for all harvesting and engineering works, including choice of harvesting and transport equipment, design specifications and maps for road-building, erosion control measures, felling practices (e.g. harvest and seed tree marking, directional felling), protection of water resources (riverine buffer zones), and slope restrictions.

5.3 Forest workers must receive training and supervision in relation to above harvesting and engineering guidelines.

5.4 Non-timber forest uses must be inventoried and continued access to such resources by local people incorporated into forest management.

5.5 Surveys and field assessments should occur which monitor environmental impacts over the long-term, providing information for mitigating adverse impacts, and, on a periodic basis (at a minimum every 2 years), formally used to revise management methods.

5.6 Any use of chemicals (pesticides, arboricides, fertilizers) should be documented, minimized and strictly monitored, and must be strictly limited to those chemicals not on "banned" lists in any country.

Principle #6: Sustained Yield

Harvesting rates of forest products must be sustainable in the long-term future.

6.1 Calculations of harvest volumes and proposed harvesting techniques must be based on reliable and site specific data on growth and regeneration from local studies and research.

6.2 An annual allowable cut (AAC) must be established, utilizing available data on regeneration and growth dynamics, and a combination of harvesting intensity, tree rotations, cutting cycles and management constraints (e.g. personnel, other resources); the AAC must provide for adequate regeneration of the utilized species.

6.3 The characteristics of the products to be harvested (e.g. minimum harvesting sizes or diameter limits, species) must be established and adhered to.

6.4 Regeneration and growth must be monitored by a systematic network of sample plots.

Principle #7: Maximizing the Forest's Economic Potential

Forest management should take into account the full range of forest products—timber and non-timber, forest functions and services, and should maximize local value-added processing.

7.1 Research must be conducted on the full range of timber and non-timber forest products and services found in the forest area, and incorporated into management planning.

7.2 Utilization and market assessments should focus on both well-known and lesser-known commercial or subsistence species.

7.3 Forest management planning and implementation should stress local value-added processing through a comparison of the costs and benefits of each potential level of local processing, including sawing, processing of non-timber forest products, air- or kiln-drying, re-sawing and machining to specifications, grading, chemical treatments, manufacturing of components or finished products (e.g. fiber and particle boards, pulp or chemical extracts).

Principle #8: True Costs

The cost of forest products should reflect the full and true costs of forest management and production.

8.1 Site specific research must be conducted that establishes the full and true financial, environmental, social, and silvicultural costs of the production of goods from the forest.

8.2 Stumpage, mill, wholesale or retail prices should incorporate ample remuneration to cover the full costs of forest management as outlined in these Principles and Criteria.

8.3 Governments, multilateral and bilateral organizations, and non-governmental organizations (NGO's), both for-profit and not-for-profit, should collaborate to establish mechanisms which ensure compensation, and provide incentives, for sustainable forestry.

8.4 Investments in forest management (e.g. silviculture, harvesting), infrastructure and processing should be evaluated economically in terms of cost-benefit, markets, national or regional interests, and/or short-term finance.

Principle #9: Appropriate Consumption

Forest production should encourage judicious and efficient use of forest products and timber species.

9.1 Forestry operations should encourage the utilization of lesser-known plant species for commercial and subsistence uses.

9.2 Forestry operations should seek the "highest and best use" for individual tree and timber species.

Principle #10: Forest Plantations

Plantations should not replace natural forest; they should augment, complement, and reduce pressures on existing natural forests.

10.1 Forest conversion to plantations must be based on extensive analysis of environmental, economic, social and biological factors, and with full and informed consent of local affected parties.

10.2 Forest plantations should test and utilize species native to the region.

10.3 The use of exotic species in forest plantations must be carefully controlled to limit negative biological impacts on native tree species which occurs through spontaneous or uncontrolled regeneration.

10.4 Forest plantations that utilize exotic species must incorporate short- and long-term trials of native species that would meet the same end use or demand.

10.5 Full environmental impact assessments must be conducted before large-scale forest conversions (a relative term that must be quantitatively defined on a local or national basis) from natural forest to plantations take place.

References

Green Cross Certification Company, "Development of a Certification System for Sustainable Forestry Management Systems," March 1991, Oakland, California.

Institute for Sustainable Forestry, "Pacific Certified Ecological Forest Products, Criteria for PCEFP Wood," from *Forestree News* (newsletter), Winter 1992.

ITTO, "Criteria for the Measurement of Sustainable Tropical Forest Management," *ITTO Policy Development Series* No. 3 , 25 March 1992.

ITTO, "Draft 4, Report of the Expert Panel on Possible

Methods of Defining General Criteria for and Measurement of Sustainable Tropical Forest Management," 28 September 1991.

IUCN/SSC Specialist Group on Sustainable Use of Wild Species and IUCN Sustainable Use of Wildlife Programme, "Criteria and Requirements for Sustainable Use of Wild Species, Proposed Policy, Second Draft 15 July 1992," Redway, California.

Poore, Duncan, and Sayer, Jeffrey, *The Management of Tropical Moist Forest Lands, Ecological Guidelines*, Second Edition, IUCN Forest Conservation Programme, 1991.

Rainforest Alliance, "Generic Guidelines for the Evaluation of Tropical Logging Operations," November 1991, New York, New York.

Rogue Institute for Ecology, "Community Forestry Certification Program," Certification Committee draft, 20 February 1992, Ashland, Oregon.

Spivey-Weber, Fran, "The Missing Forest Principles" (guest editorial), *Network '92 Newsletter*, The Centre for Our Common Future and the IFC, January 1992.

This draft of the FSC Principles and Criteria was prepared by Richard Z. Donovan, chairperson of the FSC Founding Group's Working Group on Principles and Criteria. This revision is based on comments received on the five previous drafts and a review of relevant documents (see References).

The Forest Stewardship Council
Jamison Ervin
RR 1, Box 188
Richmond, VT 05477 USA
Tel: (01) 802-434-3101/Fax: (01) 802-434-3171

Pacific Certified Ecological Forest Products: Criteria for PCEFP Wood

What is certification and who provides it?

PACIFIC CERTIFIED ECOLOGICAL FOREST PRODUCTS (PCEFP) is a project of the Institute for Sustainable Forestry, a non-profit organization headquartered in Redway, on California's North Coast. The certification program grew out of woodsworkers', consumers' and activists' growing interest in lumber produced without harm to the forest. Founders of the Institute also seek to distinguish among competing and possibly inaccurate claims about the ecological effects of wood production. The Institute has therefore drawn on the experience and knowledge of ecologists, foresters, fisheries biologists, watershed restoration workers, fallers, planters and numerous others to devise these standards for ecologically produced wood. Criteria for other forest products, also based on the Ten Elements of Sustainability, are being developed.

The Institute's other programs include public education, professional training in all facets of the ecological forest products industry; research and development into various aspects of forest management for the long-term productivity and health of the forest; and networking with others doing related work.

Geographical Scope

At present, the Institute will consider for certification wood and other forest products harvested in the redwood and Douglas-fir-hardwood forest types of northern California and southern Oregon. As experience permits, and as the Institute becomes aware of practitioners of sustainable forestry in other regions, the program may expand to those areas. Because of the diversity within this area, the certification process is designed to be flexible enough to account for site-specific circumstances as long as producers satisfy the Ten Elements of Sustainability listed below.

The Philosophical Basis for Certification

The criteria for certification are founded on several philosophical and ecological premises:

- that the health of the forest comes before human needs for products to be extracted from the forest;
- that intact natural forests provide the best laboratory for learning good forestry;
- that forests are whole living fabrics, greater than the sum of their component species, physical elements and human practices; and
- that humans will never fully understand the complexities of the forest ecosystem, although they may study the forest and work attentively with it.

The Certification Criteria

The Ten Elements of Sustainability

1. Forest practices will maintain and/or restore the aesthetics, vitality, structure, and functioning of the natural processes, including fire, of the forest ecosystem and its components.

2. Forest practices will maintain and/or restore surface and groundwater quality and quantity, including aquatic and riparian habitat.

3. Forest practices will maintain and/or restore natural processes of soil fertility, productivity and stability.

4. Forest practices will maintain and/or restore a natural balance and diversity of native species of the area, including flora, fauna, fungi and microbes, for purposes of the long-term health of ecosystems.

5. Forest practices will encourage a natural regeneration of native species to protect valuable native gene pools.

6. Forest practices will not include the use of artificial chemical fertilizers or synthetic chemical pesticides.

7. Forest practitioners will address the need for local employment and community stability and will

respect workers' rights, including occupational safety, fair compensation, and the right of workers to collectively bargain.

8. Sites of archaeological, cultural and historical significance will be protected and will receive special consideration.

9. Forest practices executed under a certified Forest Management Plan will be of the appropriate size, scale, time frame, and technology for the parcel, and adopt the appropriate monitoring program, not only in order to avoid negative cumulative impacts, but also to promote beneficial cumulative effects on the forest.

10. Ancient forests will be subject to a moratorium on commercial logging during which time the Institute will participate in research on the ramifications of management in these areas.

How To Obtain Certification

Landowners wishing to have their wood certified as ecologically harvested shall prepare a Forest Management Plan in consultation with an Institute-certified Registered Professional Forester (RPF) and in accordance with the California Forest Practices Act. This document will outline their plans for stewardship and harvest of the forest, and will indicate how these intentions satisfy the Ten Elements of Sustainability. The burden is on the preparer of the plan to demonstrate how it satisfies these criteria; a plan is assumed unsustainable unless shown to be otherwise. The Institute's certifying inspectors will visit the site before, during and after harvest, and may revoke certification if the plan or its spirit are disregarded.

All the parties to a timber operation—the forester, the landowner, and the operator—are responsible for ensuring that the promised practices are employed. For their part, consumers are encouraged to use wood only for finished products that will last at least as long as the age of the trees that were cut to supply that wood.

Long-term Certification

Landowners will submit a forest management plan and will show how it will satisfy the Ten Elements of Sustainability. The plan will contain all of the information required of the California Department of Forestry's Non-industrial Timber Management Plan (NTMP), as well as these additional specifications:

- A list and map of actively eroding areas on the site, including slides, gullies, mass movement and surface and channel erosion, and list of treatments proposed for any of these areas;

- A list and map of roads, landings, and watershed boundaries;

- A list and map of stream channels of second order or greater, and a survey of their condition;

- Whether the plan will attempt to modify plant succession after harvest, and if so, how;

- Inventory of tree species and diameter classes. Submitters may choose either to conduct a 100-percent inventory of trees on the site, or to establish a network of permanent plots that will allow a statistically reliable assessment of forest conditions;

- Inventory of major plant and animal species (as well as threatened and endangered species and species of special concern, which are already required to be inventoried for an NTMP). For herbaceous species, it is sufficient to determine the percent cover attributable to each species;

- Description of existing structure (physical elements) of forest, condition and types of soil, and projection of how structure, species composition, and ecological processes will develop under the proposed management regime, at points 50, 100, 150 and 200 years in the future;

- How the plan proposes to use fire or mimic its role in the forest;

- How the forest will be managed for a diversity of successional stages and age classes of trees in the forest, ranging from early to late successional and from tree seedling to old-growth. Plans will indicate the geographical scope over which each of these age classes will be present, now and in the future. If areas outside the management plan under consideration are invoked to meet this requirement, their management plans will be included as well;

- How managers will ensure that the growth of wood in the forest is equal to or greater than the amount of wood harvested. On young-growth forests where there exists a need to restore the forest, less wood will be cut than is grown.

Interim Certification

Landowners who have been practicing what they believe to be certifiable ecological forestry, may become certified based on their track record and on the ground effects of their previous operations. Landowners who are new to ecological forestry, will submit a copy of the documentation under which they plan to harvest timber, such as a Timber Harvest Plan. A PCEFP inspection team will visit and approve or disapprove all requests for interim certification. For examples of how some landowners act with special caution while the information for a management plan is gathered and analyzed, see the "PCEFP Forest Practice Guidelines for Certified Ecologically Produced Wood."

The Process of Certification

Because forest conditions are extremely site-specific, the Institute has granted broad latitude to its certifying inspectors to encourage practices that manifest the underlying spirit of these standards. Landowners wishing to have their wood certified will grant permission to the Institute's field staff or their designees to inspect the site of timber operations before, during and after logging. Submitters should be aware that certification is probationary: it may be suspended or revoked if the landowner's practices warrant. For a more detailed road map to certification, see "How to Become a PCEFP Wood Producer."

* For certification to remain current, the inventories of species and erosional features will be repeated every ten years or whenever the landowner proposes to harvest, whichever is less frequent. Cumulative effects, measured against baseline data, will be monitored at appropriate intervals and after major events.

* In recognition of the evolving state of the art in forest ecology, these standards will be revised periodically, allowing an adjustment period for previously certified plans. Revisions may be proposed at meetings of the Institute's Board of Directors, with changes to be adopted by the board, following a comment period, no sooner than one month thereafter.

Forest Practice Guidelines for Certified Ecologically-Produced Wood

These practices are an illustration, not a straitjacket. Not all of these techniques will be right for your forest; they describe methods that some landowners and operators have used to harvest wood in an ecologically responsible fashion. The Pacific Certified Ecological Forest Products (PCEFP) certifying inspector and your forester can help you choose the most appropriate methods for your site. Landowners may obtain interim certification by following practices such as these while they prepare a more detailed management plan to meet the PCEFP "Ten Elements of Sustainability." See Criteria for PCEFP Wood for more information on the PCEFP certification process.

The forest practice guidelines fall into several categories:

Legal Requirements

* Operations shall comply with the CDF Forest Practice Rules in effect at time of harvest, and shall follow the procedures set forth in the applicable Timber Harvest Plan or Timber Management Plan for the site.

Silviculture and Marking

* All-aged (uneven-aged) management techniques are used, including methods that have the effect of even-aged management in small openings.

* Openings created in the forest are only as large as needed, up to one-half acre, to regenerate all of the forest species native to the site.

* The following techniques are avoided:

* diameter cuts (choosing the trees to be cut primarily on the basis of their diameter class);

* high-grading (removal of only the observably superior trees in a diameter class);

* Management for conversion of timberland to other uses; or

* Whole-tree yarding.

* The area is managed to maintain all native species of flora and fauna that were present in the forest before harvest and that are appropriate to the existing stage of ecological succession.

* The age structure of stands and landscapes mimics that natural to the forest type.

* Levels of dead wood as appropriate to the ecosystem are maintained and recruited, including downed logs on land and in streams, standing snags, and cavities in living trees. The target levels shall vary depending on the forest type. For example, in redwood stands, one might aim for 20 tons per acre of large woody debris on the forest floor, including at least two pieces fifty feet or more in length, 24 inches or more in diameter at their narrow end. In the Douglas-fir-hardwood forest, targets will depend on the aspect and moisture on the site

* Over the long term, harvests remove at most the amount of sawtimber grown. Further, if more than 10 percent of the basal area is to be cut in a single entry, special attention is paid to the windfirmness of remaining trees and to possible alterations of the microclimate of the forest floor. (tabled for further discussion—need intent to maintain and improve a closed canopy; no more than x% in x years, encourage more frequent entries and smaller removal)

* At least one superior dominant or co-dominant tree per acre of each principal species (comprising 20 percent or more of the stand's basal area) are left after harvest, well-distributed through

the stand, as seed sources and "grandparent" trees, to grow until the end of their natural lifetimes. For other tree species in the stand, at least one such tree is left for every ten acres. Mature trees are marked for preservation, and younger trees are marked for recruitment into this class eventually to replace older ones that die. These trees help with the recruitment of snags and woody debris.

- Dominant and codominant trees 6 inches in dbh and greater are marked before harvest, in order to facilitate discussion with PCEFP certifying inspectors (see Criteria for PCEFP Wood.)

- Forest practices ensure the recruitment of trees to all age classes.

Regeneration

- To the extent possible, natural regeneration is employed. Where that is not feasible, nearby seedlings are transplanted or seedlings are planted that were grown from seed collected in the same seed zone as the site.

- Where openings are created, if they do not restock naturally to 150 to 300 healthy seedlings per acre (depending on site) within three years, the openings are replanted to achieve that level of stocking by the end of five years after harvest.

Falling and Slash Treatment

- To the greatest extent feasible, established regeneration and other leave trees are protected from harm, skinning or scraping during falling, limbing and yarding.

- Snags are felled only where they constitute a safety or fire hazard.

- At least three snags per acre, at least 13 inches in diameter at breast height and ten feet tall are maintained. In areas that lack this density of snags, at least one snag per acre is recruited on each entry.

- Trees are bucked to lengths that will stay on skid roads and not sideswipe leave trees or embankments, nor push sediment into streams.

- Slash is lopped and scattered to a height above the ground of 18 inches or less, hand-piled and burned, or distributed onto skid trails.

- Slash is not left at landings, on, or adjacent to roads.

Yarding

- Yarding systems are chosen to minimize potential impacts, including aerial systems such as balloon yarding where appropriate.

- Where cable yarding is used, logs are yarded through corridors 8 feet wide or narrower and at least 200 feet apart, except where they converge on the yarder.

- Yarding corridors are laid out before logging begins, and are located under closed canopy or where the canopy can be expected to close within 10 years.

- Corridors and other places where timber operations have created a water channel are waterbarred when not in use or when a chance of measurable rain is forecast. They are located where water is unlikely to collect or channel.

- Where appropriate, new skid trails are outsloped.

- All vehicles stay on roads and designated equipment trails.

- Equipment is not operated in seeps or springs.

Riparian Areas

- USFS guidelines are applied, with these revisions: WLPZ 1, Management direction: 1: Equipment exclusion zone, except at designated bridged or culverted crossings.; add 7. Harvesting permitted only to improve the quality of the riparian vegetation. Change this to more understandable standards.

Roads

The following construction methods are applied to new roads; maintenance standards are applied to all roads. To the extent possible, road alignments are permanent for as long as the area remains under management.

- Roads are planned before beginning of logging operations, and do not exceed these widths and pitches:

  - Primary roads (for log trucks): 12-foot width on straightaway, 20 feet on curves. Maximum slope 10 percent, 15 percent for up to 200 feet.

  - Secondary equipment trails (for skidding machines, four-wheel-drive pick-up and mobile mill): 10.5-foot width on straightaway, 16 feet on curves. Maximum slope 20 percent, 25% for 100 feet.

- In view of the damage to soil and watercourses

caused by roads, the density of roads and trails is kept below 400 linear feet per acre. [By the way: this means 6 miles of road for an 80-acre plan. We need to change it to something in the 50-100 range.]

- Roads are located where they will be covered and protected by overhead canopy wherever possible.

- Roads and trails are graded and watered in summer when necessary during operations to reduce dust and eventual input of sediment to streams.

- Roads and trails are waterbarred when not in use and when a chance of measurable rain is forecast.

- Skid trails cross first-order, unchanneled ephemeral streams with a rolling dip. Waterbars are placed prior to the dip, to prevent skid trail run-off from entering the stream.

- Roads and trails are outsloped or provided with ditches and culverts. Berms are avoided, except where needed to prevent sedimentation and control the flow of drainage water.

- Lower ends of culverts have downspouts and dispersion facilities. Roads have dips at culverts as back-up in case of culvert failure. Where possible, unfiltered ditch water is not drained into watercourses, but rather through sediment traps or separate culverts onto the forest floor, buffered by rocks and vegetation.

- New roads crossing Class 1 streams use bridges wherever possible. New crossings pose no barriers to species dependent on those streams, such as anadromous fish. The channel passes under the crossing at less than a 1 percent grade.

- Old culverts that are undersized, perched or impassable for migrating salmonids are replaced to correct these problems.

- Old landing at confluences of streams or adjacent to streams are identified and rehabilitated.

- New landings are no larger than 5625 square feet and cover at most 1 percent of the area harvested. Their banks are less than 6 feet high.

Employment and Economics

- Woodsworkers are drawn from communities as near to the forest as feasible.

- Wood from these operations is processed (milled, dried and remanufactured) and value added to it as close to the location of harvest as possible. The sale

of unmilled logs by the operator for use outside the watershed of harvest is discouraged.

Areas excluded from harvest

- Sites of archeological, cultural and historical significance and their immediate surroundings.

- Ancient forests are subject to a moratorium on commercial logging, during which the Institute will participate in research on the ramifications of management in these areas.

Submitting a plan

Landowners wishing to have their wood certified will grant permission to the Institute's field staff or their designees to inspect the site of timber operations before, during and after logging.

Landowners desiring interim certification will mark the trees they intend to cut (dominants and co-dominants greater than 6 inches dbh) and submit a copy of their Timber Harvesting Plan to the Institute at least 45 days before they wish to commence operations. This lead time will permit Institute staff to review the plan and schedule a pre-harvest inspection.

For more information, please contact:

The Institute for Sustainable Forestry
P.O. Box 1580
Redway, CA 95560
Tel: (707) 923-4719/Fax: (707) 923-4527

5   Forest Ecology

5

Ancient Forests, Priceless Treasures

Chris Maser

We can grow large trees, but we can never reproduce an ancient forest.

—Chris Maser

5

WE'RE GOING TO TAKE A JOURNEY into an ancient forest and see a little bit of how it functions. I'm going to start with the science at first, and then I will put it all together for you in ways that make sense in terms of relating it to land management and where we are going.

Unfortunately, scientists all too often deal with things in intellectual isolation, and this is one of our major problems. We scientists are not very good at translating data so people can understand it. What I am going to do in a very simple way is translate how parts of the forest work. We're going to look at how large trees that blow over and lie on the ground—what you would call logs — decompose and what this means in terms of the long term health and productivity of the forests of the Pacific Northwest.

I'm going to deal primarily with the ancient forest because that is the database. This is nature's forest, not humanity's. An ancient forest exists once in forever. When this is gone, ladies and gentlemen, it is not renewable. We human beings can grow large trees, but we can never reproduce an ancient forest. Nature's ancient forest is a finite entity.

Trees that fall to the ground generally do so in two ways. One is that they get blown over by the wind. The other is that they die standing. A tree is potentially immortal in that it renews all of its living tissue every year—its entire immune system. Unlike our bodies that have organs and parts that wear out and are not replaced, trees potentially can live forever. That's why some of them live over 3,500 years.

What kills trees is the rigors of the environment in which they live. When you see trees sway in the wind, big, ancient trees, their roots are being strained below ground. If the roots get strained enough and abrade on rocks, this allows pathogens to enter, and the tree starts to die unless it can wall off the pathogens. It may take a tree two hundred years to finally die. So when you are looking at the forest you are looking at a system that is in a continual stage of change.

When a tree falls to the ground, whether a freshly fallen living tree or one which fell as a snag, an already dead tree, it creates a lot of diversity. The diversity on the forest floor is not just in structure. What killed the tree determines how it will decompose internally. Its internal structure will change, allowing different functions to take place.

Now I'm going to decompose a tree for you. I'm going to do it very simply, though in fact it's very complicated. There are three major areas of a tree that are important. Just underneath the outer bark is the inner bark, or cambium, where the protein is stored. It disappears in the first year: it's eaten up. The second portion is the sap wood, which is mainly carbohydrates. Comparatively speaking, that is eaten fast.

The third part is the heartwood. The heartwood is mostly lignin, and decomposes very slowly. I'll come back to all these things. Three things happen to the wood as it decomposes. The first is it loses density; it becomes spongy. The second is it increases in moisture, and the third is it increases in nutrients.

So let's decompose a healthy tree that falls over. The bark beetles get into it within the first year. Most of the bark beetles girdle the cambium; they eat their way around the cambium, which kills the tree.

There's another group, called the ambrosia beetles, that have specialized structures called mycangia in which they carry the spores of the ambrosia fungus. These bark beetles chew their galleries in the sapwood and when the fungus germinates it grows along the galleries. If the wood is too wet the fungus explodes, and the beetle smothers in the fungus, its own food supply. If the wood is too dry, the fungus doesn't grow very well, and the beetle starves.

The other thing we're learning is that as the beetles invade the wood they also bring nitrogen-fixing bacteria with them in that first year. Nitrogen-fixing bacteria are one-celled plants. Nitrogen-fixing bacteria have a capability to pluck nitrogen out of the air and change it to an ammonia compound that makes it available to other organisms to use as fuel.

The second group that comes are flat-headed or metallic wood borers. These beetles also come in within the first year and tend to live in the sapwood. They lay their eggs on the bark. Larvae hatch, penetrate the wood and then eat their way through it. We now have a prey base in the wood and so the third group that tends to come in are predators, such as the red-bellied checker beetle. It feeds on the eggs and larvae of the first two.

As the wood continues to gradually decompose with bacteria, etc., the mites enter. Mites are related to spiders, and they do a little bit of everything. As a group they're generalists. Individually, as small groups, they're specialists. One is called the oribatid mite. It feeds on decaying vegetation. There is a group that feeds on the droppings of other animals, a group that is predacious, a group that feeds on wood, and there's a group that grazes the bacteria that are decomposing the wood. These mites do something of everything inside this wood.

Another small organism that enters the wood is called the springtail. It is a small, flightless insect and gets its name from the long appendage that is normally folded up underneath the belly area. If you touch them, they depress this very rapidly and it catapults them forward. If you cross country ski, you would know these as snowfleas. Springtails are at the bottom of the food chain; they graze on the bacteria and also eat the little thread-like parts of the fungus. So they cause an effect.

Everything in the world causes an effect, either positive or negative, for some part of the system. The world is balanced, and the thing to keep in mind as I go through this, ladies and gentlemen, is that the world functions perfectly without us. It always has. Our perception of how the world functions is imperfect, and that's what we need to deal with.

So I'm being a perception mechanic for you today. I'm going to try to help you skew your perception over a little bit to understand that the world is like a waterbed. If you punch it down over here, it's going to pop up over there. The problem is, we don't know where or how high.

When the wood becomes wet and at the right stage carpenter ants enter. Most people think of carpenter ants as the big black ants that eat up their house frames, which they do. In the forest they're extremely important. They're important not only to the ground, but also to the canopy— to the tree tops. You've noticed sawdust on the ground beneath old logs?

Carpenter ants do not eat the wood, but they chew out their galleries in the wood. Carpenter ants are primarily farmers in that they collect aphids and milk them; they herd them like cows. The aphids give off a waste product called "honeydew." That waste product is simply excess, highly sweetened plant sap. The carpenter ants actually take their aphid "cows" in the form of their eggs to the galleries in the winter and protect them over the winter and then put them out to pasture in the spring.

There's another group of carpenter ants that are predacious. Those are the ones that are important to the forest, particularly in the drier areas east of the Cascade Mountains (in Washington and Oregon). These carpenter ants and the red forest ants, which live in stumps and make mounds that you may see (ant hills, we call them), go from the ground up into the tree tops. They feed on the eggs, larvae, and pupae of the western spruce budworm and the Douglas fir tussock moth, defoliating insects that eat the needles of the conifers we want to harvest as a product.

When we get rid of the large woody material, we are removing the housing for the carpenter ants. When we cut down live ancient trees, which is where the carpenter ants have their long-term colonies (dead wood is only good for a very short time), we are losing the prime ant colonies. Viable carpenter ant colonies are like good wine. They improve with age, and they live in ancient trees. That's why, in our part of the country, you see the pileated woodpecker feeding in the large, ancient trees from the ground up to about twenty feet. This tells you that there is a carpenter ant colony in there, and carpenter ants make up the main diet of the woodpecker.

It also tells you that the tree has some rot, some defect,

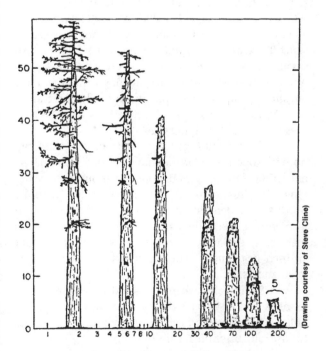

Decomposition of a Dead Douglas-fir

Height in meters is plotted against years dead. Such trees may play a role in the forest for hundreds of years after they die.

(Drawing courtesy of Steve Cline)

and part of it is dead because that's the part the ants live in. So, as we alter the habitat on the ground and liquidate the ancient trees, we're affecting the ant's habitat; that in turn affects the pileated woodpecker. This is above and beyond snags; I'm just talking about the functioning of the system at the moment. This isn't a judgment, but it does have consequences.

We know today that birds can control 80 percent of the western spruce budworm when the budworm is in an endemic stage (that is, their normal background levels). This is a particular group of birds that uses the forest and feeds on the budworm. As we alter the structure of the forest through management, we alter the bird's ability to live there. As we alter the habitat we alter the bird's ability to control spruce budworm.

Without the birds, the ants can still control about 80 percent of the budworm, but we're eliminating the large wood that constitutes their habitat. What happens when we alter both to the point that we have increased budworm outbreaks? Please understand that the western spruce budworm outbreak, the Douglas fir tussock moth, the mountain pine bark beetle, laminated root rot, red-ring rot, and black-stain root rot are all management created problems. We created them. We are the only ones who will be able to solve them.

And as we continually simplify the forest, the chances of our solving those problems, without changing our thinking, become more and more remote.

There are other organisms like millipedes. When I was a kid I played a lot with millipedes and found out they stank. The reason they stink is that in each section are two small glands that produce pure hydrogen cyanide gas. And they're poisonous enough that if you put them in a jar, stir them up and then put in a butterfly, it is usually dead in seconds. The millipedes are important because they feed on the decaying vegetation.

When the wood is good and wet, some of the long-horned wood borers or the round-headed wood borers enter. One is the ponderous borer: it's about three inches long when it's mature, a good-sized beetle. These are heartwood feeders. Because the heartwood is very low in nutrients, it takes them from three to seven years to mature. But the larvae leave behind a burrow that is about an inch in diameter. These burrows are then used by salamanders.

And finally, also when the wood is good and wet, termites get in. We have the Pacific dampwood termite. This is where the forest gets a little complicated, because this is really three organisms in one.

When termites swarm in the fall, they collect at the entrance to their colonies. They have wings, and they all mature sexually within one-half hour before flight time. Then they fly. It's called the "nuptial flight." When they have mated, they land on the wood that is right for them to inhabit; they detect this by the odors giving off by the fungi that are decomposing the wood.

Once in the wood they shed their wings. Seventy percent of the wood they eat is infected with fungi that give off the odor that tells them what part of the fallen tree is right to munch on. Termites have very strong mandibles, or jaws, but they cannot digest the wood. They can eat it. So they chew up the wood and it comes back into the gut where it is attacked by a one-celled animal called a protozoan. The protozoan can digest the cellulose in the plant wall, but the protozoan requires a constant supply of nitrogen, and wood, we know today, does not have a constant supply of nitrogen.

The nitrogen content of wood varies; wherever you go in the same tree, it's different. So nature has provided nitrogen-fixing bacteria in the gut that take nitrogen out of the air and convert it to an ammonia product that the protozoan can use; the protozoan, in turn, gives off a waste product that the bacteria use for food. Those two together cause a fermentation process that produces acetic acid that soaks through the termite's gut and fuels the termite. Thus, if one piece of this triad dies, the whole thing dies.

Other small organisms include pseudoscorpions that feed on mites, and the Pacific folding-door spider and the centipede, which are at the top of the predators in the invertebrate line. There are also things like sowbugs in the wood; they in turn are food for the clouded salamander.

We've got four salamanders in western Oregon that belong to the group called lungless salamanders, and they require the wood for two reasons: for moisture, because without having lungs they absorb the oxygen through their moist skin, and for reproduction. Even though they're amphibians they lay their eggs in the wet, rotten wood where it is available, and some of them seem to be confined to the wood in some areas.

One of these salamanders, the Oregon slender salamander, occurs in an area in Western Washington from Seattle to the Columbia River. That's a very small area. They lay their eggs in the wet, rotten wood. The eggs are very large. The larvae go through the aquatic stage inside the egg.

The salamander may only require that large fallen tree for a short time twice a year, but the wood is critical to the survival of the salamander during that time because the wet wood also acts as a reservoir for water that maintains the lifestyle of the salamander.

And then there are fungi. We're going to talk a lot about fungi because fungi are very important.

Now let's go to the wood for a moment. As wood lies on the ground decomposing, rotting if you will, it loses density. That means it becomes spongy. Residence time is the length of time in years that trees lie decomposing on the forest floor. In our forests in the Northwest, a 400-year-old Douglas fir usually lasts between 200 and 250 years as a fallen tree. That is before it is recycled. So we're talking about two and one-half centuries. This is a rough average. An 800-year-old Douglas fir takes about 400 years to decompose and recycle into the system.

So 2/3 to 3/4 of the tree's useful life is while it is living, and the last 1/3 to 1/4 is when it's dead. After death, it serves an entirely different suite of functions that are necessary to keep the forest going.

We make a lot of mistakes in science, for which I'm grateful, because that's how we learn. And one of the mistakes we've made for years in wildlife biology has been to argue for structural diversity without understanding functional diversity. What has killed the tree and how it decomposes determines how it functions once it's dead. If we should ever get rid of disease in the forest, that one act alone would alter the entire functional dynamics of the system.

And if we alter the wood that we produce, by making it grow faster and have larger annual rings, with less density, we're altering how the entire forest functions. We're altering the functional dynamics over time.

There are a number of kinds of decomposition going on in an old log: brown-cubicle rot, white-pocket rot, etc., and the ever-present beetle galleries. This is very important, because the roots of western hemlock grow into the wood and follow the white-pocket rot because the white pocket rot separates the annual rings of the wood. The hemlock roots can follow the white-pocket rot down the line of least resistance and absorb the moisture and nutrients in an ideal rooting medium. That's how they have evolved.

Now we're going to talk about ectomycorrhizal fungi. The ecto means outside, myco means fungus and rrhizal means root. I'll explain the association, the marriage, between fungi and root tips that allows the tree to take up nutrients. In the dryer east side of the Cascades, 66 percent of this relationship is in humus, which is the top organic layer, composed largely of rotting wood. We're removing that rotting wood in forest management to the best of our ability.

If we were to build a chart, 21 percent of these fungi are specialists with decayed wood, 8 percent are specialists in charcoal, and only 5 percent of this fungal association is in mineral soil. As we remove the wood from our system, we are affecting 95 percent of this fungal association that is necessary for the survival of the trees.

And what are we doing to the health of our forest? A healthy Douglas-fir has 30 to 40 species of these fungi attached to its root system at all times. In Germany, the Norway spruce has 3 to 5, and they have no wood left in their intensively managed spruce plantations. They have

altered the system. Do we necessarily want to follow suit?

A mycorrhizal fungus forms a mantle around the root tip, and that's very important because root tips are turned over very rapidly every year. This costs the tree a tremendous amount of energy. The fungus prolongs the life of the root tip, protects it, and stimulates root-tip production. A root tip that is not infected with the fungus is short-lived. It cannot take up the nutrients and water necessary for the tree to survive. With the fungus, it can do so.

What you don't see are the little mold-like threads that are torn off as we pull the roots out of the soil, that have been reaching out into the soil. These we call the hyphal mat. The fungus is an extension of the tree's root system that goes out into the soil in little fingers, picking up water, phosphorus, and nitrogen and moving it up into the tree's root tips. From there it goes up into the top of the tree.

The tree requires the fungus in order to survive. All of our conifers do! None can survive without this fungus. None of them can take up the nutrients and the water without the fungus. The tree in turn feeds the fungus sugars from photosynthesis—the conversion of sunlight, and the carbon dioxide in the sugars in the needles—that comes down the tree, out into the roots, and out into the fungus to feed it. Like the termites, these two cannot exist without each other.

So what we have here is a fungus that picks up water, phosphorus, and nitrogen, puts it through a little feeder system into the root tips and takes it up to the tree tops. The tree sends sugars down in return.

There are two types of fungi to do this. One is called the epigeous or above ground fruiting mushroom. Some are like the Boletus, in which the reproductive spores come down little tubes and out little pores. Another form is the gilled mushroom, whose spores fall down off either side of the thin, sharp gills.

There are some shortcomings to this part of the system in that these fungi depend on wind to blow the spores throughout the forest, which means the spores go hither and yon wherever the wind takes them. When they land on the soil, they have to be washed in with rainwater. On a very dry year or a very cold year the crop of mushrooms aborts. They don't grow, and the forest goes without their inoculation that year.

Another important thing about wind as a dispersal mechanism is that there is very little wind close to the ground in our dense forests. The wind increases as you get up higher. On the east coast, in the more open forests, wind is a very important factor.

In the Northwest, we have a second type of below-ground fruiting (or hypogeous) mushroom called a truffle, or false truffle. Its entire system is below ground. These look like little potatoes. They have a tough outer coat, and the spore-bearing tissue is within that coating. The problem with this system is that there is no way they can disperse their spores by themselves. They have evolved to be eaten by animals, primarily mammals.

And as the mammals disperse little fecal pellets throughout the woods they inoculate the soil with viable spores of the fungus. The fungi come in a variety of sizes and shapes. Remember—this whole system is below ground. Fruiting bodies are produced once or twice a year when the weather is right, enough sugars have been stored, and there is enough soil moisture. The fruiting bodies are then eaten by small mammals.

Now let's get back to wood for a moment. As wood lies on the ground decomposing, it increases in moisture—in water. Its water-holding capacity is tremendous. If it is under a canopy, under the tree tops, be it a young forest or an ancient forest, it forms a reservoir that holds water throughout the year. Water like this (it is called metabolic water) is produced by the respiration of wood-decayed bacteria.

Again, remember the beetle galleries and the different types of decomposition. When a fallen tree is mostly decomposed, and mostly heartwood is left, the sapwood having sloughed off, it is entirely saturated. The log becomes a Captain Marvel log: it is so wet and spongy that I can shove my hand in it, yell "Shazam!" pull it out and squeeze water out of wood. I've had people who didn't believe that. I work with fire folks a lot and I love them because there are some real skeptics in that group. It was a very hot July day in a clearcut up on the Mt. Hood National Forest in Oregon and I had forgotten my hat. (You see, I have this shiny dome that I usually think of as a solar panel for an active mind.) Anyway, out in the clearcut that day I forgot my hat. My mind was getting too active in the sun, so I wanted to go into the ancient forest for some shade.

When we got in there, there was a nice tree that was down, and it had about a quarter of an inch of rotten wood along the surface under the bark. And so I bet them (I always win with this) that they could squeeze water out of wood, and they looked at me like I already had sunstroke. I've always liked the skeptic, so I picked the skeptic and had him go over and scrape a handful of this quarter-inch of rotten wood. Then I said, "Now squeeze it."

His eyes stood out that far when drops of water started coming out of it. The point is, this is wet all year. This is actually a reservoir that holds water under a canopy, no matter how hot it gets.

Now let's look at a gentle slope, let's look at the upslope side of a fallen tree. Look at all the soil that is kept from moving down-slope by this fallen tree because it lies along the contour, across the slope. This wood serves a purpose besides just storing water. It prevents a lot of erosion. When the wood is oriented up and down the slope it does nothing for erosion. On the downhill side of the tree you'll notice an open triangle. This is cover or habitat for the small mammals that disperse the spores of the mycorrhizal fungi.

The interface between the soil and the bottom of a fallen tree is one of the richest areas in the forest in terms of nutrient cycling and exchange and we don't know much about it. This wet, fallen tree is the reservoir that keeps the forest going, this is what the salamanders use, this is what the fungi use, and this is the reservoir that the hemlock roots penetrate.

There is a specialized fungus called Rhizopogon vinicolor. It doesn't have a common name. This fungus is one that specializes in rotting wood. It forms mycorrhizae with Douglas-fir and has small "appendages" called rhizomorphs. You can think of these rhizomorphs as small siphons. They grow in the wood where they're very adept in the uptake of water that they move into Douglas-fir. This one is a specialist with Douglas-fir.

So wood is a reservoir that makes water available to the Douglas-fir throughout the drought part of the summer, because of the fungus' ability to withdraw and move water. We also know that when Douglas-fir is planted into clear-cuts in a hot site, if they have this fungus attached to the root system, they're twice as drought resistant as those that don't have it.

And then nutrients accumulate in the wood as it lies there decomposing. Nitrogen accumulates over time. You see, the longer it's there, the higher it is in nitrogen content. It might seem a minuscule amount, but we know that the forest uses more nitrogen than we've ever been able to account for, and I'll show you how we think it works.

Okay, let's recap for a moment before we go on. We've got a large, ancient tree that falls over and as it starts to decompose we've got two things that go on simultaneously. It simplifies internally because it gets eaten up, and it complicates at the same time. Everything in nature is one of these beautiful paradoxes: you think that what you see is and you find that it isn't.

As the wood simplifies, gets eaten up, the plant and animal communities increase in complexity until the sapwood is gone and all that's left is the heartwood. Then the community simplifies dramatically, almost immediately, compared to the length of time it took it to build up to the complexity. As the wood shrinks and decomposes, the plant community on the outside increases in complexity and gradually enfolds the fallen tree in leaves and branches, creating a humid environment that prolongs the life of the wood. (On the drier east side of the Cascade Range the wood decomposes much faster.)

The hemlock I was talking about earlier, a little rooting

seedling, is so designed to germinate on wood because it's an understory tree in the ancient forest; it can live in its own shade. It can grow underneath the Douglas-fir and become the climax species. Douglas-fir is not climax because it is not self-reproducing in its own shade. But the duff layer underneath the fir is so deep that these little folks can't get their roots down to the mineral soil before the summer drought kills them, so they've evolved to grow in rotting wood.

They have an ideal medium: it's spongy, it's wet, and it's high in nutrients. But they still have to have mycorrhizal fungi attached to their root tips. However, they have evolved to survive for over a year without the mycorrhizae. The other trees can't do that; they have to be inoculated within a year. These little hemlocks can live beyond a year, though there's a very high mortality for this specialization. When they've gotten this old, they have to have their roots inoculated.

That happens with small mammals, some with wind, but mostly small mammals such as deer mice, chipmunks, squirrels, etc. They "poop" on the wood, and their pooparoonies, being full of fungal spores, disintegrate and the rain washes the spores into the wood. And as the spores come in contact with the root tips, they become inoculated with the mycorrhizal fungi.

The little hemlock then can tap the resources inside this wood called a "nurse log." The wood gradually rots out from under the growing hemlock and leaves it on stilts. This is also the way the Norway spruce was designed to grow in the European Alps. And it still does. Wherever there was rotting wood, that's where we found the healthy trees.

As I said before, we make a lot of mistakes. We found a few years ago that inside the fungus were nitrogen fixing bacteria—those little folks that can take nitrogen out of the air and convert it. The way we manage, the way we tend to face life and conduct research, is to divide and conquer. Have you noticed that? We don't deal with things in relationship. We separate everything.

Well, we did this. We were good scientists; we divided and conquered and purified and killed the whole system. And we did that for a year. Then one day we ended up with a contaminated petri dish. We found that the fungus and the bacteria can only survive together because the fungus feeds the bacteria what we called the fungal extract. We don't know what it is, but it functions like the substance the protozoan fed the bacteria inside the termite.

The bacteria takes nitrogen and fixes it so that the fungus can use it. This association came from inside the fruiting bodies of the fungi and the mantle of mycorrhizal tissue that covered the root tips of the Douglas fir. That means that inside the root tips of our trees are small nitrogen pumps. For 365 days out of the year, 24 hours a day, they pump minuscule amounts of nitrogen up into the tree. We didn't know this before. We think this is where a lot of the nitrogen comes from, but we've never been able to measure it. So the way we see it now is that the tree feeds the fungus sugar from photosynthesis, the fungus goes out into the soil, picks up water, phosphorus, and nitrogen, and moves it into the tree root tips. Inside the tree root tips are bacteria that feed on the product given off by the fungus, in turn fixing nitrogen, which along with the other nutrients, is available to the tree. This is very important, because this is a symbiotic relationship which is obligatory. It has to be.

We've known for a number of years that small mammals feed on the spores of mycorrhizal fungi and that the spores remain viable. The next question was, do they also spread nitrogen-fixing bacteria? So we selected some flying squirrels and I coaxed them to give us some of their pooparoonies. The way you do that is you put them in a clean, white, cloth sack and scare them for about ten seconds. Then you wait five minutes and usually have a reward.

From those little pooparoonies we were able to grow bacteria. These bacteria are nitrogen-fixers, but we threw them out for months because we still had the divide and conquer mentality. Science has taught me a great deal of humility. We noticed there were fat ones, and round ones, and short ones, and skinny ones. We threw them out for six months to a year until a friend of ours, Dr. Telak, from the Ministry of Agricultural Research in New Delhi, India, came to visit us, and just on a hunch we asked him what these bacteria were. He said, "Oh, yes, that's *Azospirillum* spp...."

He said, "We've been experimenting with that for fifteen years on our soybean crops." (Soybeans are in the pea family; they have little lumps or nodules on the roots that house the bacteria that can make the switch with nitrogen.) "We switched bacteria and we've increased or doubled and tripled our crop." We had the best known nitrogen-fixing bacteria in the world in our trees and we didn't know it until three years ago. And it's being disseminated by the small mammals. We threw it out, however, because we were looking for something uniform.

Then in the deer mouse, the small mammals that we spent millions of dollars poisoning for years, we found another nitrogen-fixing bacteria; this one is in textbooks. It's called Clostridium butyricum.

This is an important one because the deer mouse is one of the first animals to use a clearcut. They come out of the ground even after burns—the fires don't kill them. A resting stage of the bacteria, called an endospore, can withstand temperatures of 176 degrees Fahrenheit or 80 degrees Celsius. That means they can withstand the surface temperatures of the soils that get as hot as soils do in the Sahara during summer—160 degrees Fahrenheit. So these bacteria-spreading deer mice can re-inoculate logged and burned areas with a nitrogen-fixing bacterium.

The other thing we found in small mammals were yeast propagules. Some were from the flying squirrel (our example of how this system functions in rodents). From the squirrel's stomach the small intestine goes down to a pouch called the cecum. From the cecum, the large intestine comes out to the rectum. The cecum is like an eddy along a swift stream; it collects and concentrates organisms, in this case yeast (which is a fungus), nitrogen fixing bacteria, and the mycorrhizal fungal spores. We couldn't even count these yeast propagules in the deer mouse. We found more yeast here than we found in the soil. Some of the mycorrhizal spores, when they come out of the poop, require the extract of another fungus to germinate; this in itself stimulates germination, and that's what the yeast does.

We just submitted a paper for publication in which we were able to demonstrate that yeast has to be alive. We grew the yeast from the animal droppings in nitrogen-free medium, and then we harvested it. Have you ever tried harvesting yeast? You can't even see the stuff with the naked eye. (We have very small combines that go out and harvest the yeast.)

When we have the yeast harvested we put the bacteria in. Dead yeast left no extract and the bacteria didn't survive. Where the yeast had been alive, the bacteria produced high amounts of nitrogen. So we know that the yeast has to be alive, and it comes out of the small mammals alive.

To test all this we took some droppings of deer mice — one dropping per test tube—smashed it up in sterile water, put in sterile-grown Douglas fir seedlings, and left them alone for six months. Then we did what we call "reading" them: pull the seedlings out of the tubes and examine their roots. The interesting thing was that we used three genera of fungi, two of which no one had ever been able to germinate in the lab.

One of them is a very important commercial crop in Oregon—the Oregon white truffle. After they had gone through the deer mice, we collected their droppings and inoculated the seedlings. After six months we pulled the seedlings out and found that the fungus had survived, the bacteria was fixing nitrogen beautifully, and the yeast had survived. No one had ever been able to demonstrate how that system worked. But now we have an idea of what happens in the forest floor.

I was trained as a zoologist. I want you to understand that, because wildlife biologists count pellets. They count the poops of elk and deer, and other mammals. That's how they get their biological wings. I always promised myself that I didn't want to be that kind of pilot. So what I did was spend a winter in the lab counting mouse pellets. We found—this is going to thrill you—that deer mice give off an average of sixty-six pellets in twenty-four hours. Isn't that exciting? And the little red-backed vole that looks like a meadow mouse with a red back gives off about a hundred pooparoonies in twelve hours.

The first time I told this to forest supervisors, you can imagine what they said. What this all means is that if a deer mouse has been feeding on a fungus and that's all that it's eaten, rather than the 1,000 to 10,000 spores needed to inoculate a Douglas-fir seedling, each little pellet has between 500,000 and 800,000 spores, plus yeast, plus nitrogen-fixing bacteria. It's about 300,000 per red-backed vole pellet and about 10,000,000 per deer pellet.

So one pellet has enough inoculum to inoculate one seedling and give it life. That's a dramatic function an animal plays, an animal—the deer mouse—that we used to poison because we never looked at the flip side of the coin.

Now picture the photographs you've seen of burned "clear-cuts." (We said we don't do this anymore, but once in a while fires get away, and it will still get kind of hot.) In such pictures, you'll notice that there is very little large wood; first generation forests, or "crop trees," don't leave much, and with current logging practices, we're busy removing as much of the large woody material as possible. Notice also that most of it goes up and down on the slope, because logs are pulled upward toward spar trees with cables. Few will be found along contours on the slopes. Those vertical logs have no value to speak of compared to those lying along contours of the slope.

Though such fires are hot, they don't kill deer mice whose little tunnels have lots of kinks and klinks in them so the oxygen is trapped and the heat doesn't suck it out. When the deer mice come out, they can begin to re-inoculate the soil. However, a lot of their habitat is gone, so we have lost some of their potential value in growing the next stand.

When the wood is completely rotted and only the heartwood remains as a ghost of a tree, hemlocks and other things will grow on it. There's fifty to a hundred years of nutrient cycling left in the wood and this is already free. Mother Nature has provided it. The heartwood is the most important part of the tree, not the sapwood or the cambium, but the heartwood, because inside the lignin is a substance called vanillic acid, that can be broken down by the bacteria and by the fungi who use it as their source of food.

But when we scatter this heartwood with tractors, or pull it apart with logging activities, or whatever we do with it, once its structure is gone its function is also destroyed. Here we have an option of saving something, or losing it. It's our choice: We have the technology. We have to make the choice to do something with that heartwood.

The fungi (truffle and false truffle) reproduce with those below-ground fruiting bodies we mentioned earlier. Immature fruiting bodies are white; they get darker as the spores increase in maturity. Each gives off its own odor, and we can detect some of these.

In Europe they train dogs and sows to sniff them out of the soil. The famous black truffle of Europe sells these days for $400 to $600 a pound because the Europeans are losing their forests, their truffle habitat. I said they trained sows, and I say that advisedly. In fact they used to put muzzles on them when they went truffle sniffing.

They use sows because the boars won't sniff them out. Why? The chemical odor given off by these fungi is identical to that of a boar that's ready to reproduce. Which tells us that this association has been around for a long, long time.

In the Pacific Northwest, it's the small squirrel—the chickaree of western Oregon and Washington and the red squirrel of eastern Oregon and Washington slopes—and other animals, such as shrews, that sniff out the truffles. They dig these fungi out by odor, and what they don't eat, we can glean for study. The red-backed vole of Oregon and a different species of red-backed vole in the coastal Olympic Mountains feed on these fungi 98 percent of the time, throughout the year.

When we get into the Cascade Mountains of Western Oregon and Northwestern California, the indigenous red-backed vole feeds on the hypogeous fungi 85 percent of the time. The species of red-backed vole in Washington also feeds on truffles about 75 to 85 percent of the time in the Cascade Mountains. (This last vole is native clear to the east coast, and when you study it on the east coast, it has completely shifted its diet to nuts and vegetation above ground because the below-ground food that I'm talking about here is not so prevalent on the east coast, where it's mostly hardwood forest.)

The little red-backed vole in Oregon can live for hundreds of generations in an ancient forest because it lives on the fungus. But when the forest is clearcut or burned, or whatever else might happen to remove it, that species dies out within one year because its specialized food disappears.

There's another vole called the creeping vole, which occurs only in northwestern California, western Oregon, western Washington and southwest British Columbia. It can also feed on these fungi for hundreds of years in an ancient forest, but when the canopy is removed and grasses and forbs come in, it shifts its diet completely to grasses and forbs and its numbers explode. So the red-backed vole dies out and the population of the creeping vole explodes.

When the forest returns, they reverse. In the forest, the red-backed vole is dominant; the creeping vole is subordinate.

And then there are chipmunks. Chipmunks and deer mice are very important. They visit clear-cuts from out of the ancient forest, deposit their droppings, and go back. They're inoculating the clearcut as they do that. We've noticed for years that the trees do best around the edges of a clearcut—and that also just happens to be the distance that these small mammals travel in their normal daily visitations.

In high elevations, there are the pikas, little rock rabbits, there are the mantled ground squirrels and the flying squirrels. The flying squirrel feeds on these fungi all year in southwestern Oregon. In the Pacific Northwest, and in Alaska, they feed on them spring, summer, and fall, and in the winter they switch their diet to the hair moss or lichens in the treetops. They also make their nests of these: they can have their nest and eat it too. These little guys actually come down to the ground at night to pick out the fungus they detect by odor.

That's why cougars, marten, and coyotes can catch them and eat them; that's why we've found flying squirrel remains in their droppings. These little animals flourish in forests that have a high amount of woody material on the ground because, as I said before, the fungus is attached to that woody material, and so is the moisture that keeps it going. So flying squirrels and large amounts of woody debris on the forest floor go together.

When a flying squirrel comes down to the forest floor and digs out a fungus, if it happens to expose a root tip that has not yet been inoculated and it poops right there, the spores from its droppings can germinate and inoculate that root tip. If, on the other hand, it digs out an already inoculated root tip and its droppings touch that root tip and it happens to be the same species of fungus already in the root tip, the non-reproductive portions of those fungi can fuse, and that's how genetic material is exchanged.

So in a sense, without knowing it, the squirrel can be taking care of the tree it lives in. Now here is more of the cycle: The flying squirrel is the main food of the Northern Spotted Owl. The Northern Spotted Owl requires a large amount of woody debris on the ground because its prey base feeds almost entirely on the fungi that are associated with wet, rotting wood. As we remove this from the ground, through clearcutting or burning, we're affecting the flying squirrel. As I said: "life is a waterbed."

You have probably seen photographs of the tidy forests of Europe, the German forests in southern Bavaria, for instance. You may have noted there was no wood on or in the ground; it was all picked up and burned in the homes. Even the twigs less than an inch in diameter are picked up and stacked for later use.

I've given speeches to industrial groups, and one time a German forester got very excited. When I was done, he came running up to the stage really agitated. I didn't know whether he was going to hit me or agree with me. He said, "I grew up in southern Germany and went to the University of Munich, and I can remember birds in those woods when I was a kid in 1936. I went back in 1984 and they were silent woods." He said, "Now I know what happened to all the animals."

Most of the wildlife is in the cities in central Europe; what they call wildlife is deer. In the month that my wife and I traveled around central Europe—France, Switzerland and Germany—most of the time with foresters and in the field, we saw woodpecker workings once; there were no birds. We saw a lot of deer, one mouse, and a slug. I'm not kidding. That was the third largest wildlife species we saw: a slug. We heard no squirrels. We heard no birds. The forests that are this intensively managed are silent. All they have are deer, which cause a lot of problems.

German forest management is so controlled, their forests are so stressed, so strained. Legally, they must peel all their coniferous trees to get the bark off before they take them out of the forest so that the bark beetles don't get into them. Can you imagine the costs if we were to have to do business that way here? But over there it is the law. The bark beetles manage their forest plantations. And all the "scrap" ends up in their fireplaces, even the twigs.

But you know, that isn't a whole lot different than we are doing here. Particularly when you get wood chippers on a site. I've been on clear-cuts under experimental conditions where they were chipping everything down to an inch in diameter. What do you end up with? You could play golf out there.

Think about that, folks. That is where we're headed if we continue with the thought processes and the consciousness level that we're managing forests with today. But some of this is changing. Let me finish up with this little bit.

What I'm going to do at this point is to go through some of the ideas of what we are doing, why we're doing it, and how we can change. This, by the way, usually takes me a two-day workshop. Please understand something. I do a lot of work with the Forest Service, a tremendous amount, and for any agency, any group of this size to change—yourselves included, folks—it takes an internal, personal change of every individual.

We have to learn to be gentle with each other. We're all doing our work the best we know how to. We cannot legislate values. We cannot legislate feelings. We have to evolve them ourselves. Every change in any agency, in any society, takes place at glacial speed.

As we liquidate old-growth forests, we are redesigning the forests of the future. The problem is that we've thrown away Nature's blueprint:

Nature designed a forest as an experiment in unpredictability; we're trying to design a regulated forest.

Nature designed a forest over a landscape; we're trying to design a forest on each acre.

Nature designed a forest with diversity; we're designing a forest with simplistic uniformity.

Nature designed a forest with interrelated processes; we're trying to design a forest based on isolated products.

Nature designed a forest in which all elements are neutral; we're designing a forest in which we perceive some elements as good, others bad, and we have no idea what they do.

Nature designed a forest to be a flexible, timeless continuum of species; we're designing a forest to be a rigid, time-constrained monoculture.

Nature designed a forest of long term trends; we're trying to design a forest of short-term absolutes.

Nature designed a forest to be a self-sustaining, self-repairing entity; we're designing a forest to require increasing external subsidies: fertilizers, herbicides, pesticides.

Nature designed Pacific Northwest forests to live 500 to 1,200 years; we're designing a forest that may seldom live one hundred years.

Nature designed Pacific Northwest forests to be unique in the world: 25 species of conifers, the richest conifer forests anywhere, 7 major species, the longest-lived and largest of their genera anywhere in the world; we're designing a forest based largely on a single species, in short rotation.

We can have a sustainable forest, but only if we constantly question and re-evaluate what we think we know (academically and professionally) and only if we retain all of the pieces, including ancient forests, from which to learn. We can have a sustainable forest industry to produce wood products for people, but only if we redesign industry to operate, in fact, within sustainable limits set by the forest, not by people, because the rotation concept is from Germany and it's an economic concept. It has nothing whatsoever to do with biology.

We're practicing European plantation management with all of its successes and failings, mostly failings. In both cases we must learn humility, which means we must learn to be teachable by nature. In both cases we must become students of processes, not advocates of positions. In both cases we must work together for a common goal with a common commitment, a sustainable forest for a sustainable industry for a sustainable environment for people.

How do we do this? First we have to redirect our

focus. We're focused on the wrong end of the system. We're focused only on the products. And while we argue about who gets the last ancient tree, the forest is quietly slipping away.

Our water comes from forested watersheds. In Poland, today, 90 percent of the water is too polluted for human consumption. Seventy percent of the water in major rivers is too polluted for industry. They don't have any forest watersheds. Czechoslovakia expects to lose their forest by the year 2000. What then?

We're redesigning our upper slopes. Where does our water come from in the Northwest? From snowpack. By the time the Colorado River gets to Mexico we have forgotten that it headed up in the snow pack of the Rocky Mountains of Colorado.

We're cutting the high elevation forests five times faster than we cut the low elevation forests to maintain the same output of wood fiber. At what costs to our long-term water supply?

We have to focus on that part of the system that produces the trees, and we're not. We're only focusing on trees, Spotted Owls, or deer and elk. And the way the management plans are set up will guarantee the extinction of both ancient forests and the Spotted Owl. No matter what we say—until we change our thinking and our focus to maintain a forest, we cannot have a sustainable industry. We cannot have either sustainable yield or a sustainable habitat without a sustainable forest.

We need not only some ancient forest, we also need to set aside some unmanaged mid-age forest and some unmanaged young forest because that's the only place where the genetic code for such a forest is still entirely intact as it was first evolved. This doesn't mean that we can't have large trees, and ancient trees, and owls, but they will be humanity's in the end; we have to learn from the forests how to recreate those circumstances. We can't if we liquidate the laboratory.

Nature's ancient forests are not renewable, and Chief Seattle tried to tell us this in 1855. Chief Seattle said to President Franklin Pierce:

"The Great Chief in Washington sends word he wishes to buy our land. How can you buy or sell the sky or the warmth of the land? The idea is strange to us. Yet, we do not own the freshness of the air, the sparkle of the water. How can you buy them from us? Every part of this earth is sacred to my people.

"We know that the White Man does not understand our ways. One portion of the land is the same to him as the next, for he is the stranger who comes in the night and takes from the land whatever he needs. The earth is not his brother, but his enemy and when he has conquered it he moves on. He leaves his father's grave and his children's birthright is forgotten.

"There is no quiet place in the White Man's cities, no place to hear the leaves of spring, the rustle of insect wings. But because I am a savage perhaps I do not understand. The clatter only seems to insult the ears. And what is there to life if man cannot hear the lovely cry of the whippoorwill or the arguments of the frog on the pond at night.

"The Whites, too, shall pass, perhaps sooner than other tribes. (The American Indian, the American natives, were here for 10,000 years before our forefathers arrived. In 400 years we have decimated an entire continent.) Continue to contaminate your beds and you will one night suffocate in your own waste. When the buffalo are all slaughtered, the wild horses all tamed, and the secret corners of the forest heavy with the scent of many men, and the view of the ripe hills blotted by talking warriors, where is the thicket? Gone. Where is the eagle? Gone. And what is it to say good-bye to the swift and to the hunt, the end of living and the beginning of survival?"

Chief Seattle is correct in that we ignore the four cornerstones of forestry: soil, water, air, and sunlight. We assume they are constant and so we omit them from all economic models and every management plan. But they are very delicate variables. There are only two constants in life—love and change. Everything else is a variable. Until we learn to deal with soil, water, air, and sunlight, we are killing the forests. Make no mistake about it. Fertilizing the forest does not do the job if the processes below ground are not intact to make the fertilizers available to the trees. Life is a waterbed.

We need ancient forests not for spotted owls only, not for clean water only, not for recreation only, not for spirituality only; we need ancient forests for the survival of our forests.

We invented the automobile; we designed it, we have a parts catalog, a maintenance manual, and a service station. Those parts are interchangeable, and we can design them. Our human body is a little bit similar; we know a lot about it. We have parts catalogs, anatomy manuals; we send doctors to school to learn how to read the maintenance manuals. We have service stations called hospitals, and we are to some extent interchangeable.

Where's the parts catalog, the maintenance manual, the service station for the forests? It's ancient forests, it's unmanaged mid-age forests, and it's unmanaged young forests. Unless we are willing to set some of those aside we will, if you look at world history, destroy our forests as most other nations have done, or are doing.

I know of no nation and no people that have maintained, on a sustainable basis, plantation managed trees beyond three rotations. The famous Black Forest in Europe is a plantation; it and other forests are dying at the end of the third rotation. The eastern pine plantations are dying. It's the end of their third rotation. We do not have any third rotations here.

I was quoted in a newspaper article the other day, a little out of context, but not badly. One of the gentlemen from industry said, "Well, geez, we're in our third rotation and trees are growing better than ever." He counted Nature's old-growth as one of those rotations. We're only now cutting the second rotation, and the forest is not producing as it did.

We do not value the land if we consider money to be symbolic of the value we place on something else. We harvest the land's products to a maximum and make payments in minimums. We spend the least amount possible on every acre and we harvest the maximum amount possible. We are not in any sense willing to reinvest in any natural, renewable resource.

If you have a mill and the wiring goes bad you take some of your profits and you reinvest them to get that particular wiring to do a particular job. We're not willing to re-invest a penny by leaving some old growth, some large snags, some large woody material to maintain the system through time, because we see it all as a commodity. We do not re-invest in renewable resources because we too often rely on science and technology to solve our problems.

Science and technology are human tools and are as constructive or destructive, as conservative or exploitative as their users. Science and technology have no sensitivity, they make no judgments, they have no conscience. It is neither scientific endeavors nor technological advances that affect the land. It is the degree of consciousness and the consequent thought processes with which we humans use the fruits of these endeavors that tip the ecological balance.

Visionaries, those rare individuals for whom time is at once a link to the past and a telescope into the future, have told us throughout history that we cannot survive in intellectual isolation. Yet we have tried. We have not listened.

There are those who say that we can intensify land management and have more of everything simultaneously because science and technology will find the answer. But as we simplify the above ground portion of the ecosystem for short-term profits, we simultaneously simplify the below ground portion of the ecosystem, which alters how soil, roots, nutrient cycling and nutrient uptake processes function and, consequently, how the land produces.

Is Chief Seattle's prediction of 135 years ago coming true? Are we, today, beginning to suffocate in our own wastes? Are we now beginning to fight for environmental survival because we have too little environmental consciousness?

So long as we have a commodity consciousness we will view the land as a commodity, exploit it as a commodity and destroy it as a commodity. As we elevate our consciousness, the constant human struggle, we begin to take our rightful place in the universe. Not as conquerors, for we have conquered nothing, but as universal custodians. Humanity stands today at the crossroads between the end of living and the beginning of survival. It is imperative that we heed Chief Seattle's words, and there is still time because today's choices belong to us. Tomorrow's consequences, however, belong both to us and to the future. The scale is poised in the balance. The difference is the level of our consciousness that determines our actions.

The early Native Americans gave our forefathers the key to sustainable forests and sustainable watersheds. That key is dignity and humility with respect to the land. But our forefathers did not learn from the forefathers of today's Native Americans, so now we, Native Americans and us, must learn from each other. We must take their values of relatedness and apply them to science and technology if we are to have a sustainable environment. And whatever we do, we must do it with love if we are to end survival and begin to live.

To do this, and we can, we must have a bigger dream, one in which we can all fit with dignity and unity. Our dream must be a sustainable forest and sustainable watersheds for all people, now and in the future. Ladies and gentlemen, if we want the industrialists to oil their chain saws with humility, we have to oil our words and thoughts with love, trust and respect.

The preceding was based on a presentation to the National Audubon Conference, which was meeting at Bellingham, Washington. Reprinted with permission.

The Use of Mycorrhizal Fungi and Associated Organisms in Forest Restoration

D. A. Perry and M. P. Amaranthus

Introduction

IN WIDELY VARYING ECOSYSTEMS throughout the world, intensive forest utilization, shifting cultivation, and overgrazing has led to deterioration in productive capacity, often accompanied by alteration of plant communities that appears permanent rather than transitory. Degradation of moist tropical forests (MTF) with intensified shifting cultivation is well-documented (Arnason, *et al.*, 1982; Armitsu, 1983). Site degradation is not restricted to MTF, however, but also occurs in the semi-arid Miombo woodlands of southern Africa (Maghembe, personal communication), in the montane coniferous forests of northern India (Sharma, 1983 and personal communication), in montane forests of North America (Amaranthus and Perry, 1987), and in numerous areas where overgrazed rangelands no longer support perennial grasses. Despite widely varying community types and environmental conditions, a common thread links these ecosystems and contributes to their decline when the dominant plants are too intensively utilized. That thread is the close interdependence between the indigenous plant community and both the biological and physical characteristics of soil. Depending on the environment in which they are growing, plants may divert up to 80% or more of the net carbon fixed in photosynthesis to below ground processes. Some of this goes into root growth, however a relatively high proportion may be used to feed mycorrhizal fungi and other organisms. This is energy that is lost to the plant. On the contrary, organisms living in the rhizosphere (the zone of influence of the root) improve plant growth through effects on nutrient cycling, pathogens, soil aeration, and soil nutrient and water-holding characteristics.

Of the various rhizosphere organisms, the most is known about mycorrhizal fungi. Roughly 90% of plant species belong to families whose members are thought to dominantly form mycorrhizae (the combination of fungal and root tissue is called the mycorrhizae: the fungal partner is termed a mycorrhizal forming "ectomycorrhizae" (EM)—so termed because there is an obvious external modification of the root morphology and color and those forming what are termed "vesicular-arbuscular" mycorrhizae (VAM)—the name coming from structures produced within plant cells by the fungus. Unlike EM, no external modification of the root accompanies VAM. The two types of mycorrhizae also differ in the nature of their infection with the root. In VAM, fungal hyphae always penetrate root cells, while in EM the hyphae wrap tightly around cell surfaces, but seldom form VAM. EM plants are almost exclusively woody perennials, including, in particular, members of the families *Pinaceae*, *Fagaceae*, *Ericaceae*, and *Dipterocarpaceae*. Some species—e.g., alders, eucalypts—form both EM and VAM, however this is the exception rather than the rule. Weeds, especially annuals, often do not form mycorrhizae of either type, or do so only occasionally.

Mycorrhizae improve seedling survival and growth by enhancing uptake of nutrients (particularly phosphorus) and water, lengthening root life, and protecting against pathogens (Harley and Smith, 1983). Trees forming ectomycorrhizae, including most of the important commercial species in the temperate and boreal zones and 70% of the species planted in the tropics (Evans, 1982), virtually always have mycorrhizae. The same is probably true of VAM forming dominants in the canopy of tropical forests (Janos, 1980). Ectomycorrhizae are generally thought to be crucial, if not for survival, at least for acceptable growth. Pines and oaks planted on sites that have not previously supported ectomycorrhizae die or do not grow well unless inoculated (Mikola 1970, 1973; Marx, 1980). For the trees forming VA mycorrhizae, including the majority of tropical and many temperate deciduous families, the symbiosis often is critical. Janos (1980) hypothesizes that late successional trees of moist tropical forests are usually obligately mycorrhizal, while trees of earlier successional stages and those on relatively fertile soils are facultative (i.e., they may or may not form mycorrhizae, depending on factors such as soil fertility).

Ectomycorrhiza trees often predominate on highly infertile tropical soils (Janos, 1980).

Many soil organisms other than mycorrhizal fungi influence plant growth. Tissue sloughing and organic exudates from roots, mycorrhizae and mycorrhizal hyphae support a complex community of bacteria, and protozoa and invertebrates that graze the bacteria. These organisms influence plant growth in various ways: by fixing nitrogen; by competing for nutrients but enhancing mineralization rates; by decomposing minerals; by welding aggregates; and by releasing a complex of hormones, allelochemicals, and chelators that probably affect plants both positively and negatively (chelators are organic compounds that increase the solubility, therefore availability, of certain nutrients—particularly iron). Much remains to be learned about the role of various rhizosphere organisms in plant growth, but it seems likely that their net effect on the plant is positive.

What happens to the rhizosphere community when energy inputs from plants are reduced or eliminated? In very general terms, the same thing that happens to any living system that is cut off from its energy source: it begins to die. There are, of course, many organisms in degraded soils. But so are there many organisms in a corpse; they are the agents of decay. When plants are removed, the mycorrhizal fungi—and probably various other rhizosphere organisms dependent on those plants—begin to die, and decay organisms come to predominate. This may be accompanied by changes in soil structure that reduce the soil's ability to store water and nutrients. Comparisons of soils under fallow with those under permanent pasture have shown that the former have far fewer large aggregates (Low, 1955). Clear-cuts that have remained unreforested for several years also lose large aggregates (Borchers and Perry, in press), have reduced mycorrhizal formation on tree seedlings, and lower levels of iron chelators than adjacent forest soils (Perry, *et al.* 1982; Parke, *et al.*, 1984; Perry and Rose, 1983). Although many species of ectomycorrhizal fungi produce above ground fruiting bodies (the familiar mushrooms), other—including some of the more common and important mycorrhizae of conifers—produce below ground fruiting bodies (truffles). Almost all VAM fungal species fruit below ground. Once lost from a site through death or in eroding soil, spores of these below-ground fruiters re-enter very slowly.

Little is known how rapidly the makeup of the soil community changes following removal of trees or as a consequence of overgrazing. Nor do we know enough about how these changes influence the ability of plants to re-establish and grow. However, it seems clear that, in at least some cases, reforestation failures are linked to changes

in soil biota following clearcutting. Seedling survival has been dramatically increased in both western North America and northeastern India by reinoculating clear-cuts with very small amounts of soil from healthy forests (Amaranthus and Perry, 1987; Sharma, 1983).

Loss of mycorrhizal fungi and other rhizosphere organisms will probably have the greatest negative impact on those droughty or otherwise stressful sites where seedling survival depends on rapid exploitation of soil (Perry, *et al.*, 1987). It is also on these sites that deterioration of soil physical structure is likely to have the greatest negative impact. When plants are removed and not quickly re-established, such sites may enter a positive feedback loops, in which biological and physical changes in soil lead to decreased seedling survival, which leads, in turn, to further deterioration in the soil. Often such sites become occupied by annual weeds, many of which do not require mycorrhizal fungi. Loss of important rhizosphere organisms due to overgrazing probably contributed to the widespread conversion of perennial grasslands to annuals. In the Miombo woodlands of southern Africa, sites cleared of trees for as little as two years no longer support tree growth (Maghembe, personal communication), suggesting that in at least some situations, alterations in essential soil characteristics may occur very rapidly following removal of the dominant vegetation.

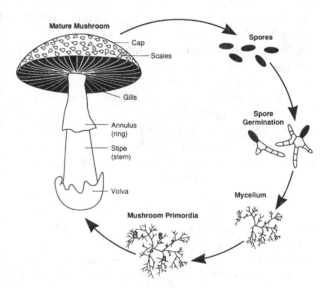

Anatomy and Life Cycle of a Typical Mushroom

This diagram shows many anatomical features that are used to characterize and identify mushrooms. Many species develop only a few of these features, and some groups have different anatomy; for example, pores rather than gills house the spores of the boletes. Credit: U.S.F.S., Molina, O'Dell, Amaranthus

Can the proper rhizosphere organisms be reintroduced as an aid to reclaiming battered and degraded ecosystems? In at least some cases the answer appears to be yes. In the following section we briefly discuss our experience on an unreforested clearcut in the Klamath Mountains of southwest Oregon.

Utilizing the rhizosphere organisms in restoration: an example

A broad band of granitic bedrock caps higher elevations of the Klamath Mountains of southern Oregon and northern California. Despite sandy soils and short, droughty growing seasons, the granites support productive forests, some of which were clearcut in the 1960's. Many clearcuts have been difficult to reforest, despite repeated attempts. One of these sites (Cedar Camp)—intensively studied over the past few years (Perry and Rose, 1983; Perry, *et al.* 1985; Amaranthus and Perry, 1987) illustrates the role of rhizosphere organisms maintaining system integrity, and how reintroducing these organisms can aid reforestation.

Cedar Camp is a 15-ha clearcut dating from 1968. It is on a 30% southerly aspect at 1720 m elevation. The adjacent forest, on the same slope and aspect, is dominated by 80-year-old white fir (*Abies concolor*), and is classed as "Site I," or the highest productivity level for that species and elevation (Amaranthus and Perry, 1987). Current vegetation consists of about 30% cover of annual grass (*Bromustectorum*), scattered patches of bracken fern (*Pteridiumaquilum*), and an occasional manzanita bush (*Arctostaphylosviridis*). The only encroachment of natural conifer seedlings from the forest into the clearcut is in association with manzanita. Despite having less than 4% clay, soils under the forest at Cedar Camp are well aggregated. Clearcut soils, in contrast, are reminiscent of beach sands. Loss of soil structure is not due to lower total organic matter, which does not differ significantly between forest and clearcut soils, but apparently to the removal of living tree roots and associated ectomycorrhizal hyphae (electron micrographs of soils in forest and clearcut are shown in Perry, *et al.*, 1987). Soil microbial communities differ dramatically between forest and clearcut at Cedar Camp. The ratio of bacterial to fungal colonies is nearly ten times greater in the latter, and mycorrhizal formation on planted seedlings is reduced (Perry and Rose, 1983). Actinomycetes are more abundant in clearcut than in forest soil, and a higher proportion of colonies express allelopathy in bioassay hydroxymatesidero-phores—microbially-produced iron chelators that are important in plant nutrition and resistance to pathogens —are also reduced in clearcut soils (Perry, *et al.*, 1984).

Various factors may a have contributed to reforestation failures at Cedar Camp, but two in particular seem likely to underlie the inability of seedlings to secure a "foothold" on this stressful site. First, loss of aggregation reduced the capacity of soils to store and deliver resources—particularly water. Second, reductions or outright loss of essential rhizosphere organisms diminished the capacity of tree seedlings to exploit sufficient soil volume to compensate for the lowered resource levels per unit of soil volume.

Had the first planting been successful, or had sprouting manzanita occupied more of the site, soil structure and microbial communities may have been stabilized at Cedar Camp. Without the proper plants, however, the system entered a positive feedback loop in which deterioration within the soil resulted in further planting failures which in turn led to further soil deterioration. Rehabilitation of such a site requires that the mycorrhizal fungi and associated organisms be re-established. At Cedar Camp, adding less than half a cup of soil from the root zone of a healthy conifer plantation to each planting hole doubled growth and increased survival of conifer seedlings by 50 percent in the first year following outplanting (Amaranthus and Perry, 1987). By the third year, only those seedlings receiving soil from the plantation were still living.

Where and How?

Under what conditions might restoring the mycorrhizal fungi and associated organisms aid restoration, and how does one go about it? Unfortunately, we do not yet have clear answers to either question. With regard to the first, the most likely candidates are sites where: a) soil resources—water or nutrients—are limiting, or b) growing seasons are short, which means that plants must exploit soil resources quickly in order to successfully establish. Because of the important role of mycorrhizal fungi and other rhizosphere organisms in creating favorable soil structure, sites with either very sandy or very clayey soils may be especially vulnerable.

With respect to nutrients, mycorrhizal fungi are especially important in gathering elements that tend to be insoluble in water, and relatively immobile in soils. This is a particular problem with phosphorus and iron, especially in acid soils such as occur in much of the moist tropics and in many (but not all) coniferous forests. Phosphorus is a primary limiting nutrient in the moist tropics, and reduced levels of soil phosphorus have been implicated in site degradation resulting from intensified shifting cultivation (Arnason, *et al.*, 1982). It seems probably that losses of mycorrhizal fungi and perhaps other rhizosphere organisms have contributed to degradation of moist tropical forests (Janos 1980). Sedge, the dominant plant in many pastures that have been converted from forest in Central and South America, is nonmycorrhizal.

Given a site where re-introducing the mycorrhizal fungi and associated organisms might help restoration, what is the best way to do it? Seedlings can be inoculated using:

a) whole soil from established plant communities (the approach we used at Cedar Camp),

b) pieces of root containing mycorrhizal hyphae, or

c) pure cultures of desirable organisms (e.g., spores or hyphae of mycorrhizal fungi).

VA mycorrhizal fungi have not yet been successfully grown in pure culture, however, spores can be produced by growing mycorrhizal plants in pots. Many EM fungi can be grown in pure culture, hence inoculation with either spores or hyphal fragments is possible.

Each of the above approaches—whole soil vs. some form of inocula—has advantages and disadvantages. Both techniques can be used either in the field, at the time of planting, or in the nursery.

Whole soil contains an entire suite of soil organisms rather than just one, and this is true to a certain extent with root fragments. There are both advantages and disadvantages to this. The collection of organisms contained in whole soils will probably include many that benefit the plant and that would not be included in pure cultures, and perhaps not in root fragments. However, whole soils may also contain pathogens or other organisms detrimental to plants. Although the possibility exists, there has been no documentation of introduction of pathogens from inoculation with healthy soil.

The source of soil for inoculation appears to be a critical determinant of its net benefit to the plant. Soil must, of course, come from the root zone of a healthy plant that is assumed to support similar rhizosphere organisms. This does not necessarily mean the same species of plant as being used in restoration; many mycorrhizal fungi, particularly VA's, are compatible with a wide variety of plant species. However, to be safe, especially when working with ectomycorrhizal plants—soils should probably be collected from the vicinity of the same plant species. Even this, however, doesn't guarantee success. Age of the plants from which soil is collected may be a factor. Mature trees often do not have the same types of mycorrhizae as younger trees of the same species, and this could influence the success of whole soil inoculation. Given all the uncertainties, the best approach is to experiment with various sources of soil and to see which, if any, works on a particular site.

The technique for whole soil inoculation is simple, but certain precautions are necessary. Little soil is needed. At Cedar Camp we added about one-half cup per seedling at the time of planting—simply dropping the soil into the planting hole with no particular attention to placement.

The time between gathering the soil and adding it to planting holes should be minimized, and the soil should not be allowed to overheat or dry out. Clearly the logistics of an operation of this type could be complicated. Careful planning is essential. Much remains to be learned about the potential benefits of reintroducing mycorrhizal fungi and associated organisms into degraded soils. We believe that some, perhaps many, reclamation projects will be aided by this approach. However, though the evidence that fuels this optimism is strong, it is also based on relatively few studies. The best advice we can give to those working in reclamation is to give it a try. One does not have to be a card carrying scientist in order to experiment. All it takes is common sense—perhaps backed up by a little intuition.

Finally, some largely philosophical musings. Even where it does benefit reclamation, reintroducing rhizosphere organisms is not some kind of magic bullet that will allow the rest of the ecosystem to be ignored. The idea that we can find, or create, some single organism or technique that will solve all of our problems is one of the great fallacies of the 20th century. This is not to say that understanding and perhaps even improving on individual species has nothing to offer. But the approach that has characterized much of modern agriculture and forestry—to consider the crop in isolation from the community and ecosystem within which it exists—is folly. As we stated elsewhere (Perry, et al., 1987): "It is increasingly clear that the rhizosphere, the soil community as a while, and the entire ecosystem...form a coherent, dynamic unit, and that stability and resilience must ultimately be understood in terms of patterns arising from interrelations within this unit. The real challenges for the future lie in the largely untilled ground of holism."

Previously published in "Restoring the Earth" National Conference Proceedings. *Reprinted with permission.*

References

Amaranthus, M. P. and D. A. Perry. 1987. "Effect of soil transfer on ectomycorrhiza formation and the survival and growth of conifer seedlings on old nonreforested clear-cuts." *Can. J. For. Res.* 17:944-950.

Arnason, T. J., D. H. Lambert, J. Gale, J. Cal, and H. Vernon. 1982. "Decline of soil fertility due to intensification of land use by shifting agriculturists in Belize, Central America." *Agro-ecosystems.* 8:27-37.

Perry, D. A., R. Molina, and M. P. Amaranthus. 1987. "Mycorrhizae, mycorrhizospheres and reforestation: current knowledge and research needs." *Can. J. For. Res.* 17:929-940.

Arimitsu, K. 1983. "Impact of shifting cultivation on

the soil of the tropical rain forest in the Benakat District, South Sumatra, Indonesia." In *IUFRO Symposium on Forest Site and Continuous Productivity*. Edited by R. Ballard and S. P. Gessel. US Dep. Agric. For. Serv. Gen. Tech. Rep. PNW-163. pp. 218-222.

Borchers, J., and D. A. Perry. "Loss of soil aggregates in old, unreforested clear-cuts in southwest Oregon." In *Maintaining long-term productivity of Pacific Northwest Forests*. Edited by D. A. Perry, R. Meurisse, B. Thomas, R. Miller, J. Boyle, J. Means, and P. Sollins. Timber Press, Portland, OR. In press.

Evans, J. 1982. *Plantation forestry in the tropics*. Claredon Press. Oxford, U.K.

Janos, D. P. 1980. "Mycorrhizae influence tropical succession." *Biotropica*, 12 (suppl.): 56-64.

Low, A. J. 1955. "Improvements in the structural state of soils under leys." *Soil Science* 6:179-199.

Marx, D. H. 1980. "Ectomycorrhizae fungus inoculations: a tool for improving forestation practices." In *Tropical Mycorrhiza Research*. Edited by P. Mikola. Oxford University Press, Oxford, U.K. pp. 13-71.

Mikola, P. 1970. "Mycorrhizal inoculation in afforestation." Int. Rev. For. Res. 3:123-196.

———. 1973. "Application of mycorrhizal symbioses in forestry practices." In *Ectomycorrhizae—their ecology and physiology*. Edited by G. C. Marks and T. T. Kozlowski. Academic Press, London, New York. pp. 383-411.

———. 1984. "Inoculum potential of ectomycorrhizal fungi in forest soil from southwest Oregon and northern California." *For. Sci.* 30:300-304.

Perry, D. A., and S. L. Rose. 1983. "Soil biology and forest productivity: opportunities and constraints." In *IUFRO Symposium on forest site and continuous productivity*. Edited by R. Ballard and S. P. Gessel, US Dep. Agric. For. Serv. Gen. Tech. Rep. PNW-163. pp. 229-239.

Perry, D. A., M. M. Meyer, D. Egeland, S. L. Rose, and D. Pilz. 1982. "Seedling growth and mycorrhizal formation in clearcut and adjacent undisturbed soils in Montana: a greenhouse bioassay." *For. Ecol. Manage.* 4: 261-273.

Perry, D. A., S. L. Rose, D. Pilz. and M. M. Schoenberger. 1984. "Reduction of natural ferric iron chelators in disturbed forest soils." *Soil Sci. Sco. Am. J.* 48:379-382.

Sharma, G. D. 1983. "Influence of humming on the structure and function of microorganisms in a forested ecosystem." *Hill Geogr.* 2:1-11.

5

Wilderness Recovery: Thinking Big in Restoration Ecology

Reed F. Noss

Abstract

DUE TO THE OVERBEARING INFLUENCE of modern humans on the land, no regional conservation strategy can be complete without a restoration component. The pinnacle of restoration ecology is the re-establishment of large wilderness landscapes replete with native predators. Big wilderness (large, roadless, essentially unmanaged areas) can maintain native biological diversity in better health than small reserves or multiple-use lands. In both of the latter, much of the original richness is always missing due to the lack of species most sensitive to human disturbance. One of the most important goals of conservation is representation of native ecosystems in reserves large enough to maintain viable populations of all native species and functional natural disturbance regimes.

Introduction

I am not a restoration ecologist. My practical experience in restorative management consists of a few times helping with prairie burns in the midwest and pine land burns in Florida. My overriding interest has been in developing ambitious conservation strategies at regional to continental scales. Through this work, a mixture of science and advocacy, I have come to realize that no big conservation project is adequate in today's world without a major restoration component. There is simply too little land left in near-prime condition, human influences are everywhere, and some ecosystem types are virtually gone.

Restoration projects and techniques, large and small, are aptly discussed in the pages of *Restoration and Management Notes*. In perusing those pages, the reader quickly notes that the vast majority of restoration projects are tiny. They typically involved a few acres of prairie, a forest stand, or a small wetland. The diminutive nature of most restoration projects is understandable. Full-blown ecological restoration at a watershed or landscape scale, often relying on high-tech engineering, can be incredibly expensive. Restoration of the Kissimmee River in South

Florida, converted to a canal by the U.S. Army Corps of Engineers between 1961 and 1971, is expected to cost $300 million—10 times the cost of the original channelization (Duplaix, 1990). Another exceptionally large restoration project, the rehabilitation of 36,000 heavily logged acres out of 48,000 acres added to Redwood National Park in 1978, was budgeted for $33 million over a 10-15 year period (Belous, 1984). As of 1990, only about $12-13 million has been spent. Although the project is considered a success so far, at least another decade of work will be needed (Lee Purkerson, National Park Service, personal communication).

The point of this article is that landscape restoration need not be prohibitively expensive, even when applied at scales that dwarf the Kissimmee River and Redwood National Park projects. Landscape-scale restoration can rely largely on the natural recovery processes of ecosystems, aided by human labor. Road closures alone can work wonders. The billions of dollars that federal agencies spend annually degrading natural ecosystems, often through such exorbitant programs as below-cost timber sales, subsidized grazing, dams, and road construction, can be diverted to restoration projects. Labor-intensive restoration, in turn, can employ many former timber workers, road engineers, and ranchers, whose prior activities have created the need for restoration in the first place. The net benefit to biodiversity and human society will be tremendous.

In the following essay, I outline a strategy and recipe for wilderness recovery based on a land ethic ("sensu" Leopold, 1949). The re-establishment of huge, wild, functional ecosystems replete with large carnivores and their prey is the pinnacle of restoration ecology and human re-harmonization with nature (Sayen, 1989). In order to achieve human dignity, we must fully respect the dignity of other life forms and pay retribution for past offenses against them; this can be achieved by assisting in the healing of ecosystems (Maser, 1990). Restoration ecology must be expanded from the local and community level to the regional landscape level in order to accomplish these goals.

A Wilderness Vision

Why wilderness? Wilderness is defined in the Wilderness Act of 1964 as "an area where the earth and its community of life are untrammeled by man, where man himself is a visitor who does not remain," and which "generally appears to have been affected primarily by the forces of nature, with the imprint of man's work substantially unnoticeable." Hence, wilderness is a place where humans do not dominate, a place to be humbled.

Ecological Values of Wilderness

Wilderness also has ecological values. It is no accident that the only ecosystems that include all native carnivores are very large roadless areas. In the lower 48 states, the only ecosystem that still regularly contains both grizzly bears and wolves is the Northern Continental Divide complex in northern Montana and adjacent Canada, the "healthiest big mountain ecosystem in America south of Canada" (Foreman and Wolke, 1989). (The North Cascades of Washington and adjacent Canada also have grizzlies and wolves, but in very tenuous populations). The presence of large carnivore populations indicates a relatively healthy ecosystem; the predators themselves may play a fundamental role in maintaining the diversity of the system through indirect effects on the food web (Terborgh, 1988). Roadlessness defines wilderness and is the key to its ecological health. Probably no single feature of human-dominated landscapes is more threatening to biodiversity (aquatic and terrestrial) than roads. Direct effects of roads include fragmentation and isolation of populations, roadkill, pollution and sedimentation of streams and wetlands, and exotic species invasions (Diamondback, 1990; Bennett, 1991). Many species of small mammals rarely or never cross roads, even two-lane roads closed to public traffic (Oxley, et al., 1974; Mader, 1984; Swihart and Slade, 1984). Roads, therefore, reduce effective population sizes and gene flow, and will be significant dispersal barriers during climate change. Another set of species—largely weeds and pests—uses roadsides as dispersal corridors. In the Northwest, Port Orford cedar root rot fungus, black-stain root disease fungus, spotted knapweed, and the gypsy moth disperse and invade natural habitats via roads (Schowalter, 1988). Sedimentation of streams and ruination of fisheries is often associated with roads, especially in steep terrain subject to landslides and debris flows. Erosion from logging roads in an Idaho study was 220 times greater than from undisturbed sites (Megahan and Kidd, 1972).

Indirect effects of roads are many, but the most important to consider here are those related to human access.

Many species associated with wilderness are there not because the habitat is ideal (it usually is not), but rather because they do not get along well with humans. In northern Wisconsin and Minnesota, road density is the best predictor of wolf habitat suitability, not because wolves avoid roads (in fact, they often use roads as travelways) but because roads bring people with guns, snares, and traps. Above 0.9 miles of road per square mile of habitat, wolves in this region cannot maintain populations (Thiel, 1985; Mech, et al., 1988). Black bears and grizzly bears show similar mortality responses with increasing road density and access to legal and illegal hunters (Brody, 1984; McLelland and Mace, 1985). Elk habitat capability also drops rapidly with increasing density of roads open to public traffic (Lyon, 1983).

Roadless areas offer refugia to those species, from wildruns of anadromous fish to large carnivores and ungulates, sensitive to the impacts of roads. Because large mammals require enormous amounts of habitat to maintain viable populations (see below), roadless areas must be large to offer sufficient security. Hence the need for Big Wilderness (Foreman and Wolke, 1989; Noss, 1991). If Americans want the symbols of American wilderness—large carnivores and herds of ungulates—to remain on their public lands (and every indication is that they do), then they should be fully informed about roads. If properly informed, many might support the concept of road closures for the restoration of Big Wilderness.

Postage-stamp nature reserves have protected some important elements of biodiversity, but they are not whole. They fail to maintain populations of area-dependent animals, do not represent complete biological communities, do not perpetuate the ecological processes necessary to assure landscape-level diversity, and are heavily influenced by phenomena beyond their borders (Noss, 1987). Furthermore, because small reserves usually require a considerable amount of manipulative management in order to maintain what diversity they have (White and Bratton, 1980), they fail the naturalness test and do little to promote humility.

Many argue that, by applying ecological principles, we can manage landscapes to maintain biodiversity and still build roads, harvest timber, drill for oil, mine, ore, graze cows and sheep, and roar around in off-road vehicles. Lawmakers have put this multiple-use philosophy on the books. Federal laws, most notably the National Forest Management Act (NFMA) of 1976, tell land-managing agencies to provide for many human uses while at the same time maintaining diversity and viable populations. But the record of multiple-use management is a sorry one; common and weedy species have prospered at the expense of rare and sensitive species and entire ecosystems are being degraded (Noss, 1983; Norse, et al., 1986;

Wilcove, 1988; Grumbine, 1990). Much of the damage is connected with road-building and other forms of habitat fragmentation (Noss 1987). Although innovative approaches to forest management, under the banner "New Forestry" or "New Perspectives" (Franklin, 1989; Gillis, 1990), are theoretically attractive, as presently applied in the Pacific Northwest they are resulting in continued liquidation of old-growth forests. Destruction of endangered ecosystems is not justified under any banner, no matter how scientifically sophisticated.

Intrinsic Value

Biologists can argue wilderness versus non-wilderness, large versus small reserves, set-asides versus managed lands, forever. In the end, they will surely agree that many conservation functions (for example, protection of rare plant populations) are served by small nature reserves, other functions (such as protection of species not overly sensitive to human disturbance) are served by multiple-use lands, while still other species (big carnivores) and processes (big wildfires) require mega-wilderness. But besides its ecological values, besides even the amenity values of inspiring humility and contemplation, Big Wilderness is essential. It has intrinsic value.

Some people, for reasons quite beyond the rational, believe that huge, wild areas are valuable for their own sake. These areas should be as free as possible from human influence in order to satisfy the criterion of sacred otherness (Reed, 1989; Birch, 1990). Science cannot prove or disprove intrinsic value in wilderness or any other entity. But if we accept that humans have intrinsic value, as do almost all ethical traditions, then only anthropocentric prejudice would keep us from recognizing such value in others. In the final analysis, intrinsic values are the only values that stand on their own, unfettered by tenuous links to utility. What good is wilderness? One might as well ask the rocks in the canyon. "Wilderness," Ed Abbey wrote, "needs no defense, only more defenders."

Balance

Implicit in conservation strategy is that a balance should be achieved between land devoted to primarily natural values and land developed for human purposes. How balanced is the ratio of wild to developed land in the United States? Conservationists often look to the tropics with greatest alarm, but many North American ecosystems are in equally critical condition and stand to lose as great a proportion of their biotas (Moyle and Williams, 1990). By 1920, the northeastern and central states had already lost 96 percent of their virgin forests (Reynolds and Pierson, 1923). Today, the Pacific Northwest holds most of the old-growth forests in the lower 48 states, yet less than 13 percent remains of the ancient forest in western Washington, western Oregon, and northwestern California (Norse, 1990). The longleaf pine forests of the Southeastern Coastal Plain, once the dominant regional ecosystem, have declines by at least 98 percent (Noss, 1989). Very little of our land is strictly protected, despite the claims of commodity interests. Designated wilderness represents only 1.8 percent of the 48 states, or 4 percent of the U.S. including Alaska, and many of these areas are open to grazing, mining and other disruptive uses (Watkins, 1989). Only about 3 percent of the 48 states is protected in wilderness, parks, or equivalent reserves and conservationists generally do not expect to more than double that figure (Scott et al., 1990-a).

To set aside only 3 percent of the 48 states in reserves, and only 1.8 percent as wilderness, does not seem very balanced. No one can say how much land is "needed" to maintain biodiversity; where we draw the line is a reflection of our values. My values tell me that an order of magnitude increase—to 50 percent—is a reasonable compromise, and that large-scale wilderness recovery is needed to restore that balance. Many people will think that asking for 50 percent of our land as wilderness is either utopian or insane (or worse). But then again, most people (and nearly all elected officials) believe in infinite economic growth. Few accept the inevitability of catastrophe if we stay on our present course. I rest my case.

Recovery Principles

Wherever we draw the line between wilderness and development, the degraded condition of most ecosystems means that preservation, strictly speaking, is seldom a tenable option. Clear-cuts and abandoned fields must be reforested, cows and fences removed, roads obliterated, natural fire and hydrological regimes restored, native carnivores and other species returned to their former range. Wilderness must be allowed to recover.

If we accept that some level of wilderness recovery is a worthy conservation goal, where do we begin? First, it must be recognized that preservation and restoration are complementary elements of any regional conservation strategy (Noss, 1985-a; Sayen, 1989). A common environmentalist criticism of restoration is that it will divert attention or resources from preserving the last pristine areas, and may even be used to justify further habitat degradation if a "don't worry, we can fix it" attitude prevails. This unfortunate situation must not be allowed to develop; restoration must be seen as a healing art, not as "an environmental license to kill" (Jordon, 1990). Using "no net loss" of habitat or biodiversity as a guiding principle, all existing, relatively unaltered natural areas must be protected in addition to restoring habitats critical to regional biodiversity. The following are some general principles to consider in designing a wilderness recovery project.

Ecosystem Representation

Habitat destruction, like biodiversity, is not uniformly or randomly distributed over the land. The most productive and often most diverse habitats were the first to be settled and converted to intensive production. Forty years ago, Kendeigh, et al., (1950-51) noted that no areas of "virgin vegetation...of sufficient size to contain all the animal species in the self-maintaining populations historically known to have occurred in the area" remained in deciduous forest, prairie, or lower elevations in the Rocky Mountains. Opportunities for creating large reserves were limited to inaccessible southern swamps, boreal forests, higher elevations in the western mountains, desert, and tundra. Today of 261 major terrestrial ecosystems in the United States and Puerto Rico, defined by a combination of Bailey's ecoregions and Kuchler's potential natural vegetation, 104 (40%) are not protected in designated wilderness areas (Davis, 1988). Wilderness boundaries often coincide with timberline: the "rock and ice" phenomenon.

Representation of all ecosystem types in wilderness and other protected areas is one of the most important and widely accepted goals of conservation. In 1987, delegates of 62 nations at the Fourth World Wilderness Conference voted unanimously for a resolution to preserve "representative examples of all major ecosystems of the world to ensure the preservation of the full range of wilderness and biological diversity" (Davis, 1988). Because any major ecosystem type will vary across its geographic range in such attributes as species composition, vegetation structure, and natural disturbance regime, multiple examples of each major ecosystem should be protected or restored. Restoration priorities can be established by determining which ecosystems types in the region have declined most markedly from pre-settlement condition.

Bigness

The desirability of large reserves, "bigness," is one of the few generally accepted principles of conservation (Soule and Simberloff, 1986). Protected examples of ecosystem types must be large enough to maintain viable populations of all native species (Kendeigh, et al., 1950-51) and to persist in concert with natural disturbances (Pickett and Thompson, 1978). Large reserves are easier to defend against encroachment from outside, suffer less intensive edge or boundary effects, and require less management per unit area (White and Bratton, 1980; Noss, 1983).

How large must a wilderness area or other reserve be to maintain native biodiversity? Estimates by conservation biologists of minimum viable populations and corresponding reserve sizes are alarmingly high. A recent review of empirical studies (Thomas, 1990) concluded

that an average population of 1,000 individuals may be adequate for species of normal population variability, but 10,000 individuals may be needed for long-term persistence of highly variable birds and mammals. How these minimum population estimates translate into area requirements depends on factors such as habitat quality and social behavior, that determine population density and dispersion. Hubble and Foster (1986) suggested that tens to hundreds of km^2 are required to maintain populations of tropical trees, which occur in low densities. Thiollay (1989) concluded that rainforest reserves in French Guiana must be between 1 and 10 million ha to maintain a complete bird community, including viable populations of diurnal raptors and large game birds. Schonewald-Cox (1983) estimated that reserves of 1,000 to 100,000 ha might maintain viable populations of small herbivorous and omnivorous mammals, but reserves of 1 to 10 million ha are needed for long-term viable populations of large carnivores and ungulates.

Natural disturbances must also be taken into consideration, as reserves that are small relative to the scale of natural disturbance may experience radical fluctuations in the proportions of different serial stages, which in turn will endanger populations dependent on particular stages. Shugart and West (1981) estimated that landscapes 50-100 times the largest disturbance patch may approach a steady state in habitat diversity. Because boreal forests experience natural fires covering up to 1 million ha might be necessary to achieve a steady state in boreal regions. In the Greater Yellowstone Ecosystem, landscape stability by some measures (constant heterogeneity) is reached at about 1 million ha (Romme and Despain, 1990). For ecosystems that experience small disturbances, such as eastern deciduous forests characterized by treefall gaps and occasional watershed-sized fires, existing national parks and forests (at 100,000 ha or so) may be in approximate steady state (Shugart and West, 1981). The current system of protected areas in this region fails to represent most ecosystem types, however (Davis, 1988). Furthermore, the most space-demanding species in these forests, eastern cougar and wolves (if re-introduced), would require larger reserves, again on the order of 1 million ha.

How well do existing reserves meet these ambitious size criteria? Research natural areas (RNAs), designated for their ecological and scientific values, are far too small by our criterion. Of the 213 Forest Service RNAs (as of 1990), 93% are smaller than 1000 ha; the remaining 7% are smaller than 5000 ha (Fig. 1; Noss 1991). The 320 units in the National Park system (as of 1983) are distributed more evenly among size classes, though only 10% are larger than 100,000 ha and 3% (10 areas) are larger than 1 million ha (Schonewald-Cox 1983). Most (81%) of the 474 units in the National Wilderness Preservation System (as of 1989) are between 1000 and 100,000 ha, and only 1% (6 areas) are larger than 1 million ha. Thus, few protected areas approach the approximately 1 million ha needed to maintain natural disturbance regimes (for some ecosystem types) and viable populations of large mammals. Society has to face the fact that its existing protected areas are too small (Grumbine, 1990).

Hence the need for wilderness recovery. In almost all cases, representing ecosystems in protected areas of sufficient size to assure viability is possible today only through restoration. For future parks or wilderness areas to represent the diversity that greeted the first European visitors, they will have to be "grown rather than decreed" (Janzen, 1988). The tall grass prairie of the American midwest, for example, has been reduced by at least 98 percent. In Missouri, only 0.5 percent remains, all of it in fragments too small to maintain the native flora or fauna (Risser, 1988). Preserving or restoring small pieces of prairie has produced depauperate "museum pieces" (Noss and Harris, 1986), not viable ecosystems. An unprecedented project of the Nature Conservancy seeks to restore an entire prairie landscape in the Osage Hills of Oklahoma, starting with an initial 30,000-acre (12,000 ha) core area (Madson, 1990). The prairie preserve will someday contain a herd of bison and a fire regime that replicates the original. But what about wolves? To be complete, restoration needs to be considered at a scale of millions of hectares.

Implementation

Accepting that all ecosystem types, across their range of natural variation, should be represented in reserves large enough to assure long-term viability, what steps can the wilderness restorationist take to put a project on the ground? The answer lies in looking to the landscape and seeing where the conservation needs and opportunities are.

Spatial Context

Spatial context is a key to determining where to locate landscape-scale restoration projects. The goal is a regional landbase where protected areas representing all ecosystem types are enclosed or otherwise linked by continuous natural habitat. Such a system of interconnected reserves can form a whole greater than the sum of its parts (Noss and Harris 1986). Although each reserve individually might be too small to assure viability of a carnivore population, for example, the network as a whole might suffice. Small, satellite reserves protecting local biodiversity hotspots, such as a rock outcrop with an endemic plant, complement the regional network but cannot be allowed to substitute for it.

A map of all public and private managed areas in the region of interest is a good place to start. Parcels can be rated in terms of the degree of protection given to them,

as is done for all managed areas by the Nature Conservancy. Such a map portrays the skeleton to which you add flesh: designate critical areas on public land in protected status, fill in gaps (such as inholdings) in public ownership, acquire surrounding lands to increase reserve size, identify restoration priorities, and establish linkages between reserves.

Next, consult the best available vegetation maps of remote sensing information to determine the current distribution of ecosystem types in the region. The land ownership and protection map can then be overlaid on the vegetation map, ideally using a Geographic Information System (GIS), to determine how well existing protected areas and other public lands represent ecosystem types. The "gap analysis" project of Mike Scott and colleagues (Scott, et al., 1990-b) is ideally suited to this type of analysis. At a state or regional scale, Scott's group is mapping the distribution of current vegetation and associated species (based on habitat suitability), determining centers of species richness and endemism, and identifying gaps in the coverage of ecosystems and species ranges in protected areas. Hot spots of high species richness outside of existing reserves become priorities for protection. Conservationists can apply this basic approach at any geographic scale, and at whatever level of resolution is desired, to identify protection and restoration needs.

Once the ecosystems most in need of representation in the wilderness recovery system are identified, proposed reserve boundaries must be delineated on a map. Boundaries should be drawn to encompass areas of adequate size; conform to topography, watersheds, and natural geomorphic features; and, take advantage of existing undeveloped areas with low road density. Within your idealistic boundaries, depict (perhaps by color coding) on the map which private land should be acquired, which existing public lands need upgraded protective designation, which roads need to be closed (perhaps all!), and other restoration needs. Draw linkages or broad habitat corridors between reserves and clusters of reserves (Harris 1984, Noss and Harris 1986, Noss 1987, Noss in press) to allow for seasonal wildlife migration, dispersal of plants and animals, and long-range movements in response to climate change.

At this stage, you have mapped a prospective wilderness recovery system. It covers perhaps 50 percent of your region, more or less depending on the extent of landscape modification and the existing public land base. Now you need to buffer the preserves from surrounding, intensive-use land (clear-cuts, corn fields, cities, etc.). A gradation of buffer zones, with intensity of use increasing outwards, can surround each core wilderness preserve and comprise a "multiple-use module" (MUM) (Harris 1984, Noss and

Harris 1986), patterned after the biosphere reserve model (UNESCO, 1974). Corridors can be zoned in a similar fashion (Noss, 1987). Such zoning can indeed provide for multiple human uses, but its primary function must be to insulate core areas from adverse human influences. The core area must provide sufficient roadless acreage to protect the most sensitive species (generally, large carnivores) that live or will be reintroduced there.

Design and Management Considerations

A wilderness recovery proposal is obviously idealistic. It is not something you take to your friendly public lands managers and legislators, and expect to be greeted with enthusiasm. Many will balk at its apparent unreasonableness. But nothing is more unreasonable than the willful destruction of biodiversity. For conservationists to put forth something less than what is really needed, to compromise nature, is foolhardy. You will never get all you ask for, but the higher you shoot, the higher you will score. If anything, it is human nature to underestimate real needs; perhaps million-hectare reserves are too small.

My wilderness recovery proposal for Florida (Noss, 1985a, 1987), portrayed on a map that encompassed half the state in protected areas (see diagram), has probably inspired more public enthusiasm than backlash, (although the Farm Bureau happily provided some of the latter). A gubernatorial candidate supported the proposal, it was endorsed in principle by members of the Florida Panther Technical Advisory Council and the Florida Department of Natural Resources in its nongame plan, and some of the key linkages have been purchased by state and federal agencies, assisted by the Nature Conservancy. Despite the rapid pace of habitat destruction in Florida, piece by piece much of the system is coming together.

The greatest failure of the Florida proposal so far relates to the refusal of public land-managing agencies to close roads and restore natural conditions on the lands entrusted to them. National forests and other existing public lands constitute most of the "core preserves" in the diagram, yet most are not being managed in a way that protects biodiversity. As an illustration of the limitations of the current system, the large core preserve in the northeastern corner of Florida, overlapping Georgia, is the Okefenokee National Wildlife Refuge-Osceola National Forest complex. Pinhook Swamp, a linkage between Okefenokee and Osceola, was purchased in 1988 and added to the National Forest, a significant conservation achievement (Noss and Harris, 1990).

This complex of nearly 500,000 ha is the first priority reintroduction site for the Florida panther, an endangered species with an 85 percent probability of extinction within 25 years, according to population viability analysis (Ballou, *et al.*, 1989). To test the feasibility of panther reintroduction into the Okefenokee-Osceola complex, 5 neutered and radio-collared Texas puma were released within the complex in 1988. The cats did not fare well; within 6 months, three died, two of gunshot. The two remaining puma discovered domestic animals (on private lands) and had to be recaptured (Noss and Harris, 1990). Clearly, some management changes—especially road closures to minimize human access and removal of domestic animals and inholdings—will have to be made before Okefenokee-Osceola can regain its top carnivore and be considered a recovered ecosystem.

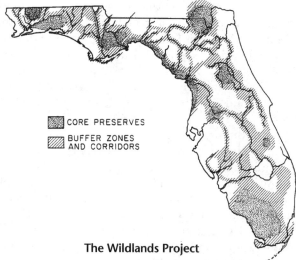

The Wildlands Project

A proposed statewide network for Florida (adapted from Noss, 1985-a and 1987). Note the wide inter-regional corridors which are intended to maintain resident populations of target animals, such as the Florida panther and Florida black bear.

Putting it on the ground

On-the-ground implementation of a wilderness recovery strategy is contingent on factors specific to each regional landscape. Some general guidelines apply:

1. close and revegetate roads;
2. remove fences and other human structures;
3. eradicate exotic species whenever feasible, including (perhaps especially) livestock;
4. reintroduce populations of extirpated native species, including large predators;
5. restore hydrological regimes and soils; and
6. reintroduce or mimic natural disturbance regimes. Many American ecosystems are naturally shaped by fire. Prescribed burning, preceded where necessary by manual removal of artificially dense vegetation that developed due to fire suppression, may be needed to restore habitat structure to a condition where wildfires will have effects approximating those in a presettlement system.

As emphasized throughout this paper, closure and rehabilitation of roads is perhaps the single most important ingredient in a recipe for wilderness recovery. Many land-managing agencies close roads, at least seasonally, to protect wildlife such as elk or bears. Barriers erected by land managers are often inadequate, however. A study on the Flathead National Forest in Montana found that some 80 percent of "obliterated" roads inventoried by the Forest Service were driveable by ordinary passenger vehicles and 38 percent of the barriers erected for road closures involve "ripping" (physical obliteration) and revegetation (Hammer, 1990). Obliteration of roads can be relatively expensive (but not as expensive as building new roads). In the Redwood National Park restoration, rehabilitation of logging roads has proceeded at any average rate of 15 miles per year. Costs for "worst-case" roads have reached $40,000 per mile, but ordinarily have ranged between $8,000 and $25,000 per mile (Belous, 1984). Many roads that pose minor erosion threats can be allowed to recover through natural revegetation, at zero cost, so long as their entrances are effectively blocked to vehicles, including off-road vehicles.

Much of the restoration of ecosystems at a landscape scale can rely on natural revegetation; the exceptions are mostly sites with severe soil destruction or dominance by exotic species, which must be dealt with case by case. In most human-modified landscapes being considered for wilderness recovery, fragments of remnant natural habitat are embedded in a matrix of agriculture, clear-cuts, or tree farms. Restoration, then, is primarily "the initiation and coalescence of *growing habitat fragments*" (Janzen, 1988, emphasis in the original). The degraded habitat between fragments must be returned to a physical condition where it can be reseeded by native plant propagules. This will often require clearing sites of foreign vegetation (including tree plantations) and will require manual planting of native species if seed sources are too distant or seed dispersal too slow to overcome the invasion of exotics.

One of the most challenging tasks in restoration is determining the target, the natural patterns and processes you are trying to replicate. Reconstructions of presettlement vegetation and disturbance regimes (Noss 1985b) and comparison with existing wilderness baselines, though not perfect, are all there is to work from. The target, of course, is always moving; any point in time specified as "natural" is just one frame in a very long movie. Furthermore, because of long-range transport of pollutants, enhanced UV-B levels due to ozone depletion, and global warming, an ecosystem can never be fully restored as long as industrial humans dominate the planet. Discussion of other elements in a wilderness recovery strategy can be found in Mueller (1985), Noss (1985a, 1986), Sayen (1987), Friedman (1988), and Foreman and Wolke (1989).

Conclusion

Preservation and restoration are essential partners in a comprehensive conservation strategy. Conservationists must insist that every wild and natural area be saved, and that many degraded areas be restored to viability by closing roads and reintroducing missing species and processes. Wilderness recovery must not be compromised in an effort to appear reasonable; the time for compromise, if ever, was when North America was still a wilderness continent.

Restoration is a life-affirming art (Jordan, 1990; Maser, 1990). It offers the only hope of true victory in conservation. Normally, conservation battles are never won; defeat is simply postponed. Designation under the Wilderness Act creates no new wilderness; for every acre officially designated, many more acres of wilderness are destroyed. The Oregon Wilderness Act of 1984, as a case in point, protected a mere 853,062 acres out of 4 million acres of eligible roadless areas on national forests; the remaining acres were "released" for multiple-abuse management (Foreman and Wolke, 1989). Wilderness recovery seeks simply to bring back ecosystems that contain all of their parts and to keep them healthy.

Without enough wilderness America will change. Democracy, with its myriad personalities and increasing sophistication, must be fibred and vitalized by regular contact with outdoor growths—animals, trees, sun warmth and free skies—or it will dwindle and pale.

—Walt Whitman

Originally published in The Environmental Professional, *Vol. 13, 1991, pp. 225-234. Reprinted with permission.*

Acknowledgments

I have been greatly inspired by the wilderness recovery ideas of Jasper Carlton, Bill Devall, Ed Abbey, Dave Foreman, Mitch Friedman, Ed Grumbine, Keith Hammer, Bob Mueller, Tony Povilitis, Jamie Sayen, David Wheeler, Howie Wolke, George Wuerthner, Bob Zahner, and other unrealistic dreamers.

Literature Cited

Ballou, J. D., T. J. Foose, R. C. Lacy and U. S. Seal, 1989. "Florida panther (*Felis concolot coryi*): Population viability analysis and recommendations." Captive Breeding Specialist Group, Species Survival Commission, IUCN, Apple Valley, MN.

Belous, R. 1984. "Restoration among the redwoods." *Restoration and Management Notes* 2: 57-65.

Bennett, A. F. 1991. "Roads, roadsides, and wildlife conservation: A review." In *Nature Conservation: The Role of Corridors*, D. A. Saunders and R. J. Hobbs, eds. Surrey Beatty and Sons, Chipping Norton, NSW, Australia. (In press.)

Birch, T. H. 1990. "The incarceration of wilderness: Wilderness areas as prisons." *Environmental Ethics* 12: 3-26.

Brody, A. J. 1984. "Habitat use by black bears in relation to forest management in Pisgah National Forest, North Carolina." M.S. Thesis. University of Tennessee, Knoxville.

Davis, G. D. 1988. "Preservation of natural diversity: The role of ecosystem representation within wilderness." Paper presented at National Wilderness Colloquium, Tampa, Florida, January, 1988.

Diamondback. 1990. "Ecological effects of roads" (or, "The road to destruction"). Pages 1-5 in *Killing Roads: A Citizens' Primer on the Effects and Removal of Roads*, J. Davis, ed. Earth First! Biodiversity Project Special Publication. Tucson, AZ, pp. 1-5.

Duplaix, N. 1990. "South Florida water: Paying the price." *National Geographic* 178(1): 89-112.

D. Foreman and H. Wolke. 1989. *The Big Outside*. Ned Ludd Books, Tucson, AZ.

Franklin, J. F. 1989. "Toward a new forestry." *American Forests*, Nov./Dec.: 37-44.

Freidman, M., ed. 1988. *Forever Wild: Conserving the Greater North Cascades Ecosystem*. Mountain Hemlock Press, Bellingham, WA.

Gillis, A. M. 1990. "The new forestry." *BioScience* 40:558-562.

Grumbine, R. E., 1990. "Viable populations, reserve size, and federal lands management: A critique." *Conservation Biology* 4: 127-134.

Hammer, K. J. 1986. "An On-site Study of the Effectiveness of the U.S. Forest Service Road Closure Program in Management Situation One Grizzly Bear Habitat, Swan Lake Ranger District, Flathead National Forest, Montana." Unpublished report.

Hammer, K. J. 1988. "Roads Revisited: A Travelway Inventory of the Upper Swan and Lower Swan Geographic Units, Swan Lake Ranger District, Flathead National Forest." Stage 2, Report No. 4.

Hammer, K. J. 1990. "A Road Ripper's Guide to the National Forests." In *Killing Roads: A Citizens' Primer on the Effects and Removal of Roads*, J. Davis, ed. Earth First! Biodiversity Project Special Publication, Tucson, AZ, pp. 6-8.

Harris, L. 1984. *The Fragmented Forest*. University of Chicago Press, Chicago, IL.

Hubbell, S. P. and R. B. Foster. 1986. "Commonness and rarity in a neotropical forest: Implications for tropical tree conservation." In *Conservation Biology: The Science of Scarcity and Diversity*, M. E. Soulé, ed. Sinauer Associates, Sunderland, MA, pp. 205-231.

Janzen, D. H. 1988. "Management of habitat fragments in a tropical dry forest: Growth." *Annals of the Missouri Botanical Garden* 75: 105-116.

Jordan, W. R., III. 1990. "Two psychologies." *Restoration and Management Notes* 8: 2.

Kendeigh, S. C., H. I. Baldwin, V. H. Cahalane, C.H.D. Clarke, C. Cottam, W. P. Cottam, I. McT. Cowan, P. Dansereau, J. H. Davis, F. W. Emerson, L. T. Haig, A. Hayden, C. L. Hayward, J. M. Linsdale, J. A. MacNab, and J. E. Potzger. 1950-51. "Nature sanctuaries in the United States and Canada: A preliminary inventory." *Living Wilderness* 15 (35): 1-45.

Leopold, A. 1949. *A Sand County Almanac*. Oxford University Press, New York.

Lyon, L. J. 1983. "Road density models describing habitat effectiveness for elk." *Journal of Forestry* 81: 592-595.

Mader, H. J. 1984. "Animal habitat isolation by roads and agricultural fields." *Biological Conservation* 29: 81-96.

Madson, J. "On the Osage." *Nature Conservancy* 40(3): 7-15.

Maser, C. 1990. 'On the "naturalness" of natural areas: A perspective for the future.' *Natural Areas Journal* 10:129-133.

McLellan, B. N., and R. D. Mace. 1985. *Behavior of Grizzly Bears in Response to Roads, Seismic Activity, and People*. British Columbia Ministry of Environment, Cranbrook, B.C.

Mech, L. D., S. H. Fritts, G. L. Radde, and W. J. Paul. 1988. "Wolf distribution and road density in Minnesota." *Wildlife Society Bulletin* 16: 85-87.

Megahan, W. F., and W. J. Kidd. 1972. "Effects of logging and logging roads on erosion and sediment deposition from steep terrain." *Journal of Forestry* 70: 136-141.

Moyle, P. B., and J. E. Williams. 1990. "Biodiversity loss in the temperate zone: Decline of the native fish fauna of California." *Conservation Biology* 4: 275-284.

Mueller, R. F. 1985. "Ecological preserves for the

eastern mountains." *Earth First!* 5(8): 20-21.

Norse, E. A. 1990. *Ancient Forests of the Pacific Northwest.* The Wilderness Society and Island Press. Washington, D.C.

Norse, E. A., K. L. Rosenbaum, D. S. Wilcove, B. S. Wilcox, W. H. Romme, E. W. Johnson, and M. L. Stout. 1986. *Conserving Biological Diversity in Our National Forests.* The Wilderness Society, Washington, D.C.

Noss, R. F. 1983. "A regional landscape approach to main diversity." *BioScience* 33: 700-706.

Noss, R. F. 1985-a. "Wilderness recovery and ecological restoration: An example for Florida." *Earth First!* 5(8): 18-19.

Noss, R. F. 1985-b. "On characterizing presettlement vegetation: How and why." *Natural Areas Journal* 5(1): 5-19.

Noss, R. F. 1987. "Protecting natural areas in fragmented landscapes." *Natural Areas Journal* 7: 2-13.

Noss, R. F. 1989. "Longleaf pine and wiregrass: Keystone components of an endangered ecosystem." *Natural Areas Journal* 9: 211-213.

Noss, R. F. 1991. "What can wilderness do for biodiversity?" In *Proceedings of the Conference: Preparing to Manage Wilderness in the 21st Century,* P. Reed, ed. USDA Forest Service, Southeastern Forest Experiment Station, Asheville, NC (in press).

Noss, R. F. In press. "Wildlife corridors." In D. Smith, ed. *Ecology of Greenways* (Publisher to be determined).

Noss, R. F., and L. D. Harris. 1986. "Nodes, networks, and MUMs: Preserving diversity at all scales." *Environmental Management* 10: 299-309.

Noss, R. F., and L. D. Harris. 1990. "Habitat connectivity and the conservation of biological diversity: Florida as a case study." In *Proceedings of the 1989 Society of American Foresters National Convention,* Spokane, WA. Sept. 24-27. Pp. 131-135.

Oxley, D. J., M. B. Fenton, and G. R. Carmody. 1974. "The effects of roads on populations of small mammals." *Journal of Applied Ecology* 11: 51-59.

Pickett, S.T.A., and J. N. Thompson. 1978. "Patch dynamics and the design of nature reserves." *Biological Conservation* 13: 27-37.

Reed, P. 1989. "Man apart: An alternative to the self-realization approach." *Environmental Ethics* 11: 53-69.

Reynolds, R. V., and A. H. Pierson. 1923. "Lumber Cut of the United States, 1870-1920." USDA Bulletin No. 1119, Washington, D.C.

Rissler, P. G. 1988. "Diversity in and among grasslands." In *Biodiversity,* E. O. Wilson, ed. National Academy Press, Washington, D.C., pp. 176-180.

Romme, W. H. and D. G. Despain. 1990. "Effects of spatial scale on fire history and landscape dynamics in Yellowstone National Park." Paper presented at Fifth Annual Landscape Ecology Symposium: The Role of Landscape Ecology in Public-Policy Making and Land-use Management. March 21, 1990. Oxford, OH.

Sayen, J. 1987. "The Appalachian Mountains: Vision and Wilderness." *Earth First!* 7(5): 26-30.

Sayen, J. 1989. "Notes towards a restoration ethic." *Restoration and Management Notes* 7: 57-59.

Schonewald-Cox, C. M. 1983. Conclusions. "Guidelines to management: A beginning attempt." In *Genetics and Conservation: A Reference for Managing Wild Plant and Animal Populations,* C. M. Schonewald-Cox, S. M. Chambers, B. MacBryde, and W. L. Thomas, eds. Benjamin-Cummings, Menlo Park, CA, pp. 141-145.

Schowalter, T. D. 1988. "Forest pest management: A synopsis." *Northwest Environmental Journal* 4: 313-318.

Scott, J. M., B. Csuti, and K. A. Smith. 1990-a. "Playing Noah while playing the devil." *Bulletin of the Ecological Society of America* 71: 156-159.

Scott, J. M., B. Csuti, K. Smith, J. E. Estes, and S. Caicco. 1990-b. "Gap analysis of species richness and vegetation cover: An integrated conservation strategy for the preservation for biological diversity." In *Balancing on the Brink: A Retrospective on the Endangered Species Act,* K. Kohn, ed. Island Press, Washington, D.C.

Shugart, H. H., and D. C. West. 1981. "Long-term dynamics of forest ecosystems." *American Scientist* 69: 647-652.

Soulé, M. E., and D. Simberloff. 1986. "What do genetics and ecology tell us about the design of nature reserves?" *Biological Conservation* 35: 19-40.

Swihart, R. K., and N. A. Slade. 1984. "Road crossing in Sigmodon hispidus and Microtus ochrogaster." *Journal of Mammalogy* 65: 357-360.

Terborgh, J. 1988. "The big things that run the world—a sequel to E. O. Wilson." *Conservation Biology* 2: 402-403.

Thiel, R. P. 1985. "Relationship between road densities

and wolf habitat suitability in Wisconsin." *American Midland Naturalist* 113: 404-407.

Thiollay, J. M. 1989. "Area requirements for the conservation of rain forest raptors and game birds in French Guiana." *Conservation Biology* 3: 128-137.

Thomas, C.D. 1990. "What do real population dynamics tell us about minimum viable population sizes?" *Conservation Biology* 4: 324-327.

UNESCO. 1974. "Task Force on Criteria and Guidelines for the Choice and Establishment of Biosphere Reserves." *Man and the Biosphere Report* No. 22, Paris. France.

Watkins, T. H. (ed.). 1989. "A special report—Wilderness America: A vision for the future of the nation's wildlands." *Wilderness* 52 (184): 3-64.

White, P. S., and S. P. Bratton. 1980. "After preservation: Philosophical and practical problems of change." *Biological Conservation* 18: 241-255.

Wilcove, D. S. 1988. "National Forests: Policies for the Future." *Vol. 2. Protecting Biological Diversity*. The Wilderness Society. Washington, D.C.

5

Old Growth and the New Forestry

Dr. Jerry F. Franklin

Abstract

RESEARCH ON OLD-GROWTH and other natural forests during the last two decades has provided a wealth of new information and perspectives on forest ecosystems and how they function. Among the findings are a greatly enhanced appreciation of the complexity of natural forest ecosystems, mechanisms for ecosystem recovery following natural disturbances and the necessity to consider larger spatial scales. Natural forests have a richness of organisms and processes, much of which is linked to their characteristic structural complexity. Recent research on natural disturbances has increasingly clarified the importance of biological legacies of living organisms and organically-derived structures, such as snags and down logs, in providing for perpetuation of complex natural ecosystems. The importance of large-scale or landscape perspectives has been clarified by research on issues such as cumulative effects and forest fragmentation.

There are strong indications that alternative approaches to forest management are needed. These should reflect the need to base stewardship on the most current scientific information; and to incorporate societies' increasing concern with sustained productivity and ecological values, including biological diversity. "New Forestry" is a concept which attempts to do this.

The objective of New Forestry is development of forest management systems which better integrate commodity production with maintenance of ecological values. At the stand level the basic principle of New Forestry is maintenance of structurally complex managed forest systems; this contrasts with the structural and compositional simplification that is characteristic of current intensive forest management practices. At the landscape level the basic principle of New Forestry is to consider effects of management practices over large spatial and temporal scales. This includes such issues as the arrangement of different types and sizes, and integration of reserved areas with commodity lands to produce a diversified landscape.

Introduction

I appreciate having this opportunity to discuss old-growth forests as well as some different ways of looking at our managed forests. I want to begin by simply reminding you that here on the northwestern coast of North America, we share the most incredible temperate forests in the world, bar none. They really do not take a back seat even to the tropical forests in terms of their complexity and richness. The Pacific coastal region supports the most massive and among the most productive forests that exist anywhere in the world. They represent the largest organic accumulations of any of the world's ecosystems. The trees species composing the forest are both the largest and longest-lived representatives of their genera and are further noteworthy because of their ability to sustain significant growth for several centuries.

The use of these forests has become increasingly controversial. Indeed, what we're looking at, in forestry and in forest resources management is a revolution. This is not very surprising when you reflect upon it, because the practices that we're using today were, in their fundamentals, laid down many decades ago—in the late 1940's on national forest lands in Oregon and Washington.

So much has happened in the last few decades—in terms of increased knowledge about these forests and changes in our societal objectives—that a reassessment of forest practices is long overdue. We need to step back and take a fresh look at what we're doing and why we're doing it.

I think that most parties to the controversies recognize the need to develop some practices which do a better job of accommodating ecological values at the same time that we're trying to provide for some level of commodity production; to create what I've sometimes called a "kinder and gentler" forestry or, as its popularly known, a "New Forestry."

I want to talk about old-growth, some of the controversies, and the potential role of New Forestry.

Scientific Underpinnings of New Forestry

The scientific knowledge that is both driving the need, and providing the basis, for some changes in our forestry practices is a good place to begin. I emphasize the scientific underpinning because there are people on both sides of the issue who suggest that new forestry is a facade—smoke and mirrors—lacking scientific substance. In fact, it is most emphatically based on peer-reviewed scientific research, particularly research during the last 20 years on natural forest ecosystems and how they work.

It is only very recently that we examined these forests as ecosystems. Indeed, serious ecosystem research on natural forests in the Pacific Northwest began just a little over two decades ago, with National Science Foundation Support of the International Biological Program's Coniferous Forest Biome project in 1969 (Edmonds, 198_). This project and other ecosystem research programs have yielded a tremendous wealth of new knowledge. I will present, some of it here under three topical headings:

1. ecosystem complexity;
2. "biological legacies" or aspects of ecosystem regeneration following catastrophic disturbances; and
3. landscape ecology perspectives. While these subject areas are not new, I think that the richness of the scientific information base and its relevance to forest management issues really is new.

Ecosystem Complexity

We have discovered from our research that natural forests are very complex, more complex than we could have imagined, as Chris Maser is fond of saying.

To begin with, these natural forests contain a richness of species. We can take mammalian species as one example. Diversity of mammal species varies with successional stage in Douglas-fir forests. This pattern exhibits high levels of diversity (many species) in the open ecosystem prior to tree canopy closure. This diversity is a mixture of both forest species and weedy pioneer species. Diversity collapses to much lower species numbers when the forest canopy closes and then recovers to intermediate levels of diversity in the mature and old-growth stages. This is a very common pattern; it is similar for many other groups of organisms including birds, fish and many types of invertebrates.

A critical point is that, although the early successional (pre-canopy closure) stage includes more total species, many of the species found in the mature and the old-growth forests have specialized habitat requirements. They often require conditions that are only found in older stages of forest succession and, hence, are found primarily in those kinds of forests. The northern spotted owl is a good example of that kind of organism.

Equally or perhaps more important, and as yet largely unrecognized, are the incredible levels of invisible or "hidden" diversity which exist in natural forest, diversity which is critical to the functioning of these forests. The diversity of invertebrates, for example, and of fungal species, groups of organisms that we really don't think much about, let alone catalog and study. For example, old-growth forests, to the degree that they have been studied, appear to be very rich in invertebrate species. Schowater (1988) found 61 species of arthropods in canopies of old-growth forests and only 16 species in adjacent young, managed stands. Furthermore, most of the old-growth invertebrates were species that prey upon or parasitize other kinds of invertebrates—insects that kill bark beetles or aphids, for example. This is a much healthier situation than in the young stands which were dominated by organisms that prey on plants, such as the aphids. So, there is not only a richness of species in these natural forests, but many that do specialized and very important kinds of "work".

The studies of species richness boils down to the simple recognition that mature and old-growth forests are biologically diverse ecosystems and not biological deserts. They never were deserts; they only seemed to be, as viewed from such narrow perspectives as production of some game species.

We also see in natural forests a great richness of process. Sources of nitrogen for the forest ecosystem provides a good illustration. Thirty years ago, we had few ideas about how nitrogen was brought into these systems; as you know, the air is full of elemental nitrogen but a few organisms can convert or "fix" it into biologically useful forms. In recent years ecosystem scientists have identified numerous pathways by which nature provides for nitrogen additions to the ecosystem. An important early discovery in IBP was the role of foliose lichens, large leafy lichens which live in the canopies of old-growth Douglas-fir trees in nitrogen cycling. These lichens are estimated to fix five to nine kg/ha/yr of nitrogen, a significant addition to these forest systems. Other routes for nitrogen additions include fixation by microbes living in rotting logs and in the rhizosphere or regions immediately around the tree roots.

Scientists have also discovered that the mature and old forests are very productive by any kind of ecological or biological definition. It really couldn't be any other way given the amount of "green" or chlorophyll that's out there in those old-growth forests. Trees do not retain leaves that lack a net benefit in terms of photosynthesis. And there are a lot of leaves out there, as anyone can see! So the older forests are , in ecological terms, as productive as most young forests. The difference is that in older forests a lot of the productivity is being used in respiration—to maintain the incredible accumulated biomass—rather than for production of additional wood. Hence, from a forester's perspective, older forests are viewed as unproductive forests because they are not growing many additional "boards". Much of the tree growth is offset by tree mortality. To the degree it has been studied, however, older forests are very stable in terms of wood volumes and may even continue to gradually accumulate additional merchantable wood (DeBell and Franklin 198—); virtually all of these old forests continue to have net accumulations of organic matter (stored carbon).

Another thing that we see increasingly are the incredible linkages that exist in these forest ecosystems; the richness of webs of various kinds, of functional relationships. One very fine example is the part of the forest that exists below ground. Although the below ground subsystem makes up only twenty percent of the biomass of the forest, it has such high turnover that as much as fifty to seventy percent of the photosynthate produced by the forest may be required for its maintenance. This certainly underlines the importance of trees as energy sources fueling the soil subsystem. Dave Perry identifies the tree roots as "white holes" providing the very lifeblood of soils by pumping energy into them. And, of course, there are the mycorrhizae and mycorrhizal relationships which are increasingly recognized as critical linkages not just between trees and their soil environment but also between trees and between plants in the overstory and in the understory. Through fungi and other organisms the soil subsystem is, in fact, a highly interlinked living system.

The extremely high quality water yielded by the old-growth forest systems is a consequence of the complexity and richness of the below ground system. Tight biological linkages reduce nutrient leaching and, hence, levels of dissolved materials in these water. The extensive root mass helps reduce levels of various kinds of erosional events thereby reducing sediment levels in surface waters.

The forest canopies in old-growth Douglas-fir forest represent truly immense surface areas which are interfaces between the forest and the atmosphere. We can imagine the canopy as a giant atmospheric scavenger which condenses large amounts of moisture from the atmosphere and precipitates dust and other atmospheric particulates, bringing these materials into the ecosystem. Of course, these canopies also provide diverse areas of habitat for various kinds of organisms.

Imagine the volume of space that is occupied by one of these ecosystems where the canopy extends seventy or eight meters into the atmosphere. A single old-growth Douglas-fir tree, has around an acre of foliar surface area! So you can imagine the canopy surface area of a whole forest of these trees. That is one reason that these forests are so effective at scavenging the atmosphere. In some of our forests condensation from fog and low clouds adds vary significantly—a net of mm/yr in one case (Harr)—to the moisture inputs into old-growth dominated watersheds and, consequently, to the level of streamflow.

Riparian areas provide a third example of a highly interlinked and ecological rich subsystem which previously we had not adequately appreciated. The linkages between forests and streams are proving numerous, complex, and critical to stream functioning. For example, we started 20 years ago by thinking about forests primarily in terms of their influence on temperature regimes of streams. More recently we have recognized that forests also provide the critical structural features for streams (e.g., in the form of woody debris) and diverse allochthonus inputs (litter and other organic materials) that are the streams' energy and nutrient base.

Structural complexity or diversity in natural forests is recognizable as the key to much of the richness of organisms, of habitat, and of processes. Some of this structural complexity can be defined in terms of individual structural features, as has been done in many current definitions of old-growth forests. These individual structures include large old-growth trees, large snags or standing dead trees, and large downed logs.

Coarse woody debris—standing dead trees and downed logs—is an important element of structure. In reflecting on my career as a forester I find it difficult to understand why it took me so long to appreciate the contribution that dead wood structures make to ecological functioning in a forest. Those contributions range all the way from geomorphic functions, such as in influencing erosional processes; to biological diversity, such as in providing habitat for a broad array of vertebrate and invertebrate organisms; and to providing long-term sources of energy and nutrients for these systems. From an evolutionary point of view we need to remember that large, woody structures have been around for a long time and that there has been a lot of animal and microbial evolution in association with these kinds of habitats.

Wood, big pieces of wood, is at least as important to stream as to forest ecosystems. It is a major element in creation of stepped structures in these systems and moderates various erosional processes. Woody debris is important in the larger rivers and estuaries, as well as in small streams although it plays different roles; your fisheries people can provide you with detailed information.

One of the keys to the overall structure, the "gestalt" of the old-growth forest, is the spatial heterogeneity that is present. Large trees, large snags, and large down logs are important individual structural components of old-growth forests, but we also have to recognize that the forest as a whole has some structural attributes. It is not just the sum of a few individual pieces. For example, there are gaps in the natural forest—places where light levels are higher and there is rich development of the understory. And areas that are the reverse of the gap ("antigaps")—very heavily shaded locales where a dense overstory of hemlock and cedar prevent the establishment of almost any green plant on the forest floor. This variability in light conditions helps create the incredible complexity and richness of the understory in these forests. The importance of diverse and well-developed understories is illustrated by the critical relation between old-growth forest structures and Sitka black-tailed deer in the coastal forests of the Tongass National Forest. Research by Paul Alaback and others has also shown that the development and maintenance of these diverse understory plant communities is complicated—not just a matter of allowing more light, for example.

What can we conclude with regards to forest complexity? The essence is that most (all?) of the parts of a forest ecosystem have value—fulfill some functional role. That complexity has value. The inference is that simplification should be approached with considerable caution.

Research has also shown us that old-growth forests have intrinsic value; rather, they are rich and diverse ecosystems that fulfill many ecological functions very well.

Biological Legacies

"Biological legacies" is a short-hand identification of the second scientific concept that I want to discuss. It relates to the way ecosystems recover from disturbances. Mount St. Helens provided a unique object lesson to scientists, one that presumably won't be repeated in my lifetime; a lesson in the way that nature perpetuates complexity, for richness, in the regenerating ecosystems which develop following a catastrophic disturbance.

As we looked at our TV sets on May 18,1980 we thought that Mount St. Helens had provided us with a moonscape to study. "Oh, boy, we get to watch succession start from scratch! It's got to start all over again." However, from our first minutes on the ground in the devastated zone ten days later, we encountered incredible legacies of living organisms, survivors of the eruption. As I took my first steps from the helicopter I encountered hundreds of fireweed sprouts, ants scurrying about, the excavations of pocket gophers, etc.

We discovered that many kinds of organisms had survived within the devastated Mount St. Helens landscape utilizing a wide variety of strategies. Essentially the only organisms that had been lost were the birds and the large mammals that lived above ground. Anything which was living below ground or could regenerate from parts protected below ground or was buried in a snow bank or in the mud at the bottom of a lake, or in any of a number

of other environments, was able to survive. From seeds to spores to full size organisms, an important key to early recovery at Mount St. Helens was survivors. In addition to that living legacy, there was also an immense legacy of organic matter and, most importantly, biologically derived structures—snags and downed logs, large soil aggregates, etc., in the landscape.

The importance of biological legacies, both living and dead, stimulated us to rethink ecosystems responses to other catastrophic events. "Now what does happen following a fire? What happens following a windstorm? What happens following clearcutting? Our review quickly reminded us that while natural catastrophes typically kill trees and other organisms, they leave behind most of the wood, most of those structures or dead legacies, as well as many living organisms.

In most cases natural forest systems do not really start from scratch at all; biological legacies provide them with a running start at richness and complexity. Hence, we see young natural forests with substantial structural and compositional diversity. For example, a 70-year-old Douglas-fir stand at Mount Rainier National Park, developed following a wildfire, has large-standing dead trees, many large down logs, and some large and old green trees which survived the fire, as well as an abundance of young trees.

The concept of biological legacies really isn't new, but it has been nearly ignored in our textbooks. We have emphasized the need for migration and re-establishment of individuals in barren areas. Although we knew about biological legacies we really did not appreciate their significance. (Perhaps one reason is the historical emphasis on old-field succession in ecological research; such environments probably offer minimum levels of legacies compared with other types of secondary succession, e.g., those that follow fire.) And so one of the things that we have tended to do in talking about forestry practices is to persist in representing practices like clearcutting and broadcast slash burning as being similar to natural processes. This is clearly not an accurate portrayal. It is not generally the way that nature does it and never was. Although clearcutting is often a very effective way of accomplishing some of our objectives, it is not the way that nature perpetuates ecosystems.

Landscape Perspectives

The landscape perspective is the third scientific topic that I want to discuss. This refers to the need to consider larger spatial and temporal scale that has been traditionally been the case of forestry. It means thinking beyond the individual stands or patches to drainages and to mosaics of patches and to long-term changes in these mosaics. Here in coastal northwestern Northern America we can recognize immediately that the kinds of landscapes that nature created were mosaics of large heterogeneous patches. We can also recognize, as in the Washington Cascade Range, that the landscapes often had complex attenuated boundaries between patches. This contrasts starkly with the landscape pattern that we have been creating through our management practices on National Forest lands in Oregon and Washington—small homogeneous patches with sharp, straight boundaries.

We resource managers first began to consider landscapes seriously in dealing with management of large animals—ungulates, such as elk, or wide ranging predators, such as the grizzly bear. I suspect that this was the first widespread recognition that, "Oh, yeah, we've got to think about more than just 25 or 40 acres. We've got to think about large areas."

That got us into landscape ecology. Unfortunately, we've learned more about landscape ecology from dysfunctional landscapes, landscapes that are not working well, than we have by studying really healthy landscapes. One example is in the southeastern United States where we have created extensive pine monocultures that are outstanding opportunities for outbreaks of the southern pine bark beetle.

Closer to home, the cumulative effects issue has exposed us to another class of dysfunctional landscapes. Many of our cumulative effects are in consequence of the fact that, after you clearcut an area, there is a period of time where you have increased potential for certain kinds of undesirable hydrologic or geomorphic events, such as landslides or more intense rain-on snow flood events.

Rain-on snow events are an interesting phenomenon. They are a consequence of the fact that along the Pacific northwestern coast much of the mountain landscape is part of a "warm snow zone." This is an area where snowpacks develop during cold fronts; then a warm front may bring in warm air and rain which melts the snow pack. High flows result from the combined run-off of melted snowpack plus an additional rainfall. Essentially all significant flood events in northwestern North America are rain-on-snow events, from Alaska to northern California.

Looking at the hydrology of these events we find that old-growth forests have a low potential for contributing to rain-on-snow events compared to cutovers or young forests. Several factors are involved. For one thing those huge canopies with their stiff branches intercept a lot of the snow which then evaporates or sublimates back into the atmosphere.. Much more of it melts, drips to the ground, and enters the soil. Some snow does form a snowpack on the forest floor, of course. as any of you who've been in an old-growth forest after a wet snow knows, it gets in there in big blobs, and sets up in irregular hard snowpacks in the understory. So there is less snow and its is well protected by the forest cover from both the

warm air and rains in the old growth forests than in the cutovers. Hence, the contributions of old-growth forests to rain-on-snow flood events are typically much lower than those from recently cut areas.

In clear-cuts, snows accumulate to maximal depths because none of it is intercepted. And it is exposed to the warm air and rains which melt it and convert it to runoff. Consequently, you can dramatically exacerbate flood events if you do not pay close attention to how much of your landscape is in a freshly cut over state at any point in time.

Fragmentation is another example of landscape dysfunction and a stimulus to think at larger spatial scales. Fragmentation results when forest cover is broken into small pieces or patches they cannot function effectively in providing interior forest environments. This has been a particular problem for us on federal lands in Oregon and Washington where we have used a clearcutting system, as I will point out later. Please note, that if you create large continuous clear-cuts, as has been done in much of coastal British Columbia, there is no problem with fragmentation. You have to leave some forest behind in order to have concern with fragmentation!

One element of the problem is that when you break forests down into small patches, surrounded by cutovers, the patches are effectively all edge. For example, using dispersed patch clear-cuts as adopted by the U.S. Forest Service, the forest is quickly converted to small patches; the landscape may still be half covered with forest but because it's all in patches of 10 to 15 ha. this is a problem because of 15 ha patch is all edge environment. From studies of forest edges we have found that you must move two to four tree heights into a forest from its boundary with a clearcut before the microclimate returns to the conditions found in a large intact forest patch; this can be as much as 400 to 500 m in extreme cases. Hence, a landscape of small forest patches interspersed with cutovers effectively lacks interior forest conditions; no habitat remains suitable for species requiring interior forest environments.

This problem is a very serious one if you have an interest in retaining interior forest conditions, such as for some wildlife. The fragmented landscape is also very vulnerable to wind-throw.

Summary of Scientific Underpinnings

We have now considered scientific findings in ecosystem complexity, biological legacies and the landscape perspective. There is obviously a large and rapidly-growing body of knowledge which is substantial, quantitative and provides some fundamental principles that we might use in creating some alternative forestry practices.

We are beginning to appreciate the complexity of

the natural forest ecosystem. Furthermore, as each piece and process is identified and studied we can recognize that essentially all play significant, often essential, roles. None can be discarded without consequences. Hence, forest simplification should be approached with caution and humility.

We can see that nature provides for the rapid re-creation of ecologically complex young forests through the mechanism of biological legacies. These carryovers of live and dead organic materials help insure that natural young forests are structurally and compositionally diverse. In effect, nature perpetuates ecosystems rather than simply regenerating trees.

We can see that much larger land areas—landscapes—and time periods must be considered in forest planning. Without these grander perspectives we almost certainly will create undesirable cumulative impacts on forest resources.

Have we foresters been incorporating this knowledge into our philosophy and recommended practices? In general, no; at least not to appropriate degrees. Some concepts have been picked up by some foresters, such as providing for coarse woody debris. But we foresters have resisted the notion that major problems exist with traditional practices.

Traditional forest practices are based on principles of simplification, homogenization. They seemed satisfactory to us until fairly recently. I was taught, and I think most foresters have been taught, that good forest stewardship is simply regenerating new trees that can grow freely and rapidly and produce boards. And we really felt—and based upon the science that we've had up until fairly recently—that was a reasonable assumption. A healthy forest was one that was growing lots of wood. What would be good for wood production would be good for other forest values! This clearly "just ain't so!" but, not knowing otherwise we developed our current practices such as clearcutting, broadcast slash burning, disposal of large woody debris (at very substantial costs, in the case of the U.S. Forest Service), and establishment of even-aged monocultures. At least we've made an effort to establish those monocultures even though we haven't always succeeded. (Fortunately, nature hasn't always allowed us to do everything we thought that we wanted to do.) And we've been applying these practices on a very large scale.

Now, although I'm a forester, I think foresters need to acknowledge that they have been slow to recognize problems with current practices. We really have been reluctant to acknowledge that a lot of ecological values are being sacrificed using traditional forest practices and to accept the principle that what is good for the production of wood fibre is not necessarily good for other resource values.

In conclusion, I think that in the interests of maintaining options for future generations, in the interests of sustainable productivity, in the interests of biological diversity, and, fundamentally, in terms of responsible global stewardship, we need to reconsider our practices with increased respect for the complexity of these forest systems and with a humility that reflects our true level of knowledge about those systems and how they work.

Based on a talk given on January 19, 1990 at "Forests Wild and Managed: Differences and Consequences," a symposium at the University of British Columbia. Only the first half of the talk is reprinted here. Dr. Franklin is Bloedel Professor of Ecosystem Analysis at the College of Forest Resources, University of Washington, Seattle. He is Chief Plant Ecologist with the USDA Forest Service.

Natural Enemies in Forest Insect Regulation

Torolf R. Torgersen, PNW Research Station, La Grande, Oregon

NATURAL ENEMIES are an important component among the factors that regulate forest insect pests. I will describe what natural enemies are and what they do, how they influence pest insect populations, and what management options are avail able to enhance their effects.

Forest insects are a continual problem in the forests of Northeastern Oregon and the Pacific Northwest. The most devastating of these in sects are the bark beetles and the defoliators. Northeastern Oregon is currently experiencing an outbreak of one of these defoliators—the western spruce budworm (*Choristoneura occidentalis*). Budworms feed on the foliage of Douglas-fir (*Pseudotsuga tnenziesii glauca*) and true firs (*Abbies* spp.) causing growth loss and sometimes killing trees in localized areas.

The western spruce budworm and another important defoliator, the Douglas-fir tussock moth (*Orgyia pseudotsugata*), are always present in the forest in low numbers. At such levels, they may cause some small-scale mortality or growth loss among host trees. But occasionally a change in some factors, such as weather, food supply or forest stand conditions, allows insect populations to explode. Populations then reach outbreak proportions, damaging thousands, tens of-thousands, or even millions of acres of mixed conifer forests.

Populations of many kinds of insects commonly build up and fall again, often in largely unpredictable sequences over long periods. While not every build-up develops into a full fledged outbreak, over the course of an 80- to 120-year rotation, some insects will almost certainly reach outbreak one or more times. But for decades, these same insects and their damage will be almost invisible in the very same stands.

What causes outbreaks to occur is a complex question whose answers differ with the insect involved. For some forest insect pests, entomologists have identified the dominant regulatory factors, but for many others, outbreak dynamics is still a puzzle. Outbreaks of the Douglas fir tussock moth last from two to three years and are somewhat predictable. For insects like the western spruce budworm, there seems to be no pattern that can be narrowly defined or reliably predicted. If most forest pests occur at essentially innocuous levels most of the time, the processes that tend to maintain such low levels are important for managers to know about.

Forest insect ecologists are only beginning to understand some of even the most simple interrelationships in the forest. Predation processes, or the relation between the "hunter" and the "hunted," are among some of the inner workings of insect pest systems that have been examined. Naturalists and agriculturists have known for millennia that natural enemies of insects play important roles in preventing outbreaks of crop pests. Let me describe what kinds of organisms are included as natural enemies.

Natural enemies of forest pests fall into three categories: diseases, parasites and predators. Insect diseases are caused by viruses, bacteria, fungi or protozoa, and are generally most important at high populations of the pest insect. Disease organisms can also be used as biological insecticides; an example is the widely used *Bacillus thuringiensis*, also known as "BT." Commercially produced BT bacteria are incorporated into a formulation much like a chemical insecticide and sprayed from an aircraft. The recent U.S.D.A. Forest Service budworm spray projects in the Cascades and Blue Mountains used this material. (During the spring of 1988, the Forest Service sprayed 164,571 acres with *Bacillus thuringiensis*, a bacterium that is used to combat the spruce budworm. These acres are in the Tollgate and Meacham units. The operation was completed by July 1, 1988.) Biological materials such as BT are desirable because they affect primarily the target insect without the toxic side effects to non-target organisms such as birds and most other insects.

Most parasites, or more specifically parasitoids, of insects are wasps or flies specialized to lay eggs in or on other insects. Their developing larvae feed on the host and eventually kill it. Parasites are common in the forest environment, and insect pests may be attacked by many different species. Parasites can dampen rising insect populations and may play a role in the collapse of an outbreak.

Predators of insects in the forest include a wide variety of organisms from arthropods to vertebrates. Among the predaceous arthropods, spiders and insects are dominant. All spiders are predators and most major orders of insects have some predaceous forms. But ants and wasps, true-bugs, beetles and lacewings are the most numerous on the forest floor and in the forest canopy. Predatory insects and spiders stalk, pursue, ambush or snare their prey, killing and consuming large numbers of insects in the course of their lifetime.

Parasites can also be propagated and used much like biological insecticides. A fine example of the use of laboratory-reared parasites in a biological control program was accomplished in northeastern Oregon.

The larch casebearer (*Colephora laricella*) is a serious forest pest accidentally introduced into North American from Europe. Since it was introduced without its natural enemies, its number quickly grew until it threatened larch (Larix spp.) as a timber species. Casebearer parasites collected from Europe and Japan were reared in the laboratory and released in infested stands. Dr. Roger Ryan, a researcher at the Forestry and Range Sciences Laboratory in LaGrande, guided the project. He obtained the parasites from abroad and determined how to rear them under lab conditions where he let them reproduce before releasing them. These parasites have virtually annihilated the casebearer in some larch stands, and are now becoming a natural part of the beneficial insect community in western forests.

Vertebrate predators include various ground dwelling and arboreal rodents and shrews, as well as bats and birds. Although small mammals may kill many insects, birds are the main insect consumers. Because of their mobility and diverse feeding habits, they forage everywhere that insects feed, fly or rest. Early studies identified woodpeckers as predators of bark beetles and wood-boring insects. More recent studies of major pests like the Douglas-fir tussock moth and western spruce budworm were likewise directed in part at understanding predation by birds and other predators.

Next, I will describe some of the studies that identified what natural enemies preyed on the tussock moth and the budworm. These studies also indicated the magnitude of the beneficial effects of these organisms in the forest environment, and how they affected pest insect numbers.

In studies of the Douglas-fir tussock moth, researchers discovered many larvae were disappearing from study branches. By keeping a daily watch on individual larvae, several species of spiders, true-bugs, ants and a dozen species of birds were found to prey on the tussock moth.

When we designed studies to similarly assess mortality of western spruce budworm in north-central Washington, we also chose to use a selective exclosure method. Our objective was to determine what would happen if certain predators were kept away from budworm-infested trees. Preliminary studies had already shown that ants and birds might be important predators of the budworm. For our exclosure study, we hypothesized that if birds and ants were important predators of the budworm, then more budworms should survive if birds and ants were excluded from infested trees. To test this hypothesis, we designed and built a series of 30 foot-tall whole-tree exclosures. The exclosures were plastic pipe frameworks covered with netting to keep birds out. Sticky barriers around the base of the tree stems kept ants from climbing them. Some trees were protected by both netting and sticky barrier, and some were left unprotected.

At the end of the study season when the budworm had completed development, we counted all the surviving budworms on the trees in each of the treatments. We determined that when the birds and ants had access to the trees and could forage normally, very few budworms were left. When either birds or ants, or both birds and ants were denied access to the trees, many more budworms survived. In fact, we found that without these predators, there were about 10 times as many budworms on the trees! We repeated the experiment in Oregon, Montana and Idaho, and observed similar results. We saw 12 to 18 times as many budworms surviving in the absence of birds and ants!

The studies illustrated how these predators could have a significant impact on budworm. I want to distinguish here that the regulatory role these predators play is most important at low, non-outbreak levels of the pest. In the strictest sense, they don't control outbreaks. Their influence, in effect, is to lengthen the periods of forest stability between pest outbreaks. In other words, they function to help dampen or regulate insect numbers before an outbreak occurs, rather than to terminate or control an outbreak. This is an important distinction! Natural enemies do, in fact, have some role in outbreak collapse, but is it not usually a dominant one.

A dozen species of ants (*Formica* spp. and *Camponotus* spp.) and over two dozen species of birds are predators of the western spruce budworm and Douglas-fir tussock moth. These creatures have diverse requirements for food, shelter and living space. Forest birds build nests concealed in grasses or low shrubs, high in the canopy, in their own bark slabs on trees or snags. Territories may be large, as they are for woodpeckers, or small or nonexistent as for pine siskin and evening grosbeak. Feeding requirements also differ widely. Some search for seeds and insects on or near the ground, others forage in mid-or high canopy layers, and some perch on vantage points and make aerial forays to capture flying insects.

Nesting and foraging requirements for ants are less well known than for birds. Ants normally nest in rotting logs or stumps, in or on the ground. These colonies are usually in proximity to the trees where the ants forage for prey or tend colonies of aphids. Colonies are slow-growing and long-lived; sometimes attaining an age of 20 or more years. Disruption of the nest site can have devastating consequences for the 30,000 or more individuals comprising it.

But birds and ants can only perform as well as their habitat allows. If food, or cover, or some other requirement is inadequate to support them, they cannot occupy a site and fulfill their role as regulators of pest insects. That may be why some of our forests appear to be increasingly susceptible to serious insect outbreaks.

So why should any of this be of interest to the landowner or manager? I'll explain why an understanding of natural enemies is important, and what the concerned and interested person, corporation or agency can do to reap the benefits of conserving and enhancing them.

In particular, we found that birds and ants appeared to be dominant predators of the budworm. Further, we found that in the absence of these predators, about 10 times as many budworm survived as on trees where these natural enemies had full access to the trees and the budworm on them. The studies illustrated how these predators could have a significant impact on pest insect numbers. I distinguished between the regulatory role of such predators as opposed to the concept of controlling outbreaks. I explained that regulation is a process that is most important at low, non-outbreak levels of the pest insects. This is an important distinction—one that is critical to understanding how natural enemies can be used to the forest manager's advantage.

The question I left you with was "Why should natural enemies be of any interest to the landowner or manager?" My intent in the following discussion is to explain how the manager can influence the activity of natural enemies. I'll discuss why it is important, and what the concerned manager can do to reap the benefits that accrue from considering natural enemies in stand management plans.

Researchers have found that the ability of a stand to resist insect pests has at least two interdependent components: its physical structure and vegetational composition, and the diversity and adaptability of the natural enemies that live in the stand.

The stand can be viewed as the supporting matrix within which both forest pests and their natural enemies exist. Some research suggests that forest practices can increase or decrease the resistance of stands to attack and damage by insect pests. Silvicultural prescriptions that create structurally simple stands with tree species favored by insect pests can lead to more outbreaks and the losses associated with them. Practices that favor a variety of the tree species and age classes, that maximize edge-effect, and encourage structural diversity are likely to support a diversity of natural enemies.

Forest practices are not categorically beneficial or detrimental to the natural enemy community. Certainly, for many questions about the effects of management actions, there are no definitive answers. But failing to act because we don't know all the answers may compound our problems. Suppose a manager wants to develop stands with features that favor natural enemies. What techniques are available?

Guidelines developed for increasing numbers of insect-eating birds apply generally to many other natural enemies. Consider the following forest management options:

- Interspersing irregularly shaped cutting units to maximize edges, to mix successional stages and to create a variety of crown closures and canopy layers. This will encourage a broad assemblage of predators.

- Planting or providing for regeneration by a variety of tree species suitable for a given site.

- Conserving riparian corridors. The value of streamside or pond habitat goes far beyond their proportional representation in the landscape. Small impoundments or catchment basins at a rate of one to four per 60 acres can improve bird nesting success and benefit other wild and domestic animals as well.

- Standing and down dead woody material is a vital source of diversity in all forest habitats. It provides critical substrate and shelter for a wide variety of vertebrates and invertebrates. Large diameter logs, stumps and snags provide nesting sites for ants, and avian and mammalian cavity nesting canopy and bole foragers. Consider augmenting natural habitat with bird boxes where needed in special sites. Limit ground disturbances by heavy equipment to protect established ant colonies and prevent destruction of dead-wood habitats.

- Herbicides must be used with care so as not to reduce the diversity and physical structure created by deciduous shrubs, grasses and common forbs that predators and other organisms depend on. Many insecticides affect not only the target pest insect, but also many beneficial insects and spiders and other non-target organisms. Use these substances with care!

- Regulating cattle grazing in riparian zones and other fragile areas to minimize the impact in these sensitive habitats. Overgrazing can profoundly affect plant diversity and natural enemy habitat.

Reducing damage to forest lands by insect pests demands that natural enemies be viewed as a resource to be conserved and enhanced by management actions. One of the great challenges, for landowners and managers alike, is to insure that new knowledge is used to broaden management perspectives and increase the range of management options to mitigate losses from forest insect pests.

Reprinted with permission from the Newsletter of the Northeast Oregon Natural History Society, *1988–89.*

5

Landscape Pattern and Forest Pests

David A. Perry

Introduction

FOREST BIOLOGISTS AND MANAGERS around the globe are facing issues never before confronted. In the Pacific Northwest, we have been and still are, for the most part, harvesting forests that were established long before Europeans arrived on the continent. This bounty is coming to an end and, if forests are to remain a viable part of the economy of this region, we must change our focus from tree cutting to tree growing. Of course, foresters have been planting and growing trees in the Northwest for several decades. Nonetheless, we are setting off into uncharted territory.

Forests west of the Cascades crest ("west-side"), growing for several hundreds of years before Europeans arrived, were remarkably productive and apparently quite stable. We know relatively little about why this was so. Hence, we don't know whether the forests now being established also will be productive and sustainable over the long term. One certainty is that any analysis of current forest management practices must address both productivity and sustain ability. Fast growing trees are of little use if they never reach maturity, and to trade short-term yields for longer-term degradation of ecosystems is to abdicate our responsibility to the future.

The transition from wild to managed forests is accompanied by many changes and uncertainties. "A vast experiment is underway," said Burgess and Sharpe (1981). "Its unplanned and unwitting de sign is changing the spatial and temporal structure of terrestrial ecosystems." This paper deals with one facet of this unplanned experiment. I examine, in particular, how changes in spatial structure (the pattern of forest communities and age classes across the landscape) might influence forest stability. Much uncertainty exists regarding this issue. The factors underpinning ecosystem stability are in general complex and poorly understood. The role of landscape pattern is very difficult to study experimentally. Despite these caveats, it seems clear that the mechanisms stabilizing natural ecosystems are largely ecological in nature.

That is, stability cannot be understood solely as a property of individual organisms (e.g., toxic chemicals in tree foliage). Rather, it emerges from a complex of factors that includes, among other things, interactions among organisms (e.g., how predators find and feed on their prey) and the manner in which biological communities are arrayed across the landscape (e.g., Schowalter, Hargrove, and Crossley, 1986).

Stability does not mean "no change." Much evidence indicates that forests, even the old growth that we tend to view as constant and unchanging, are quite dynamic. Historically, disturbance was a common feature of forests throughout the Northwest. Much of the Cascades was burned over in a massive forest fire during the fourteenth century, and many smaller fires have burned since then. Most forests in the Oregon Coast Range date from a large fire during the middle of the nineteenth century. In the interior forests east of the Cascades and extending into the northern Rockies, both wildfire and periodic insect outbreaks appear to be part of a normal historic pattern. These historic disturbances were part of the environment to which the organisms comprising our forests were adapted.

On the other hand, "foreign" disturbances—those that in one way or another defeat the adaptive mechanisms that confer stability on ecosystems—are potentially destabilizing. For example, fire volatilizes large amounts of nitrogen, shortages of which limit forest productivity in our region. However, historic wildfires have not (as far as we know) reduced forest productivity, because certain plants within the system are capable of pumping nitrogen from the atmosphere back into the soil. When, as sometimes happens in forest management, these "nitrogen-fixing" plants are seen as undesirable and eliminated from sites that have been clearcut and burned, their function must be replaced by fertilizers, or site productivity will eventually decline. This decline is not a direct result of the clearcut or the slash burn, but of a "foreign" disturbance that eliminated an important part of the ecosystem—nitrogen-fixing plants that are important to system recovery following tree death and fire. A central issue to be addressed is whether the pattern of new forests that we are imposing on the landscape is sufficiently "foreign" to alter the stability of forest ecosystems. However, I shall also discuss instances where natural landscape patterns exacerbate pest problems, and the proper management strategy is the imposition of a "foreign" pat tern.

I first discuss how forest management alters landscape patterns. Second, I provide examples of pest problems in the Northwest that are linked to changes in landscape pattern. I then raise what I believe to be one of the more significant questions to be addressed in Northwest forestry: How might landscape pattern influence the susceptibility of forests to a major "pest"—catastrophic wildfire? Finally, I close with some thoughts on where landscape management in the Northwest should be headed.

Predicting Pest Problems Associated With Landscape Pattern

Except for a few instances to be discussed in the following section, there is little evidence that landscape patterns, either natural or resulting from logging, have increased pest problems in the North west. This statement must be taken in context, however, because no one has systematically looked for such a connection, and unrecognized problems might exist. Moreover, lack of a problem today does not guarantee that none will appear in the future. This is the time to ask where management is taking the forested landscape, and how susceptible this future forest might be to pests. Once the future pattern is established, it will be too late. Landscape pattern influences the dynamics of pest populations in two general ways: (1) through the homogeneity, or lack thereof, in the distribution of food sources; and (2) through the habitat provided for natural enemies of pests. Not surprisingly, pests multiply and disperse much more effectively when suitable food plants are distributed uniformly across the landscape (Schowalter, Hargrove, and Crossley, 1986). Depending on the particular pest, suitable may mean "a given species or set of species, or a certain age or size class of plants," as is the case with mountain pine beetle (discussed in the following section).

Defoliating insects and bark beetles are the most serious pests of interior forests. These insects—particularly the defoliators—also are present in west-side forests; but, for reasons that are unclear, they rarely reach outbreak levels. Landscape patterns almost certainly influence the survival and spread of these insects. Larvae of spruce budworm and tussock moth, the two principal "outbreak" defoliators in interior conifer forests, are dispersed largely by wind cur rents (Stock and Willhite 1979;

Wickman and Beckwith, 1978). Larval survival, hence the rate with which an infestation spreads, depends (among other things) on the proportion of dispersing larvae that lands on a suitable host which depends, in turn, on the relative distribution of host and non-host plant species across the landscape.

There are many kinds of pests with many different behaviors. No single landscape pattern is likely to protect against all. Although extensive even-aged stands are vulnerable to at least some insects, close intermingling of old and young stands can facilitate movement of some pests from one to another. For example, dwarf mistletoe, a plant that parasitizes many conifer species, spreads by seeds that are ejected from one tree and land on another. Young trees are much more likely to be infected when they are growing in proximity to older, infected trees than when they are at some distance from older trees (see Baker, this volume). In other cases, older trees may be at risk when near early successional vegetation. Some pests, particularly rusts (foliar pathogens such as white pine blister rust) and aphids, have complex life cycles in which different stages require different hosts. For both rusts and aphids, the proximity of the alternate host influences population dynamics (Dixon, 1985; Manion, 1981).

Landscape pattern also influences the habitat provided for birds, mammals, and invertebrates, such as spiders, that prey on defoliators and bark beetles. Woodpeckers eat large numbers of bark beetles, and may converge on the rich food source provided by beetles invading wind-thrown trees (Koplin, 1969). Bird communities in western conifer forests are dominated by species that feed on foliage insects, though they comprise a lower proportion of total bird species than they do in forests of the eastern United States (Wiens, 1975). Wiens (1975) calculates that roughly 80% of the food consumed by Northwestern birds is animal prey, most of which is foliage-feeding insects. Takekawa and Garton (1984) estimated that it would cost $1,800 per square km per year in insecticides to kill the same number of spruce budworms that are eaten by birds in forests of north central Washington.

Predators, however, simply cannot increase in numbers fast enough to keep up with an outbreaking insect population. With some exceptions (e.g., woodpeckers congregating in response to localized bark beetle outbreaks), birds and mammals are unlikely to stop an insect epidemic once it has started. However, these animals almost certainly play an important role in regulating insect populations and thereby decrease the chance of an outbreak starting (Wiens 1975; DeGraff, 1978; Carlson, et al., 1984). Wiens (1975) quotes Gibb (1961) on New Zealand forests:

With their low reproductive potential, birds cannot cope with plagues of insects once they have broken out; but at the more prevalent endemic levels of their prey they can eat a significant fraction of their foodstocks...and under certain circumstances their predation can dampen down oscillations in insect numbers which might otherwise develop into serious outbreaks.

Birds and other predators of insect pests depend on certain age classes of forest for nesting, and their numbers decline if the landscape does not contain these habitats. Meslow (1978) listed preferred nesting habitats of 84 birds common to west-side forests. In general, the more favored nesting sites for many insectivorous songbirds are in young conifer forests prior to crown closure (the "shrub-sapling stage"), although these birds are at least somewhat flexible in their choice of nest sites. On the other hand, 20 species listed by Meslow (1978), including various woodpeckers, owls, nuthatches and swifts, are cavity-nesters. Cavities are equally important for many insectivorous birds in forests of the interior West (Balda, 1975; Thomas, 1979). Cavity-nesting birds have little or no flexibility; they require either the snags that are common in old growth forests or a suitable substitute. (Nest boxes are an acceptable substitute for some species but not others.)

Meslow (1978) concludes, as have others in both North America and Europe, that the middle stages of succession in conifer forests provide relatively poor habitat for most birds. The middle stages comprise the period following crown closure and preceding "old growth" which is characterized by an increase in structural complexity (the combination of snags, fallen logs, shade-tolerant understory plants, etc.). In a study encompassing forests throughout North America, James and Warner (1982) concluded that "...both bird species richness and density are minimal in coniferous forests characterized by high tree density, low canopy, and few species of trees."

The middle stages of succession in coniferous forests also are the period of highest wood productivity. Hence, the direction of much forest management is toward early dominance of the site by conifers, and stands are harvested well before forests develop the bird and mammal habitats (snags, logs) found in older forests. The resulting managed landscape, dominated by middle-stage forests, provides less habitat than unmanaged forests for many animal species, including some that are important predators of forest pests. There is, however, a growing trend among forest managers to leave some trees within harvest units as a future source of snags for cavity nesters.

Birds that characterize the early successional shrub-sapling stage appear to be more flexible in their habitat requirements than cavity nesters. Morrison and Meslow (1984) found that vegetation control (with herbicide) in young plantations in the Siuslaw National Forest had only transitory effects on numbers of birds. However, management practices that accelerate crown closure of conifer plantations—a desirable goal from the standpoint of timber production—seem likely to result in fewer eventual nesting opportunities for birds that prefer the shrub-sapling stage.

Predatory and parasitic spiders, ants, and wasps also kill large numbers of insect pests (e.g., Campbell and Torgersen, 1982). Carlson, et al. (1984) found that predation by ants and birds reduced spruce budworm damage to Douglas-fir by 50%. Comparatively little is known about the habitat requirements of predatory and parasitic invertebrates. Some supplement their diets with the nectar produced by flowering plants, and, hence, require some non-coniferous plants on the landscape. Schowalter and Means (1988) found that old growth forests in the Cascades supported far more predatory invertebrates—primarily spiders—than plantations (160 g/ha vs. 60 g/ha, respectively). This raises the question of the degree to which insect pests within plantations could be controlled by insect predators that originate in old-growth. Spiders are the primary invertebrate predator of the eastern spruce budworm, a close relative of the western spruce budworm (Morris 1963). The importance of spiders in controlling budworm in west-side forests has not been studied.

The implications of reduced numbers of predators are impossible to predict with any certainty. Other factors also influence the population dynamics of insect pests, including chemical defenses of the trees and climatic factors that affect both insect survival and the production of tree defenses. Most ecologists and entomologists agree that these factors act in concert to regulate insect pests and prevent their populations from reaching destructive levels (Schowalter, Hargrove, and Crossley 1986). Reduced numbers of predators, the equivalent of relaxing one of a set of regulating factors, could increase the probability of pest outbreak, particularly when other regulating factors also are weakened (e.g., during drought years). This may be especially true in west-side forests, which appear to have limited foliar defenses against western spruce budworm (Perry and Pitman 1983). Apparently, at least in the two west-side forests that have been studied (Perry and Pitman 1983), some combination of climate and predators has effectively controlled defoliating insects, and trees have experienced little evolutionary pressure to produce chemical defenses against this defoliator. It remains to be seen whether the same pattern holds for other west-side forests. In both east-side and west-side forests, reduction in the number of predators, coupled with stresses to trees associated with the anticipated changes in global climate, may well increase the level of insect pest activity.

Harvest Pattern and Pest Problems: Examples from the Northwest

Since the 1950s, forest harvest on federal lands in much of the Northwest has followed what is called a "staggered setting" pattern. This simply means that clear-cuts are interspersed within the matrix of old growth forest, rather than being concentrated, resulting in a patchwork of old growth and young growth.

Because harvest units are scattered, rather than concentrated, in the staggered-setting system, an extensive road network is required, and much forestry-related and recreational traffic follows. The spread of at least five pest species in the Northwest has been facilitated by the corridors and traffic resulting from logging roads. These pests include: gypsy moth, Port Orford cedar root rot, black stain root disease, tansy ragwort, and spotted knapweed (Strang, Lindsay, and Price, 1979; Hansen, et al., 1986; Daterman, Miller, and Hanson, 1986). In general, any pest, whether it flies, is borne by the wind, or is carried in the mud on the underside of a truck, will move much more readily along corridors than through undisturbed forest.

Staggered-setting logging produces a patchwork pattern in which different age-classes of forest exist in relatively small, isolated is lands. Logging old growth in this fashion is like eating a pancake by punching small pieces out of its interior instead of starting from the edge and working inwards. At first, the bites exist as small islands surrounded by the uneaten pancake, but eventually it is the pieces of uneaten pancake that become the isolated fragments. Harris (1984) documented the situation on the Siuslaw National Forest. "Of the 319 old-growth stands remaining, 196 (61%) are less than 40 acres (16 ha) in size…. There are only 8 stands larger than 350 acres (140 ha)." These numbers vary, depending on how much of a particular forest has been logged, but the trend is common to all public lands in the Northwest that are open to logging. Forest fragmentation is occurring in many areas of the world, and ecologists have devoted a great deal of attention to its implications for species diversity.

For the Northwest, most of what can be said about the effects of fragmentation on species diversity, and particularly on pest problems, is speculative. Reasonable arguments can be made, but empirical evidence with which to test their validity is in short supply. There is, however, one situation in the Northwest in which the link between fragmentation and a "pest"—wind—is relatively strong. When grown in the open, trees are usually "wind-firm" (able to withstand high wind speeds). Trees growing in the interior of forests experience little wind, however, because of buffering by surrounding trees. When suddenly exposed by having neighboring trees removed, such trees are quite vulnerable to windthrow. Staggered setting harvest pattern creates a large amount of edge relative to stand size as remaining old forests are fragmented into smaller islands. Hence, a high proportion of remaining trees is exposed to high winds (Franklin et al. 1986). In areas where winds are consistently gentle, exposure probably will not result in serious wind throw. However, in areas with periodic strong winds, old growth fragments are not likely to persist. Areas with strong winds include coastal forests and those near mountain passes (which act as wind funnels). Even areas with normally gentle winds are subject to the infrequent large windstorms such as those which occurred in the mid-1950s and early 1960s.

Windthrow has been a particular problem on certain areas of the Mount Hood National Forest, because strong winds are funneled down the Columbia Gorge and up into the forest. Windthrow in forests around Mt. Hood was first associated with clearcut edges, and then a domino effect commenced; previous windthrow exposed new and more extensive edge that was vulnerable to the next large windstorm. Consequently, each windstorm blows down more trees. Forest Service silviculturists are attempting to arrest this progressive unraveling by a technique called feathering, in which diffuse (rather than sharp) boundaries between forest and non-forest (blowdown or clearcut) are created. Whether or not this works remains to be seen.

One disruption to an ecosystem often sets the stage for others. This potential exists with windthrow, which provides a large food base for some species of bark beetles. Once beetle populations have built to high levels on dead trees, it becomes easier for them to overcome the resistance mechanisms of living trees. The two most serious Douglas-fir beetle infestations on record for west-side forests occurred following major windstorms in the mid-1950s and, again, in 1962. These were catastrophic windstorms that blew down many trees over wide areas; small-scale windthrow associated with old growth islands probably would not have the same effect on beetle populations. On the other hand, old growth fragments over extensive areas will be vulnerable to the next windstorm comparable in magnitude to the 1962 storm, and sufficient wood could go down to allow beetle populations to increase and spread to living trees.

Quite the opposite pattern occurs in pine forests of the interior Northwest. There, where extensive even-aged lodgepole pine forests set the stage for bark beetle epidemics, some degree of fragmentation would be beneficial. Mountain pine beetle, a major pest of lodgepole and ponderosa pine, successfully attacks only after trees attain a certain size. Lodgepole forests usually are established by fire and tend to be even-aged over wide areas even when unman aged. Hence, extensive areas of forest become vulnerable to the mountain pine beetle at the same time (as has been happening throughout eastern Oregon for the past several years). This is a self-maintaining pattern. Beetle infestations create large amounts of fuel, increasing the probability of wildfire. Fire, in turn, initiates development of new even-aged lodgepole pine stands, which repeats the cycle at some point in the future. From the standpoint of lodgepole pine, this is a desirable sequence of events, because the interaction acts to perpetuate this fire-maintained species. From the standpoint of the forest manager, it is an undesirable cycle that only can be broken by diversifying the landscape.

Forest Fragmentation and Pest Problems

Ecologists have devoted considerable attention to the effects of habitat fragmentation on species diversity. Species diversity, by it self, is not necessarily a reliable indicator of ecosystem stability (May 1972; Pimm 1984, 1986). However, given mounting evidence of pest problems in monocultures, contrasted with their rarity in mixed stands (Schowalter, Hargrove, and Crossley 1986), an ecosystem that is losing species must be considered at risk. Predators may be particularly sensitive to landscape pattern. For a given body size, predators require more territory than do herbivores (including pests). Therefore, predators are frequently the first casualties of habitat fragmentation (a possible exception from northern California is discussed below). This raises the possibility that fragmentation could eventually result in outbreaks of pests that normally are kept at innocuous levels by natural enemies. Experience has shown that islands, the basis for much of the ecological literature on fragmented habitats, are notoriously vulnerable to invasion by exotic species— especially when the invaders have been predators or herbivores to which native species had evolved no defense (Simberloff 1981; Pimm 1986). It is not clear that an island is a reliable model of a fragmented mainland habitat, but it is argued that

The fragmentation of habitats may well create communities that not only are island-like in their species richness but in their structure. Isolated, species poor habitat fragments may surprise us in their lack of resistance to further species losses... (Pimm 1986).

Populations of breeding birds are known to be declining in forest fragments of the eastern United States. This is particularly true of ground nesters, and is at least partially due to increased levels of predation in small (compared to large) forest tracts (Wilcove, 1985). Cavity nesters are less affected. However, in the Northwest at least one cavity-nesting bird, the spotted owl, may be endangered by fragmentation. In general, however, the eastern experience is unlikely to have much relevance in western forests. Eastern fragments are usually woodlots that are truly islands in a sea of farmland and suburbs. They are vulnerable to invasion by cats and dogs, which prey on birds. Moreover, the top predators that control predators of birds (mountain lions, wildcats, and bears) have long since disappeared. The situation in old-growth fragments of the Northwest— islands in a sea of younger forest—is quite different.

I am aware of only one study of the influence of forest fragmentation on species diversity in the Northwest. In Douglas-fir forests of northern California, Rosenberg and Raphael, (1986) found the highest numbers of bird and amphibian species in the most fragmented stands. However, some species (fisher, gray fox, spotted owl, northern flying squirrel, and pileated woodpecker) appeared at least somewhat sensitive to fragmentation. Because of the difficulty in controlling environmental conditions over large areas and the often highly-individual responses of different species, studies such as this are difficult to perform and even more difficult to interpret. As Rosenberg and Raphael point out, the problem of interpretation is further confounded in the Northwest because we are early in the process of fragmentation. What we see now is not necessarily what we will get in the future.

Landscape Pattern and Wildfire

Wildfire also is an example of a "pest" that may be promoted by the trend toward younger forests. Under a given set of weather conditions, the probability of ignition (usually lightning in the Pacific Northwest) turning into a conflagration depends on the amount, flammability, and distribution (vertical and horizontal) of fuels. If they are flammable, low branches or understory trees (termed "fire ladders" or "ladder fuels") provide vertical continuity that facilitates spread of fire into the crowns of the overstory. Once in the crowns, horizontal continuity (the degree to which tree crowns are "packed") comes into play, influencing the spread of fire across the landscape. Like other pests, fire spreads most rapidly where it has a homogeneous "food" source.

Old growth conifer forests frequently are considered to be vulnerable to catastrophic fire, because of the large amounts of fuel on the ground and (sometimes) abundant ladder fuels (Heinselman, 1981). Experience in the lodgepole pine-spruce-fir forests of Yellow stone National Park indicates that older forests in the Northern Rockies, particularly those in transition from lodgepole pine to spruce and fir, are indeed the most susceptible to wildfire. The situation appears to be different in west-side forests, however. Based on patterns of burning and reburning during the catastrophic wildfires that occurred early in this century (e.g., the Tillamook and Yacalt burns), Franklin and Hemstrom (1981) conclude that west-side Douglas-fir forests are most susceptible to fire during their first 75 to 100 years.

Early indications are that patterns resulting from the 1987 wild fires in southwest Oregon are as Franklin and Hemstrom suggest. The Galice and Longwood fires, both of which burned through areas with a mix of plantations and older forests, affected the former more seriously than the latter. Relatively young natural forests, established following catastrophic fires in the 1930s, were also severely affected by the recent fires. Some old-growth forests were killed by the 1987 fires, but many survived. In contrast, few plantations between the ages of (about) 5 and 25 years (generally the oldest plantations in the forest) survived. In one case, fire spreading up a broad, uniform ridge passed through three age classes of forest that were adjacent to one another and on the same slope and aspect: a 10 to 15-year-old plantation, a 100-year-old stand established by previous wildfire, and an older mixed conifer-hardwood stand. The former two were destroyed; the latter, in which fire did not move into the crowns, had relatively little damage to overstory conifers.

If older west-side forests are indeed less vulnerable to fire than younger forests, what might account for this? One factor is the horizontal discontinuity of fuels in older forests. Whereas young stands often have tightly packed crowns—an ideal homogeneous "food source" for fire—older stands frequently have a great deal of patchiness in the crown layer, which hampers fire spread. Older stands do tend to develop fire ladders in the form of understory trees, but such an understory may or may not act as a fire ladder, depending on its flammability. In the recent southwest Oregon fires there is compelling evidence that stands with a hardwood component burned less severely than those without. In one instance, fire burned through a young plantation (trees 10 to 15 ft tall) that was the site of a "brush" control study. The only surviving Douglas-fir were those in the control plot for that study, where the hardwood component had not been previously removed. The explanation is straightforward: The hardwood foliage was not very flammable and conducted the fire very poorly.

If the structure of young west-side forests increases their vulnerability to catastrophic fire, this should be of great concern in the Pacific Northwest, where management is creating a landscape dominated by forests that are uniformly younger than 100 or so years of age. As long as the climate of our region remains roughly the same (dry summers), fires will occur periodically. In a landscape dominated by relatively young, tightly-spaced conifer plantations, future fires could be highly destructive and very difficult (if not impossible) to control. Managing the species composition and horizontal distribution of crowns may be our best tools for protecting forests against catastrophic fire losses. Inclusion of hardwoods as "fire insurance" is not a new idea. Following the 1910 Yacalt burn in south-central Washington, strips of red alder were interplanted within Douglas-fir stands as fire breaks.

Closing Thoughts: Whither Northwest Silviculture?

Can we design stands and landscapes in such a way that pest problems are minimized? Being an optimist, my answer to this question is "yes," but the problem is far from simple. Different pests respond differently to a given landscape pattern, and a pattern that reduces problems with one pest could well create problems with another. The problem is confounded because factors beyond the direct control of local managers and policymakers have a high likelihood of increasing the susceptibility of forests to pests. Air pollution and global climate change almost certainly will stress Pacific Northwest forests in the future, if they are not already doing so. Stress often translates to increased pest problems.

Global influences on the Pacific Northwest go beyond those mediated by the atmosphere. The most serious threat to insectivorous songbirds in our area may not be lost habitat here, but lost habitat on the wintering grounds in Central and South America. Roughly one-half of insectivorous songbird species in the Northwest are migratory, wintering in tropical forests. The large-scale destruction of tropical forests means lost habitat for these birds and lower numbers in the temperate forests where they return for summer.

Deteriorating global environment and consequent stresses on forests set the stage for an increase in pest problems, and underscore the need for silvicultural schemes that deal with stability as well as productivity. Just what forms that silviculture might take will depend on numerous economic and biological factors, and its definition will require the creative interaction of many people. One conclusion seems clear: While the current trend toward homogenizing the landscape may make sense from the standpoint of short-term productivity and short-term economics, it bodes ill for the longer term stability—hence economic viability—of Pacific Northwest forests (for more detailed arguments see Franklin, et al., 1986; Franklin, Perry, and Schowalter, 1988; Perry and Maghembe, 1988).

Modern forestry as practiced worldwide is a child of European silviculture. At least some European foresters, witnessing the progressive collapse of their forests over the past 10 years, are now saying that their system has failed in that it did not provide the resilience necessary to withstand the stresses of the modern environment. Whether or not European forests would have been more stable under a different kind of management is impossible to say. However, the lesson for us is to move cautiously and to learn what contributes to the robustness of the natural forests while we still have them. There is, in fact, a burgeoning interest among European foresters in the biology and ecology of old growth. Having none of their own, they are turning to ours in the Pacific Northwest for insights.

Harris (1984), Franklin et al. (1986), Franklin, Perry, and Schowalter (1988), and Newton and Cole (1987) have discussed alternatives to current silvicultural practices in west-side forests. If periodically thinned, Douglas-fir has a capacity to maintain quite good growth for 200 or more years. Moreover, such trees produce wood that is of higher quality than fast-grown short rotation trees. Based on these considerations, Newton and Cole (1987) argue that rotation lengths on the order of 200 years are economically feasible and that they duplicate at least some (but not all) of the characteristics of old growth forests. Franklin, Perry, and Schowalter (1988) recommend that current harvest patterns be replaced by "large sloppy cuts," creating a heterogeneous mosaic of intermingled successional stages across the landscape. The latter scheme would result in landscape patterns that approximate those imposed by historic wildfires in west-side forests. Some amalgamation of the large sloppy cut and long rotations—coupled with provisions for retaining both the very early and very late successional habitats—seems to be a good direction. However, this type of management is not without its own problems, both logistical and environmental. More dispersed harvest and management activity, if accompanied by more frequent entry into stands to cut trees, could result in even greater spread of some pests and perhaps exacerbate management-related impacts such as soil compaction. Creative engineering and silviculture will be required to mitigate adverse effects. Whatever our future management strategy, it should be guided by four basic principles:

1. Ecological diversity should be maintained or, where appropriate, created. This refers not only to the variety of species, but also to the variety of age classes and the sizes of openings across the landscape;

2. Harvest unit boundaries should conform as much as possible to landforms and natural landscape features, rather than being arbitrarily drawn as straight lines;

3. Silvicultural systems should be flexible. What is appropriate for one area may not be appropriate for another; and

4. We should learn from and protect the natural robustness of our forest ecosystems.

References

Balda, R. P. 1975. "Vegetation structure and breeding bird diversity." Pp. 59-80. In *Proc. symp. on management of forest and range habitats for non-game birds*, ed. D. R. Smith. USDA Forest Service Gen. Tech. Rep. WO-1. Washington, D.C.

Burgess, R. L., and D. M. Sharpe. 1981. *Forest island dynamics in man-dominated landscapes*. New York: Springer-Verlag.

Campbell, R. W., and T. R. Torgersen. 1982. "Some effects of predaceous ants on western spruce budworm pupae in north central Washington." *Environ. Entomol*. 11: 105-106.

Carlson, C. E., R. W. Campbell, L. J. Theroux, and T. H. Egan. 1984. "Ants and birds reduce western spruce budworm feeding injury to small Douglas-fir and western larch in Montana." *For. Ecol. Manage*. 9:185-19Z.

Daterman, G. E., J. C. Miller, and P. E. Hanson. 1986. "Potential for gypsy moth problems in southwest Oregon". Pp. 37-40. In *Forest pest management in southwest Oregon*, ed. O. T. Helgerson. Corvallis: Forest Research Lab, Oregon State Univ.

DeGraff, R. M. 1978. "The importance of birds in ecosystems." Pp. 5-11. In *Proc. workshop on non-game bird habitat management in the coniferous forests of the western United States*, ed. R. M. DeGraff. USDA Forest Service Gen. Tech. Rep. PNW-64. Portland, Oregon: Pac. NW For. Range Exp. Sta.

Dixon, A. F. G. 1985. *Aphid ecology*. London: Blackie.

Franklin, J. F., and M. A. Hemstrom. 1981. "Aspects of succession in coniferous forests of the Pacific Northwest." Pp. 212-229. In *Forest succession*, ed. D. E. Reichle. New York: Springer-Verlag.

Franklin, J. F., D. A. Perry, and T. Schowalter. 1988. "The importance of ecological diversity." In *Maintaining the long-term productivity of Pacific Northwest forest ecosystems*, eds. D. A. Perry, R. Meurisse, B. Thomas, D. Miller, J. Boyle, J. Means, and P. Sollins. Portland, Oregon: Timber Press. In press.

Franklin, J. F., T. Spies, D. A. Perry, M. Harmon, and A. McKee. 1986. "Modifying Douglas-fir management regimes for non-timber objectives." Pp. 373-379. In *Douglas-fir: Stand management for the future*, eds. C. D. Oliver, D. P. Hanley, and J. A. Johnson. Contr. No. 55. Seattle: College of Forest Resources, Univ. Wash.

Gibb, J. A. 1961. "Ecology of the birds of Kaingaroa Forest." *Proc. N.Z. Ecol. Soc*. 8: 29-38.

Hansen, E. M., D. J. Goheen, P. F. Hessburg, J. J. Witcosky, and T. D. Schowalter. 1986. "Biology and management of black-stain root disease in Douglas-fir." Pp. 13–19. In *Forest pest management in southwest Oregon*, ed. O. T. Helgerson. Corvallis: Forest Research Lab, Oregon State Univ.

Harris, L. D. 1984. *The fragmented forest*. Chicago: Univ. Chicago Press.

Heinselman, M. L. 1981. "Fire and succession in the conifer forests of northern North America." Pp. 374-405. In *Forest succession*, ed. D. E. Reichle. New York: Springer-Verlag.

James, F. C., and N. O. Wamer. 1982. "Relationships between temperate forest bird communities and vegetation structure." *Ecology* 63:159-171.

Koplin, J. R. 1969. "The numerical response of wood-peckers to insect prey in a sub-alpine forest in Colorado." *Condor* 71:436-438.

Manion, P. D. 1981. *Tree disease concepts*. Englewood Cliffs, New Jersey: Prentice Hall.

May, R. 1972. *Stability and complexity in model ecosystems*. Princeton, New Jersey: Princeton Univ. Press.

Meslow, E. C. 1978. "The relationship of birds to habitat structure—plant communities and successional stages." Pp. 12-18. In *Proc. workshop on non-game bird habitat management in the coniferous forests of the western United States*, ed. R. M. DeGraff. USDA Forest Service Gen. Tech. Rep. PNW-64. Portland, Oregon: Pac. NW For. Range Exp. Sta.

Morris, R. F. (ed.). 1963. "The dynamics of epidemic spruce budworm populations." *Entomol. Soc. Can. Memoir* 31:1-332.

Morrison, M. L., and E. C. Meslow. 1984. "Response of avian communities to herbicide-induced vegetation changes." *J. Wildlife Manage.* 48:14-22.

Newton, M., and E. C. Cole. 1987. "A sustained yield scheme for old-growth Douglas-fir." *West. Journ. Appl. Forestry* 2:22-25.

Perry, D. A., and J. Maghembe. 1988. "Ecosystem concepts and current trends in forest management: Time for reappraisal." *For. Ecol. Manage.* In press.

Perry, D. A., and G. B. Pitman. 1983. "Genetic and environmental influences in host resistance to herbivory: Douglas-fir and the western spruce budworm." *Z. Ang. Entomol.* 96:217-228.

Pimm, S. L. 1984. "The complexity and stability of ecosystems." *Nature* 307:321-326. 1986. "Community stability and structure." Pp. 309-329. In *Conservation biology: The science of scarcity and diversity*, ed. M. E. Soule. Sunderland, Mass.: Sinauer.

Rosenberg, K. V., and M. G. Raphael. 1986. "Effects of fragmentation on vertebrates in Douglas-fir forests."

Pp. 263-272. In *Wildlife 2000*, eds. J. Verner, M. L. Morrison, and C. J. Ralph. Madison: Univ. Wisc. Press.

Schowalter, T. D., W. W. Hargrove, and D. A. Crossley, Jr. 1986. "Herbivory in forested ecosystems." *Ann. Rev. Entomol.* 31:177-196.

Schowalter, T., and J. Means. 1988. "Pests link site productivity to the landscape." In *Maintaining long-term productivity of Pacific Northwest forest ecosystems*, ed. D. A. Perry, R. Meurisse, B. Thomas et al. Portland, Oregon: Timber Press. In press.

Simberloff, D. 1981. *Community effects of introduced species. Biotic crises in ecological and evolutionary time*, ed. M. H. Nitecki. New York: Academic Press.

Stock, M. W., and E. A. Willhite. 1979. "Origin and spread of spruce budworm outbreaks." Pp. 134-142. In *Dispersal of forest insects*, eds. A. A. Berryman and L. Saxanyik. Proc. IUFRO Conf. Evaluation, theory and management implications, Canadian Forestry Service, USDA Forest Service and Washington State University.

Strang, R. M., K. M. Lindsay, and R. S. Price. 1979. "Knapweeds: British Columbia's undesirable aliens." *Rangelands* 1:141-143.

Takekawa, J. Y., and E. O. Garton. 1984. "How much is an evening grosbeak worth?" *Jour. For.* 82:426-427.

Thomas, J. W. (ed.). 1979. *Wildlife habitats in managed forests: The Blue Mountains of Oregon and Washington*. USDA Forest Service Agric. Handbook No. 553. Washington, D.C.

Wickman, B. E., and R. C. Beckwith. 1978. "Life history and habits." Pp. 30-37. In *The Douglas-fir tussock moth: A synthesis*, ed. M. Brooks, D. Stark, and R. Campbell. USDA Forest Service SEA Tech. Bull. 1585. USDA. Washington, D.C.

Wiens, J. A. 1975. "Avian communities, energetics, and functions in coniferous forest habitats." Pp. 226-265. In *Proc. symp. on management of forest and range habitats for non-game birds*, ed. D. R. Smith. USDA Forest Service Gen. Tech. Rep. WO-1. Washington, D.C.

Wilcove, D. S. 1985. "Nest predation in forest tracts and the decline of migratory songbirds." *Ecology* 66:1211-1214.

Previously published in The Northwest Environmental Journal, *4:213-228, 1988. University of Washington, Seattle, Washington 98195. Reprinted with permission.*

5

6 Resource Guide To Forest Ecology, Restoration, and Reforestation

Forest Ecology: A Resource Guide

Forest Science in the Pacific Northwest

THE PACIFIC NORTHWEST is one of the world's leading areas in forest ecology research. People like Jack Ward Thomas, David Perry, Jerry Franklin, Chris Maser and hundreds of others are providing the scientific underpinnings for restoration forestry. Understanding the ecology of forests provides clues to forestry management. Nature is the best forester. We must learn from Her.

Exploitation of the Pacific Northwest's accumulated ecological wealth provided the money and the incentive to apply science to forestry. Much of the research monies were provided by large timber corporations, thus, the research tended to fill their needs. Ironically, the recent findings and syntheses of forest researchers ended up damning clear-cuts, forest fragmentation, plantations, and short rotation forestry which timber companies (and most foresters) espouse and practice. Researchers in the Pacific Northwest were greatly aided in their work by a relative abundance of old-growth forests to observe and study. Unfortunately, the clearcutting of old-growth forests continues.

The following references are representative of the best ecological studies on forest functioning. Most are from the Pacific Northwest.

Birds as a Link Between the Forest Health of Central American Forests and North American Forests

Insectivorous birds, like the Western Tanager, are important components of natural forest insect pest control in U.S. forests. These birds spend their winters in Central and/or South American forests. However, as their wintering forests are increasingly decimated, less and less of the bird populations make it back to U.S. forests to perform their important ecological roles in forest health.

If we want healthy forests in the U.S. we also have to look at how we can help restore and maintain forests and forest health south of our borders. Forest ecosystems operate on all scales—from the individual plant/animal interactions with their environment to the community level, landscape level, greater ecosystem level, and, as in the case of migratory birds, globally.

Ants and Aphids Important to Forest Function

Ants are very significant animals in forest ecology by virtue of their sheer number of individuals and diverse roles in soil processes, predation and seed dispersal. Seed harvesting ants may potentially alter the abundance and distribution of some trees. In Victoria, seedling density of Eucalyptus baxteri was increased 15-fold after ants were experimentally eliminated. In Europe, predatory wood ant (*Formica polyctena*) colonies take up to 100,000 arboreal insect larvae daily and birch forests have been reported with 40 metre radii of healthy trees around ants nests during outbreaks of defoliators.

In temperate forests, phloem-feeding insects such as scales, aphids and psyllids are present in very large numbers. They are an important link in the energetics of the forest through their ability to relay sugars and starch via their secretions to other animals including birds.

—Excerpt from Peter B. McQuillan.
"The Role of Invertebrates in the Conservation
of Temperate Forests."
In *Towards a Global Temperate Forest Action Plan*,
pp. 30-35.

(See international forests books section for full citation.)

Books on Forest Ecology

Analysis of Coniferous Forest Ecosystems in the Western United States
Robert L. Edmonds, ed. 1982. Hutchinson Ross Pub. Co.: Stroudsberg, PA.

Ancient Forests in the Pacific Northwest: Analysis and Maps of Twelve National Forests
P. H. Morrison, D. Kloepfer, D. A. Leversee, C. M. Socha, and D. L. Ferber. 1991. The Wilderness Society: Washington, D.C.

Biological Nitrogen Fixation in Forest Ecosystems: Foundations and Applications
J. C. Gordon and C. T. Wheeler, eds. 1983. Martines Njhoff and Dr. W. Junk. 343 pp.

Biology of Bats in Douglas-fir Forests
R. E. Christy and S. D. West. 1993. USDA Forest Service Pacific Northwest Res. Stn. Gen. Tech. Rep. PNW-308. 28 pp.

Biomass Dynamics of Dead Douglas-fir and Western Hemlock Boles in Mid-elevation Forests of the Cascade Range
Robin Lee Lambert Graham. Oct. 1981. Thesis. Oregon State University. 150 pp.

Concepts of Ecosystem Ecology
Pomeroy, L. R. and J. J. Alberts, eds. 1988. Springer-Verlag, NY.

Cumulative Effects of Forest Practices on the Environment: A State of the Knowledge
Rollin R. Geppert, Charles W. Lorenz and Arthur G. Larson. 1984. Ecosystems, Inc.: Olympia, WA.

Directing Ecological Succession
James O. Luken. 1990. Cropman and Hall: Department of Biological Sciences, Northern Kentucky University. 251 pp. $77.50.

Scientific overview, many references.

"Dynamics of Northwestern Nevada Plant Communities During the Last 30,000 Years"
Peter E. Wigand and Cheryl L. Nowak. 1992. In: *The History of Water: Eastern Sierra, Owens Valley, White-Inyo Mountains: Proceedings*, White Mountain Research Station, 4th biennial Symposium; September 1991; University of California, Los Angeles: pp. 40-62.

Ecological Applications
1993. Ecological Society of America.

New, useful book on applied ecology. Much on forestry, but it also includes management of grasslands and aquatic ecosystems. It includes an article on ecosystem management by Fred Swanson and Jerry Franklin which is one of the best overviews on the subject to date.

Ecological Characteristics of Old Growth Douglas Fir Forests
J. F. Franklin et al. 1981. USDA Forest Service, Pacific Northwest For. and Rg. Exp. Stn., Gen. Tech. Rep. PNW-118.

The Ecological Effects of Slashburning with Particular Reference to British Columbia. A Literature Review
M. C. Feller. 1982. B.C. Ministry of Forests, Land Management Report. No. 13: Victoria, B.C., Canada.

Ecology and Management of Oak and Associated Woodlands: Perspectives in the Southwestern United States and Northern Mexico
USDA Forest Service, Rocky Mountain For. and Rg. Exp. Stn. Gen. Tech. Rep. RM-218. Proceedings of a conference held April 27-30, 1992, Sierra Vista, Arizona.

Ecology and Conservation of Neotropical Migrant Landbirds
John M. Hagan III and David W. Johnston. 1992. Smithsonian Institution Press. 610 pp. $17.95.

A resource book on the importance of Neotropical migrant songbirds as key indicators of ecological collapse. It argues for overall landscape protection.

The Ecology of Even Aged Plantations
E. D. Ford and M. Cannell, eds. 1979. Institute of Terrestrial Ecology: Abbotswood, U.K.

Ecology of Natural Disturbance and Patch Dynamics
S. T. Pickett and P. S. White. 1985. Academic Press. 472 pp.

"Ecology of the Pileated Woodpecker In Northeastern Oregon"
Evelyn L. Bull. *Journal of Wildlife Management*. Vol. 51 (2): pp. 472-481.

Ecosystem Management for Parks and Wilderness
James K. Agee, and Darryll R. Johnson. 1988. University of Wash. Press. 237 pp. $20.00.

Ecotones. The Role of Landscape Boundaries in the Management and Restoration of Changing Environments
Marjorie M. Holland, Paul B. Risser and Robert J. Naiman, eds. 1991. Chapman & Hall. 142 pp. $35.00.

Contains the proceedings of a 1989 symposium. Discusses the characteristics of ecotones, how they respond to environmental change and ways to appropriately manage them.

Ecotones are the boundary areas between different habitats such as forest/meadow, riparian zones, and seashores. Ecotones are rich in species and play important roles in ecosystems. This book gives an excellent look at a subject that is all too infrequently addressed in land management.

Federal Research Natural Areas in Oregon and Washington: A Guidebook for Scientists and Educators
J. F. Franklin, F. C. Hall, C. T. Dyrness, and C. Maser. 1972. USDA Forest Service, Pacific Northwest For. and Rg. Exp. Stn.

6

Forest Ecology

S. H. Spurr and B. V. Barnes. 1980. John Wiley & Sons.

One of the preferred college texts on the subject.

Forest Ecosystems, Concepts and Management

Richard H. Waring and William H. Schlesinger. 1985. Academic Press: Orlando, FL.

Forest Influences

Joseph Kittredge. 1948. Dover Books: McGraw Hill.

Still one of the best texts on microclimate influences in forests.

Forest Island Dynamics in Man-Dominated Landscapes

1981. Springer-Verlag: New York.

Forest Primeval: The Natural History of An Ancient Forest

Chris Maser. 1989. Sierra Club Books. 282 pp. $25.00.

The history of one forest area in the Cascades, from its birth 1,000 years ago to the present time, is used by the author to frame a detailed chronicle of the life cycles of the myriad plant and animal species who live there. Maser is one of the most fluent and moving writers in the field of restoration forestry and beyond. Maser brings out the awe and mystery of the forest.

Forest Stand Dynamics

Chadwick D. Oliver and Bruce C. Larson. 1990. McGraw-Hill. 624 pp. $29.95 paper.

How can one manage forests without understanding their dynamics? Incorporates many of the latest ecological findings on forest disturbances such as fire, wind and floods, as well as climate change.

Forest Succession and Stand Development Research in the Northwest

J. E. Means, ed. 1982. Oregon State University, Forest Research Lab.: Corvallis.

Forest Succession: Concepts and Application

H. H. Shugart and D. B. Botkin, eds. 1981. Springer-Verlag: New York.

Forests—Fresh Perspectives from Ecosystem Analysis

Richard Waring, ed. 1980. Proceedings of the 40th Annual Biology Colloquium, Oregon State Univ. Press: Corvallis, OR. 197 pp. $16.95.

A large collection of papers on forest ecology, mainly from researchers in the Pacific Northwest.

From the Forest to the Sea: Story of Fallen Trees

Chris Maser, Jerry F. Franklin, Robert F. Tarrant and James M. Trappe. Sept. 1988. USDA Forest Service Gen. Tech. Rep. PNW-GR-224.

This is a state-of-the art book on the ecological processes of large dead trees. What functions does it play while decomposing, in streams, in rivers, estuaries and finally out at sea. Follow giant tree trunks on their fascinating journey to the sea.

This publication presents information for managers making resource management decisions on the impact that large fallen trees in various stages of decay have on many ecological processes in the Pacific Northwest. Much of the information is relevant to forests in other parts of the world. This kind of study would not have been possible in the many parts of the world that no longer have significant stands of old-growth forest left.

Impact of Intensive Harvesting on Forest Nutrient Cycling

Proceedings of a Symposium held at the State Univ. of New York College of Env. Sci. and Forestry, Syracuse, NY, Aug. 1979.

Dozens of papers. Not limited to the Eastern USA. Brought together many of the leading authorities on the subject.

The Internal Element Cycles of an Old-Growth Douglas Fir Ecosystem in Western Oregon

P. Sollins, *et al.* 1980. *Ecological Monographs*. Vol. 50 (3): 261-285.

Landscape Boundaries: Consequences for Biotic Diversity and Ecological Flows

A. J. Hansen and F. di Castri, eds. 1992. Springer-Verlag: New York. Chapter 15, pp. 305-323.

Includes a chapter "Landforms, Disturbance, and Ecotones" by Pacific Northwest authors: Frederick J. Swanson, S. M. Wondzell and G. E. Grant.

Landscape Ecology

R. T. Forman and M. Godron. 1986. John Wiley and Sons: New York. 619 pp.

Text focusing on landscape dynamics, structure, and function including forest and hedgerow landscapes.

Maintaining the Long-Term Productivity of the Pacific Northwest Forest Ecosystems

D. A. Perry, R. Meurisse, B. Thomas, R. Miller, J. Boyle, J. Means, C. R. Perry, and R. F. Powers, eds. 1989. Timber Press: Portland, Oregon. 256 pp.

One of the most current state-of-knowledge reports on the ecology underpinning restoration forestry. The contributors list reads like a Who's Who of PNW forest ecologists.

Old Growth Definition Task Group, Interim Definitions for Old-Growth Douglas-Fir and Mixed-Conifer Forests in the Pacific Northwest and California

Jerry Franklin, et al. July, 1986. USDA Forest Service, Research Note PNW-447.

"Old-growth Forests and History of Insect Outbreaks"
Boyd E. Wickman. 1990. *Environmental Journal*. Vol. 6(2): 401-403.

Old-growth Forests in the Southwest and Rocky Mountain Regions: Proceedings of a Workshop
Merrill R. Kaufmann, W. H. Moir, and Richard L. Bassett, (tech. coords.) 1992. USDA Forest Service, Rocky Mountain For. and Rg. Exp. Stn. Gen. Tech. Rep. RM-213. 201 pp.

Old Growth in the Pacific Northwest, A Status Report
Peter Morrison. November, 1988. Wilderness Society.

A statistical analysis of Forest Service inventories, checked against scientists' definition of old growth. This study shows that less than half remains of the old growth Forest Service managers have counted on.

Pattern and Process in a Forested Ecosystem
F. H. Bormann and F. E. Likens. 1979. Springer-Verlag.

Proceedings—Symposium on Ecology and Management of Riparian Shrub Communities
August 1992, USDA, Forest Service, Intermountain For. and Rg. Exp. Stn. Gen. Tech. Rep. INT-289.

Research Natural Areas in Oregon and Washington: Past and Current Research and Related Literature
S. E. Greene, T. Blinn, and J. F. Franklin. 1986. USDA Forest Service, PNW-GTR-197.

Research Natural Areas often represent our only examples of low elevation old growth forests remaining. It is a shame that they are usually small, isolated fragments of forest ecosystems.

The Role of the Genus Ceanothus in Western Forest Ecosystems
Susan G. Conard, Annabelle E. Jaramillo, Kermit Cromack, Jr., and Sharon Rose. 1985. USDA Forest Service, Pacific Northwest For. and Rg. Exp. Stn. Gen. Tech. Rep. PNW-182. 72 pp.

Ceanothus is an important nitrogen-fixing shrub in Pacific Northwest forests. It includes an extensive bibliography and a listing of forest researchers involved in Ceanothus research.

The Seen and Unseen World of the Fallen Tree
Chris Maser and James M. Trappe, eds. USDA Forest Service, Gen. Tech. Rep. PNW-164. 56 pp.

Snag Habitat Management: Proceedings of the Symposium
J. W. Davis, G. A. Goodwin, and R. A. Ockenfeis (tech. coords.). USDA Forest Service, Rocky Mountain For. and Rg. Exp. Stn. Gen. Tech. Rep. RM-99. 226 pp.

Conference held June 7-9, 1983, Northern Arizona University, Flagstaff.

"Tree Death as an Ecological Process: The Causes, Consequences, and Variability of the Tree Mortality"
Jerry F. Franklin, H. H. Shugart, and Mark E. Harmon. *BioScience*. Vol. 37(8): 550-556.

This paper examines the critical importance of understanding and predicting tree mortality in calculating forest stand yields and allocating efforts in tending and protecting forests.

Wildlife and Vegetation of Unmanaged Douglas Fir Forests
May 1991. USDA Forest Service, Pacific Northwest Res. Stn. Gen. Tech. Rep. PNW-283. 531 pp.

A state-of-knowledge book for Pacific Northwest maritime forests. One of the most in-depth looks at the ecology of natural forests conducted so far in the world. Not exactly what you'd call a layperson's readable style, but serious students of PNW forest ecology will want to spend some time with this book. The book has 40 chapters on such topics as composition, function, and structure of old-growth Douglas fir forests, diurnal forest birds, small mammals, amphibians, old-growth community studies, wildlife and forest management, fire history, inventories, status and definitions. There is an extensive list of references. Contributors include Jack Ward Thomas, Jerry Franklin, Thomas Spies among many others.

Video

"Natural Enemies of Forest Insect Pests"
Torolf Torgersen, producer. Available from: Pacific Northwest For. and Rg. Exp. Stn, Publications Dept., PO Box 3890, Portland, OR 97208-3890. Tel: (503) 326-7135.

This video gives some fascinating insights into the complex web of life in forest ecosystems that regulate forest tree "pests." It explores the role of insectivorous birds and the very important (but previously little-known) role that ants play as predators of insect pests. The conclusion of the video is that many of the forest practices of the past decades have increased the susceptibility of forests to insect pest outbreaks. It also suggests forest management methods to curtail insect pest outbreaks. The video is a good educational tool for children and adults who get more from visual presentations than written ones.

Many of the most important insectivorous birds are cavity nesting birds, so it is very important to have lots of standing snags and down logs for habitat of our natural enemies of forest insect pests. (See Torgersen's article in *Restoration Forestry*.)

6

Biodiversity: A Resource Guide

Greater Ecosystem Alliance

AN ESTIMATED 12.5 MILLION SPECIES inhabit the earth today. These are mainly insects and micro-organisms, animals, simple and complex plants, algae, invertebrates and fishes.

Biodiversity is defined by ecologist Reed Noss as "a full complement of the native plant and animal species in their natural or normal patterns of abundance." Biodiversity is the foundation of evolution in any bioregion.

Habitat is defined as an interdependent community of life that supports the various species that live within it. Habitat is the foundation of biodiversity.

Ecosystem conservation is, according to conservation biologist Mitch Friedman, a strategy for sustaining biodiversity by maintaining and/or restoring sufficient habitat and integrity of ecological processes for entire ecosystems to remain functional with long-term viability.

Ecosystem conservation and preservation of biodiversity is the cutting edge of both the science of ecology and the environmental movement. This approach is vital to forest restoration. Fortunately, there are many organizations and individuals promoting ecosystem conservation.

What we are proposing in a way, is a treaty with the animals. Humans have been steadily pushing wildlife back. Large predators are the first to go. Besides calling a truce, the treaty can include giving back part of the territory humans have taken. This can be done on a personal and neighborhood level by creating local wildlife corridors as well as a societal level by returning high mountain cutover forests to wilderness status. Who knows, maybe someday you'll have a grizzly bear come down your neighborhood wildlife corridor.

Biodiversity Organizations

Some of the leading environmental organizations addressing biodiversity issues include: Earth First! Biodiversity Project, Greater Ecosystem Alliance, Alliance for the Wild Rockies, Superior Wilderness Action Network, WILD Cam-paign (BC, Canada), Greater Yellowstone Coalition, Preserve Appalachian Wilderness and Superior Wilderness Action Network. (See addresses in Environmental Organizations section.)

The Wildlands Project
P.O. Box 5365
Tucson, Arizona 85703
Tel: (602) 884-5106

The mission of The Wildlands Project is to help protect and restore the ecological richness and native biodiversity of North America through the establishment of a connected system of reserves. The most ambitious and well-done proposal for a continent-wide plan to preserve biodiversity. The Wildlands Project was outlined in a special issue of Wild Earth journal (available for $6.00).

Books for the Big Outside
(See address in the Book Sources section.)

This mail-order book store has the biggest selection of books on biodiversity available.

Biodiversity Periodicals

Biodiversity and Conservation
Chapman and Hall
29 West 35th St.
New York, NY 10001-2291

Quarterly journal focusing on all aspects of biological diversity.

Conservation Biology
Society for Conservation Biology
Blackwell Scientific Publications, Inc.
Three Cambridge Center, Suite 208
Cambridge, MA 02142

Quarterly.

Update
Center for Conservation Biology
Dept. of Biological Sciences, Stanford University
Stanford, California 94305

Bi-annual. Free ($15.00 donation accepted).

Wild Earth
P.O. Box 455
Richmond, Vermont 05477

Wild Earth is a quarterly journal serving the biocentric grassroots elements within the conservation movement. It advocates the restoration and protection of all natural elements of biodiversity. *Wild Earth* is filled with cutting-edge political analysis and updates from activists and activities from around the country. Full of provocative writings on the subject of biodiversity. $25/yr.

"For creatures who care about their habitat."

Books and Articles on Biodiversity

A Preliminary Biodiversity Conservation Plan for the Oregon Coast Range
Reed F. Noss. 1992. Coast Range Association, P.O. Box 148, Newport, OR 97365. 40 pp. $6.50.

Biodiversity
E. O. Wilson, ed. 1988. National Academy Press: Washington DC. 521 pp. $19.50.

A synthesis of information on the consequences of destruction of biological diversity. One of the most comprehensive compilations by leaders in the field. A global perspective.

Biodiversity: Culture, Conservation and EcoDevelopment
Margery L. Oldfield and Janis B. Alcorn. Westview Press. £26.95.

Emphasizes the urgent need for collaboration between those who plan the future of biodiversity from afar and the rural people who know what it means to live with biodiversity in the longterm.

Biodiversity in Sub-Saharan Africa and its Islands. Conservation, Management and Sustainable Use
Simon N. Stuart and Richard J. Adams, eds. 1990. IUCN. 242 pp. $25.00 paper.

Biodiversity of Northwestern California: Symposium Proceedings
Contact: Richard Harris, Biodiversity Symposium, 163 Mumford Hall, University of California, Berkeley, CA 94720

Proceedings of a symposium held October 28-30, 1991 in Santa Rosa, California. The Symposium was sponsored by the University of California. It includes a notable article by Tim McKay and Felice Pace, "New Perspectives on Conservation and Preservation in the Klamath-Siskiyou Region."

The Conference objectives were to: Determine the status of scientific knowledge on the major topics of concern in the region. Review current and emerging approaches to management for biodiversity in the region. Develop a broad research agenda to fill gaps in knowledge and initiate a network for communication among researchers, managers, environmental activists and decision-makers.

Cascadia Wild
Greater Ecosystem Alliance. 1993.

GEA's latest book on biodiversity in the Greater North Cascades ecosystem.

Conservation Biology and National Forest Management in the Inland Northwest: A Handbook for Activists
1993. Greater Ecosystem Alliance: P.O. Box 2813, Bellingham, WA 98227. 250 pp. $20 postpaid.

The book brings together a wealth of scientific information on biodiversity in a digested form that is accessible to non-scientists. Topics ranging from landscape ecology and habitat fragmentation to forest health and fisheries with fact sheets, annotated bibliography and lists of issues to consider when reviewing Forest Service plans.

Conservation Biology: The Science of Scarcity and Diversity
Michael E. Soulé and Bruce A. Wilcox. 1980. Sinauer Associates. 584 pp. $38.00.

This book contains 25 chapters by leading experts which cover topics such as Fitness & Viability of Populations, Patterns of Diversity, and Rarity.

Conservation Biology: The Theory and Practice of Nature Conservation, Preservation, and Management
Peggy K. Fiedler and S. K. Jain, eds. 1992. Chapman & Hall. 507 pp. $35.00.

A theoretically sound book which offers specific scientific guidance to the problems encountered in the real world of nature conservation.

Conserving Biological Diversity In Our National Forests
The Wilderness Society. 1986. Washington D.C.

The Diversity of Life
Edward O. Wilson. 1992. Harvard University Press. 424 pp. $29.95.

Highly recommended as the best of all the new books in the Spring 1993 "Books for the Big Outside" catalogue.

Ecosystem Management for Parks and Wilderness
James K. Agee and Darryll R. Johnson. 1988. Univ. of Wash. Press: Seattle. 236 pp.

Mainstream approach to large-scale biodiversity.

*Forever Wild: Conserving the Greater North
    Cascades Ecosystems*
Mitch Friedman, ed., 1988. Greater Ecosystem
Alliance. $12.80.

A comprehensive ecology-based proposal to conserve the greater North Cascades Ecosystem including an 8.2 million-acre "ecosystem wilderness." Natural and human history in the area, present management, conservation needs of wolves, grizzly bears and spotted owls. It also explains in simple language the concepts of island biogeography, population viability, ecosystem management and other conservation biology ideas.

*The Fragmented Forest: Island Biogeography Theory
    and the Preservation of Biotic Diversity*
Larry D. Harris. 1984. University of Chicago Press:
Chicago, Ill. 211 pp.

The author employs the principles of island biogeography to provide a set of guidelines for rural planning. The isolation of small fragments of biodiversity in Parks and Ecological Reserves decline over time due to their isolation. One of the seminal books in developing the need for biological corridors and large areas of natural ecosystems to preserve world biodiversity. Much of the fieldwork and data behind the study concentrate on the Douglas-fir zone of Washington-Oregon.

"It is frequently asserted that clearcutting is analogous to the catastrophic fires that occurred naturally, and therefore contemporary forestry practices essentially mimic the natural situation. This analogy is incorrect for several reasons, but even if it were true it would be tangential to the issue. Early accounts report that fire had destroyed the timber on only about 10 percent of the forest acreage at any one time. This meant that the landscape was predominantly mature or old-growth forest. Currently, the proportions are reversed such that as little as 10 percent remains in mature or old growth forests while 90 percent occurs as second growth. This ratio of old-growth and mature forest to second-growth is the parameter of most concern to wildlife biologists and ecologists."

*Global Biodiversity: Status of the Earth's
    Living Resources*
World Conservation Monitoring Center. 1992.
Chapman-Hall. 585 pp. $59.95 (printed in large
format).

An estimated 12.5 million species inhabit the earth today. These are mainly insects and micro-organisms, animals, simple and complex plants, algae, invertebrates and fishes. This book attempts to look at them all. Contains information on uses, law and status. Probably the most comprehensive overview to date.

*The Greater Yellowstone Ecosystem: Redefining
    America's Wilderness Heritage*
Robert B. Keiter and Mark S. Boyce, Eds. 1991. Yale
Univ. Press. 424 pages

Sections on fire policy and management controversy; conservation biology and wildlife ecology; and wolf recovery. An up-to-date view on management of large "wild" ecosystems.

**"Lessons from Natural Forests: Implications for
    Conserving Biodiversity in Managed Forests"**
A. J. Hansen, T. A. Spies, F. J. Swanson and J. L.
Ohmann. 1991. *Bioscience* 41(6): pp. 382-92.

The authors offer guidance on the management of Coastal Northwest forests that are dedicated to both wood production and conservation of biodiversity.

Landscape Linkages and Biodiversity
Wendy E. Hudson, ed. 1991. Island Press. 214 pp.
$19.95.

Explores the conservation of biodiversity and the use of conservation corridors to link up remaining fragments of healthy ecosystems to allow species to move between them more easily. The authors include leaders in this field such as: Reed F. Noss, Michael E. Soulé, Larry D. Harris and Douglas H. Chadwick.

Natural Diversity in Forest Ecosystems
James. L. Coley and Jane H. Coley, eds. 1984. Institute
    of Ecology, University of Georgia: Athens, GA.

Proceedings of a workshop.

Nitrogen, Corn & Forest Genetics
Roy Silen. USDA Forest Service Pacific Northwest
Res. Stn. Short paper.

Draws analogies between industrial production in agribusiness and the timber industry. Outlines the faults of low genetic variability in corn and also in forest plantations. Draws on research which shows the poor performance of "super tree" plantations as compared to natural regeneration in the Pacific Northwest. One of the earliest influential writings on the hazards of low genetic diversity in PNW tree plantations.

Our Living Legacy Symposium
Research Branch, B.C. Ministry of Forests, 31 Bastion
Square, Victoria, B.C. V8W 3E7. Tel: (604) 387-6710.

Proceedings of a symposium on biological diversity held in British Columbia, Feb. 29-March 2, 1991.

Preserve Appalachian Wilderness (PAW) Proposal
Preserve Appalachian Wilderness (PAW), 81 Middle
Street, Lancaster, New Hampshire 03584.
Tel: (603) 788-2918

The PAW proposal calls for a system of large "evolutionary preserve" areas along the Appalachian Mountain

Range connected by wide migration corridors to enable the movement of individual species and genetic information up and down the length of the mountain range. The preserves would maintain a variety of viable habitat areas and characteristic ecosystems in a protected landscape large enough to support the largest, native carnivorous predators and diverse enough to maintain all representative native species.

Restoring Biodiversity in the Southern Appalachians

Proceedings of a conference held October 27, 1989 at the Owens Conference Center, University of North Carolina, Asheville.

Wilderness Management

John C. Hendee, George H. Stankey, and Robert C. Lucas. 1990. North American Press. 546 pp. $40.00.

A text on managing wilderness areas with contributions from over 100 wilderness experts.

Wildlife and Habitats In Managed Landscapes

Jon E. Rodiek and Eric G. Bolen, eds. 1991. Island Press: Washington DC. 216 pp. $24.95.

An anthology which discusses methods of protecting wildlife habitat by using landscape concepts. This is not an overview book. Rather it has nine chapters on particular species or regions, including: windbreaks, forests in the Appalachians, and southeast Alaska forests.

The Role of Fire in Forest Ecosystems: A Resource Guide

WILDLAND FIRE is a subject most people do not often consider. It is, however, one of the most potent factors in many terrestrial ecosystems. Wildfire is a part of almost all ecosystems, albeit at increasingly longer intervals between fires as annual precipitation increases. Fire suppression and logging practices in much of the PNW has led to a much worse fire situation than occurred naturally or under Native American management.

Foresters should know the ecological roles of fire in the habitats they are working in and how to make management decisions with fire in mind. Fire prevention can involve pruning, thinning, fuelbreaks, firelines, and strip-planting of fire-resistant fuelbreak plant species.

Increasingly, forest managers are beginning to deliberately use controlled burning (prescribed burning) in the forest to emulate nature and maintain a desired mix of tree and understory species. Fire suppression and controlled burning are controversial subjects. Where are they appropriate? To what extent should humans intervene? When is prescribed burning appropriate? When is slash burning appropriate?

Reintroducing controlled burning (following traditional Native American practices) to interior Pacific Northwest forests requires great care and up to decades of preparatory work. Work can include: reducing fuel loads; cutting up slash to get it on the ground where it decays faster; digging firelines; pulling fuel away from around trees; and raking needles from under large trees over a period of years to drive their feeder roots deeper into the ground.

Following are several short articles and references to some of the outstanding books in this field. Their bibliographies can lead you to further sources. (Also see articles and fire bibliography in the Native American section.)

I particularly recommend Steve Radosevich's book, *Natural & Prescribed Fire in PNW Forests,* as state-of-the-art knowledge on the ecological role of wildfire.

Fire in the Forest

In 1988, a drought year, 70,000 fires in America's forests burned five million acres. Fire continues to dramatically shape the structure and function of forest ecosystems in the Pacific West. Forest organisms are adapted to survive or reproduce following fire. Fire is a vital factor in the maintenance and sustenance of forest health and diversity. Fire suppression has had as much impact on some forests as road building and logging. If we, as the public, are to redeem the management of our Pacific forests, we should begin with understanding, accepting and helping to direct and imitate the role of fire. Fire is, as forest ecologist Tom Atzet says, "nature's reset button."

—Reprinted with permission from
The Public Forester, 1990, Issue 1

Fire Regimes

Thomas Atzet

A fire regime can be defined by its frequency, intensity, duration and extent. High frequency is related to low intensity; the reverse is also true. Fire behavior, a function of weather, fuel, and terrain, varies with latitude, elevation and regional topography. The infrequent fires of the cool, moist Olympic coast often burn over 65 percent of the area at high intensities. Conversely, fires in the hot, dry, flats of eastern Oregon burn less than 20 percent of the area at high intensities.

Fire directly or indirectly determines the structure and composition of the forest, rivers, and meadows, including insects, birds, fish and wildlife. Rates of ecosystem processes are a function of the amount of time since burning. Fire, a primary agent of change for millions of years, provides the ecosystem with the stress needed to evolve, maintain biological diversity and remain stable. It is an essential component of ecosystem health.

Without total control of fuels and modification of the landscape, complete control of fire is not operationally possible.

Although some degree of control and risk reduction is possible, risk cannot be totally eliminated. In terms of risk, all landscapes are fire's floodplain. Maximum modification of fuels and their distribution should be concentrated in the forest/urban interface, where risk and hazard are high. In wilderness, where values are ecocentric, every effort should be made to maintain fire's role. That role has helped provide the productive, resilient system we depend upon today.

Tom Atzet is a forest ecologist with the Forest Service with over twenty years of field experience in the Siskiyou, Rogue and Umpqua Forests.

Reprinted with permission from The Public Forester *(1990, Issue 1).*

Tree Plantations Susceptible to Wildfire

...In some cases there simply are no human substitutes for natural stabilizing mechanisms. Resistance to catastrophic fire is a case in point. Catastrophic wildfire may be the most serious threat to sustainability that we face, particularly in areas where the climate is going to become drier. It is clear that humans have increased the susceptibility of moist tropical forests to fire, and the weight of evidence in the Pacific Northwest suggests that conversion of structurally heterogeneous old growth forests to structurally homogeneous plantations increases the severity of wildfires. In the 1987 fires of southwest Oregon, for example, plantations and young stands established by wildfires in the 1930's were much more heavily impacted than old growth forests.

—Excerpt reprinted with permission from "An Overview of Sustainable Forestry," by David Perry.
Journal of Pesticide Reform, Vol. 8 (3). pp. 8-12.

Burning to Get the Cut Out

Salvage logging in burns opens up a pandora's box, when Forest Service incentives are to "get the cut out." There are disturbing reports of loggers setting fires and Forest Service personnel misusing backfires during wildfires to burn timber stands which could then be opened to salvage logging.

Alternatives to Burning Logging Slash

… There are compelling reasons to question the need for fire as presently used and as envisioned for reducing fuel loads in mixed conifer stands of the interior Pacific

Northwest. In addition to the potential losses in sustainable productivity because of nutrient losses, burning aggravates the problem of carbon-loading of the atmosphere, creates air and stream pollution problems, alters soil architecture (structure) and soil microenvironment, and in many cases destroys larger woody debris that serves as a refuge for early-to mid-seral shrub species. Some of these shrubby species are nitrogen fixers that may also play an important role in accumulation of essential plant nutrients such as phosphorus and calcium.

A key question is: How can we manage forest residues and large accumulations of biomass without relying solely on fire? Many (and perhaps most) of the goals accomplished by fire can be achieved with mechanical management of residues and mechanical management of the new tree crop. Practical measures that can be implemented as part of harvest include leaving residues in place and by rearrangement with lop and scatter. Excessive residues can be removed for chipping in many instances or by a combination of mechanical and fire management techniques. Chipping and leaving residues on the site is an alternative that needs to be explored for effects on soil nutrient availability and forest successional dynamics.

From: *Potential Impacts of Prescribed Burning on Sustainable Forest Productivity.* Arthur R. Tiedemann and James O. Klemmedson. 1992. Blue Mountains Natural Resources Institute: La Grande, OR. Vol. 2 (2).

Compost from Fuelbreaks—An Added Layer of Benefits

Jean Pain has done much work on how to create fuelbreaks in highly flammable Mediterranean scrub forests, to reduce big forest fires. Pain uses the forest thinnings and prunings from the firebreaks to create high value compost for agriculture. The compost piles heat water for warming buildings and greenhouses. the compost piles also supply methane for fuel. To generate high heat compost, Pain developed a special shredder/grinder to create high surface area to volume material as compared to conventional chippers. Pain was able to demonstrate that fuelbreaks could pay for themselves through the sale of compost. Pain's work bears careful scrutiny for land managers concerned with creating fuelbreaks and controlling wildfire. California chaparral residents especially take note.

Equipe Jean Pain is the source of Pain shredders and of Pain's book, *Another Kind of Garden* (Ida and Jean Pain, 1982 edition), which describes Pain's ideas and operating models. Equipe Jean Pain, B.P. 16 Treigny, F. 89520 St. Sauveur En Puisaye, FRANCE. Tel: (33) 86.74.72.20

Resources on Fire

International Association of Wildland Fire
P.O. Box 328,
Fairfield, Washington 99012
Tel: (509) 283-2397/Fax: (509) 283-2264

An excellent networking service for people concerned with wildland fire and prescribed burning, and useful to serious forestry networkers. Services include printing and publishing *Wildland Fire: The International Journal of Wildland Fire* ($90); an annual *International Bibliography of Wildland Fire* ($225—the 1993 edition has 34,000 entries); specialized *Fire Bibliographies*; FRI Library; mailing labels; and the *International Directory of Wildland Fire* ($90). (See review in the Directory section.) All of these directories and bibliographies are available on IBM disc. Membership in IAWF is $30. Members receive $30 off on the journal and 10% discount on books and discs.

IAWF also has a mail-order bookstore for texts on just about any fire-related publication. Send for a catalog.

Fire Ecology and Management in the Blue Mountains—a series of 5 seminars
Sept./Oct. 1993. Blue Mountains Natural Resources Institute, 1401 Gekeler Lane, LaGrande, Oregon 97850. Contact: Patty Burel, (503) 962-6546.

The seminars brought together the public and forest agencies to discuss whether fire should be reintroduced in the Blue Mountains, i.e. wide-scale use of prescribed fire. The seminars were broadcast via two-way television systems to seven locations in eastern Oregon. Fire ecology and its use in fire management is a special concern at the BMNRI, so it is a place for up-to-date information.

Books on Fire and Forests

Burning Bush: A Fire History of Australia
Stephen J. Pyne. Henry Holt Press: Australia.

Recent book. Fire from pre-human, aboriginal until the 1983 Ash Wednesday fires.

Ecology of Natural Underburning in the Blue Mountains of Oregon
Frederick C. Hall. 1977. USDA Forest Service, Pacific Northwest Region R6-ECOL-79-001. 11 pp.

Effects of Fire Management of Southwestern Natural Resources
J. S. Krammes, tech. coord. USDA Forest Service, Rocky Mountain For. and Rg. Exp. Stn. Gen. Tech. Rep. RM-191. 293 pp. Proceedings of symposium in Tucson, AZ, November 15-17, 1988.

Effects of Fire on Flora: A State-of-Knowledge Review
March 1981. USDA Forest Service, Gen. Tech. Rep. WO-16. 71 pp.

Reviews the effects of wildfire on ecosystems of the United States. Emphasis is on the western states. The information on any given ecosystem is scanty given the small number of pages. 300 references enable the serious researcher to locate references for specific ecosystems.

Fire and Ecosystems
Academic Press: 465 S. Lincoln Dr., Troy, MO 63379.

Fire and the Environment: Ecological and Cultural Perspectives
Stephen C. Nodvin and Thomas A. Waldrop (eds.). USDA Forest Service, Southeastern For. Exp. Stn. Gen. Tech. Rep. INT-290. Proceedings of an International Symposium, March 20-24, 1990. Knoxville, TN.

Fire Ecology of Forests and Woodlands in Utah
Anne F. Bradley, Nonan V. Noste and William C. Fischer. 1992. USDA Forest Service, Intermountain Res. Stn. Gen. Tech. Rep. INT-287.

Fire Ecology of Montana Forest Habitat Types East of the Continental Divide
William C. Fischer and Bruce D. Clayton. 1983. Intermountain For. and Rg. Exp. Stn. Gen. Tech. Rep. INT-141. 83 pp.

Fire Ecology of Pacific Northwest Forests
James K. Agee. 1993, Island Press. 490 pp. $50.

A thorough examination of the effects and use of fire in Pacific Northwest wildlands. Ecological role of fire, historical and cultural aspects and political considerations. Probably the hottest new book on PNW fire ecology in 1993.

Fire Ecology of the Forest Habitat Types of Eastern Idaho and Western Wyoming

Anne F. Bradley, William C. Fischer and Nonan V. Noste. September 1992. USDA Forest Service Intermountain Res. Stn. Gen. Tech. Rep. INT-290.

Fire History and Pattern in a Cascade Range Landscape

Peter H. Morrison and Frederick J. Swanson. 1990. USDA Forest Service, Pacific Northwest Res. Stn. Gen. Tech. Rep. PNW-GTR-254. 77 pp.

Fire in America: A Cultural History of Wildland and Rural Fire

Stephen J. Pyne. 1982. Princeton University Press.

Region by region fire history of fire control policy.

Fire in North American Tallgrass Prairies

Scott L. Collin and Linda L. Wallace. 1990.

Proceedings of conference held in 1987.

Fire in Pacific Northwest Ecosystems: Exploring Emerging Issue

Oregon State University. 1992.

Proceedings of a conference held January 21-23, 1992 in Portland, Oregon. Includes article: "Relationships Between Fire, Pathogens, and Long-term Productivity in Northwestern Forest" by Alan E. Harvey, G. I. McDonald and M. F. Jurgensen.

Fire in the Tropical Biota: Ecosystem Processes and Global Challenges

J. G. Goldammer, Ed. 1990. Ecological Studies 84. Springer Verlag: Berlin.

Described in the book's preface as the "first pan-tropical and multidisciplinary monograph on fire ecology." The book is written in a readable, narrative style, is well illustrated, and each chapter is accompanied by an extensive list of literature citations.

"Forest Fire History in the Northern Rockies"

Stephen F. Arno. 1980. *Journal of Forestry*. Vol. 78 (8): pp. 460-465.

Fire scarred trees were used to interpret forest fire history. This article provides fire history, pattern, and intensity for many different forest types. Useful information for restoring natural fire-based ecosystems.

Guidelines for Prescribed Burning Sagebrush-Grass Rangelands in the Northern Great Basin

Stephen C. Bunting, Bruce M. Kilgore, and Charles L. Bushey. 1987. USDA Forest Service, Intermountain Res. Stn. Gen. Tech. Rep. INT-231. 33 pp.

Natural & Prescribed Fire in Pacific Northwest Forests

Steve Radosevich, John D. Walstad, and David Sandberg. 1990. Oregon St. Univ.: Corvallis. 316 pp. $25.00.

I recommend this book as the place to start in understanding the role of fire in restoration forestry. Focuses on prescribed burning for silvicultural purposes primarily in Oregon and Washington.

"Past and Present Fire Influences on Southwestern Ponderosa Pine Old Growth"

Michael G. Harrington and Stephen S. Sackett. 1992. In: *The Southwest and Rocky Mountain Regions: Proceedings of a Workshop*, March 9-13, 1992. Portal, AZ USDA Forest Service Rocky Mountain For. and Rg. Exp. Stn. Gen. Tech. Rep. RM-213. pp. 44-50.

Prescribed Burning in California Wildlands Vegetation Management

Harold H. Biswell. 1989. Univ. of Colorado Press. 255 pp.

History—Indians—wildfire. Present use, planning, and techniques.

"The Role of Fire in Forest Ecosystems"

Inner Voice. Vol. 4 (2). March/April, 1992.

A special issue of the association of Forest Service Employees for Environmental Ethics (AFSEEE) newsletter with many good articles on the role of fire in restoration forestry.

Wilderness and Wildfire

Tom Walsh, ed. June 1989. Wilderness Institute, Montana Forest and Range Experiment Station, Misc. Pub. No. 50, School of Forestry, Univ. of Montana. 23 pp.

Published in the wake of the great fires of 1988, this collection of articles takes a progressive view of wildfire, its natural role in forest ecosystems, and how humans cope with wildfire. Includes articles on the "let burn" policies, economics, liability of fire managers, fire ecology, and climate change and wildfire.

Notes on Fire Hazard Reduction and Forest Stand Improvement

thoughts by Jan Iris, transcribed by Peggy Iris

The first in a series of informational handouts from the Institute for Sustainable Forestry.

Background

MOST HOMESTEAD LAND in the Southern Humboldt/Northern Mendocino area has been logged to varying degrees. This, combined with suppression of frequent low-intensity natural fires, has left much of the land in a state which is overcrowded with vegetation, creating a fire hazard and a forest that's hard to walk in.

If you're interested in reducing this fire hazard and improving the general health and aesthetic quality of your forest, particularly around your house and roads, the first step is to thin.

A Common Mistake

Enthusiasm too often inspires folks to take out too many trees too quickly, leaving holes in the canopy. This lets in too much sun which: l) encourages sun-loving brush species such as poison oak and whitethorn, 2) encourages resprouting of tanoak and other highly invasive natives, bringing the forest back to a high risk fire hazard very quickly, and 3) can hurt the remaining trees and change the microclimate, affecting all living things therein.

The Goal

Instead of opening up the canopy too fast, the goal is to raise the canopy, and clear the area below of much of the brush, logging slash and some small trees, so that flames can not climb up into the canopy. Over a long period of time, this modifies the light coming in to produce a dappled effect, restoring the old growth qualities of its pre-logged condition.

The How-To's

The first step involves encouraging your larger, healthier trees. Identify the least healthy trees, those that are twisted, leaning and damaged by disease or previous logging. Cut some of those out, slowly. If in doubt, don't cut! As you progress, slowly opening up your forest, some trees that you pick to save might have some damage that wasn't visible on first inspection and they might die back, becoming easier to identify. Leaving some twisted and leaning trees may be desirable for aesthetic composition.

The next step is to "limb up" (remove some of the branches of) your remaining trees with a chainsaw and/or a pole saw to reach the higher branches. Limb slowly in a series of entries. Limb carefully. Look for the round collar on the trunk at the base of the limb. Make your cut parallel and as close to the collar as possible.

NOTE: Never limb up more than 1/3 of the total height of the tree, (for example, for a nine foot tree, limb up about three feet from the ground).

The trees that are removed are then cut into firewood or sometimes are large enough to be milled for lumber. Branches and slash are piled and burned. Burn in clearings and keep fires small to avoid scorching overhead branches. Be fire safe, if in doubt consult your local fire department or California Department of Forestry and Fire Protection.

Example Scenario

Thirty trees exist in a small crowded stand. On the first entry you cut ten trees. Upon second entry, three to five years later, you cut five more trees. You make the third entry three to five years later and cut five more trees. You are now left with ten specimen trees. Now you can limb up higher. A thirty foot tree can be limbed up to ten feet. The ten remaining trees will now grow faster with more available sunlight, moisture and nutrients from the soil. Following this model, after thirty to forty years you could have five, ninety foot trees with limbed up branches thirty feet above the ground creating a beautiful, healthy forest to walk and live in. Because of the shade, most of the unpleasant brush will be absent. Huckleberries grow under these conditions and they are fire resistant, easy to deal with, and delicious!

Forest Soils & Mycorrhizae: A Resource Guide

A KNOWLEDGE OF SOILS AND SOIL ECOLOGY is critical to restoration forestry in all parts of the world. So much depends on soil processes, but so little is known about the ecology of life in the soil. For instance, mycologists and forest researchers are finding that most trees die or perform poorly without their symbiotic partner fungi. Mycorrhizal fungi inoculation can mean the difference between success and failure in reforestation efforts.

Denizens of the Soil: Small, but Critical

...A *mycorrhizae* is a symbiosis between a fungus and a plant root. The fungus makes an attachment to the plant root and grows out into the soil. As it grows out into the soil, the plant pumps fuel into the mycorrhiza (sugars fixed in photosynthesis), the mycorrhiza dissolves its surroundings, and what it doesn't want it sends to the plant root.

...There are literally hundreds of thousands of individual arthropods per square meter of soil. These are all things you can see walking around in your hand; they've got eyes, they've got legs, they get hungry, they get tired, they lust after mates, they do little mating dances, they have behavior. These are not bacteria, they are not amoebae, these are rather highly complicated organisms.

...There are a few morals I'd like you to get. First, soils are alive. They are biogenic. All the upper layers are in fact nothing but living critters or the feces of living critters. Second, soil arthropods are the regulators in most soil processes. They are the system catalysts that drive the microbial processes of chemical excitement. All of those processes would stop if we didn't have the critters here feeding upon them. Third, soils are by far the most biologically diverse part of any terrestrial ecosystem.

Excerpts from a fascinating article by Andy Moldenke, Research Entomologist, Oregon State University, Corvallis, Oregon. Article appeared in Natural Resource News, *published by Blue Mountains Natural Resources Institute, August 1993 issue, pp. 3-5. Reprinted with permission.*

"120,000 Little Legs"

Andy Moldenke. *Wings*, Journal of the Xerxes Society. Summer, 1990, Pages 11-14. Xerexes Society, 10 SW Ash St., 3rd Fl., Portland, OR 97204. Tel: (503) 222-2788

Moldenke says he hasn't published much of his fascinating soil lore, but recommends this article for those who hunger for more soil ecology.

"Creatures of the Forest Soil"—Video

Andy Moldenke, *et al.* Communications Media Center, Oregon State University, Corvallis, Oregon 97331

A 20-minute video with close-up filming of many soil creatures. A worm's-eye view of a little-seen, fascinating world. The commentary gives an introduction to soil ecology and its importance to forest functioning.

Mycorrhizal Organizations

Mycorr Tech

University of Pittsburgh Applied Research Center 440 William Pitt Way, Pittsburgh, Pennsylvania 15238 Tel: (412) 826-5488

A commercial source for ectomycorrhizal inoculum for trees.

North American Mycological Association

3556 Oakwood Ann Arbor, Michigan 48104

Dues are $15 a year (newsletter, annual journal) and should be sent to NAMA, Ann Bornstein (membership secretary), 336 Lenox Ave., Oakland, CA. 94610

List of Pacific Northwest Mushroom Clubs

This list of addresses of 26 mushroom clubs is an Appendix from the publication: *Biology, Ecology, and Social Aspects of Wild Edible Mushrooms in the Forests of* the *Pacific Northwest* (see review this section). The list was compiled from the North American Mycological Association's 1990 membership list.

Multipurpose Trees and Shrubs: Sources of Seeds and Inoculants

Peter G. Von Carlowitz. 1991. 334 pp. International Center for Research in Agroforestry (see Agroforestry section).

Chapter 5 provides addresses of suppliers of inoculants and pure cultures and explains the principles of inoculation.

Periodical

Mushroom: The Journal of Wild Mushrooming

Box 3156, University Station
Moscow, I D 83843.
$16 a year for 4 issues. Back issues are $4 postpaid.

Since 1983, one of the most interesting mushroom journals in the English language.

Books and Articles on Soil

The Belowground Symposium: A Synthesis of Plant-Associated Processes

S. A. Marshall, ed. 1978. Col. State Univ. Sci. Series 26: Ft. Collins, CO.

Biology, Ecology, and Social Aspects of Wild Edible Mushrooms in the Forests of the Pacific Northwest: A Preface to Managing Commercial Harvest

Randy Molina, Thomas O'Dell, Daniel Luoma, Michael Amaranthus, Michael Castellano, and Kenelm Russell. 1993. USDA Forest Service, Pacific Northwest Research Station, General Tech. Report PNW-GTR-309. 42 pp. Available on request from the Pacific Northwest Research Station (See US Forest Service section for address).

The commercial harvest of edible forest fungi has mushroomed into a multimillion dollar industry with several thousand tons harvested annually. Anyone seriously interested in mycorrhizal ecology and/or edible mushrooms will want a copy of this report. A page is devoted to the 11 major mushrooms harvested currently. Useful for its color photos, information and technical literature references for each species. The appendices include a list of Field Guides to Mushroom Identification and PNW Mushroom Clubs.

Degradation of Forested Land: Forest Soils at Risk

Lousier, J. and G. Still, eds. *Proceedings of 10th B.C. Soil Science Workshop, February 1986*. British Columbia Ministry of Forests, Victoria. Land Management Report 56.

The Ecology of the Nitrogen Cycle

Janet I. Sprent. 1987. Cambridge Studies in Ecology. 149 pp. $16.95.

Detailed, scientific, and useful.

Forest Soils of the Douglas-Fir Region

Paul E. Heilman, Harry W. Anderson, and David M. Baumgartner, eds. 1979. Wash. State University Cooperative Extension Service, Pullman, WA 99164. 298 pp.

The Importance of Mycorrhiza to Forest Trees

by Nicholas Malajczuk, Norman Jones and Constance Neely. The World Bank Asia Technical Department Agriculture Division. Land Resources Series—No. 2., 28 pp.

This booklet gives an overview of soil-plant relationships, mycorrhizal fungi as a key species and its diversity and forest productivity. Also covered are: mycorrhizal dynamics, diversity, disturbance, and site rehabilitation. Good contact persons working with mycorrhiza are listed, 13 contacts world wide, and an extensive reference list.

"Interactions Among Mycorrhizal Fungi, Rhizosphere Organisms, and Plants"

Elain R. Ingham and Randy Molina. 1991. In: *Microbial Mediation of Plant-Herbivore Interactions*. Pedro Barbosa, Vera A. Krischik and Clive G. Jones, eds. John Wiley and Sons, Inc.: New York. Chapter 6: pp. 169-197.

"This chapter summarizes data on the influence of mycorrhizal colonization on plant processes, such as root exudation, carbon allocation, and nutrient uptake. In the remainder of the chapter we discuss the effects of mycorrhizal colonization on: 1) the below-ground food web (including bacteria, saprophytic fungi, protozoa, nematodes, and microarthropods); 2) pathogen attack of plants; 3) litter decomposition rates; 4) above-ground grazing by herbivores; (5) plant growth hormones; (6) soil aggregation; and (7) plant competition, community structure, and succession." From the Introduction.

"Long-Term Forest Productivity and the Living Soil"

Michael P. Amaranthus, James. M. Trappe and R. J. Molina. in *Maintaining the Long-Term Productivity of Pacific Northwest Forest Ecosystems*. 1989. Timber Press, Portland, Oregon.

"Mycorrhizae, Mycorrhizospheres and Reforestation: Current Knowledge and Research Needs"

David A. Perry, Randy Molina, and Michael P. Amaranthus. *Canadian Journal of Forest Research*. Vol. 17 (8): pp. 929-40.

Readers of Restoration Forestry are already familiar with David Perry and Michael Amaranthus. Randy Molina, a research botanist at the USDA Forest Service,

Corvallis, Oregon, is another of Oregon's underground ecology experts.

Mycorrhizal Symbiosis
J. L. Harley and S. E. Smith. 1983. Academic Press: New York.

Management and Productivity of Western-Montane Forest Soils
Alan E. Harvey and Leon F. Neuenschwander, compilers. 1991. Gen. Tech. Rep. INT-280; USDA FS Intermtn. Res. Stn. 254 pp.

Proceedings of a seminar held April 10-12, 1990 in Ogden, Utah. Includes 35 papers presenting state-of-the-art knowledge on the nature and problems of integrating soils information and expertise into management of inland western forest resources.

Properties and Management of Forest Soils
William L. Pritchett and Richard F. Fishe, 1987. 2nd ed. John Wiley & Sons: New York.

The Rhizosphere
J. M. Lynch, ed. 1990. Wiley and Sons.

Soil Microbial Ecology: Applications in Agricultural and Environmental Management
F. Blaine Metting, Jr., ed. New York: Marcel Dekker, Inc.

Soil-Plant Relationships; An Ecological Approach
David W. Jeffrey. 1987. Timber Press: Portland, OR. 295 pp.

Recommended.

Symbiotic Nitrogen Fixation in the Management of Temperate Forests
J. C. Gordon, C. T. Wheller, and D. A. Perry, eds. Proceedings of a workshop held April 2-5, 1979, Oregon State Univ., Corvallis, OR.

Forestry, Fish, Wildlife and Livestock: A Resource Guide

IN ANY FORESTED LANDSCAPE, wetlands and riparian zones are vital links between the forest and aquatic systems. Water is the blood of the system, carrying nutrients, sediment, and organic debris from the forest into the aquatic system. While water drives the system, forest vegetation, in what eco-forester Herb Hammond calls the "Riparian Zones of Influence," regulates and controls the dynamics of water's influence. For example forest vegetation slows the rate of water delivery into the system and minimizes peak flows and flooding.

Riparian vegetation provides numerous important functions for the aquatic ecosystem including: shading to regulate water temperature; delivering nutrients and organic debris and litter; and filtering pollutants. The large woody debris from streamside forests provides crucial fish and insect cover, regulates stream flow and erosion, and creates pools and gravel bars for fish reproduction.

Riparian zones are equally important to the terrestrial ecosystem. They provide corridors for wildlife and plant migration.

Any forestry practices which remove riparian forests result in a chain reaction of negative impacts throughout the system. Ultimately, these impacts, such as flooding and loss of salmon, cost us much more than the value of timber removed from such areas.

The Economic Benefits of Managing Rivers on an Ecosystem Basis

Restoration and management of rivers and watersheds on an ecosystem basis will insure the sustainability of healthy native fish populations and watershed health. Regional economic benefits resulting from ecosystem management of rivers and streams, include: 1) sustainable harvest of native fish populations; 2) development of sustainable riparian silviculture; 3) reduced litigation and downstream mitigation and clean-up; 4) development of specialty tree crops for pulp and fiber; 5) export of watershed restoration and management expertise; 6) improvement of human health through recreation, and 7) a sustained ecological tourism industry.

Reprinted with permission from Streamside Runoff, *Winter/Spring 1993, Center for Streamside Studies, University of Washington, Seattle.*

Clear-cuts increase runoff in the short-term.
Clear-cuts result in increased run-off for a number of reasons:

- Lost interception and re-evaporation from standing forest.
- Loss of immense transpiration from forest.
- More soil compaction increases runoff.
- Increased snow accumulation and melt during rain-on-snow events.
- Snow melts quicker in the spring due to lack of shade.

Books on Forests and Water

Adopting a Stream: A Northwest Handbook
Steve Yates. 1988. Adopt-A-Stream Foundation: Seattle. 114 pp. $9.95.

Adopting a Wetland: A Northwest Guide
Steve Yates. 1989. 144 pp. $5.95.

Better Trout Habitat: A Guide to Stream Restoration and Management
Christopher J. Hunter. 1990. Island Press. 320 pp.

A detailed, readable book describes the science of trout stream restoration. It includes 14 detailed case studies of successful stream restorations.

Bibliography of Forest Service range, wildlife and fish habitat, and related research publications: 1977-89
Gale L. Wolters, comp. and ed. 1990. Bibl. and Lit. of Agric. No. 95. Washington, DC: U.S. Department of Agriculture, Forest Service. 288 pp.

Cumulative Effects of Forest Management on California Watersheds: An Assessment of Status and Need for Information
Richard B. Standiford and Shirley I. Ramache, eds. 1981. Agricultural Sciences Publications, Univ. of California, Special Publication 3268. 109 pp. $4.00.

Proceedings of The Edgebrook Conference. Includes chapters on economics and legalities. Useful references.

"An Ecosystem Approach to the Conservation and Management of Freshwater Habitat for Anadromous Salmonids in the Pacific Northwest"
Gordon H. Reeves and James R. Sedell. 1992. *Transactions of the 57th North American Wildlife and Natural Resources Conference.* pp. 408-415.

"An Ecosystem Perspective of Riparian Zones"
S. V. Gregory, F. J. Swanson, W. A. McKee, and K. W. Cummins. 1991. *BioScience* 41 (8): pp. 540-551.

A reprint of the article is available from the lead author at: Department of Fisheries and Wildlife, Oregon State University, Corvallis, OR 97331.

"Effects of Logging on Winter Habitat of Juvenile Salmonids in Alaskan Streams"
J. Heifetz, M. L. Murphy, and K. V. Koski. 1986. *North American Journal of Fisheries Management.* Vol. 6: pp. 52-58.

The Forest Ecosystem of Southeast Alaska— Part 8: Water
Donald C. Schmiege, Austin E. Helmers, and Daniel M. Bishop. 1974. USDA Forest Service Gen. Tech. Rep. PNW-28. 26 pp.

Data on water regime, temperature, sedimentation, and chemistry as basis for protection of high quality water.

Forests and Water: Effects of Forest Management of Floods, Sedimentation, and Water Supply
H. W. Anderson, M. D. Hoover and K. G. Reinhart, 1976. USDA Forest Service, Pacific Southwest For. and Rg. Exp. Stn. Gen. Tech. Rep. PSW-18. 115 pp.

A summary of what is known about the forest's influence on water resources, particularly the effects of current forestry practices.

Freshwater Marshes: Ecology and Wildlife Management
Milton W. Weller. 1987, 2nd edition. University of Minnesota Press.

The Hydrological Role of Forests
A. A. Molchanov. 1963. Israel Program for Scientific Translating.

A Soviet view of forests and water.

Improving Southwestern Riparian Areas Through Watershed Management
Leonard F. DeBano and Larry J. Schmidt. 1989.

USDA Forest Service, Rocky Mountain For. and Rg. Exp. Stn. Gen. Tech. Rep. RM-182. 33 pp.

Intended to serve as a state-of-the-art report on riparian hydrology and improvement in both naturally occurring and man-made riparian areas in the SW. Many references.

Influences of Forest and Rangeland Management on Salmonid Fishes and Their Habitats
William R. Mechan, ed. 1992. American Fisheries Society. 751 pp.

Influence of Habitat Complexity and Food Availability on the Fish Community in an Oregon Coastal Stream
Steve Fieth and Stan Gregory. In: COPE Report, July 1993, Vol. 6 (2). Coastal Oregon Productivity Enhancement Program, Oregon State University, Corvallis, OR.

Part of the larger, fundamental COPE study "Fish Habitat and Riparian Zone Interactions."

International Symposium: Integrated Management of Watersheds for Multiple Use
Carlos E. Gonzalez-Vicente, John W. Russell, Avelino B. Villa-Salas, and R. H. Hamre. 1990. USDA Forest Service, Rocky Mountain For. and Rg. Exp. Stn. Gen. Tech. Rep. RM-198. 190 pp.

Proceedings of a conference held in March 1990, in Morelia, Mexico. Several dozen papers, about half in Spanish and half in English. Includes a number of case studies.

Methods For Evaluating Stream, Riparian, and Biotic Conditions
William S. Platts, Walter F. Megahan, and G. Wayne Minshall. 1983. USDA Forest Service, Intermountain For. and Rg. Exp. Stn. Gen. Tech. Rep. INT-138. 70 pp.

"Northwest Salmon at the Crossroads"
High Country News. April 22, 1991, Vol. 23 (7). (Address in Environmental Periodicals section.)

A special issue on salmon and land management. The Columbia Basin's eight mainstem dams on the Columbia account for nearly all (95.3 to 98 percent) of the Northwest's annual salmon slaughter. These dams could be modified.

Off-site Effects of Roads and Clearcut Units on Slope Stability and Stream Channels
Richard L. Farrington and Mary E. Savin. Jan. 1977. Fox Planning Unit, Six Rivers National Forest. 54 pp.

Riparian Forests in California, Their Ecology and Conservation
Anne Sands, ed. 1980. Agricultural Sciences Publications, Univ. of Calif. Publication No. 4101. 121 pp. $4.00.

Salmonid-Habitat Relationships in the Western
United States: A Review and Indexed Bibliography
Michael D. Marcus, Michael K. Young, Lynn E. Noel,
and Beth A. Mullan. 1990. USDA Forest Service,
Rocky Mountain For. and Rg. Exp. Stn. Gen. Tech.
Rep. RM-188. 84 pp.

Habitat requirements, human impacts and management. Most of the report is taken up with the hundreds of bibliographic entries with keywords.

Techniques for Increasing the Natural Production
of Anadromous Salmonoids:
A State of the Art Review
Gordon H. Reeves and Terry D. Roelofs. 70 pp.

Good bibliography.

Watershed Management: Balancing Sustainability
and Environmental Change
R. J. Naiman, ed. 1992. Springer-Verlag: New York.
542 pp.

Forestry and Wildlife

Research on cavity nesting birds, such as the pileated woodpecker has shown that standing dead trees are an integral component of the ecosystem. They provide nest and roost sites for cavity nesters, as well as harbor insects that woodpeckers prey upon. When they fall, dead trees contribute to nutrient recycling, provide habitat for carpenter ants, and function as cover for small mammals that are preyed upon by owls.

The important role of ants as a decomposer in the forest ecosystem has been understood to some extent. A new insight from recent research is the important role of ants in forest health. Ants are a major predator of forest insects, notably tree herbivores such as tussock moth caterpillars and spruce budworm. If management practices decrease ant habitat, increased susceptibility to insect pests ensues. Thus, a good forester manages with ant habitat in mind. Another example of the intricate web of life found in healthy forest ecosystems.

Books and Articles on Wildlife

Biogeography and Ecology of Forest Bird Communities
1990. SPB Academic Pub.: The Hague, The
Netherlands.

Ecology of the Great Gray Owl
Evelyn L. Bull and Mark G. Henjum. 1990. USDA
Forest Service Gen. Tech. Rep. PNW-GTR-265. 39 pp.

Study of the great gray owl led the authors to specify management practices for enhancing habitat for great gray owls, including: providing artificial nest platforms, protecting existing nest platforms and large-diameter dead trees, providing dense tree cover around

or adjacent to the nest, and providing perches for recently fledged young.

Evelyn L. Bull, is a Research Wildlife Biologist at the USFS, Forestry and Range Sciences Laboratory, 1401 Gekeler Lane, La Grande, OR 97850. Tel: (503) 963-7122.

Fish and Wildlife Data Sources
Elizabeth Rodrick and Ruth Milner, Tech. Eds. April
1991. Pacific Northwest Forest & Range Exp. Stn.
Portland, OR.

Describes how to order data.

Forest and Range Land Birds of the United States:
Natural History and Habitat Use
Richard M. DeGraff, Virgil E. Scott, R. H. Hamre, Liz
Ernst, and Stanley H. Anderson. 1991. Agric.
Handbook 688, USDA Forest Service. 625 pp.

This book provides managers with information on the assemblage of bird species that might be expected in forest and rangeland habitats. Natural histories are provided for each bird species, including taxonomic information, range and status, key habitat requirements, nest site descriptions, and food habits.

Management of Wildlife and Fish Habitats in Forests
of Western Oregon and Western Washington
E. Reade Brown, tech. ed. 1985. USDA Forest Service,
PNW Region R6-FOWL-192-1985. Part 1, 332 pp.,
Part 2 , 302 pp.

Over 60 authors. I don't think much of their recommendation of a 95-year forest rotation; but there is a good deal of useful information on 460 wildlife species and 178 aquatic organisms. Very good species index for habitat requirements.

"Master Carpenter–Species Profile: Pileated Woodpecker (*Dryocopus pileatus*)"
Evelyn Bull and Michael Snider. *Wildbird*, February,
1993.

The life history of the pileated woodpecker and the importance of this primary cavity-nester in providing cavities for secondary cavity-nesters are presented in this popular article. The differences between nest trees and roost trees and the need for both are discussed, as well as foraging strategies, diet, behavior, and management.

Methods Of Killing Trees For Use By Cavity Nesters
Evelyn Bull and Arthur D. Partridge. 1986. Wildlife
Society Bulletin. Vol. 14: 142-146.

Population Ecology, Habitat Requirements and
Conservation of Neotropical Migratory Birds
Deborah M. Finch. 1991. USDA Forest Service,
Rocky Mtn. For. and Rg. Exp. Stn. Gen. Tech. Rep.
RM-205. 26 pp.

Recent analysis of data on forest dwelling species,

many of which are neotropical migrants, show population declines in many North American areas. The literature review summarizes current information. Opportunities for research, monitoring and conservation of these migrants on Forest Service lands are discussed.

30 Birds That Will Build in Bird Houses
R. B. Layton. 1977. Nature Books Pub. 220 pp.

Describes birds, habitats, and plans for birdhouses sizes for owls, woodpeckers, and others. Valuable information for the restoration of urban forests and neighboring forests.

Training Guide for Bird Identification in Pacific Northwest Douglas-Fir Forests
Andrew B. Carey, Valen E. Castellano, Christopher Chappell, Robert Kuntz, Richard W. Lundquist, Bruce G. Marcot, S. Kim Nelson, and Paul Sullivan. 1990. Pacific Northwest Res. Stn. Gen. Tech. Rep. PNW-GTR-260; 28 pp.

Wildlife and Habitats in Managed Landscapes
Jon E. Rodiek and Eric G. Bolen. 1991. Island Press.

Wildlife & Woodlands
Gary Schneider. 1991. Environmental Coalition of Prince Edward Island (address in Canadian Environmental Organizations section). 32 pp.

This booklet is an introduction to forestry practices that benefit wildlife. Especially oriented to Canada's eastern seaboard forests, but useful in other northern forests as well. Schneider gives short overviews on why we need diversity, wildlife trees, healthy soil, trees along streamsides, etc. Especially valuable are each section's list of "what you can do" which give practical ideas on how the individual and landowner can help.

Several excerpts are printed in *Restoration Forestry* in the Eastern Forests section.

Wildlife, Forests and Forestry: Principles of Managing Forests for Biological Diversity
Malcolm L. Hunter, Jr. 1990. Prentice-Hall.

Reed Noss considers this the best single treatment of modern ecological notions about forestry and wildlife management. A strong recommendation from one of biodiversity's most respected spokespersons.

Wildlife Habitat Relationships in Forested Ecosystems
David R. Patton. 1992, Timber Press: Portland, Oregon. 392 pp. $45.

The author's problem-solving techniques for analyzing habitat relationships will be of assistance to forest managers and policy planners.

Wildlife Habitats in Managed Forests: The Blue Mountains of Oregon and Washington
Jack Ward Thomas, et al. 1979. USDA Forest Service.

Forests and Livestock

Since a large proportion of the world's forests are grazed by livestock, restoration forestry must address the impact of livestock on forest ecosystems. Currently, most livestock grazing practices around the world result in ecosystem degradation. For example, poor livestock management can: eliminate preferred forage species; delay or prevent tree regeneration through browsing and trampling; cause soil erosion and compaction of soils; eat desired seeds; and spread non-native seeds. For instance, in Northern California both feral pigs and introduced turkeys gobble up acorns and eat and root-up seedlings. As a result, the forest composition is changing as oaks and other native species are having a hard time growing young replacement trees. Overgrazing by the livestock of European settlers wiped out much of the semi-wild "gardens" which helped feed Native American tribes.

Reducing stocking rates in many forest areas will help ecosystem restoration. In some forests, domestic livestock should be removed altogether for a decade, or even more, to promote recovery. After a healthy, functioning forest ecosystem has been restored, livestock could, in some cases, be re-introduced on carefully monitored rotations where culturally appropriate.

Livestock can also be used for beneficial forest management. For example, livestock grazing can reduce fire danger by reducing vegetation. Sheep have been used for vegetation control to reduce competition for young trees. Livestock distribute nutrients in their waste and can also be used for seeding (by feeding them seeds which benefit from passing through a ruminants stomach and are expelled in a packet of fertilizer and mulch).

Organizations for Grazing Reform

Public Lands Action Network
P.O. Box 5631
Santa Fe, NM 87502
Tel: (505) 984-2718

Rest the West
P.O. Box 68345
Portland, Oregon 97268
Tel: (503) 645-6293

Periodical on Rangeland Management

Journal of Range Management
Society for Range Management
1839 York Street
Denver, Colorado 80204

USA's most prestigious journal on range management. Articles range from traditional, anti-ecological, pro-livestock range management to more progressive, wildlife-centered research on rangeland ecology.

Books on Rangeland Management

Can Livestock Be Used as a Tool to Enhance Wildlife Habitat?

Keith E. Severson, tech. coord. 1990. Rocky Mountain For. and Rg. Exp. Stn. Gen. Tech. Rep. RM-194. 123 pp. Proceedings of the 43rd Annual Meeting of the Society for Range Management, Reno, NV, Feb. 1990.

Forest Grazing Management in California

University of Calif. Coop Extension Leaflet 21388. 1984. Extension Forester, 145 Mulford, U.C. Berkeley, 94720.

Kill the Cowboy: A Battle of Mythology in the New West

Sharman Apt Russell. Addison-Wesley: Reading, MA. 217 pp. $12.95.

Russell presents the "cowboy" as a foe of environmental conservation on the public lands of America. The book includes profiles of people, such as Denzel Ferguson, Allan Savory, Don Oman, Steve Johnson, and others, exposing the environmental impact of grazing and finding solutions to the problem.

Public Trust Betrayed: Employee Critique of Bureau of Land Management Rangeland Management

Public Employees for Environmental Responsibility. 1993. 24 pp.

That the BLM grossly mismanages its rangelands may not be news, but the difference with this scathing criticism of grazing on BLM lands is that its authors are current BLM employees fed up with their agency's conduct. The anonymous group outlines the basics of rangeland mismanagement: the extreme political pressure to cater to livestock interests; the agency's various attempts to deceive the public about the condition of grazing allotments; the reality of destructive range "improvements;" and the damaging impacts of livestock on wildlife and ecosystems. The group concludes with a set of recommendations to facilitate rangeland improvement on BLM lands.

(Review by Erika Zavaleta. Contact AFSEEE for the report).

Inner Voice: Special issue on Grazing Management

July/August, 1993, Vol. 5 (4), and Summer 1991, Vol. 3 (3). American Forest Service Employees for Environmental Ethics (AFSEEE).

These two issues of *Inner Voice* are dedicated to the problem of livestock grazing on public lands in the U.S. and includes articles on grazing reform and specific impacts of grazing on natural resources.

Sacred Cows At the Public Trough

Denzel and Nancy Ferguson. 1983. Maverick Publications, Drawer 5007, Bend, OR 97708. 250 pp.

One of the best critiques of Western public land ranching by the managers of the Malheur Field Station, one of Oregon's largest wildlife reserves.

Southwest Riparian Habitat—Then and Now

Robert D. Ohmart, in Inner Voice, July/August, Vol. 5 (4), 1993.

"Domestic livestock grazing is the most insidious threat to riparian habitats in the 11 Western states. ...Fisheries biologists have unquestionably led the conservation effort in riparian habitats since aquatic organisms reflect dramatic declines as botanical, stream bottom, and bank channel conditions deteriorate. Many species of native trout have been pushed to the brink of extinction and through the attempted recovery of these species our understanding of the effects of cattle grazing in riparian habitats has been clarified."

Symposium on Ecology, Management, and Restoration of Intermountain Annual Rangelands, May 18-21, 1992

Contact: Nancy Ness, BSU, Div. Continuing Education, University Library L-247, 1910 University Dr., Boise, ID 83725. Tel: (208) 385-1689 in Idaho; outside Idaho (800) 824-7017 (ext. 1689).

Waste of the West: Public Lands Ranching

Lynn Jacobs. 1991. Free Our Public Lands!, PO Box 5784, Tucson, Arizona 85703. Tel: (602) 578-3173. 602 pp. $28.00.

This is a controversial book in grazing circles. It is probably the most complete, up-to-date look at the environmental effects of livestock grazing in the arid and semi-arid West. It is a political (and scientific) expose' of destructive practices, and a guide to improved management.

If you are interested in sustainable management of grass and shrub ecosystems, this book is a must. Easy reading, heavily illustrated, many ideas for activism, many statistics, a 500-item bibliography and a thorough index.

Restoration Ecology and Ecosystem Restoration: A Resource Guide

"Restoration is the deliberate attempt to compensate in an ecologically precise and effective way, for human influence on a natural system."

—*William R. Jordan III, a founder of the Society for Ecological Restoration*

"Restoration—as in the restoration of a work of art, is not the re-creation of the original masterpiece. Rather, attempts are made to return the work of art to conditions more closely resembling its original state."

—*Robert "Bobcat" Brothers. Headwaters Alliance.*

RESTORATION ECOLOGY has a very short history compared to the long history of environmental degradation. For example, restoration in the Mediterranean region will be difficult because degradation has left few intact native ecosystems, many extinct native plants, erosion of topsoil, and even subsoil down to bedrock. In contrast, restoration of a recently clearcut rainforest in Amazonia can draw upon the genetic bank of neighboring intact rainforest ecosystems.

Ecosystem restoration is needed in every neighborhood. It is a massive worldwide task, that can only be accomplished by many, small, simple steps by many, many, individual people. Everyone can help.

How much does restoration cost?

Pacific Rivers Council has a draft plan for regional watershed and salmon restoration in western Oregon and Washington. Their budget is predicated on stormproofing the 137 key public land watersheds identified by the Scientific Panel on Late Successional Forest Ecosystems (The Gang of Four). At this time, projected cost of the program would be $156 million and would generate 7,000 to 11,000 jobs. This cost deals with just a small portion of the total PNW watersheds, and the least impacted ones at that. Discouraging figures for small town folk, but peanuts in the face of military budgets. This is significant as one of the most ambitious restoration proposal made thus far. It gives estimates of budgets to accomplish the work and how many jobs would be created and possible mechanisms to generate the money to do the work.

The working document is titled: *Watershed and Salmon Habitat Restoration in the Pacific Northwest: Rationale and Framework for Legislation*. January, 1993 version. The Pacific Rivers Council, Inc., P.O. Box 309, Eugene, OR 97440. Tel: (503) 345-0119.

Restoration Ecology Periodicals

Restoration Ecology
Society for Ecological Restoration. (Price and address in Restoration Organizations.)

A peer-reviewed scientific journal on restoration ecology.

Restoration & Management Notes
Society for Ecological Restoration. (Price and address in Restoration Organizations.)

This twice-yearly journal is the best source of information on restoration ecology and restoration projects. It is the first journal in this field. Each issue contains quality articles, plus many reviews of the latest books, updates on projects, member activities and advertising by companies and consultants doing professional restoration work. Editor, William R. Jordan III, is one of the most respected and well-known restorationists. A subscription to R & M Notes and the quarterly newsletter comes with SER membership.

Restoration Ecology Organizations

Mattole Restoration Council
P.O. Box 60
Petrolia, California 95558
Tel: (707) 629-3670

One of the best examples of grass-roots stream restoration, erosion control and restoration forestry. The Council seeks to restore and sustain the Mattole River Watershed, including forests, fisheries, soils, flora and fauna. Involvement of local residents is a founding principle. Accomplishments include:

- Published a survey of erosion sources
- Organized erosion control work, including tree planting, seeding and slope stabilization
- Rehabilitation of salmon and steelhead habitat
- Mapped Mattole timber harvest history and remaining old growth habitat.

MRC has developed a systematic approach to identifying erosion on a watershed basis and prioritizing areas to restore first; called "Elements of Recovery."

Queen Salmon. Theater as an Educational Forest Tool.

The Mattole Restoration folks prepared one of the premier environmental theatrical performances of 1992 which played in many venues on the West Coast.

"Queen Salmon" is the true-to-life story of the often heroic, equally comic efforts by people in a remote northwestern California river valley to save their once great salmon runs from extinction.

"Queen Salmon" uses music, dance and outrageous humor to point directly at the transformation of society. "Queen Salmon" is, in the end, a love story—of female to male, human to salmon and of people to the place they live. It reveals a new possibility for human interaction with the natural world. It is inspirational, funny and fun."

—From *Talking Leaves*, 1993.

I have heard from several viewers that "Queen Salmon" was one of the funniest shows ever. Theater and humor are two of the best ways to reach people with restoration messages. . You can obtain a video by writing the Mattole Council.

Rehabilitation Program: Redwood Creek
Redwood National Park, National Park Service.

A massive, multimillion-dollar program. One of the larger scale restoration efforts to date.

Restoring the Earth
1713-C Martin Luther King Jr. Way
Berkeley, California 94709-2113
Tel: (510) 843-2645

They have hosted several major conferences and have proceedings available.

Sand County Foundation
P.O. Box 3037
Madison, Wisconsin 53704
Tel: (608) 244-351

The Foundation assists landowners to do ecological restoration with particular emphasis on restoring ecological processes such as fire, predation, and seasonal water table fluctuations. They assist landowners by putting them in touch with scientists; training; and assistance with legal, political and fund-raising concerns. The Foundation does not field general inquiries or have literature to send out. They wish to hear from landowners who are interested in their services, not only in Wisconsin, but in other parts of the USA as well.

Society for Ecological Restoration
University of Wisconsin-Madison Arboretum,
1207 Seminole Highway,
Madison, Wisconsin 53711
Tel: (608) 263-7889

SER is concerned exclusively with the restoration and creation of historic ecological communities, especially those that occur in an area naturally. It is the most eminent, scientific organization in restoration. SER has chapters in California, the Pacific Northwest and other regions of the USA.

There are several levels of membership. $69 for membership + newsletter + both journals Restoration & Management Notes and Restoration Ecology. $32 for membership + newsletter + Restoration & Management Notes. The 1993 SER Member Directory is available for $8.00.

The Society for Ecological Restoration holds annual conferences. The sixth SER Conference will be held in 1994. Contact SER for information on obtaining Proceedings of the conferences.

Restoration Ecology Books and Articles

Annotated Bibliography on the Ecology and Reclamation of Drastically Disturbed Areas
M. M. Czapowsky. 1976. USDA Forest Service, Northeastern For. Exp. Stn. General Technical Report: NE-21. 98 pp.

Literature on mining effects and reclamation in coal regions of the United States.

Bringing Back the Bush: The Bradley Method of Bush Regeneration
Joan Bradley. 1988. Landsdowne Press. $14.95.

The work of Eileen and Joan Bradley. An inspirational account of what two people can do to regenerate disturbed land and bring back native plant communities. Their work has influenced many people around Australia and beyond. Their three principles are:

1. Work from areas with native plants and weed out the non-native plants.

2. Make minimal disturbance.

3. Let native plant regeneration dictate rate of weed removal.

British Trust for Conservation Volunteers Practical Handbook Series
Available from agAccess. $33.00 each.

An exceptional series of books, each containing comprehensive construction & maintenance advice for restoration work. Titles especially pertinent to foresters are:

♦ *Woodlands: A Practical Handbook*. 1986. 171 pp.

- *Waterways & Wetlands*. 1987. 186 pp.
- *Fencing: A Practical Handbook*. 1986. 140 pp.
- *Hedging: A Practical Handbook*. 1975. 120 pp.
- *Footpaths: A Practical Handbook*. 1983. 192 pp.

The Ecological Restoration of the Northern Appalachians

Jeff Elliot and Jamie Sayen. 1990. Loose Cannon Pub.: North Stratford, NH. (See PAW in Environmental Organizations section.)

Environmental Restoration: Science and Strategies for Restoring the Earth

John J. Berger, ed. 1990. Island Press: Washington D.C. and Covelo California. 398 pp. $19.95.

This book is the result of the Restoring the Earth Conference held at the University of California at Berkeley. The authors present the need for and feasibility of restoring a wide variety of natural resources including forests, deserts, barrens, wetlands, mined lands, lakes, and streams.

Helping Nature Heal: An Introduction to Environmental Restoration—A Whole Earth Catalog

Richard Nilsen, ed. 1991. Ten Speed Press: Berkeley, CA. 160 pp. $14.95.

This resource-laden book follows the Whole Earth catalog's approach to information display by giving short reviews of books, periodicals, videos and organizations along with examples of many imaginative, ambitious projects in restoration. Recommended as the best overview and easiest to read book on the subject.

Living with the Land: Communities Restoring the Earth

Christine Meyer and Faith Moosang, eds., 1992. New Society Pub.: Gabriola Island, BC.

A series of articles by people that are restoring the earth. The back-to-the-landers, farmers, local activists, squatters, indigenous people, parents and other "folks." Reports from grassroots people that are doing it. The cultural, community dimensions are especially explored.

Prairies, Forests and Wetlands: The Restoration of Natural Landscape Communities in Iowa

Janette R. Thompson. 1992

A layperson's how-to book.

Readings in Watershed Management and Rehabilitation

A bibliography containing several hundred references, most of them for northern California. Distributed at the August, 1981 Redwoods Rehabilitation Symposium. No address or agency/organization listed as the source, but can be ordered from Redwood National Park.

Restoration Ecology-A Synthetic Approach to Ecological Research

William R. Jordan III, Michael Gilpin, and Vorn D. Aber (eds.). 1987. Cambridge U. Press. 342 pp.

A compilation of writings by restoration leaders. Gives addresses of many contributors.

Restoration of Aquatic Ecosystems: Science, Techniques, and Public Policy

1992. Academy Press. 555 pp. $39.95.

Many experts made contributions to this book, which also has an extensive reference section, many case studies, recommended readings, and an excellent overview. Generally up-to-date on the state of knowledge.

Restoration of Arid and Semi-arid Ecosystems in Afghanistan

N. S. Hassanyer. 1977. Ph.D. Thesis, Colorado State Univ.

Streamside Runoff: Restoration of Salmonid Habitat in the Pacific Northwest

Winter/Spring 1993, Vol. 7 (1). Center For Streamside Studies, University of Washington, AR-10, Seattle, WA 98195.

Watershed Rehabilitation in Redwood National Park and Other Pacific Coastal Areas

R. N. Coats, ed. Center for Natural Resources Studies of JMI and National Park Service. 360 pp.

Proceedings of a symposium held August, 1981 includes 33 papers on restoring vegetation, hillslope procedures and rehabilitation, stream channel processes and fisheries restoration, and case studies. Good bibliography.

Wetland Creation and Restoration: The Status of the Science

Jon A. Kusler and Mary E. Kentula, eds., 1990. Island Press. 594 pp. $39.95 cloth.

This book provides the first major national assessment by region of the capacity to implement a goal of no-net-loss of wetlands. Extensive treatment. Includes bibliography, recommended reading, and evaluation of case studies. A voluminous work with much practical and technical information from the people doing wetland restoration. Many references.

Whole Earth Review—Special Issue on Environmental Restoration

Spring 1990, No. 66. U.S. $5 (address in Environmental Periodicals section).

Erosion Control: A Resource Guide

SOIL EROSION is one of the most insidious and dangerous threats to human welfare. Healthy soils are the basis for healthy forests, healthy agriculture, and ultimately, healthy human societies. Stopping human-induced, accelerated erosion is one of the most important tasks facing humanity and a prerequisite for restoration forestry.

There are two kinds of erosion:

1. natural erosion, and

2. human-induced, accelerated erosion. The world has suffered and continues to suffer, catastrophic, human-induced accelerated erosion rates. Natural rates of erosion vary widely depending on steepness of slope, precipitation patterns, soil type, plant cover, soil surface texture, humus content, surface litter, orientation of joints and bedding planes, etc. On vegetated sites, natural rates of erosion are slow, although over time they level mountains.

Since 1920, 50% of the world's soils have been lost and an additional 30% degraded. 14 million arable acres/year are lost to production. India is losing 6 billion tons soil/yr. In Australia, during the 1980s, 180 tons soil/minute were lost.

Erosion process: bare soil > rain splatter > puddling > sheet erosion > rill erosion > gully > arroyo > slips/slumps > landslides > mass movement.

Erosion effects: loss of soil & fertility, declining forest yields, silting of reservoirs, harbors and channels, flooding, and stream ecology disruption and eutrophication. Accelerated erosion effects the whole aquatic food chain; microorganisms, non-vertebrates, fish and aquatic mammals.

Wetlands need protection. They perform a valuable cleansing function for ecosystems and on the biosphere and planetary level. Wetlands could be likened to the Earth's kidneys; fine tubes filtering the flow. Like kidneys though, they can only handle a certain flow of toxins without being damaged.

Trees offer one of the best tools for stopping erosion and building soil. Trees stabilize slopes by providing root reinforcement (lateral, horizontal and arch buttressing) and by pumping water. The most important characteristic in selecting trees/plants for erosion control is adaptability to the site. The plants should be tough, competitive against less desirable plants and trouble-free.

Some erosion control techniques include: plugs, dams, gabions, aprons, weirs, silt traps, keyline subsoiling, swales, barrier hedges, and alley cropping on contour.

Some bioengineering/biotechnical erosion control techniques include: vegetated gabion wall, vegetated concrete crib wall, contour wattling, staking with live cuttings, vegetated terraces, brush layering, grass plugs, plant establishment, reed trench-layering, brush matting, toe walls with vegetated slopes, and vegetated revetments with rip rap. You can find out about all these and more, from Hugo Schiechtl's book, *Bioengineering for Land Reclamation and Conservation*.

Organizations

International Erosion Control Association

P.O. Box 4904
Steamboat Springs, Colorado 80477
Tel: (303) 879-3010/Fax: (303) 879-8563.

The IECA is a professional organization promoting erosion control as a necessary and effective means of protecting the limited resources of the world. IECA publishes a quarterly bulletin, the REPORT as well as a Products and Services Directory and Proceedings of their annual conference. The 25th annual Conference of the IECA will be held February 15-18, 1994 in Reno, Nevada.

Soil Conservation Service

12th and Independence Ave., SW
Washington, DC 20250
Tel: (202) 447-4525/Fax: (202) 447-7690

Periodical

Land Degradation and Rehabilitation

John Wiley and Sons, Inc.,
Department "C"
605 Third Avenue
New York, New York 10158

Quarterly. Subscriptions: Institutions–US$150/year; reduced rates for individuals; sample copy available upon request.

Books on Erosion Control

Annotated Bibliography on Soil Erosion and Erosion Control in Subarctic and High-Latitude Regions of North America

C. W. Slaughter and J. W. Aldrich, compilers, 1989. Pacific Northwest Research Station General Technical Report PNW-GTR-253. 234 pages.

The bibliography is divided into two sections, one specific to Alaska and similar high-latitude settings and one relevant to understanding erosion, sediment production and erosion control.

An Investigation of Soil Characteristics and Erosion Rates on California Forest Lands

Marvin Dodge, *et al.*, 1976. State of California Resources Agency; Dept of For. Sacramento. 105 pp.

Soils, erosion, mass movements, timber harvesting. Good references.

Bioengineering for Land Reclamation and Conservation

Hugo Schiechtl, 1980. University of Alberta Press. 400 pp.

My favorite book on soil erosion control methods. Much of the information is from European experience. Extensive lists of plants for erosion control. Profusely illustrated.

Biotechnical Slope Protection and Erosion Control

Donald H. Gray and Andrew T. Leiser, 1982. Van Nostrand Reinhold Co.: NY. 271 pp.

One of the best books on the subject. Some parts are quite technical. Includes good descriptions of contour wattling, brush layering, and other methods.

The Earth Manual: How to Work on Wild Land Without Taming It

Malcolm Margolin, 1985 revised ed., 1975, 1st edition. Heyday Books, P.O. Box 9145, Berkeley, CA 94709. 237 pp.

Ecological sound land management for the small landowner. Practical applications in erosion control, tree planting and care, seeding, ponds, and forestry.

Forest Amelioration

O. Riedl and D. Szchar, 1984. Elsevier: Amsterdam. 623 pp.

Biotechnical erosion control. Quite technical.

Native Woody Plants of The United States: Their Erosion-Control and Wildlife Values

William R. Van Dersal, 1938. USDA Miscellaneous Publication No. 303: Washington DC. 362 pp.

This publication presents an indexed list of woody plants growing in the United States, and gives all available data pertinent to their use in erosion control and wildlife conservation (at that time). Over 2000 species.

Research Needs and Applications to Reduce Erosion and Sedimentation in Tropical Steeplands

R. R. Ziemer, C. L. O'Loughlin and L. S. Hamilton, 1990. 396 pp. $50. IAHS, 2000 Florida Ave NW, Wash. DC 20009.

Fifty papers from an international symposium held in Suva, Fiji in June 1990. The fifth in a series of meetings held over the past decade on the state of erosion and sedimentation research related to steeplands around the Pacific Rim. This was the first to concentrate on tropical areas.

6

Reforestation & Tree Planting: A Resource Guide

Miguel Guizar

IN A HEALTHY FOREST ECOSYSTEM there should be little reason to plant trees. The forest will plant itself. Reforestation, or tree planting, is an emergency measure which will hopefully be largely dispensed with after several decades of restoration forestry.

Relying on natural regeneration from local genetic stock is the preferred method in restoration forestry. However, in today's ravaged world, tree planting is extremely important, especially in waste places, eroding hillsides, and other damaged areas. Tree planting should rely on a wide mix of native species to promote and restore forest ecosystems with their complete set of native species and structures. On the harsher sites, it may be necessary to start with tough, pioneer plants, and years or decades later, plant in later successional species.

To promote forest regeneration and advance, various levels of intervention are possible. In some cases, we just get out of the way and let nature do the planting. It might mean fencing an area to protect natural regeneration from livestock or wildlife. A simple means of intervention is to collect seeds and plant them in nearby suitable habitats. Depending on soils, moisture, and animal pressure, the seeds can be favored by mulching, fertilizing, screening, caging, watering, etc. The next level of intervention is to collect local seeds, grow seedlings in nurseries and plant them in nearby, suitable habitats.

Tree planting should be the last resort. To succeed, trees need to be planted correctly and at the right time of year. There are many things which can be done to improve tree survival rate; including shading, mulching, fertilizing, screening, caging, irrigating, using bud-caps to protect leaders from browsing, and digging of microcatchments for water supply.

The more of these extra tasks you do, the more expensive reforestation becomes. The cost of reforestation in the Pacific Northwest currently ranges from $150 to $800 an acre. Planting rates average one acre per person per day but vary from half an acre to two and a half acres per person per day. The harsher the environment, the more extra steps need to be taken and the more energy it takes to do reforestation.

Tree Planting Figures for the United States

Since 1982, the U.S. Forest Service has compiled data on acreage of forest land planted annually in the U.S.A. In 1988, 3.4 million acres were planted or direct seeded nationwide (only 1% is direct-seeded). Eighty percent of this planting was in the Southern states, 13% in the Pacific Coast states, and 6% in the rest of the nation. Of the area planted, 40% was forest industry land, 47% other private lands, and 13% public lands. Artificial regeneration in the Pacific Coast region has involved around 400,000 acres per year, primarily on public and forest industry lands. The Pacific Northwest region of North America has one of the most sophisticated and largest tree planting programs in the world. Between 400 and 500 million trees a year were planted in the late 1970's.

The November 1989, *National Geographic* claimed that U.S. corporations and private landowners plant 6,000,000 trees a day. It is also commonly stated by the industry that the U.S. has more trees on its 730 million acres of forest land than 70 years ago. While these numbers may be true, they do not tell the whole story. How many tiny seedlings equal an 18-foot diameter old growth tree?

At first glance this giant tree-planting effort sounds commendable. But on closer look, it is the symptom of poor forestry practices (i.e. clearcutting). Why is the system so damaged that people have to plant trees?

The figures from the Forest Service and industry do not distinguish between tree plantations and forest ecosystems. Most of the trees planted in the U.S. are in tree plantations, both on private and public land. These plantations are intensively managed for tree growth and wood quality with one or a few dominant conifer species. This is not reforestation, i.e. the restoration of fully functioning forest ecosystems.

Tree Planting Organizations

Northwest Reforestation Contractors Association
> P.O. Box 2034
> Eugene, Oregon 97402
> Tel: (503) 344-6179

Reforestation News, a quarterly publication of the NRCA provides information about the reforestation industry to reforestation contractors, timber companies, logging companies, federal and state natural resource agencies, and reforestation suppliers.

NRCA's main clientele are small reforestation contractors rather than tree planter employees. The association began in 1989 as an informal network of eight contractors to address the high costs of workmen's compensation. The association has grown rapidly and now has over 55 active members found in five states of the West. Besides tree planting, the NRCA covers other forest jobs as well, such as thinning, fire-fighting, site prep, and release.

Western Silvicultural Contractors Association
> Suite 310, 1070 W. Broadway,
> Vancouver, British Columbia, V6H 1E7, CANADA
> Tel: (604) 736-8660/Fax: (604) 738-4080.

An organization representing the interests of tree planting contractors. They publish the *Canadian Silviculture Magazine*.

Books on Reforestation

Afforestation in Israel
> Efraim Orni. 1978. Jewish National Fund. 80 pp.

History of the forests, recent afforestation, types of trees used, and methods.

Birth of a Cooperative: Hoedads Inc. A Worker Owned Forest Labor Co-op
> Hal Hartzell, Jr. 1987. Hulogosi, P.O. Box 1188, Eugene, OR 97440. 351 pp. $12.95.

The story of the largest and most successful hippy tree planting cooperative. Entertaining reading for professional tree planters and would-be planters.

Collecting, Processing and Germinating Seeds of Wildland Plants
> James A. Young and Cheryl G. Young. 1986. Timber Press: Portland, Oregon. 236 pp. $24.95.

An excellent resource for the serious seed collector. Concentrates on the western U.S., but includes species from other parts of the world. Covers trees, shrubs, herbaceous plants and grasses. Very well referenced.

Establishment Techniques for Forest Plantations
> G. W. Chapman and T. G. Allan. 1978. FAO, Resources Div., Forestry Dept.

Forest Tree Planting in Arid Zones
> Goor and Barney. 1976. The Ronald Press.

One of the best books on the subject, especially with reference to "non-over-developed" countries in the tropical, subtropical and Mediterranean areas. Good information on establishing nurseries with limited resources, planting techniques in deserts, and utilizing micro-climates.

Forgotten Men: The Civilian Conservation Corps
> Robert Allen Ermentrout. 1982. Exposition Press. 102 pp.

A Guide to Forest Seed Handling: With Special Reference to the Tropics
> FAO. 1985. 394 pp.

Integrating Plant Autecology and Silvicultural Activities to Prevent Forest Vegetation Management Problems
> R. G. Wagner and J. C. Zasada. 1991. The Forestry Chronicle. Vol. 67 (5): pp. 506-513.

Reforestation without the use of herbicides is a key practice in eco-forestry. This article shows how an understanding of the reproduction, growth habits, and habitats of early successional plant species can be used to gain benefits or naturally eliminate them from forest stands without herbicides.

Opportunities for Reforestation Work in the Pacific Northwest
> Northwest Reforestation Contractors Association. May 1990.

Prepared by the NRCA to appraise reforestation opportunities on lands of the U.S. Forest Service, BLM, private industry forest lands, and non-industrial lands. The NRCA calculates that over 6,000 economically and environmentally sound rural jobs could be created, including reforestation on over 1.3 million acres of unstocked and understocked land in Oregon.

Proceedings, Intermountain Forest Nursery Association
> August, 1989, Bismarck, ND. Rocky Mtn., For. & Range Exp. Stn. USDA FS, 146 pages. Gen. Tech Rep. RM-184

The papers presented in the proceedings are technical and of interest to the specialist. The noteworthy aspect of this publication is the summary of meetings and contents of Proceedings of the Intermountain Forest Nursery Assoc. from 1960 to 1989. Hundreds of papers written on nursery production over the past three decades are listed and make this publication a great research tool for the serious nurseryperson from cold temperate latitudes.

6

The Reference Manual of Woody Plant Propagation: From Seed to Tissue Culture

Michel A. Dirr and Charles W. Heuser. 1987. Varsity Press, P.O. Box 6301, Athens, GA 30604. 338 pp.

"A practical working guide to the propagation of over 100 species, varieties and cultivars."

Reforestation in Arid Zones

Fred R. Weber with Carol Stoney. 2nd ed. 1986. Volunteers In Technical Assistance (VITA), 1815 N. Lynn St., Suite 200, Arlington, VA 22209. 335 pp.

Highly recommended for field workers, this book covers project design, soil properties, site and species selection, nursery management, agroforestry methods, and information on 200 species for use in arid Africa. Useful appendix with resources including many organizations, periodicals, and a bibliography of suggested reading.

Reforestation Practices for Conifers in California

Gilbert H. Schubert and Ronald S. Adams. 1971. State of California, The Resources Agency, Dept. of Conservation, Div. of Forestry. 358 pp.

Cone and seed handling practices, nursery practices, site preparation, planting, and seeding.

Reforestation Practices in Southwestern Oregon and Northern California

Oregon State Univ. For. Res. Lab., Corvallis, Oregon. 465 pp. $27 postpaid.

The book summarizes the results of $20 million in research involving 65 scientists. Looks closely at reforestation failures and successes.

Reforestation Programs and Timberland Suitability

Henry H. Carey, V. Alaric Sample, Stephen P. Greenway, and Nicholas Van Pelt. September, 1988. 57 pp.

Available from the CHEC (Cascade Holistic Economic Consultants) Catalog.

The Forest Service has always considered reforestation to be important. But its forest plans fail to screen out lands that are impossible to reforest. This paper examines several forests in detail to show that reforestation problems are more severe than claimed by the forest plans.

Reforesting the Earth

Sandra Posel and Lori Heise. 1988. Worldwatch: Washington, D.C.

This study advocates a variety of reforestation approaches including shelterbelts, plantations, conservation of wood, and giving deforested land to poor people for rehabilitation.

Regenerating British Columbia's Forests

D. P. Lavender, et al., eds. 1990. Univ. of B.C. Press: Vancouver, B.C.

Regenerating Oregon's Forests

Brian D. Clearny, R. D. Greaves and R. K. Hermann, eds., 1978. Oregon State Univ. Ext. Serv., Corvallis, OR. 286 pp.

A look at the reforestation effort that has made the Pacific Northwest the site of some of the biggest acreages of plantation forest in the world. The ecology of plantations, nursery and planting techniques, and aftercare are covered. Many useful appendices and references.

Seed Propagation of Trees, Shrubs and Forbs for Conservation Planting

Charles F. Swingle. 1939. Soil Conservation Service Publication No. SCS-TP-27. 198 pp.

A gold mine of information! Over 2,000 species are covered! Most of them are North American natives, including many obscure species.

Seeds of Woody Plants in North America

J. A. Young and C. H. Young. 1992. Discorides Press: Portland, OR. 407 pp.

The "bible" for seed collectors and nursery people. This book is an updated edition of the invaluable, out-of-print USDA Agriculture Handbook 450. Covers hundreds of species, both native and non-native. Information includes suitable growing conditions of native woody plants, identification and collection of seeds, and germination. Methods of vegetative propagation are presented when applicable. An extensive listing of literature citations for further information on propagation is included.

Sowing Forests from the Air

BOSTID. 1981.

Justifies and recommends reforestation by aerial seeding based on experiences in North America, the Pacific and the tropics.

Strategies and Design for Afforestation, Reforestation and Tree Planting

K. F. Wiersum and Hinkeloord, eds. 1984. PUDOC: Wageningen, The Netherlands. 350 pp.

These proceedings of an International Symposium describe a systematic framework for strategies of afforestation which encompass both small and large-scale private and industrial schemes.

A Technical Guide for Forest Nursery Management in the Caribbean and Latin America

Leon H. Liegel and Charles R. Venator. 1987. USDA Forest Service General Technical Report SO-67. 156 pp.

Based on 20 years of research at the Institute of Tropical Forestry, Puerto Rico, this manual details nursery planning, seed management, pest control, nutrition and methods of plant production. Actual and recommended practices are discussed, and the pros and cons of each with many specific examples. Oriented towards large-scale, chemical-heavy monoculture plantations.

Tropical Trees: Propagation and Planting Manuals, Vol. 1. Rooting Cuttings of Tropical Trees
Longman, K. A. 1993. 137 pp.

Wastelands Afforestation
Irshadkhan. 1987. Oxford and IBH Pub.: New Delhi.

Part I is on the degraded land problem including forest lands and wastelands. Part II is on afforestation techniques and systems. Appendices include species to use for different climate zones. Chapter 8 is on tree planting on difficult sites.

Sources of Tools, Equipment & Supplies for Foresters, Tree Planters and Woodsworkers

Here are a few of the larger, mail-order supply companies in the U.S. and Canada.

Bailey's
P.O. Box 550
Laytonville, California 95454
Tel: (707) 984-6133

Mail order logger's, woodcutter's and reforestation supplies at discounted prices. Has outlets in New York and Tennessee also.

Ben Meadows Co.
P.O. Box 80549
Atlanta, Georgia 30366
Tel: 1-800-241-6401

Tools and equipment for forestry, reforestation, cruising, logging, fire fighting, outdoor living. Also has a separate catalog for Civil Engineering supplies.

Canadian Forestry Equipment, Ltd.
17309 107 Ave.
Edmonton, Alberta T5S 1E5 CANADA
Tel: 1-800-661-7959

Forestry Suppliers, Inc.
P.O. Box 8397
Jackson, Mississippi 39284
Tel: 1-800-647-5368/Fax: 1-800-543-4203

Large selection of forestry, engineering and environmental equipment. Free 420-page catalog.

International Reforestation Suppliers
2100 W. Broadway
Eugene, Oregon 97402
Tel: 1-800-321-1037

Recommended by tree-planters as having the lowest prices. Free catalog.

Terra Tech, Inc.
P.O. Box 5547
Eugene, Oregon 97405
Tel: 1-800-321-0597

International reforestation suppliers.

6

6

7 Resource Guide To Forestry in the USA

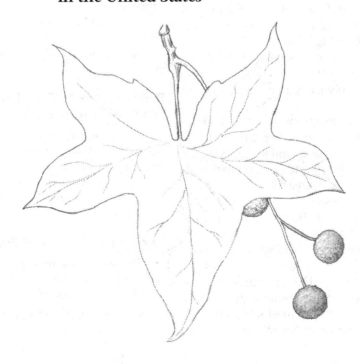

Forests of the United States: A Bibliography

Credit: Natural Areas Association

The United States Forest Service— Can It Be Reformed?

THE U.S. NATIONAL FOREST SYSTEM comprises 191 million acres on 155 National Forests, 20 National Grasslands, and 84 Experimental forests, with a total staff of more than 30,000 men and women.

The United States Forest Service (USFS) once had a proud reputation in the U.S. public mind, but its reputation is becoming increasingly tarnished. Here in the rural areas of the Pacific Northwest, it is commonly referred to as "the Forest Circus." Alas for the forests, US Forest Service timber harvest levels have been largely dictated from the White House and Congress for the past half-century and the politicians have largely been in the pockets of the financial and industrial cartels including the timber industry.

One of the latest, and biggest, scandals to rock the Forest Service is the expose' of massive timber theft from the National Forests, sometimes with the collusion of USFS personnel. Under-calculation of timber cut is commonplace, often at the scaling station.

Environmentalists have been fighting the USFS for decades and the more cynical suggest the USFS is beyond reform and should be dismantled and replaced. But replaced with what?

From my personal grass-roots view of the Forest Service there is reform needed. I have spent over 20 years living next to, traveling through, and working in National Forests around the Pacific Northwest. I drive the backroads the tourists never see. I have covered tens of thousands of road miles and seen thousands of clear-cuts. I have planted trees in the burned-out, bombed-out remains of forest ecosystems on slopes so steep you could barely climb up them. I am appalled at how the Forest Service is damaging the forests.

There are good people in the USFS. The question is not whether the Forest Service needs reforming, the question is how. For a start, instead of the timber sale people, the biologists should run the Forest Service. This includes from the district level on up.

From this particular grass-roots view, the battle over forest management is as contentious as ever. There has been no significant change in attitude in the National Forest Service's superior staff. In fact, a recent report from AFSEEE (Association of Forest Service Employees for Environmental Ethics), details the ongoing purge of progressive employees at all ranks of the US Forest Service. Restoration forestry is still frowned upon and discouraged in the Forest Service. It is, however, becoming harder to resist the movement for reform both from within and outside the agency.

There are signs of change in the agencies, but the "old guard" still holds sway. Stay tuned for further developments. Will the Forest Service be reformed, will they be disbanded by an angry public? Will the public's forests continue to shrink in size and health? Today, the overcutting continues. The last of the old trees continue to fall.

1987 and 1988 saw record breaking timber harvests in the United States. In 1987, USA exported $8.2 billion of wood products and imported $13.0 billion in wood products.

Proposal for Reforming the Forest Service From Within the Agency

See article on page 2 in the September/October 1993 issue of *Inner Voice* for some well-thought-out ideas on how to reform the U.S. Forest Service. The AFSEEE proposals have particular merit since they are prepared by people who work for, or who have worked for, the Forest Service.

Saving Our National Forests from Waste

[The following is a statement from AFSEEE (Association of Forest Service Employees for Environmental Ethics).]

U.S. National Forests:

+ Supply only 14% of U.S. wood products.

- Comprise only 8.5% of our country's land area.

- Contain 50% of remaining wildlife habitat in the U.S.

- Supply 50% of the remaining cold-water fisheries habitat in the U.S.

- Provide abundant clean water and clean air.

- Represent the last vestiges of functioning ecosystems, critical for the preservation of remaining biological diversity.

These environmental values cannot be supplied anywhere else: They can only be found on our remaining public lands, including national parks, state and county land.

The U.S. does not need wood from our national forests. Consider the following simple conservation and recycling strategy which would more than make up for the current 14% of wood products coming from U.S. National Forests:

- Increasing the efficiency of our mills in the U.S. to literally cut more wood from each log. Technology already available and being used in Japan would increase our "supply" a full 27%, almost double what comes from National Forests!

- Using more post-consumer, recycled paper products, double-sided recopying, reducing use of disposable paper products, eliminating wood waste in the construction process in addition to mill efficiency would save us 50% of the trees we are cutting now—nearly four times the wood coming from national forests!

While AFSEEE is not necessarily advocating a halt to public lands development and logging, we do advocate a complete moratorium on any development of remaining roadless areas or old growth.

Dismantle the Forest Service and Replace it With a New Federal Department of Conservation?

The Center for Biodiversity has printed full page ads in various journals calling for the dismantling of the U.S. National Forest Service and placing the national forests under the jurisdiction of a new federal department of conservation. Obviously they have been doing some thinking on the subject. If you are interested in this scenario, contact them for details.

"A Department of Natural Resources is the Best Reorganization Alternative"
Gene Peterson. *Headwaters Journal*, Winter 1993–94 issue, pp. 18–19. (Address in Environmental Periodicals section.)

Peterson is a career BLM employee and former District Manager of the Medford BLM. In this article, he looks at the history of federal land agencies in the U.S. In the light of history, dismantling the Forest Service may not be so radical an idea. The last effort to create a Department of Natural Resources was undertaken by Interior Secretary Cecil Andrus (1878–82), but his efforts were thwarted by vested interests.

Watch Out for Proposals to Privatize the U.S. National Forests and Sell the Land Off to the Highest Bidder.

There have been sporadic calls over the past century to sell off U.S. federal forest lands. It would not be unexpected to have this broached more seriously in the decade ahead. The U.S. Federal Government is in debt over 3 trillion dollars—more than all the Third World (who owe less than 2 trillion combined). U.S. creditors may ask the federal government to sell off its assets. This is exactly what happened in New Zealand in the late 1980's. New Zealand divided its forest holdings into two parts. Part was kept and put under the administration of a new Ministry of Conservation. The production forests were sold off to large corporate interests.

The World Bank and the IMF are forcing many countries to go through restructuring because of their debts. The U.S. might be forced to go through restructuring in the next decade. The U.S. standard of living is shrinking and might shrink even faster.

It is ironic that corporate interests will most likely try to capitalize on calls by some environmentalists for dismantling the Forest Service by pushing for a selling off of the production forests, similar to New Zealand.

Books on Forest Politics

Timber And The Forest Service
David A. Clary. University Press of Kansas. 1986.

An analytic history of how timber production came to dominate the US Forest Service. 252 pp. $12.95.

Last Stand: Logging, Journalism, and the Case for Humility
Richard Manning. Penguin Books. 192 pp. $10.00.

A hard-hitting exposé that ties together key issues of conservation and corporate/government repression.

Clearly illuminates the root cause of our current forest crisis: the overcutting by private companies seeking to maximize their profits.

Reforming the Forest Service
Randal O'Toole. Available from Cascade Holistic Economic Consultants (see index).

Reforming the Forest Service presents a comprehensive proposal to protect endangered species, clean water, wilderness, local community stability, and other resources. Based on years of research, reviews of over 40 forest plans and thousands of timber sales, and a detailed analysis of Forest Service behavior.

Clear-cutting: A Crime Against Nature

Edward C. Fritz. 1989. 124 pp. $16.25 ppd. Available from Forest Reform Network, 5934 Royal Lane, Suite 223, Dallas, TX 75230.

Ned Fritz is one of those indefatigable people who manage to accomplish a lot in their field. Ned's goal is stopping clear-cutting on US National Forests. This book explains why it needs to be stopped and the progress to date. Ned covers clear-cutting from coast to coast in the USA.

On page 113-114, Fritz gives names, addresses and phone numbers of 15 notable forest managers around the USA who are practicing Selection Management.

Cut and Run

Grace Henderson. 1991. Western Eye Press. 239 pp. $9.95.

In an easy-to-read, journalistic style, the author takes us on a basic tour of all the forests of the West, from Arizona to Washington, with a chapter for each state. Through interviews and personal profiles, she captures the main points of the different sides of the National Forest logging debate.

History of U.S. Forest Service and Timber Policy

U. of Kansas or Univ. of Nebraska Press.

Recommended by Jerry Franklin.

Books About Forests & Forestry in the United States

Following is a selection of books, the first section with nationwide relevance followed by publications from the Western US.

The Eastern USA and the Pacific Northwest have separate Book Review sections. Further books are reviewed throughout Restoration Forestry.

Atlas of United States Trees

E. L. Little. USDA Misc. Pub. 1146, 1293, 1314, 1342, 1361.

Five volumes of information about the distribution of native tree species with detailed range maps.

An Analysis of the Timber Situation in the United States: 1989-2040

USDA Forest Service Rocky Mountain For & Range Exp. Stn., Gen. Tech. Rep. RM-199. December 1990. 268 pp.

A technical document supporting the 1989 USDA Forest Service RPA Assessment. A great deal of data which the forest researcher and forest activist can utilize. It shows where the Forest Service expects our national wood supply to come from/go to over the next 50 years. It includes domestic timber resources; trends in the consumption of timber products, both domestically and internationally; economic importance of the timber processing industries; international trade in forest products; the forest products sector in main competitor and customer countries; alternative futures, and opportunities for increasing productivity on timberlands.

Clear-cut: The Tragedy of Industrial Forestry

Bill Devall, ed. 1993. 300 pp. Sierra Club Books and Earth Island press. Clear-cut is available for $50 from Patagonia Company. Call 1-800-638-6464.

A coffee table book on clear-cutting. 180 pages of color photographs of the most powerful images of industrial clear-cutting across North America ever published.

Must reading for restoration foresters. The authors in this book offer the best-articulated and ecologically-based arguments against clear-cutting. The book also addresses alternatives to clear-cutting. The text contains writings by notable environmentalists and by restoration foresters such as Chris Maser, Orville Camp, Herb Hammond, and Reed Noss. Bill Devall, a proponent of Deep Ecology, teaches at Humboldt State University, in Arcata, California.

Starting January, 1994, 12,000 copies will be given to forest activists for presentation to policy-makers, foresters and the media. If you are a forest activist you can request free copies by calling Rainforest Action Network in San Francisco (415) 398-4404. Ask for Kate Cissna, Mike Roselle or Eric Johnson.

Free copies for activists to distribute are available in Canada from: Canada's Future Forest Alliance in New Denver, British Columbia (604) 358-2660.

Defining Sustainable Forestry

Greg Aplet, Nels Johnson, Jeffrey T. Olson and V. Alaric Sample, eds. November, 1993. Island Press. 320 pp. $24.95.

This book is the result of a national conference convened by the Wilderness Society, American Forests and the World Resources Institute to help establish a common framework upon which to guide the future development of forestry.

The book was not released as Restoration Forestry went to press, so all I can do is offer a guess that it will represent some of the latest thinking from the large, Washington DC-based, environmental think-tanks. Well-thought out, reasoned proposals to reform forestry. I expect it will be one of the best compilations of restoration forestry writings to date; but don't expect grass-roots.

Forest Cover Types of North America

F. Y. Eyre, ed. 1982. Soc. of Am. Foresters: Washington, D.C.

Forestry Handbook

Karl F. Wenger Ed.; 1984, 2nd ed. John Wiley & Sons. 1335 pp. $75.

For the working forester. This handbook gives details on just about anything a forester would ever want to know that has to do with linear thinking. Very good graphs, tables, and species lists. For instance, it gives waterlogging tolerances for trees, shade tolerance. Allelopathic trees, short overviews of ecology, management, logging, timber measurements, range, urban forestry, law, roads, drains, statistics, terminology, regeneration site prep. etc. etc. A huge amount of information.

Global Imperative: Harmonizing Culture & Nature

Chris Maser. 1992. Stillpoint Publishing: Walpole, NH. $12.95

Chris Maser offers one of the most penetrating insights into the roots of our current ecological dilemma and how to go about building a world based on restoration. Maser asks, can our post-industrial society once again learn nature's ways and become conscious co-creators? A look at the social side of forestry by one of restoration forestry's best ecologists and philosophers.

History of Sustained-Yield Forestry: A Symposium

H. K. Steen ed. 1984. IUFRO. 470 pp.

Proceedings of a 1983 Symposium in Portland, Oregon. Many articles.

Holistic Resource Management

Alan Savory. 1988. 564 pp. $24.95.

Holistic Resource Management (HRM) is an integrated design approach to natural resource management. Alan Savory brought the concepts to the U.S. from Rhodesia. HRM has been applied to many livestock properties and has achieved notable fame in the cattle grazing circles of the USA. High-intensity, short-duration grazing is its hallmark. HRM is not limited to livestock operations; HRM as a design methodology can be successfully applied to restoration forestry.

North American Terrestrial Vegetation

Michael G. Barbour and William Dwight Billings, eds. 1988. Cambridge University Press: New York. 434 pp.

An overview. The authors cite the most noteworthy plant surveys for each major habitat area in North America.

Principles of Silviculture

T. W. Danel, J. A. Helms and F. S. Baker; 1979; McGraw-Hill

Silvicultural challenges and opportunities in the 1990's

Proceedings of the national silvicultural workshop. held July 10-13, 1989, Petersburg, Alaska. Published 1991. Intermountain Research Station, US Forest Service.

Silvics of North America: Vol. 1, Conifers

Russell M. Burns, Barbara H. Honkala, Tech. coords. U.S. Department of Agriculture, Forest Service. 1990. Washington, DC. Agriculture Handbook 654

The silvical characteristics of over 80 forest tree species and varieties are described. Most are native to the United States, but a few are introduced and naturalized.

Silvics of North America. Vol. 2, Hardwoods

Russell M. Burns, Barbara H. Honkala, Tech. Coordinators. 1990. US Dept. of Agriculture, Forest Service, Wasington, DC; 877 pp. Agricultural Handbook 654.

"The silvical characteristics of about 200 forest tree species and varieties are described. Most are native to the United States and Puerto Rico. Information on habitat, life history, and genetics."

Silvicultural Systems for the Major Forest Types of the United States

Richard L. Williamson and Asa D. Twombly. 1983. USDA Forest Service. Handbook No. 445, Washington DC

This Well-Wooded Land: Americans and Their Forests from Colonial Times to the Present

Thomas R. Cox. 1985. Univ. of Nebraska Press: Lincoln.

One of the more complete histories of American forests.

Trees, Prairies, and People: A History of Tree Planting in the Plains States

Wilmon H. Droze. 1877. Texas Woman's University: Denton.

This book is a history of shelterbelt planting in the U.S. during the 1800's and 1900's, including the dust bowl era.

Western USA, Excluding Pacific Northwest

Coniferous Forest Habitat Types of Central and Southern Utah

Andrew P. Youngblood and Ronald L. Mauk. 1985. USDA Forest Service, Intermountain Res. Stn. Gen. Tech. Rep. INT-187. 89 pp.

Coniferous Forest Habitat Types of Northern Utah

Ronald L. Mauk and Jan A. Henderson. 1984. USDA Forest Service, Intermountain Res. Stn. Gen. Tech. Rep. INT-170. 89 pp.

The Distribution of Forest Trees in California
James R. B. Griffin and William Critchfield. USDA Forest Service Res. Paper PSW- 82/1972. 118 pp.

Excellent range maps for every native California tree. Includes text explaining maps. A good way to help locate seed stands.

Ecology and Management of Oak and Associated Woodlands: Perspectives in the Southwestern United States and Northern Mexico
Gen. Tech. Rep. RM-218. Fort Collins, CO: USDA, Rocky Mountain Forest and Range Experiment Station.

Proceedings of a symposium, April 27-39, 1992 in Sierra Vista, Arizona.

Ecology of Western Forests: Peterson Field Guide
John C. Kricher and Gordon Morrison. 1993. Houghton Mifflin. $16.95.

Forest Resources of Arizona
Roger C. Conner, Alan W. Green, J. David Born, and Rennee A. O'Brien. 1990. USDA Forest Service, Intermountain Res. Stn. Resource Bulletin INT-69. 92 pp.

Forest Trust Silviculture Manual
Forest Trust, P.O. Box 519, Santa Fe, New Mexico, 87504. $25.00.

Developed for grassroots activists in the four corners states. The silviculture manual provides a comprehensive introduction to forest ecology and silvicultural methods currently used in national forest management.

Forest Trust Water Quality Manual
Forest Trust. $25.00.

Forest Trust has been in the forefront of restoration forestry in the Southwest.

Forest Trees of the Pacific Slope
George B. Sudworth. 1967. Dover: New York.

Written in 1908 by a man who had first-hand knowledge and experience with most Western forests before they were despoiled. The book's best points are its exact descriptions of each tree's range, habitat, site tolerances and reproduction habits.

History of the Coniferous Forests, California and Nevada
D. I. Axelrod. 1976. Univ. of Calif., Berkeley.

Major Habitat Types, Community Types, and Plant Communities in the Rocky Mountains
Robert R. Alexander. 1985. USDA Forest Service, Rocky Mountain For. and Rg. Exp. Stn. Gen. Tech. Rep. RM-123. 105 pp.

Multiple-Use Management of California's Hardwood Resources
General Technical Report PSW-100. Berkeley, California: U.S. Department of Agriculture, Pacific South West Forest and Range Experiment Station.

Proceedings of a symposium.

Multi-Resource Management of Ponderosa Pine Forests
Proceedings of a symposium, Nov. 14-16, 1989. Flagstaff, AZ.
Aregai Tecle, W. Wallace Covington, R. H. Hamre, technical coordinators. 1989. Rocky Mountain Forest and Range Experiment Station General Technical Report RM-185; 282 pp.

A Natural History of Western Trees
Donald Culross Peattie. 1953. Houghton-Mifflin: New York.

A detailed, readable and enjoyable introduction to Northwest and California trees.

Oaks of California
B. M. Pavlik, P. C. Muick, S. G. Johnson and M. Popper. 191. 184 pp.

Gorgeous color photographs and attractive layout. Good text, although it doesn't go into much detail on management. Taxonomy, ranges, species, Indian uses, ecology, wildlife, the decline of oak in California and the efforts to restore oak woodlands. Oak fanatics would buy a copy, general tree fanatics would borrow a copy from the library.

"Old-Growth Ponderosa Pine-Western Larch Forests in Western Montana: Ecology and Management"
James R. Habeck. *The Northwest Environmental Journal,* 1990, 6(2): 271-292.

A Southwestern Mosaic: Proceedings of the Southwestern Region New Perspectives University Colloquium
D. C. Hayes, Jon S. Bumstead, Merton T. Richards (editors). 1992. General Technical Report RM-216. Rocky Mountain Forest and Range Experiment Station, USDA Forest Service, Fort Collins, Colorado, 80526 52 pp.

A look at what New Perspectives means to US Forest Service managers in the Southwest.

Terrestrial Vegetation of California
M. G. Barbour and J. Major, eds. 1977. Wiley: New York.

Forestry Organizations in the United States

THIS IS A SOMEWHAT ECLECTIC SELECTION of organizations in this section. Most are national in scope. Hundreds of other U.S. organizations are reviewed in other *Restoration Forestry* sections.

American Forestry Association

P.O. Box 2000
Washington, D.C. 20013
Tel: (202) 667-3300. Fax: (202) 667-7751.

The American Forestry Association (AFA), founded in 1875, has a total membership of 112,342. Membership in AFA ($24/yr.) includes subscription to *American Forests* (6 issues/yr.) as well as discounts on publications, invitations to meetings and conferences, voting privileges, access to the AF library, and technical assistance from AFA's professional staff using their toll-free number. The AFA is the leading force behind operation Global ReLeaf, which aims to stimulate tree planting throughout U.S. cities and towns.

American Forest Council

1250 Connecticut Ave. NW
Washington, DC 20036
Tel: 1-800-648-6699.

American Society of Ecological Education

c/o College of Environmental and Applied Sciences
Governors State University
Park Forest South, Illinois 60466

Association of Consulting Foresters of America, Inc.

5410 Grosvenor Lane, Suite 205
Bethesda, Maryland 20814-2194
Tel: (301) 530-6795.

High standards of training and professional ethics are criteria for ACF membership. There are currently about 400 members. ACF professionals service individuals, banks, attorneys, accountants, industry and others.

Association of Forest Service Employees for Environmental Ethics (AFSEEE)

P.O. Box 11615
Eugene, Oregon 97440
Tel: (503) 484-2692

The Association of Forest Service Employees for Environmental Ethics was formed in 1989 as Employees Speaking as Concerned Citizens of the United States. The first issue of it's newsletter, *Inner Voice*, was published in Summer 1989. By the second issue in Fall 1989, it's membership was already close to 1000 current, retired, or former Forest Service employees and another 1,000 non-Forest Service subscribers.

Other AFSEEE publications for sale include:

The Cycle of An Agency by Chris Maser–$15.

Crisis on the Clearwater–$3.

Ten Questions to Ask About Salvage Logging Programs–$2.

Notes on the 1993 FS Budget–$2.

AFSEEE Chapters:

Colville Chapter AFSEEE
1903 East Ivy
Colville, Washington 99114
Tel: (509) 684-8376

Ketchikan Chapter AFSEEE
Tongass NF
P.O. Box 9113
Ketchikan, Alaska 99901

Lolo Chapter AFSEEE
2161 S. 10th West
Missoula, Montana 59801
Tel: (406) 549-5243.

Los Padres Chapter AFSEEE
P.O. Box 1282
Goleta, California 93116

Tel: (805) 962-2415.

Stanislaus Chapter AFSEEE
P.O. Box 1323
Pine Crest, California 95364
Tel: (209) 965-4271

Umpqua Chapter AFSEEE
P.O. Box 196,
Glide, Oregon 97443

Willamette Chapter AFSEEE
P.O. Box 11339
Corvallis, Oregon 97440
Tel: (503) 747-2336.

Forest Island Project
1017 University Ave.
Berkeley, California 94710
Tel: (415) 548-1778.

A nonprofit organization whose goals are to preserve remnant tropical forest lands, promoting their integrated use along with sustainable agriculture practices. The idea is to create "living bridges" of sustainable agriculture plantations to serve as wildlife corridors between remaining forest patches and to provide local people with economic alternatives to deforestation through the marketing of native plant products. The pilot project is in the Los Tuxtlas rain forest in Vera Cruz, Mexico, involving 7 communities.

Forest Trust
P.O. Box 519
Santa Fe, New Mexico 87504
Tel: (505) 983-8992

The Forest Trust promotes restoration forestry in the Southwest and beyond. The Forest Trust conducts research in the areas of silviculture, reforestation, timber sale economics, water quality protection, water resource values, wildlife habitat protection, and multiple resource modeling. Current projects include research on endangered species recovery, ecosystem and biodiversity modeling, and cross-cultural perspectives on forest ecosystems and forestry.

The Trust's staff provides assistance with assessments of decision-making procedures, identification of alternative approaches to issues, and development of effective strategies for achieving group objectives.

The organization holds in trust some 13,000 acres of forest lands in New Mexico and Colorado.

Forest Trust publishes *Network News: Environmental Protection for National Forests.*

The Forest Trust's Mora Forestry Center teaches forestry skills to adults and young people in the area. In cooperation with the state Labor Department, the center has trained about 20 people each summer in forestry property management, fire fighting and business skills.

In summer, 1993, the Forest Trust announced publication of a new newsletter: *Practitioner: Newsletter of the Forest-Based, Rural Development Practitioners' Network.* The goal of the practitioners is to resolve the conflict between environmental protection and economic development. Some 80 individuals attended the 1992 Forest-Based, Rural Development Practitioners' Working Session in Arcata, California.

Forest Trust has also publishes a *Directory of Forest-Based, Rural Development Groups.* The 1993 edition is a compendium of organizations throughout the U.S. engaged in rural community development based on forest resources. *The Directory* lists groups whose goals include restoring and enhancing the forest environment; developing consensus within rural communities; supporting and creating good jobs; creating and managing value-added industries; empowering local users to manage resources for local benefit; providing training and education for the labor force; and promoting state and national policies that further these goals.

International Society of Tropical Foresters
Address in International Forestry Organizations section.

ISTF has been providing information services on the wise use, management and protection of the global tropical forests since 1950. ISTF is working to develop a more effective networking and information clearinghouse called Tropical Forestry Network Clearinghouse.

Los Amigos del Mesquite (The Friends of Mesquite)
Center for Semi-Arid Forest Resources
Texas A&M University
Kingsville, Texas 78363
Fax: (512) 595-3713

Established in 1982 to encourage and promote research on the utilization of mesquite (*Prosopis sp.*). They held their 11th annual conference in 1993.

The National Arbor Day Foundation
100 Arbor Avenue
Nebraska City, Nebraska 68401

National Association of State Foresters
444 North Capitol St. NW
Washington, DC 20001

National Big Tree Program
American Forestry Association
See address at beginning of this section.

The program has been keeping records since 1940 of the largest trees of each species in the USA.

Natural Areas Association

320 S. Third St.
Rockford, Illinois 61104
Tel: (815) 964-6666

The Natural Areas Association was formed in 1978 as a non-profit organization of persons concerned with natural areas. Members include professional and volunteer researchers, natural area managers, naturalists, conservationists and other interested persons. They sponsor an annual conference and publish the quarterly *Natural Areas Journal*, one of best places to find out about current research and stewardship activities, rare species management, land preservation techniques, and natural area legislation. $25 Individual member.

Nature Conservancy

1815 N. Lynn Street
Arlington, Virginia 22209
Tel: (703) 841-5300

The Nature Conservancy owns and manages more than 1,600 preserves throughout the US, which is the largest private system of nature sanctuaries in the world. Since 1953, the Conservancy has saved 5.5 million acres and managed 1,300,000 acres in the US. The Conservancy has 585,000 members, 500 corporate associates, and employs over 1,000 professional staff in all 50 states. They have many restoration projects. Collectively, the Conservancy staff constitute one of the largest sources of restoration knowledge in the U.S.

Public Employees for Environmental Responsibility

810 First St. NE, Suite 680
Washington DC 20002-3633
Tel: (202) 408-0041/Fax: (202) 842-4716.

PEER is building on the success of AFSEEE Association of Forest Service Employees for Environmental Ethics. Jeff DuBonis got AFSEEE up and running and now has started PEER to provide a voice for reform for all public employees. Publishes *PEEReview*, a quarterly newsletter. Membership is $30 or more.

Society of Wetland Scientists

Box 296
Wilmington, North Carolina 28402

Washington State Big Tree Program

College of Forest Resources
University of Washington AR-10
Seattle, Washington 98195

Founded in 1989 to keep track of the largest and tallest trees in Washington. An updated list is published each year which includes both native and non-native conifers and deciduous trees. Locations are given. Citizens are encouraged to seek out and submit nominations for this list. Hundreds of species are listed. One of the nation's best

state-wide programs.

World Forestry Center

4033 SW Canyon Rd
Portland, Oregon 97221
Tel: (503) 228-1367

The World Forestry Center (WFC) is a local, independent, non-profit educational institution dedicated to the establishment, protection, conservation, and management of forests, soils, water, wildlife and other renewable resources. WFC operates a research institute, conference facility, a museum and exhibit hall and a 70-acre demonstration forest in Wilsonville, Oregon.

Sounds like restoration forestry, but it has been pointed out that WFC is closely aligned with the timber industry, albeit left of center on forest policy and management.

The World Forestry Center publishes a quarterly *Forest Perspectives*. WFC also publishes one issue per year of *Forest World*, with educational information on conservation of the world's forests. Subscription comes with membership. $25/year.

Woodworkers' Alliance for Rainforest Protection

One Cottage St.
Easthampton, Massachusetts 92075
Tel: (619) 481-0442

WARP works for rainforest conservation on an international level, but they are also involved with sustainable forestry and certification. Their newsletter, *Understory*, provides a valuable perspective of restoration forestry from the viewpoint of small-scale wood artisans.

State Forest Farm Associations

About 25 states have associations of small timberland/woodlot owners, some more than one. Their members offer sources of forestry information. Here are names and addresses of some of these associations, and the address for the national center which looks after all their interests. Collectively these state associations represent tens of thousands of small woodland owners. Certainly they include many restoration forestry models. Collectively they represent a tremendous amount of forestry knowledge. Most of the small landowners love their land and forests, and some are practicing, or open to, restoration forestry ideas and techniques.

Nearly 60 percent of U.S. forest land is owned by private individuals. Of the 70,000 tree farmers, two thirds are family operations of less than 100 acres. Private industry owns another 15 percent.

This group of people is under quite a bit of pressure to log their forests. Small woodland owners have been targeted as the next best place to log after the federal timber lands give out. Stumpage prices are high in 1993. In Idaho, the unprecedented high stumpage prices have resulted in the fifth consecutive year of record high logging on private forest lands. In late 1993, the Public Forestry Foundation reported that the timber cut on Oregon's private lands doubled during the past year. Plenty of forestland owners in my neck of the woods have been logging; some clear-cut, some highgrade, some precommercial thin. Few practice what I would call restoration forestry, but I believe many would, if approached with a clear presentation and with some models to look at. If restoration forestry is to work on the national scale it will have to be through the thousands of small forestland owners.

National Woodland Owners Association
374 Maple Ave. E., Suite 210
Vienna, Virginia
Tel: (703) 255-2700

Keith Argow, President. They publish a quarterly magazine, *National Woodlands* and a newsletter on legislation, *Woodland Report*, eight times a year. Membership is $25. Any new member with 20 acres or more of forestland receives a free on-site consultation by a certified forester. The consultation usually lasts a half day.

New Hampshire Timberland Owner's Association
54 Portsmouth St.
Concord, New Hampshire 03301

New York Forest Owners Association
9 Grant St.
Cobleskill, New York 12043

Oregon Small Woodlands Association
1149 Court St. NE
Salem, Oregon 97301
Tel: (503) 588-0050

Small Woodland Owners Association of Maine
South Gouldsboro, Maine 04678
Tel: (207) 963-2331

Washington Farm Forestry Association
P.O. Box 7663
Olympia, Washington 98507
Tel: (206) 943-3875.

The Washington Farm Forestry Association has 1200 members. They publish a quarterly magazine and a management newsletter. Membership is $25/yr.

Wisconsin Woodland Owners Association, Inc.
505 Togstead Glen
Madison, Wisconsin 53711

Forestry Periodicals in the United States

OTHER U.S. PERIODICALS can be found in the Pacific Northwest and Eastern U.S. sections as well as scattered throughout *Restoration Forestry*. The only complete list would be the index to periodicals at the back of the book.

Directories To Forestry Periodicals

Directory of Selected Tropical Forestry Journals and Newsletters

Includes many U.S. publications which have relevance outside the tropics. See address/review in International Periodicals section.

International Directory of Wildland Fire

Disc version, 1993. Printed version, 1990. International Association of Wildland Fire. 671 pp.

This directory lists 500 forestry journals and newsletters from around the world. See review and address in the Directory section.

U.S. Forestry Periodicals

American Forests

"The Magazine of Trees and Forests" is published by the American Forestry Association. See organizations section for address.

The issues in the late 1980's reflected a wide variety of progressive viewpoints on conservation, urban forest, and small woodlot management. Oriented to the general public. AFA also publishes a newsletter titled *Resource Hotline*.

Biologue

National Wood Energy Association
777 North Capitol St. NE, Suite 805
Washington, DC 20002
Tel: (202) 408-0664/Fax: (202) 408-8536.

National and international news on development in the field of biomass energy production. Quarterly.

Ecology Law Quarterly

Boalt Hall School of Law
University of California
Berkeley, California 94720
Tel: (510) 642-0457

A journal of environmental law and policy. A 1990 Winner of United Nations Global 500 Award. $27.50/yr. $12 single issue.

Environmental Science and Forestry

State University of New York, College of Environmental Science and Forestry
Bray Hall, Rm. 123
Syracuse, New York 13210
Tel: (315) 470-6644

Newsletter.

Flora of North America Newsletter

Missouri Botanical Garden
P.O. Box 299
St. Louis, Missouri 63166

The Flora of North America (FNA) project is an ambitious cooperative program to produce a flora of the vascular plants of North America north of Mexico. Many volumes are projected to be published over the course of several decades. The newsletter is published bimonthly to communicate news about the FNA project and other topics of interest to North American floristic researchers. FNA is centered at the Missouri Botanical Garden in St. Louis, Missouri but involves hundreds of taxonomists and botanists around North America.

Forest Industries

500 Howard St.
San Francisco, California 94105

Pro-industry. Free subscription to individuals in the logging, lumber and plywood industries. $55/yr. to others.

Forestry Support Program Memo

USDA Forest Service (IF)
Forestry Support Program
P.O. Box 96090
Washington D.C. 20090-6090

Quarterly newsletter on technical and general information about forestry issues to USAID and Peace Corps staff. Free of charge.

Inner Voice

Association of Forest Service Employees for Environmental Ethics (AFSEEE)
PO Box 11615
Eugene, Oregon 97440

Inner Voice conveys a feeling that there is a rebellion going on within the ranks of the Forest Service. An inside view of the Forest Service's scandals (and there are lots of them), but also an inside view of what is being done to swing the Forest Service towards a gentler and more sustainable forestry. If you are interested in what is happening in the national forests, you will want to read *Inner Voice*.

Besides the politics, there are practical articles on forest management. *Inner Voice* has become one of the best forums for developments in restoration forestry. If you are a current, former or retired Forest Service employee you can become an AFSEEE member. If not, you can become an associate member for $20. Limited income $10. *Inner Voice* back issues $2.

Journal of Environmental Education

4000 Albermarle St. NW, Suite 500
Washington DC 20016

Journal of Forest History

Forest History Society
701 Vickers Ave.
Durham, North Carolina 27701-3147
Tel: (919) 652-9310

Journal. $20/yr.

Journal of Forestry

Society of American Foresters
5400 Grosvenor
Bethesda, Maryland 20814
Tel: (301) 897-8720/Fax: (301) 897-3690

Twelve issues per year. Subscriptions: US $7/issue; $110/year overseas.

Journal of Sustainable Forestry

The Haworth Press, Inc.
10 Alice Street
Binghamton, New York 12094

The first issue (quarterly) was issued in early 1993. Although it takes up 134+ pages it contains only 7 articles and an abundance of ads for Haworth Press' other publications. Four of the articles are technical and would be applicable to few people. The three general-interest articles include an article by Chris Maser, one on forestation of mined lands, and one on the Palcazu project in Peru. There are no book reviews, timely information, conference announcements, editorial columns, etc.

All in all, a disappointing showing for the first issue of a magazine with such an interesting title. Hopefully it will improve in future issues. $24/year individual. $36 institution.

Mountain Research and Development

University of California Press
2120 University Way
Berkeley, California 94720

A quarterly with an international focus. Articles deal with land use, forests, soil erosion and control, reforestation, and social systems. Subscriptions: Individuals $34/yr., institutions $70. Overseas postage extra.

Natural Areas Journal

Natural Areas Association
Address in U.S. Organizations.

A quarterly on the management of natural areas. Oriented to career professionals. $25/year.

Natural Resource Rehabilitation

502 East Sussex
Missoula, Montana 59801
Newsletter.

Northern Journal of Applied Forestry

Southern Journal of Applied Forestry

Western Journal of Applied Forestry

Published by the Society of American Foresters
Address in U.S. organizations.

The above three journals are read by many US foresters. Reports from leading, practicing foresters.

Social Sciences in Forestry

c/o Jean Albrecht, Librarian
110 Green Hall, 1530 N. Cleveland Ave.
St. Paul, Minnesota 55108
Newsletter.

Women in Natural Resources

Laboratory of Anthropology
University of Idaho
Moscow, Idaho 83843
Tel: (208) 885-6754

An international journal by/for professional women in forestry and natural resource fields. $15/yr.

University Forestry Departments in the U.S. and Canada

Forestry Education on the Rise in the U.S.

The Society of American Foresters (SAF) released a survey in 1993 on enrollments and degrees granted in schools of natural resources during the 1992–93 school year. In 1992–93, total undergraduate and graduate enrollments were 19,849, an increase of four percent from the previous year. Women made up 29.5 percent in 1991–92. By discipline fxorestry had the highest enrollment (7,624 students), followed by wildlife (3,936), natural resources conservation (2,513), environmental science (2,076), recreation (1,595), wood technology (1,117), fisheries (742), and range (246). A copy of the complete survey which includes more than 74 pages of individual school data, regional totals, and graphs is available for $15 from the Society of American Foresters, 5400 Grosvenor Lane, Bethesda, MD 20814. Excerpt from article in National Woodlands, October 1993.

Where To Obtain Lists of Forestry Schools Outside the USA

The SILVA-Network
See International Organizations section for address.

An organization including 21 academic forestry institutes from 14 European countries.

World List of Forestry Schools
Food and Agriculture Organization of the United Nations. Forestry Department. Rome. FAO Forestry Paper 3. 1977. 88 pp. (Ask for a most recent list.)

A list of university-level institutions and non-university level schools.

U.S. Universities and Colleges Offering Forestry Degrees

Association of State College and University Forestry Research
University of Minnesota College of Forestry
Saint Paul, Minnesota 55108
Tel: (612) 624-1234

Forestry Schools in the United States

The U.S. Forest Service publishes a directory, which is updated periodically.

School of Forestry
Auburn University
108 M. White Smith Hall
Auburn, AL 36849-5418
Tel: (205) 844-1007/Fax: 205-844-1084

Natural Resources Management Dept.
California Polytechnic State University
San Luis Obispo, CA 93407
Tel: (805) 756-2702/Fax: 805-756-1402

College of Forest & Recreation Resources
Clemson University
130 Lehotsky Hall
Clemson, SC 29634-1001
Tel: (803) 656-3215/Fax: 803-656-0231

Dept. of Forest Sciences
Colorado State University
Ft. Collins, CO 80523
Tel: (303) 491-6911/Fax: 303-491-6754

Connecticut Ag Experiment Station
P.O. Box 1106
New Haven, CT 06504
Tel: (203)789-7214/Fax: 203-789-7232

Department of Environmental Resources
Cook College, Rutgers University
New Brunswick, NJ 08903
Tel: (201)932-9631/Fax: 201-932-8644

Dept. of Natural Resources
Cornell University
Fernow Hall
Ithaca, NY 14853
Tel: (607)255-2298/Fax: 607-255-0349

7

School of The Environment
Duke University
216 Biological Sciences Building
Durham, NC 27706
Tel: (919) 684-2135/Fax: 919-684-8741

Department of Forestry
Iowa State University
Ames, IA 50011
Tel: (515) 294-1166/Fax: 515-294-1337

Department of Forestry
Kansas State University
215 Call Hall
Manhattan, KS 66506
Tel: (913) 532-5752/Fax: 913-539-9584

Department of Forestry
Michigan State University
East Lansing, MI 48824-1222
Tel: 517/355-0093/Fax: 517-353-1143

School of Natural Resources
The Ohio State University
210 Kottman Hall
2021 Coffey Road
Columbus, OH 43210
Tel: 614-292-2265/Fax: 614-292-7162

Dept. of Forestry and Natural Resources
Purdue University
West Lafayette, IN 47907
Tel: (317) 494-3591/Fax: 317-494-0409

School of Forestry
Stephen F. Austin State University
Box 6109, S F A Station
Nocogdoches, TX 75962-6109
Tel: (409) 568-3304/Fax: 409-568-2489

Faculty of Forestry
SUNY College of Environmental Science and Forestry
Syracuse, NY 13210
Tel: (315)470-6536/Fax: 315-470-6535

Department of Horticulture, Forestry, Landscape & Parks
South Dakota State University
Box 2207-C
Brookings, SD 57007
Tel: 605/688-5136/Fax: 605-688-6065

Dept. of Horticulture & Forestry
North Dakota State University
Fargo, ND 58102
Tel: (701) 237-8474/Fax: 701-237-8520

School of Forestry, Wildlife and Fisheries
Louisiana State University
227 Forestry-Wildlife-Fisheries Bldg.
Baton Rouge, LA 70803-6200
Tel: (504)388-4131/Fax: 504-388-4227

School of Forestry
Louisiana Tech University
Box 10138, Tech Station
Ruston, LA 71272
Tel: 318-257-4985/Fax: 318-257-4288

School of Forestry & Wood Products
Michigan Tech University
Houghton, MI 49931
Tel: (906) 487-2454/Fax: 906-487-2915

School of Forest Resources
Mississippi State University
P.O. Drawer F R
Mississippi State, MS 39762-5726
Tel: (601) 325-2952/Fax: 601-325-8726

Horticulture Department
New Mexico State University
Box 3530
Las Cruces, NM 88003
Tel: (505) 646-1522/Fax: 505-646-6041

College of Forest Resources
North Carolina State University
2028 Biltmore Hall, Box 8001
Raleigh, NC 27695-8001
Tel: (919) 515-2883/Fax: 919-515-7231

School of Forestry
Northern Arizona University
Box 4098
Flagstaff, AZ 86011
Tel: (602) 523-3031/Fax: 602-523-1080

Department of Forestry
Oklahoma State University
011 Agricultural Hall
Stillwater, OK 74078
Tel: (405)744-5437/Fax: 405-744-9693

College of Forestry
Oregon State University
Corvallis, OR 97331
Tel: 503-737-2221/Fax: 503-737-2668

Dept. of Forestry
Southern Illinois University
Carbondale, IL 62901
Tel: (618)453-3341/Fax: 618-453-1778

Department of Forest Science
Texas A & M University
Horticulture Forest Science Building
College Station, TX 77843-2135
Tel: (409) 845-5000/Fax: 409-845-6049

School of Agriculture & Land Resource Management
Ag Exp. Station
University of Alaska Fairbanks
172 AHRB
Fairbanks, AK 99775-0100
Tel: (907)474-7083/Fax: 907-474-7439

School of Renewable Resources
University of Arizona
Tucson, AZ 85721
Tel: (602)621-7257/Fax: 602-621-7196

Department of Forest Resources
University of Arkansas
P.O. Box 3468
Monticello, AR 71655
Tel: (501)460-1052/Fax: 501-460-1092

Dept. of Forestry & Resource Management
University of California, Berkeley
145 Mulford Hall
Berkeley, CA 94720
Tel: (510) 642-0376/Fax: 510-643-5438

Ag Experiment Station
University of Delaware
Newark, DE 19717-1303
Tel: (302)451-2501/Fax: 302-292-3651

School of Forest Resources and Conservation
University of Florida
118 Newins-Ziegler Hall
Gainesville, FL 32611-0303
Tel: (904) 392-1791/Fax: 904-392-1707

School of Forest Resources
University of Georgia
Forest Resources Bldg., Room 231
Athens, GA 30601
Tel: (404) 542-2686/Fax: 404-542-8356

College of Tropical Agriculture & Human Resources
University of Hawaii
3050 Maile Way, Room 202
Honolulu, HI 96822
Tel: (808) 956-8234/Fax: 808-956-6442

College of Forestry, Wildlife & Range Sciences
University of Idaho
Moscow, ID 83843
Tel: (208) 885-6442/Fax: 208-885-6226

Dept. of Forestry
University of Kentucky
205 Thomas Poe Cooper Building
Lexington, KY 40546-0073
Tel: (606)257-7596/Fax: 606-258-1031

College of Forest Resources
University of Maine
Orono, ME 04469
Tel: (207) 581-2844/Fax: 207-581-2858

Ag Exp. Station
University of Maryland
College Park, MD 20742
Tel: (301) 405-1210/Fax: 301-314-9089

Department of Forestry & Wildlife Management
University of Massachusetts
Amherst, MA 01003
Tel: (413)545-2665/Fax: 413-545-4358

School of Natural Resources
University of Michigan
Ann Arbor, MI 48109-1115
Tel: (313) 764-2550/Fax: 313-936-2195/313-763-9694

School of Natural Resources
University of Missouri
Columbia, MO 65211
Tel: (314) 882-6446/Fax: 314-882-1977

School of Forestry
University of Montana
Missoula, MT 59812
Tel: (406) 243-5522/Fax: 406-243-4510

Department of Forestry, Fisheries, and Wildlife
University of Nebraska, East Campus
101 Plant Industry Building
Lincoln, NE 68583-0814
Tel: 402-472-2944/Fax: 402-472-2964

Department of Range, Wildlife and Forestry
University of Nevada
Reno, NV 89512
Tel: (702) 784-4000/Fax: 702-784-4583

Dept. of Natural Resources
University of New Hampshire
James Hall
Durham, NH 03824
Tel: (603)862-1020/Fax: 603-862-4976

Dept. of Forestry, Fisheries, & Wildlife
University of Tennessee
Knoxville, TN 37901-1071
Tel: (615) 974-7126/Fax: 615-974-2765

School of Natural Resources
University of Vermont
330 Aiken Center
Burlington, VT 05401
Tel: (802) 656-4280/Fax: 802-656-8683

Research and Land Grant Affairs
University of the Virgin Islands
Route 2, Box 10,000
Kingshill, St. Croix, VI 00850
Fax: ## need to get this #!

College of Forest Resources
University of Washington
Seattle, WA 98195
Tel: (206) 545-1928/Fax: 206-545-0790

College of Natural Resources
University of Wisconsin
Stevens Point, WI 54481
Tel: (715)346-4617/Fax: 715-341-0089

Dept. of Forestry
University of Wisconsin
Russell Labs
Madison, WI 53706
Tel: (608) 262-1780/Fax: 608-262-9922

School of Natural Resources
University of Wisconsin–Madison
146 Agriculture Hall
Madison, WI 53706
Tel: (608) 262-6968/Fax: 608-262-6055

Division of Range Management
University of Wyoming
Laramie, WY 82070
Tel: (307) 766-2263/Fax: 307-766-3379

Department of Forest Resources
Utah State University
Logan, UT 84322-5215
Tel: (801) 750-2455/Fax: 801-750-3798

Department of Natural Resource Sciences
Washington State University
Pullman, WA 99164-6410
Tel: (509) 335-6166/Fax: 509-335-7862

Division of Forestry
West Virginia University
Morgantown, WV 26506
Tel: (304)293-2941/Fax: 304-293-2441

School of Forestry & Environmental Studies
Yale University
New Haven, CT 06511
Tel: (203) 432-5107/Fax: 203-432-5942

Canadian Universities Offering Forestry Degrees

Lakehead University
School of Forestry
Thunder Bay, Ontario, P7B 5E1, CANADA
Tel: (807) 343-8507.

Université de Moncton
L'École de Sciences Forestieres
165 Boulevard Hebert
Edmundston, New Brunswick E3V 2S8, CANADA
Tel: (506) 735-5068/Fax: (506) 739-5373.

Université Laval
Laval, Quebec, GIK 7P4 CANADA

University of New Brunswick
Bag Service #44555
Frederickton, New Brunswick E3B 6C2, CANADA
Tel: (506) 453-4501/Fax: (506) 453-3538.

University of Toronto
Faculty of Forestry
Earth Sciences Centre, 33 Willcocks St.
Toronto, Ontario M5S 3B3 CANADA
Tel: (416) 978-6152/Fax: (416) 978-3834

University of Alberta
Faculty of Agriculture & Forestry
Edmonton, Alberta, T6G 2P5, CANADA
Tel: (403) 492-4931

University of British Columbia
207-2357 Main Mall
Vancouver, British Columbia V6T 1Z4, CANADA
Tel: (604) 822-2727/Fax: (604) 822-8645

U.S. Government Forest Agencies and Publications

THERE ARE THOUSANDS of government agencies and offices concerned with forests. Here are a few addresses for the U.S. Forest Service, mainly in the Pacific Northwest. For a complete guide to government forest agencies at federal and state levels ask the appropriate government agencies.

Superintendent of Documents

USP.O. Washington DC. 20402-8325

Orders with VISA & MasterCard can be called in to (202) 783-3238.

U.S. Forest Service Headquarters

Chief, Forest Service

U.S Department of Agriculture
Auditors Building 14th & Independence, S.W.
201-14th Street SW
Washington, DC 20250

Cooperative Forestry Department
Tony Dorrell, Director
U.S. Forest Service
210-14th Street SW
Washington, DC 20250
Tel: (202) 205-9389

Extension Forestry
Larry E. Biles, National Program Leader
U.S. Forest Service address above
Tel: (202) 447-2728 Fax: (202) 475-5289

Forest Service-USDA
14th & Independence, S.W.
P.O. Box 96090
Washington, DC 20090-6090
USDA General Information Tel: (202) 720-USDA
Public Inquiries Tel: (202) 205-0957

Forest Service-Info Central
Information Systems Staff
Forest Service—USDA
10301 Baltimore Blvd., Rm. 112
Beltsville, Maryland 20705
Tel: (301) 344-4173

Forest Service Research
Dr. Jerry A. Sesco, Deputy Chief for Research
USDA Forest Service
P.O. Box 96090
Washington, DC 20090

New Perspectives Group
Address as above.
Tel: 202) 205-1974/Fax: (202) 205-1978

New Perspectives is the US Forest Service's new initiative to practice more ecologically sound forestry and ecosystem management.

United States Forest Service Research Stations Regional Headquarters

All of the following Experiment Stations put out *Monthly Alerts* listing new publications available to the public, usually at no charge.

Forest Products Laboratory
One Gifford Pinchot Drive
Madison, Wisconsin 53705
Tel: (608) 231-9200

Intermountain Forest and Range Experiment Station
324 25th Street
Ogden, Utah 84401
Tel: (801) 625-5412

North Central Forest Experiment Station
1992 Folwell Avenue
St. Paul, Minnesota 55108
Tel: (612) 649-5000

Northeastern Forest Experiment Station
P.O. Box 6775
Radnor, Pennsylvania 19087-4585
Tel: (219) 975-4222

Pacific Northwest Forest and Range Experiment Station
(See following section)

Pacific Southwest Forest and Range Experiment Station
P.O. Box 245
Albany, California 94710-0011
Tel: (510) 559-6300

Rocky Mountain Forest and Range Experiment Station
240 West Prospect
Ft. Collins, Colorado 85026
Tel: (303) 498-1100

Southeastern Forest Experiment Station
P.O. Box 2680
Asheville, North Carolina 28802
Tel: (704) 257-4390

Southern Forest Experiment Station
701 Loyola Avenue
New Orleans, Louisiana 70113
Tel: (504) 589-6800.

Pacific Northwest

Pacific Northwest Forest and Range Experiment Station
P.O. Box 3890
Portland, Oregon 97208
Tel: (503) 326-5640
Publications Dept. Tel: (503) 326-7128

Recent publications of the Pacific Northwest Research Station. Published quarterly. Free subscription.

Videos available from Pacific Northwest Forest Experiment Station

Videos are available on loan without charge. Borrowers pay only return postage. Portland Habilitation Center, 2750 SE Mailwell Dr., Milwaukie, OR 97222

FS INFO NW Monthly Alert
Mail Stop AQ-15
University of Washington
Seattle, Washington 98195

The *FS INFO NW Monthly Alert* announces recent publications in forestry and related fields, emphasizing forestry in the Northwest. Each issue lists hundreds of articles or books in 30 subject categories.

All items listed in the *Monthly Alert* are available from FS INFO NW to USDA Forest Service employees and to other authorized users. FS INFO services also includes obtaining any material listed in the *Monthly Alert* or from any other source, and a computer-based literature searching, citation verification, quick information and referral to other sources or contacts for information.

Pacific Northwest U.S. Forest Service Research Stations

Anchorage
Anchorage Forestry Sciences Laboratory
201 E. 9th Ave., Suite 303
Anchorage, Alaska 99501

Bend
Silviculture Laboratory
1027 NW Trenton Ave.
Bend, Oregon 97701

Corvallis
Forestry Sciences Laboratory
3200 SW Jefferson Way
Corvallis, Oregon 97331

Fairbanks
Institute of Northern Forestry
308 Tanana Drive
Fairbanks, Alaska 99775-5500

Juneau
Forestry Sciences Laboratory
2770 Sherwood Lane, Suite 2A
Juneau, Alaska 99801

La Grande
Forestry Sciences Laboratory
1401 Gekeler Lane
La Grande, Oregon 97850

Olympia
Forestry Sciences Laboratory
33625 93rd Ave. SW
Olympia, Washington 98502

Portland
Forestry Sciences Laboratory
P.O. Box 3890
Portland Oregon 97208-3890

Seattle
Forestry Sciences Laboratory
4043 Roosevelt Way NE
Seattle, Washington 98105

Wenatchee
Forestry Sciences Laboratory
1133 N. Western Ave
Wenatchee, Washington 98801

Forest Conservation Organizations in the USA

THE PHENOMENON of citizen's groups organizing to have more say in local forest management is happening in every country to a greater or lesser extent. I estimate there are now hundreds of thousands of local forest conservation organizations in the world and the number is growing rapidly.

Contributions of Environmental Groups To Forestry Practices

Forest conservation groups do more than lobby for forest conservation and preservation. Collectively they have some of the best knowledge on sustainable forestry practices for their region. After years of effort, research, training and interaction with the forest, some environmentalists have become more knowledgeable about forest ecology, forest conditions and ecologically-sound logging methods than their counterparts in the Forest Service or industry. Citizen's groups are starting to come up with forest management plans clearly superior to those prepared by government agencies. Not all environmental groups have reached this capability. The prerequisites seem to be a core group of skilled and knowledgeable local people, including people who live and work in the woods, a decade or more of working together to build vision and knowledge, recurrent interaction with land management agencies, a great love for the forests, and dedication. Some groups which have come up with credible forest plans include the Slocan Valley Watershed Coalition of the Selkirk Mountains, British Columbia; Willits Environmental Center, California; Friends of Greens Springs, Ashland Oregon; Forests Forever Initiative in California; Cortez Island, British Columbia; Ecoforestry Institute's Stella Peak Forestry Plan, southwest Oregon, and the Year 2000 Proposal by TREES, Garberville, California.

To reflect this broadening of forestry knowledge in the community, people are demanding greater participation in decision making. Citizen advisory boards for National Forests at the district level are increasing in number and influence. Through these small beginnings, local citizens are laying the groundwork for increased local participation in decision-making in National Forests.

When I want to locate the whereabouts of restoration forestry practitioners, I call the environmental organizations for that region and ask them. If forestry practices can pass the scrutiny of the environmentalists, it is likely to be exemplary of restoration forestry.

The environmental movement in the USA is a true bioregional movement. Local people organizing around a specific issue or a particular forest, river or place they love. There are few National Forests which do not have at least one watchdog environmental group. Over time, many of these small, local, grassroots groups grow in size and maturity. They find their struggle often leads to Washington D.C. and multinational corporate headquarters. To effect change at these larger levels they join forces with nearby grassroots groups. Thus regional coalitions are formed. Over time, these regional coalitions ally with adjacent coalitions to cover whole states or bioregions (such as the Northern Rockies or Appalachians). Over the past few years these larger coalitions have been uniting on a national level. One example is the Western Ancient Forest Campaign (WAFC).

A bioregional movement starts from the grassroots and works up, rather than from the top down. This grassroots nature of the environmental movement is what makes it such a strong force for change.

The list of forest conservation groups in *Restoration Forestry* represents the tip of the iceberg. Coverage is most comprehensive in the Pacific Northwest. This large section has been divided into various categories: major national organizations, national coalitions of grassroots organizations, regional organizations, and local grassroots groups. I have done my best to place groups in the appropriate category, but there is some subjectivity, due to not having detailed information for all groups.

Directories To Environmental Groups

Conservation Directory

National Wildlife Federation. 1993. 430 pp. See address this page.

The 1993 *Directory* is the 38th edition. This directory lists addresses, phone numbers, and officers of hundreds of conservation organizations by state. Mostly big organizations; not very good coverage of grass-roots groups. It also lists members of Congress, federal and state wildlife and conservation agencies, and universities with forestry and wildlife programs. Some international listings. Copies of the *Directory* cost $15.

The Nature Directory: A Guide to Environmental Organizations

Susan D. Lanier-Graham. 1991. Walker & Co.: New York. 190 pages. $12.95.

One-page overviews of about 100 major environmental groups. Not much grass roots here, but a fairly detailed coverage of most of the big ones.

U. S. Environmental Directories

P.O. Box 65156
St. Paul, Minnesota 55165

[Also see: WAFC Directory, Western Ancient Forest Coalition in national grass-roots coalitions.]

Major National Environmental Organizations

We have included a few of the more prominent national groups working on forest issues. Grassroots activists sometimes refer to them as the "Big Ten," although there are more then ten. Each of these national organizations has dozens or even hundreds of local chapters. Only the national headquarters addresses are listed here. See *National Wildlife Federation's Conservation Directory* for a comprehensive list.

Biodiversity Legal Foundation

P.O. Box 18327
Boulder, Colorado 80308

A national, non-profit organization dedicated to the preservation and restoration of all native wild plants and animals, communities of species, ecosystems and natural landscapes in all regions of North America. Cutting-edge administrative and legal work on behalf of sensitive, rare, threatened, and endangered species and the natural ecosystems upon which their survival depends.

Environmental Action Fund

P.O. Box 22421
Nashville Tennessee 37202
Tel: (615) 2544-4994

Environmental Defense Funds, Inc.

475 Park Ave. S.
New York, New York 10016

Friends of the Earth

218 D St. SE
Washington, DC 20003
Tel: (202) 544-2600

Greenpeace

1436 "U" St. NW
Washington, DC 20009
Tel: (202) 462-1177/Fax: (202) 462-4507

Greenpeace

4549 Sunnyside Ave. N.
Seattle, Washington 98103
Tel: (206) 632-4326
Environet: The Greenpeace Computer Bulletin Board System

National Audubon Society

950 Third Ave
New York, New York 10022
Tel: (212) 832-3200

National Audubon is different from others in the Big Ten, because it is more of a bottom-up organization and its member groups are autonomous. Audubon Society's Adopt-a-Forest Program helps local groups organize to monitor and influence the activities of National Forests, and conduct mapping of ancient forests.

National Wildlife Federation

1400 Sixteenth St. N.W.
Washington, D.C. 20036-2266
Tel: (202) 797-6800

Natural Resources Defense Council

40 West 20th St.
New York, New York 10011
Tel: (212) 727-2700

Sierra Club

730 Polk St.
San Francisco, California 94109

Sierra Club Legal Defense Fund

2044 Fillmore St.
San Francisco, California 94115

Sierra Club Legal Defense Fund

216 1st Ave. S, #330
Seattle, Washington 98104

The Wilderness Society

1400 I St., NW, 10th Fl
Washington, DC 20005-2290
Tel: (202) 842-3400

National Coalitions of Grassroots Forest Groups

Forest Reform Network

Ned Fritz
5934 Royal Lane, Suite 223
Dallas, Texas 75230
Tel/Fax: (214) 352-8370

Ned Fritz and the Forest Reform Network have been conducting a crusade to end clear-cutting for several decades. The Forest Reform Network initiated and has helped organize an Annual National Forest Reform Pow Wow for seven years with the aid of a growing number of forest groups. It is one of the largest, and longest running, national get-togethers of forest activist's in the USA. The 5th Annual Pow Wow was sponsored by Lighthawk and was an impressive display of unity and common will for 300 attendees from 29 states and over 65 organizations. Those present worked out a "National Forest Protection Pledge." The 1993 Pow Wow (the 7th) was hosted by Heartwood in May in eastern Kentucky.

Save America's Forests

4 Library Court SE
Washington DC 20003
Tel: (202) 544-9219/Fax: (202) 544-7462

By May 1993, Save America's Forests nationwide coalition included over 300 grassroots forest protection groups and businesses across the U.S., and represented over 2.2 million people. Their lobbying and organizing office in Washington DC has enabled a stronger presence by grassroots groups in D.C. Their *Citizen Action Guide* contains information on how to be an effective forest activist and lists many resources.

Save the West

3578 SE Milwaukie
Portland, Oregon 97202
Tel: (503) 234-0093

Founded in 1992 in order to build a new institution which could independently support and truly empower grassroots conservationists throughout North America.

Western Ancient Forest Campaign (WAFC)

1400 16th St. NW #294
Washington, DC 20036
Tel: (202) 939-3324, hotline: 939-3328
Fax: (202) 939-3326

A network of grassroots organizations and individual activist working to protect America's ancient forests for the future. Founded in 1991. WAFC's *1993 Activist Directory* has addresses of over 650 people, most of them representing environmental groups, both national and grassroots.

Regional Coalitions of Grass-roots Forest Groups

Alliance for the Wild Rockies

Box 8731
Missoula, Montana 59807
Tel: (406) 721-5420/Fax: (406) 721-9917

The Alliance was formed to initiate a bioregional approach to protect Wild Rockies ecosystems. An example of bioregional organizing which transcends national borders, as the coalition has member groups in British Columbia and Alberta as well as in Montana, Idaho, and Wyoming. Their membership includes more than 135 member organizations and businesses and 1000 individual paid members. Quarterly newsletter *The Networker*.

Alliance for a Paving Moratorium

P.O. Box 4347
Arcata, California, Ecotopia 95521

Every clear-cut has a road.

American Wildlands

7500 E. Arapahoe Road, Suite 355
Englewood, Colorado 80112

Formerly the American Wilderness Alliance. The 2,500 member group has broadened its focus to include timber policy and reform, riparian habitat, rangeland restoration, and economic analysis. In recent years, AWL has appealed 60 timber sale projects; 95 percent of those appealed have been either settled by negotiation or withdrawn by the Forest Service. Publishes a quarterly journal *On the Wild Side*.

California Ancient Forest Alliance

P.O. Box 1749
Quincy, California 95971
Tel: (916) 283-1007/Fax: (916) 283-4999
or: 156 Barlock Ave
Los Angeles, California 90049
Tel: (310) 471-4278

California Wilderness Coalition

2655 Portage Bay East, Suite 5
Davis, California 95616
Tel: (916) 758-0380/Fax: (916) 753-2935

Coast Range Association

P.O. Box 148
Newport, Oregon 97365
Tel: (503) 265-8105

Colorado Environmental Coalition

777 Grant St. #606
Denver, Colorado 80203
Tel: (303) 837-8704

Earth First!
P.O. Box 1415
Eugene, Oregon 97440
Tel: (503) 741-9191/Fax: (503) 741-9192

The most notorious forest activists to date. Each issue of the *Earth First! Journal* contains a directory of grass-roots Earth-First! groups around the USA and in other countries. About 80 groups in all.

Greater Yellowstone Coalition
P.O. Box 1874
Bozeman, Montana 59771
Tel: (406) 586-1593

Yellowstone/Teton protection.

Heartwood
Rt. 3, Box 402
Paoli, Indiana 47454
Tel: (812) 723-2430

A coalition for central Midwest forests.

Inland Empire Public Lands Council
P.O. Box 2174
Spokane, Washington 99210

This is one of the most active organizations speaking out for the forests of the interior Pacific Northwest.

They have initiated a program called Forest Watch, similar to Audubon's Adopt-a-Forest, which helps groups organize, monitor and appeal timber sales. They produce a monthly newsletter called *Transitions*.

"The Inland Empire" is another term for the interior Columbia River watershed in the United States, comprising eastern Washington, northeast Oregon, northern & central Idaho and western Montana. The Columbia River watershed includes a large part of southern British Columbia. Floristically, all of the watershed of the Columbia could be considered a bioregion. Some people call this bioregion "Columbiana."

Klamath/Siskiyou Coalition
Box 654
Cave Junction, Oregon 97523

Promoting a Siskiyou National park.

Lake Superior Alliance
c/o Upper Peninsula Environmental Coalition
Contact: Jerry Smith

A coalition of twenty US and Canadian environmental groups which monitor and promote the Binational Program to Restore and Protect the Lake Superior Basin.

North Carolina Wilderness Federation
1020 Washington St.
Raleigh, North Carolina 27605
Tel: (919) 856-1581

Olympic Environmental Council
P.O. Box 950
Port Townsend, Washington 98368

A coalition of organizations and individuals on the Olympic Peninsula.

Oregon Ancient Forest Alliance
Western Cascades Region
P.O. Box 11664
Eugene, Oregon 97440

Preserve Appalachian Wilderness (PAW)
81 Middle St.
Lancaster, New Hampshire 03584
Tel: (603) 788-2918

The *PAW Journal* is a "journal of eco-ecstasy, rage and action" illuminating the issues facing the many Appalachian bioregions. Offering solutions based on the Preserve Appalachian Wilderness Plan.

Protect Our Woods
P.O. Box 352
Paoli, Indiana 47454
Tel: (812) 723-2430

A Midwest Forest Activist Network focusing on issues related to the remnant central hardwood forest ecosystems.

"We are focusing on sustainable forest practices on those private forestlands that are going to be cut anyway, and on restoration of native diversity, productivity and health for the public forests, none of which should be logged."

Protect Our Woods has been organizing and lobbying since 1985. They monitor Hoosier National Forest operations and influence project decisions. They have prepared a no-logging management plan for Hoosier National Forest, which is the first of its kind.

Public Lands Action Network
P.O. Box 5631
Santa Fe, New Mexico 87502

Redwoods Coast Watersheds Alliance
11800 Anderson Valley
Boonville, California 95415
Tel: (707) 895-2111/Fax: (707) 895-3442

Sky Island Alliance
1639 E. 1st St.
Tucson, Arizona 85719

Southeast Alaska Conservation Council
Box 021692
Juneau, Alaska 99802
Tel: (907) 586-6942

Quarterly newsletter *RavenCall*.

Southern Utah Wilderness Alliance
P.O. Box 518
Cedar City, Utah 84720

SouthPAW
P.O. Box 2193
Asheville, North Carolina 28802
Tel: (704) 298-2636

Trees Foundation
PO Box 2202
Redway, California 95569
Tel: (707) 923-4377

A service for northern California environmental groups. Sustainable forestry is one of their main foci.

Upper Peninsula Environmental Coalition
Box 34
Houghton, Michigan 49931
Tel: (906) 339-2961

Utah Wilderness Coalition
177 East 900 S., Suite 102,
Salt Lake City, Utah 84111
Tel: (801) 483-4156

Virginia Wilderness Committee
95 Hope St.
Harrisonburg, Virginia 22801
Tel: (703) 434-1318

Washington Environmental Council
Forest Resources Committee
5200 University Way NE, Suite 201
Seattle, Washington 98015
Tel: (206) 527-1599

Washington Wilderness Coalition
P.O. Box 45187,
Seattle, Washington 98145-0187
Tel: (206) 633-1992/Fax: (206) 633-1996

A coalition of 40 environmental groups in Washington. Their Washington *Wildfires Journal* is published 5 times a year.

Western North Carolina Alliance
70 Woodfin Pl., Suite 03
Asheville, North Carolina 28801
Tel: (704) 258-8737/Fax: (704) 258-9141

West Coast Ancient Forest Activists Conference
Headwaters
P.O. Box 729
Ashland, Oregon, 97520
Tel: (503) 482-4459/Fax: (503) 482-7282

This annual event is the largest and most representative get-together of forest conservation organizations on the West Coast. The 2nd annual event was held in February, 1993 with over 300 forest activists. The 3rd annual conference was held in Ashland, Oregon in early February, 1994. The conferences are hosted by Headwaters, whose work is focused in southwest Oregon. The theme is region-wide strategy for ancient forest preservation.

Grassroots Forest Conservation Groups

Adopt-A-Grove
Hal Hushbeck
39450 Mohawk Loop
Marcola, Oregon 97454
Tel: (503) 933-2415

Adopt-A-Timber Sale
5 1/2 W. Cottage Ave.
Flagstaff, Arizona 86001
Tel: (602) 774-0604

American Wildlands
7500 E. Arapahoe
Englewood, Colorado 80110

Ancient Forest Defense Fund
P.O. Box 151
Leggett, California 95455

Applegate New Forestry Advocates
6285 Thompson Ck.
Applegate, Oregon 97530

Audubon Society
Washington State Office
P.O. Box 462
Olympia, Washington 98507

Biodiversity Network, EPIC
P.O. Box 397
Garberville, California 95542

Biodiversity Legal Foundation
P.O. Box 18327
Boulder, Colorado 80308-8327

Black Hills Audubon
4946 Beverly Dr. NE
Olympia, Washington 98506

Blue Heron Environmental Center
P.O. Box 155
White Salmon, Washington 98672
Tel: (509) 493-2737

Blue Mountains Biodiversity Project
HCR-82
Fossil, Oregon 97830
Tel: (503) 468-2028

Blue Mountains Conservation Council
209 N. Clinton St.
Walla Walla, Washington 99362
Tel: (509) 525-0054

Blue Mountains Environment Council
2319 Balm St.
Baker City, Oregon 97814
Tel: (503) 523-3357

Blue Mountains Natural Forest Alliance
Rt. 4, Box 640
Walla Walla , Washington 99362

Bull Run Interest Group
P.O. Box 3426
Gresham, Oregon 97030

Butte Environmental Council
708 Cherry St.
Chico, CA 95928

Butte Falls Forest Advocates
9510 Butte Falls Hwy.
Eagle Point, Oregon 97524

Carson Forest Watch
P.O. Box 15
Llano, New Mexico 87543
Tel: (505) 587-2848

California Forest and Watershed Council
7346 Baker lane
Sebastopol, California 95472

Central Oregon Forest Issues Comm.
1399 NW Saginaw
Bend, Oregon 97701
Tel: (503) 388-4651

Center for Environmental Information, Inc.
46 Prince St.
Rochester, New York 14607
Tel: (716) 271-3550

Chemeketans
500 Rose NE
Salem, Oregon 97301

Citizens for Better Forestry
P.O. Box 1510
Hayfork, California 96041

Citizens for Ecosystem Protection
6919 NW 179th St.
Ridgefield, Washington 98642
Tel: (206) 574-1130

Citizens for Responsible Logging
P.O. Box 21
Chewelah, Washington 99109

Columbia Gorge Audubon Society
1208 Snowden Rd.
White Salmon, Washington 98672
Tel: (509) 493-4428

Concerned Friends of the Winema
HC 30, Box 160
Chiloquin, Oregon 97624

Earth First! Biodiversity Project
2365 Willard Road
Parkersburg, West Virginia 26101-9269

Earth First! Southern Willamette
P.O. Box 10384
Eugene, Oregon 97440
Tel: (503) 343-7305

East Fork Preservation Coalition
P.O. Box 9307
Santa Fe, New Mexico 87504
Tel: (505) 983-2703

Eastern Forests
Box 283
Swarthmore, Pennsylvania 19081

Environmental Protection Information Center (EPIC)
P.O. Box 397
Garberville, California 95440
Tel: (707) 923-2931

The Environmental Protection Information Center has been one of the leaders for the protection of old-growth in northern California.

Environmentally Concerned Citizens of the Lakeland Area
P.O. Box 537
Minocqua, Wisconsin 54548
Tel: (715) 588-3568

Finger Lakes Wild!
P.O. Box 4542
Ithaca, New York 14852

A grassroots, biocentric environmental organization dedicated to the ecological restoration of central New York.

Forest Action Workshop
P.O. Box 1444
Cave Junction, Oregon 97523
Tel: (503) 592-3083

The Forest Action Workshop is a traveling resource available to environmental groups that want to expand their repertoire of effective tactics.

Forest Concerns of the Upper Skagit (FOCUS)
P.O. Box 93
Rockport, Washington 98283
Tel: (206) 873-2542

Forest Guardians

616 Don Gaspar Ave.
Santa Fe, New Mexico 87501
Tel: (505) 988-9126

Protecting archeological sites in Jemez Mts.

Forest Trust

P.O. Box 519
Santa Fe, New Mexico 87504

Noteworthy for their work in sustainable forestry as well as preservation.

Fort Bragg Environmental Center

110 Laurel
Fort Bragg, California 95437
Tel: (707) 961-0554

Friends of Breitenbush

1109 Church St. NE
Salem, Oregon 97301
Tel: (503) 362-6704/Fax: (503) 375-9334.

Friends of the Coquille River

HC 86, Box 158
Myrtle Point, Oregon 97458
Tel: (503) 572-3253

Friends of Del Norte

180 Oak St.
Crescent City, California 95531
Tel: (707) 464-2960

Friends of Dixie

P.O. Box 190085
Brian Head, Utah 85719

Friends of Mount Hood

P.O. Box 82876
Portland, Oregon 97282

Friends of the Bow

P.O. Box 6032
Laramie, Wyoming 82070

Friends of the Gila River

P.O. Box 218
Gila, New Mexico 88038

The Friends of the Gila River have been successfully interacting with the Forest Service to affect management, lower timber sales, and phase out some grazing allotments. They are part of a community forest advisory forum.

Friends of the Green Springs

15097 Hwy 66
Ashland, Oregon 97520
Tel: (503) 482-2307

This local community group has prepared its own set of forest plans to counter the BLM's plan for nearby forests.

Friends of Lake Fork

P.O. Box 806
Halfway, Oregon 97834

Forest preservationists in the Wallowa mountains of northeast Oregon.

Friends of the Loomis Forest

790 North Pine Cr.
Tonasket, Washington 98855

The Loomis Forest borders the North Cascades National Park and the Pasayten Wilderness. It contains the largest population of lynx in the lower 48 States.

Friends of the South Fork

P.O. Box 2085
Trinidad, California 95570

Friends of Opal Creek

P.O. Box 318
Mill City, Oregon 97360
Tel: (503) 897-2921

Courageous efforts have kept the chainsaws out of one of Oregon's last remaining lowland, old-growth forests. At the end of 1992, the Persis Corporation gave a large land grant of mining leases to Friends of Opal Creek. Once FOC comes up with $56,000 in lease fees, they "are off to a grand start at establishing the finest education and scientific research facility in the nation." Programs already include Educator's Retreat; Native American school program; Docents (hike leaders) and greeters; and a Cultural Botanical Inventory.

Gifford Pinchot Task Force

10102 NE 10th St.
Vancouver, Washington 98664
Tel: (206) 892-5643

Coordinates all the groups working on this forest. Monthly newsletter.

Gila Watch

P.O. Box 309
Silver City, New Mexico 88062

Grande Ronde Reserve Council

2211 Cedar St.
La Grande, Oregon 97850
Tel: (503) 963-0905

Great Old Broads for Wilderness

P.O. Box 368
Cedar City, Utah 84721
Tel: (801) 586-1671

The Greater Ecosystem Alliance

P.O. Box 2813
Bellingham, Washington 98227
Tel: (206) 671-9950 Fax: (206) 671-8429

GEA promotes protection of biological diversity

through the conservation of greater ecosystems. Geographic areas of concern are the North and Central Cascades, the Olympic Peninsula and the Selkirks. They are working to establish the North Cascades International Park. Their newsletter is a good forum on biodiversity.

Greater Gila Biodiversity Project
P.O. Box 742
Silver City, New Mexico 88062
Tel: (505) 538-0961/Fax: (505) 538-3540.

Headwaters
P.O. Box 729
Ashland, Oregon 97520
Tel: (503) 482-4459/Fax: (503) 482-7282

The major environmental group working for the forests of southwest Oregon.

Hells Canyon Preservation Council
P.O. Box 908
Joseph, Oregon 97846
Tel: (503) 432-8100/Fax: (503) 432-9061

The Hells Canyon ranks with the Grand Canyon in depth, although its isn't as sheer-walled. The Canyon, which runs between the Wallowas of northeast Oregon and the Seven Devils of Idaho, is a spectacular piece of country with very few people. Huge dams on the Columbia, livestock grazing and overlogging are a few of the problems negatively impacting the ecosystem.

Hoosier Environmental Council
RR 3, Box 286
Nashville, Indiana 47448
Tel: (812) 988-2717/Fax: (317) 686-4794

Idaho Conservation League
P.O. Box 2671
Ketchum, Idaho 83340

ICL has been in the forefront of conservation of roadless areas in Idaho.

Idaho Environmental Council
P.O. Box 1708
Idaho Falls, Idaho 83403
Tel: (208) 523-6692

Illinois Environmental Council
313 West Cook St.
Springfield, Illinois 62704

Jackson Hole Alliance
40 E Simpson, Box 2728
Jackson, Wyoming 83001
Tel: (307) 733-9417

Jemez Action Group
P.O. Box 40445
Albuquerque, New Mexico 87196
Tel: (505) 277-3736

Kettle Range Conservation Council
Tim and Sue Coleman
8504 W. Fork Trout Creek
Republic, Washington 99166
Tel: (509) 775-3754

Klamath Forest Alliance (KFA)
P.O. Box 820
Etna, California 96027
Tel: (916) 467-5405

King Mountain Advocates
800 Railroad Ave.
Wolf Creek, Oregon 97497

Labor Coalition for Environmental Responsibility
P.O. Box 732
McMinnville, Oregon 97128
Tel: (503) 472-1562

Grass roots—union and non-union.

Laytonville Center
45501 N. Hwy. 101
Laytonville, California 95454
Tel: (707) 984-8354

Leavenworth Adopt-a-Forest (LEAF)
Deborah Seyler
P.O. Box 688
Leavenworth, Washington 98825
Tel: (509) 548-6035

LightHawk "The Environmental Airforce"
P.O. Box 8163
Santa Fe, New Mexico 87054-8163
Tel: (505) 982-9656/Fax: 984-8381

From small planes, Lighthawk offers environmentalists, politicians and photographers a birds-eye view of what is happening in the forests of North America. Lighthawk has had a major impact for forest conservation. Seeing is believing. It is easy for people to stay at home and say "we are not overcutting the Pacific Northwest forests," but fly around in an airplane and you'll hardly believe your eyes how much destruction is out there!

LightHawk—Seattle Field Office
311 First Ave. S, #301
Seattle, Washington 98104
Tel: (206) 324-5338/Fax: (206) 329-6998

Lynn Canal Conservation
P.O. Box 964
Haines, Alaska 99827

Mattole Restoration Council
P.O. Box 160
Petrolia, California 95558

Mary's Peak Alliance
P.O. Box 2285
Corvallis, Oregon 97339

McKenzie Guardians
51013 McKenzie Hwy
Finn Rock, Oregon 97488

Mendocino Environmental Center
106 W. Standley
Ukiah, California 95482
Tel: (707) 468-1660/Fax: 462-2370

Methow Forest Watch
P.O. Box 473
Twisp, Washington 98856
Tel: (509) 996-2326

Michigan Forest Advocates
7015 Thilhorn Rd
Sheboygan, Michigan 49721
Tel: (616) 627-6691

Wilderness restoration and forestry issues in northern Michigan.

MidPAW
Box 309
Nellysford, Virginia 22958

Montana Environmental Information Center
P.O. Box 1184
Helena, Montana 59624
Tel: (406) 443-2520

Mountaineers Timber Watch
4016 8th Ave. NE, #403
Seattle, Washington 98105
Tel: (206) 443-1199

Mt. Adams Ranger District Adopt-a-Forest
111 Alder Spr.
Lyle, Washington 98635

Native Forest Action Council
P.O. Box 2171
Eugene, Oregon 97402
Tel: (503) 249-2958

The Native Forest Council works to increase public awareness of the issues affecting our nation's remaining native forests. To date the Council has produced and distributed 800,000 copies of the *Forest Voice*, a tabloid packed with photos and facts documenting the decimation of America's native forests.

The NFC uses economic arguments. Taxpayers subsidize the timber industry with over $2 billion a year.

The US forest Service has a budget of $2.5-3.5 billion a year, and returns less than $400 million to the US Treasury. The NFC's Native Forest Protection Act proposes to redirect the $2.1 billion Forest Service deficit to employ or

retrain dislocated timber workers in restoration ecology and ecosystem restoration.

North Applegate Watershed Protection Association
1340 Missouri Flat
Grants Pass, Oregon 97527
Jack Shipley

North Cascades Audubon Society
1515 J St.
Bellingham, Washington 98225
Tel: (206) 671-0430

North Cascades Conservation Council
7217 Sycamore Ave. NW
Seattle, Washington 98117
Tel: (206) 783-9340

North Central Washington Audubon Society
Marv and Sue Hoover
212 S. Iowa
E. Wenatchee, Washington 99802
Tel: (509) 884-3272

Northcoast Environmental Center
879 Ninth St.
Arcata, California 95521

Northwest Coaltion for Alternatives to Pesticides (NCAP)
P.O. Box 1393
Eugene, Oregon 97440
Tel: (503) 344-5044

Their work involves forest management alternatives to herbicide and pesticide spraying.

Northwoods Citizens for a Sustainable Forest
8333 Bemidji Road NE
Bemidji, Minnesota 56601
Tel: (218) 751-7676

See review in Eastern USA Organizations.

Northwoods Conservation Association
Box 222
Boulder Junction, Wisconsin 54512
Tel: (715) 543-2944

Oachita Watch League
P.O. Box 124
Welling, Oklahoma 74471
Tel: (918) 456-3235

Ohio Alliance for the Environment
445 King Ave.
Columbus, Ohio 43201

Oregon Natural Resources Council
522 SW 5th Av. #1050
Portland, Oregon 97204

Tel: (503) 223-9001

Oregon Natural Resources Council
1161 Lincoln
Eugene, Oregon 97401

Pacific Rivers Council
P.O. Box 309
Eugene, Oregon 97440
Tel: (503) 345-0119/Fax: (503) 345-0710

PAHAYOKEE
P.O. Box 557735
Miami, Florida 33255

Pend Oreille Environmental Team (POET)
2081 Deer Valley Rd
Newport, Washington 99156
Tel: (509) 447-2644

Pilchuck Audubon Society
Bonnie Phillips-Howard
7207 Lakewood Rd.
Stanwood, Washington 98292
Tel: (206) 652-9619

Coordinates and communicates with groups working in the North Cascades.

Predator Project
P.O. Box 6733
Bozeman, Montana 59711
Tel: (406) 587-3389

Quilcene Ancient Forest Coalition (QUAFCO)
90 Magnolia Ave.
Port Townsend, Washington 98368
Tel: (206) 385-6271

A coordinator for groups working on the Olympic Peninsula. Newsletter and workshops.

Redwood Coast Watersheds Alliance
Box 209
Comotche, California 95427
Tel: (707) 468-1253

Regional Association of Concerned Environmentalists
Pomona General Store
Pomona, Illinois 62975
Tel: (618) 893-2997

RIDGE
P.O. Box 927
Roslyn, Washington 98941
Tel: (509) 649-2377

Rocky Mountain Front Advisory Council
Box 8442
Missoula, Montana 59807

Originally founded in 1982, the RMFAC was re-organized in 1992. Especially concerned with the Bob Marshall ecosystem and the Badger-Two Medicine.

Salmon River Concerned Citizens
Butler Cr.
Somes Bar, California 95568

Sanctuary Forest
P.O. Box 166
Whitethorn, California 95489

Santiam Wilderness Society
7665 NW McDonald Circle
Corvallis, Oregon 97330

Save Chelan Alliance
PO Box 1205
Chelan, Washington 98816
Tel: (509) 687-3180

Save-the-Redwoods League
114 Sansome Street, Room 605
San Francisco, California 94104
Tel: (415) 362-2352

The Save-the-Redwoods League started their efforts to save the Redwoods in 1918. One of their main tactics has been to raise money to buy Redwood forest for preservation (five million dollars in 1991). In its 75 years they have purchased more than 250,000 acres of Redwood forest and watershed land for public parks. Anyone who has visited the lowland old-growth Redwood forests will be glad they did!

Save the Trees
2850 Meinhold Rd.
Langley, Washington 98260
Tel: (206) 221-2434

Sierran Biodiversity Institute
P.O. Box 29
North San Juan, California 95960

Selma Citizens Advocating Responsible Forestry
5701 Deer Cr.
Selma, Oregon 97538

Sequoia Forest Citizens
6776 Milner Rd.
Hollywood, California 90068

Siskiyou Environmental Council
P.O. Box 858
Cave Junction, Oregon 97523

Siskiyou Regional Education Project
P.O. Box 220
Cave Junction. Oregon 97523
Tel: (503) 592-4459/Fax: (503) 592-2653

The home of Low Gold, famous forest activist who gained notoriety for his vigils atop Bald Mountain in the

Kalmiopsis Wilderness. Few have done as much as Lou to safeguard the Siskiyou forests. Newsletters, videos and other educational material available.

Siskiyou Mountains Resource Council
P.O. Box 4376
Arcata, California 95521

Sisters Forest Planning Committee
P.O. Box 1211
Sisters, Oregon 97759

SouthPAW
P.O. Box 3141
Asheville, North Carolina 28802

Superior Wilderness Action Network
c/o Biology Dept.,
Univ. of Wisconsin-Oshkosh
Oshkosh, Wisconsin 54901

Support the Wild Rockies Action Fund
P.O. Box 8395
Missoula, Montana 59807

An organization which supports The Northern Rockies Ecosystem Protection Act (NREPA). NREPA is the first legislation based on ecosystems and the connection corridors between them, rather than arbitrary state boundaries.

Swan View Coalition
P.O. Box 1901
Kalispell, Montana 59901
Tel: (406) 755-1379

Talent Watershed Intercommunity Group (TWIG)
P.O. Box 994
Talent, Oregon 97540

Ten Mile Creek Association
P.O. Box 496
Yachats, Oregon 97498
Tel: (503) 547-4097

They have put together a proposal for a Coastal Oregon Rainforest Reserve of approximately 65,000 acres. It represents the most significant nesting area for the marbled murrelet in Oregon.

Texas Committee on Natural Resources
5934 Royal Lane, Suite 223
Dallas, Texas 75230

Ned Fritz and company work on Texas forest issues as well as the nationwide Forest Reform Network.

Thompson Creek Watershed Defenders
P.O. Box 99
Dillard, Oregon 97432

Tonasket Forest Watch
P.O. Box 313
Tonasket, Washington 98855

Tongass Conservation Society
P.O. Box 3377
Ketchikan, Alaska 99901

Umatilla Forest Resources Council
219 Newell
Walla Walla, Washington 99362
Tel: (509) 529-2540

Umpqua Wilderness Defenders
P.O. Box 714
Roseburg, Oregon 97470

Upper Pecos Association
Rt. 1, Box 7
Glorieta, New Mexico 87535
Tel: (505) 438-0200

Virginians for Wilderness
Rt. 1, Box 250
Staunton, Virginia 24401

Watershed Ecosystems
P.O. Box 9226
Santa Fe, New Mexico 87504
Tel: (505) 986-9804

Western North Carolina Alliance
P.O. Box 18087
Asheville, North Carolina 28814-0087
Tel: (704) 258-8737/Fax: (704) 258-9141

Whatcom Watch
P.O. Box 1441
Bellingham, Washington 98227

Whidbey Environmental Action Network (WEAN)
P.O. Box 53
Langley, Washington 98260
Tel: (206) 221-2332

White River Forest Management Committee
12031 Northup Way
Bellevue, Washington 98005

Willits Environmental Center
316 S. Main
Willits, California 95490
Tel: (707) 459-4110

They have put together a well-prepared proposal for an Ancient Forest Reserve system for the Mendocino National Forest which can serve as a model for proposals in other National Forests. The complete proposal costs $45.

Wind River Ranger District Adopt-a-Forest

12195 SE 106th Ave
Portland, Oregon 97268

Wisconsin Forest Conservation Task Force
Don Waller and Bill Alverson
Botany Dept., Birge Hall, University of Wisconsin
Madison, Wisconsin 53706

The task force is a group of botanists who have sued the U.S. Forest Service for managing in such a way that biological diversity is reduced in national forests.

Youth and Student Environmental Organizations

Associated Students Environmental Center
Western Washington University
V.U. 106, Box A-3
Bellingham, Washington 98225
Tel: (206) 650-6129

Children's Alliance for Protection of the Environment, Inc. (CAPE)
P.O. Box 307
Austin, Texas 78767
Tel: (512) 476-CAPE; (512) 258-0557
Fax: (512) 258-9025

CAPE is an international, nonprofit organization enlisting the world's children to repair the global environment.

They have arranged, with the Neotropical Foundation, to establish a Children's Rainforest on 2,500 acres of tropical forest land in Southern Costa Rica, which will be the second in the world and will eventually include a Tropical Forest Youth Center.

Children For Old Growth (CFOG)
Trees Foundation
P.O. Box 2202
Redway, California 95569
Tel: (707) 923-4377

CFOG has established an international network designed to give children a voice in determining the future of their world.

CLEARING Magazine
John Inskeep Environmental Learning Ctr.
19600 S. Molalla Ave.
Oregon City, Oregon 97045

Bimonthly resource and activity guide for environmental education in the Pacific Northwest bioregion. Subscriptions $15/yr. (5 issues), sample $1.

Earth Information Center
P.O. Box 387,
Springfield, Illinois, 62705

Publishes *Environmental Connections* five times a year

to provide educators and students with information on environmental activism. $25/yr.

Envirolink Action
Josh Knauer at Carnegie Mellon University
using e-mail: env-link@andrew.cmu.edu,
Tel/Fax: (412) 268-4949

The Student EnviroLink Network is using new computer networking techniques to help activists communicate quickly and inexpensively. Activists receive an electronic mailbox (e-mail) which is capable of receiving messages from all over the world.

Environmental Youth Alliance
P.O. Box 34097, Stn D.
Vancouver, B.C., V6J 4M1, CANADA
Tel: (604)737-2258/Fax: 739-8064

EYA is part of a Canada-wide network of local coalitions of student groups. They publish the newsletter *Environmental Youth Alliance.*

Environmental Youth Alliance West Coast
Victoria International Development Education Assoc.
Tel: (604) 383-2062. Fax: (604) 721-8997

The EYA West Coast is a correspondence network of youth stretching from Alaska to Chile. A computer network is being set up with nodes in Chile, Costa Rica and Victoria, BC.

Earthstewards Network
Holyearth Foundation
Box 10697
Bainbridge Island, Washington 98110
Tel: (206)842-7986

Between 1992 and 1996, the Earthstewards will coordinate a series of environmental restoration projects in the Cascadia bioregion (northwest US and BC). Young adults from all parts of the planet are brought together to learn to live and work together across cultural, ethnic and racial boundaries while positively impacting deteriorating ecosystems.

Student Conservation Association
P.O. Box 550
Charlestown, New Hampshire 03604
Tel: (603) 826-5741

Survival Center
Environmental Students OSU
Ground Floor EMU, Oregon State University
Corvallis, Oregon 974
Tel: (503) 346-4356/Fax: (503) 346-2573

Student Environmental Action Coalition
P.O. Box 1168
Chapel Hill, North Carolina 27514
Tel: (800) 700-SEAC

A national coalition of 1500 high school and college groups. They published a resource guide in 1993.

Wildlands Studies and Information Center

Room 207, Forestry Bldg.
University of Montana
Missoula, Montana 59812
Tel: (406) 243-5361

In early 1994, WSIC published the *Wilderness Directory* of all groups working in wildlands issues in the Northern Rockies bio-region.

Environmental Periodicals in the United States

THERE ARE THOUSANDS of environmental periodicals, ranging from small newsletters to glossy magazines. Most environmental groups have a newsletter or journal. Here are a few of the larger magazines and/or ones with a noteworthy coverage of restoration forestry.

For more environmental periodicals see also the British Columbia Environmental section and the International Environmental section.

Amicus
Natural Resource Defense Council
40 West 20th St.
New York, New York 10011

A professional magazine from one of the larger environmental NGOs. $10/yr.

Buzzworm's Earth Journal
2305 Canyon Blvd., Ste. 206
Boulder, Colorado 80302
Tel: (303) 442-1960.

Slick and glossy. Not radical. Good gift for someone just cutting their environmental teeth. Once a year they publish a directory of the largest environmental organizations in the USA. Special emphasis on eco-tourism.

Different Drummer
Cascade Holistic Economic Consultants (CHEC)
14417 SE Laurie
Oak Grove, Oregon 97267
Tel/Fax: (503) 652-7049.

Different Drummer is a quarterly newsletter published by Cascade Holistic Economic Consultants which analyzes specific resource management topics such as grazing, park service, and forestry. Both economic and ecological factors are addressed. The first issue was Winter '93-'94 (64 pages). Subscriptions are $12.95/year for individuals. $27.50/year for agencies/companies.

Editor, Randall O'Toole, the founder of CHEC, is a legendary figure in forestry circles. Few people read Forest Service budgets faster and his eagle eye has spotted millions of dollars in errors. He has thrown many monkey wrenches into Forest Service planning—and he does it with a pen and a calculator.

Earth First! Journal
P.O. Box 1415
Eugene, Oregon 97440
Tel: (503) 741-9191. Fax: (503) 741-9192.

A large tabloid journal full of radical environmentalism. Earth First! has gone through a lot of changes in the last 10 years, but it is still grassroots.

Earth Island Journal
See Earth Island Institute in International Environmental Organizations based in the US.

E Magazine
P.O. Box 5098
Syracuse, New York 13217

E for Environmental. One of the most commonly seen environmental magazines at newsstands. $20/6 issues/yr.

Environmental Action
6930 Carroll Ave, Suite 600
Takoma Park, Maryland 20912
Tel: (301) 891-1100

Quarterly. $25/yr.

Forest Watch
Cascade Holistic Economic Consultants
Address under *Different Drummer*.

In the late 1980's and early 1990's *Forest Watch* was one of the best environmental magazines to cover forest issues and restoration forestry practices. As of late 1993, *Forest Watch* is not being published by Cascade Holistic Economic Consultants (CHEC). Former editor, Jeffrey St. Clair, is publishing a new magazine, *Wild Forest Review*, which will be similar in content and coverage of forestry issues as *Forest Watch*. Back issues of *Forest Watch* are available from CHEC. Bound and indexed annual volumes are $20.

Green Disk
Paperless Environmental Journal
P.O. Box 32224
Washington, D.C. 20007
Tel: (202) 337-4175/EcoNet: <greendisc>

US $35/6 issues(disks)/yr., elsewhere $40. Information on environmental matters is distributed on computer discs (IBM or Macintosh). Organizations involved include Greenpeace, Sierra Club and Worldwatch.

Headwaters Journal
P.O. Box 729
Ashland, Oregon 97520
Tel: (503) 482-4459/Fax: (503) 482-7282

I regard the *Headwaters Journal* as one of the top environmental journals covering Pacific Northwest forestry issues with an eye to restoration forestry alternatives. Membership $20/yr.

High Country News
Box 1090
Paonia, Colorado 81428
Tel: (303) 527-4898

High Country News is one of the premier periodicals covering natural resources and public lands issues across the West (over 9,000 subscribers think so). One year subscription is $24 for 24 issues. *The Northwest rediscovers its ancient forests*, Vol. 22 No. 22, Nov. 1990 is a special issue on ancient forests. $3/single copies.

Northwest Conservation
Greater Ecosystem Alliance
P.O. Box 2813
Bellingham, Washington 98227
Tel: (206) 671-9950. Fax: (206) 671-8429 .

A focus on the North Cascades ecosystem. Excellent articles on biodiversity, wilderness, charismatic megafauna and forest management.

Sierra
730 Polk St.
San Francisco, California 94109.
Tel: (415) 776-2211

The official magazine of the Sierra Club. Membership is $35/yr. Non-member subscriptions are $15/yr. for 6 issues/yr.

Whole Earth Review
PO Box 38
Sausalito, California 94966
Tel: (415) 332-1716

The *Whole Earth Review* has consistently been one of the premier journals reporting on progressive trends in society. Quarterly. $27/yr.

Wild Earth
See Biodiversity section for review.

Wild Oregon
Journal of the Oregon Natural Resources Council
1050 Yeon Bldg., 522 SW 5th Ave.
Portland, Oregon 97204
Tel: (503) 223-9001

Its focus is on forestry and conservation issues in the Pacific Northwest.

Wild Forest Review
3578 SE Milwaukie
Portland, Oregon 97202
Tel: (503) 234-0093

The first issue was published in November, 1993. It's editor, Jeffrey St. Clair, was the editor of *Forest Watch* (published by Cascade Holistic Economics Consultants) since 1987. St. Clair is continuing his gutsy, grass-roots, forest reporting in Wild Forest Review. Published 11 times a year by Save the West, Inc. $25/yr.

Wild Rockies Review
Box 9286
Missoula, Montana 59807
Tel: (406) 728-5733

An Earth First! regional publication.

Worldwatch
Worldwatch Institute
1776 Massachusetts Ave N.W.
Washington, DC 20036
Tel: (202) 452-1999/Fax: (202) 296-7365.

Worldwatch monitors global problems such as deforestation and pollution and reports on efforts to reverse the negative trends. $15/yr. in the U.S. $30/yr. overseas airmail. $5/single back issue.

Eco-warriors: Understanding the Radical Environmental Movement
Rick Scarce. 1990. Noble Press.

A book about Earth First!ers, Sea Shepherd sailors, tree-sitters and other eco-activists. Rick Scarce recently served a federal prison term for writing this book (without being formally convicted of breaking any federal law) for refusing to reveal his sources to a U.S. Grand Jury. He is now speaking out about the unchecked power of the Grand Jury and its ability to harass environmental activists for information regarding alleged crimes committed defending the Earth. He is also fighting for the right of journalists and researchers to not reveal sources of potentially incriminating information.

Thinking Like A Mountain: Towards A Council of All Beings
John Seed and Joanna Macey. 1988. New Society Publishers. 128 pp. $7.95.

A handbook on how to lead "Councils of All Beings." Environmental education and deep ecology.

International Environmental Organizations Based in the United States

See also Environmental Organizations based outside the USA in the International Environmental Organizations section.

Ancient Forest International
P.O. Box 1850
Redway, California 95560
Tel: (707) 923-3015

AFI is working for preservation of temperate rainforests. See Chile, South America section for details.

Arctic to Amazonia Alliance
1 Main St., PO Box 73
Strafford, Vermont 05072
Tel: (802) 765-4337/Fax: (802) 765-4262

An advocate for cross-cultural communication, tribal activism, traditional technologies and grassroots organizing strategies for preserving forests.

Center for International Environmental Information
300 E. 42nd St.
New York, New York 10017

Conservation International
1015 18th St. NW, Suite 1000
Washington D.C 20036
Tel: (202) 429-5660

A large NGO. Its quarterly report to members is *Tropicus*.

Earth Island Institute
300 Broadway, Suite 28
San Francisco, California 94133
Tel: (415) 788-3666/Fax: $415) 788-7324

The Earth Island Institute, founded by David Brower, is an umbrella for 20 specialized environmental groups. The institute publishes a quarterly magazine which is one of the best environmental magazines covering a broad range of topics. Annual membership $25.

Friends of the Earth
218 D St. S.E.
Washington, DC 20003
Tel: (202) 544-2600

Global Response
Environmental Action Network
P.O. Box 7490
Boulder, Colorado 80306-7490
Tel: (303) 444-0306

GR is an effective environmental letter-writing campaign center. GR alerts thousands of readers/letter-writers to the most pressing environmental hot-spots around the world. GR names culprits and gives addresses of who to write to demand environmental justice. They update readers on further developments and the effect their letters have. GR's network has become a thorn in the side of national governments and multinational corporations. Check it out.

Greenpeace
1436 "U" St. NW
Washington, DC 20009
Tel: (202) 462-1177/Fax: (202) 462-4507

Greenpeace initiated a tropical forests campaign in 1992 and has been working to protect the forests of the Northern Wild Rockies.

Greenpeace
139 Townsend St.
San Francisco, California 94107
Tel: (415) 512-9025

Pam Wellner is the coordinator for Greenpeace's tropical rainforest campaign.

Native Forest Network
Western North America Resource Center
P.O. Box 60271
Seattle, Washington 98160
Tel: (206) 542-1356/Fax: (206) 632-6122

The Native Forest Network is working in behalf of

forests throughout the U.S., Canada, Australia, Russia, Chile, United Kingdom and Sweden. Their campaigns often target multinationals such as Weyerhaeuser, Champion, Hydro-Quebec and Hyundai. (For the address of NFN's Tasmania office see Environmental Organizations in the International section.)

The Native forest Network is a non-hierarchical umbrella organization which utilizes lobbying, research, litigation, education and direct action. Membership is free. The quarterly newsletter is $20/yr.

Native Forest Network
Eastern North America Resource Center
P.O. Box 57
Burlington, Vermont 05402
Tel: (802) 863-2345/Fax: (802) 863-2532

The Nature Conservancy
1815 N. Lynn St.,
Arlington, Virginia 22209
Tel: (703) 841-5300

One of the largest conservation organizations in the world. The Conservancy owns millions of acres in the USA and in many other countries.

New England Tropical Forest Project
P.O. Box 73
Strafford, Vermont 05072

New Internationalist
Box 1143
Lewiston, New York 14902

An international magazine reporting on environmental and human rights issues (mainly on countries of the South). NI has editorial offices in other countries as well. $35/12 issues/yr.

Rainforest Action Center
6321 Roosevelt Way NE, Apt. A
Seattle, Washington 98815
Tel: (206) 524-0194

Rainforest Action Network (RAN)
450 Sansome, Suite 700
San Francisco, California 94111
Tel: (415) 398-4404

RAN has become one of the most vocal US groups for rainforest preservation. RAN has 30,000 members, attesting to the growing movement to preserve forests. The World Rainforest Report contains reports from around the world. Also available are monthly *Action Alerts* and *Rainforests: A Teacher's Resource Guide* by Lynne Chase. To become a member of the Rainforest Action Network send $15 or more.

Rainforest Action Groups (RAGs)
Eileen Pole (Information Department) at the Rainforest Action Network address.

One of the largest networks of rainforest activists. There are over 50 independent RAGs, while RAN acts as a general coordinator for the RAG network and helps to facilitate communication among the RAGs. Included in their publications is a directory of related organizations, information pamphlets, and lists of publications for sale.

Rainforest Alliance
270 Lafayette St., Suite 512,
New York, New York 10012
Tel: (212) 941-1900/Fax: (212) 941-4986

The Rainforest Alliance coordinates efforts with Third World groups that strive to protect the rights of rainforest peoples and serves as an international clearinghouse for information about rainforest conservation.

The Rainforest Alliance has established the Kleinhans Fellowship to promote research on sustainable forestry in tropical forests. The fellowship provides US$30,000 for two years.

Rainforest Information Center
1300 Park St.
Santa Rosa, California 95404

Rainforest Information Center
DeVargas Center, Suite 504-G
Santa Fe, New Mexico, 87501
Tel: (505) 988-5300. Fax (505) 988-1642

R.I.C. (US) is the US contact point for a large permaculture project in Ecuador. (See C.B.I.T. in Latin America section.)

Woodworkers Against Rainforest Destruction (WARD)
20 Stearns Court
Northampton, Massachusetts 01060
Tel: (413) 586-6126

7

7

188   Restoration Forestry: An International Guide to Sustainable Forestry Practices

8 Restoration Forestry in North America's Eastern Forests

8

Resources on Eastern North American Forests

RESTORATION FORESTRY IS NEEDED as badly in the eastern U.S. as anywhere, and is as difficult to find. By 1900 almost all of the primeval forest of the East had been cut. Many parts of the eastern landscape are intensively settled and forests have been managed for hundreds of years. There is a wide range in degree of forestation and intensity of human impact, ranging from the urban forest, to the suburban forest, to the woodlands in the farm landscapes, to the wilder forests higher up in the mountains. Each area needs different strategies.

Much of the wilder second growth is now growing into economic maturity and ecological maturity. Plants and animal species are gradually migrating from the wildest areas to surrounding habitats that are becoming habitable. These second growth forests are at a crossroads, a human crossroads. We can let them grow toward old-growth status. Or we can clear-cut them and start over again. Restoration forestry perhaps offers a third way, or actually, a range of options. With natural selection ecoforestry (Orville Camp's methods), a timber flow can come from some managed forests while they continue to grow in stature and maturity. Other parts of the landscape can be in reserves where logging is not allowed.

Despite a study by the Southeastern Forest Experiment Station that determined the recreational value of the national forests is nine times greater than the economic value of the forest's timber, timber harvest levels on central hardwood public forests over the last two decades have increased dramatically.

Throughout the central hardwood region, grassroots groups have sprung up to protest the logging of their public forests.

Eastern Old Growth

It was generally thought that all eastern old growth has been gone for over a hundred years, but a study of old growth stands in the southern New England Appalachians has found at least 32 confirmed sites in Massachusetts alone. Unfortunately most of them are small groves.

For more information on finding eastern old growth, or to send descriptions of potential old growth you have located, write:

Robert T. Leverett
52 Fairfield Ave.
Holyoke, Massachusetts 01040

Eastern Old-Growth Forests Conference
UNCA Environmental Studies
Asheville, North Carolina 28804-3299

A conference was held the fall of 1993 to discuss the value of old growth forest ecosystems of the eastern U.S.

Organizations in Eastern North America

Center for Woodlands Culture and Alternative Forestry Research
1 Main St., PO Box 73
Strafford, Vermont 05072
Tel: (802) 765-4337/Fax: (802) 765-4262

The Arctic to Amazonia Alliance has begun the process of establishing a center to research and demonstrate alternative, sustainable, and community forest management techniques applicable to the New England and Atlantic Maritime forest regions.

Cloquet Forestry Center
Cloquet, Minnesota
Tel: (218) 879-0850

Robert Stein, Director. The CFC is managed by the University of Minnesota. Established in 1910, it is one of the oldest forestry research centers in the Midwest. CFC manages 3600 contiguous acres of forestland at the Center as well as 3700 acres in other holdings.

Forest Resources Center
Rt. 2, Box 156-A
Lanesboro, Minnesota 55949
Tel: (507)-467-2437

FRC is a non-governmental research center for sustainable forestry, which offers a model for other states and regions. Much of their work is with education of children and adults. They lead tours to their 40+ demonstration sites for sound forestry practices. Each site comprises 1 to 15 acres. FRC has several forestry demonstrations that show both natural and artificial oak regeneration. They also have a hedgerow/shelterbelt project for farmland. The FRC works with private woodland owners and publishes a newsletter *Friend of the Forest*. Joe Deden, Director.

Forest Resource Information System (FORIS)

Tree Talk, Inc.
431 Pine St.
Burlington, Vermont 05451
Tel: (802) 863-6789/Fax: (802) 863-4344

FORIS is a computer database on over 8,000 species of trees which covers sources and conservation status of each species, physical characteristics of the wood, and impacts of harvesting.

Preserve Appalachian Wilderness (PAW)

81 Middle St.
Lancaster, New Hampshire 03584
Tel: (802) 297-1022

PAW publishes *A Journal of Eco-Ecstacy, Rage and Action*. With a journal subtitle like that it is not surprising to find references to Earth First! and forest activism inside. There are also well-articulated ideas for sustainable forest management, ecological science and conservation biology. Each issue contains a directory of affiliated environmental organizations and individuals.

The PAW Proposal by Jeff Elliot and Jamie Sayen is one of the largest wilderness preserve proposals for the Eastern U.S. and calls for a contiguous Appalachian Wilderness reuniting the Florida Keys with maritimes of Canada and beyond. They call for the National Forests to be set aside as Evolutionary Preserves, managed solely for evolutionary integrity and the maintenance of a healthy, diverse, biotic community. These evolutionary preserves would be linked together by corridors allowing for the migration of species, and linking currently isolated genetic communities. The Appalachian Ridge would serve as the backbone of this corridor.

Northern Forest Forum

P.O. Box 52
Groveton, New Hampshire 03582

Northwoods Citizens for a Sustainable Forest

8333 Bemidji Road NE
Bemidji, Minnesota 56601
Tel: (218) 751-7676

Northwoods Citizens for a Sustainable Forest (NCFS) is educating people about the effects of clear-cut forestry, and promoting alternatives. In a well-documented comment to the Minnesota Environmental Quality Board on the draft report *Generic Environmental Impact Study on Timber Harvesting*, NCFS pointed out the advantages of selection management, and the disadvantages of even-age logging of aspen and other species.

Judy Johnson reports that there has been a big upswing in logging in Minnesota over the past 10 years. In the early 1980s, the area's annual cut (including the Chippewa National Forest) was around 2 million cords. Now it is running 4 million cords/yr. and there is talk of taking it up to 5 million. 90% or more of the cutting is done by clear-cutting. There has been lots of industry investment in feller bunchers and equipment, and there are reports of loggers and logging equipment coming in from the Pacific Northwest. As the clear-cuts mount, so does local opposition.

Penobscot Experimental Forest, USFS

5 Godfrey Dr.
Orono, Maine 04473
Tel: (207) 866-7257
Robert M. Frank: Research Forester

A 4,000 acre demonstration and research forest since 1950. The forest has long-term experiments with a wide range of silvicultural methods. Comparisons of growth and yield, species composition, and other stand variables are being made among several intensities of selection and shelterwood silviculture and strip and "biomass' clear-cutting. Diameter-limit harvesting and commercial clear-cutting are also being compared with an undisturbed natural area. They were one of the first places to experiment with strip clear-cutting in the 1960s. New Forestry techniques are being added. The forest is located near the University of Maine and is utilized by U. of M. forestry students. Visitors are welcome. They have many publications available.

Society for the Protection of New Hampshire Forests

54 Portsmouth St.
Concord, New Hampshire 03301
Tel: (603) 224-9945

A conservation organization which has managed 20,000 acres of forest since the turn of the century. They demonstrate environmentally sound forest management on woodlots across the state and publish a bi-monthly newsletter *Forest Notes*.

Waldee Forest

Walton R. Smith
221 Huckleberry Creek Road
Franklin, North Carolina 28734
Tel: (704) 524-3186

Waldee Forest is one of the best long-term examples of restoration forestry management in the Eastern U.S.

Walton has written a 50-page *Manual on Managing a Small Hardwood Forest* which is available from him at the above address. See also article by Walton Smith in Restoration Forestry.

Woodland Steward Newsletter
P.O. Box 155
Butlerville, Indiana 47223

The newsletter is an organizing tool for timberland owners in Indiana and surrounding areas, who want to manage their land for timber production but preserve the quality and integrity of their forests. Contains information about prices, taxes, property law, timber management, and government assistance.

Books and Articles on Eastern North American Forests

Beyond the Beauty Strip: Penetrating the Myths of the Industrial Forest
Mitch Lansky, 1992. $15.95. 400 pp.

A "beauty strip" is what Mainers call the strip of trees that is left between a road (or lake or river) and a clear-cut after industrial landowners have taken their harvest. It creates the illusion that selective cutting has taken place and that all is well in the forest.

Lansky references scientific information, to help demolish the myths, both common and uncommon, on forest management. Lansky offers concrete actions which citizens can take to help change our direction.

One Man's Forest: Pleasure and Profit from Your Own Woods
Rockwell R. Stephens. 1974. The Stephen Green Press: Brattleboro, Vermont. 159 pp.

Hardwood Management Techniques of Natural Stands
F. W. Shropshire. 1971. Proceedings of a Symposium. USDA Forest Serv. State and Private For. Branch, Atlanta.

The Deciduous Forests of Eastern North America
E. Lucy Braun. 1967. Hafner Publishing Company: NY. 596 pp.

One of the best textbooks on the plant associations, plant geography and ecology of eastern forests. Includes many photographs. Braun uses botanical plant names.

Eastern Forest Recovery
Dave Foreman. Summer, 1993. Wild Earth. Vol. 3 (2). pp. 25-28.

A thorough summary of what needs to be done to restore public and private owned forests throughout the Eastern U.S. from an ecosystem conservation and wilderness protection approach.

The Ecological Restoration of the Northern Appalachians: An Evolutionary Perspective
Jeff Elliot and Jamie Sayen. Preserve Appalachian Wilderness: RFD 1, Box 530, N. Stratford, NH 03590.

Chapter 9 is on Ecological Forestry.

Forests and Forestry in the Eastern United States
The December 1991, issue of *Inner Voice* (Volume 3, Issue 6) is a special issue on the National Forests of the East. It contains a number of excellent articles, plus smaller notes of interest.

The Forests of Maine: Yesterday, Today and Tomorrow
Routley, R. and V. Routley. 1974. Orono, University of Maine.

Managing the Family Forest in the South
H. L. Williston et al. 1982. General Report SA-GR22, Available free from USFS, SE Area, 1720 Peachtree Rd. NW, Room 901, Atlanta, GA 30367.

The Monongahela Forest: An Alternative Vision
Ed Lytwack, Jr. Allemong Wilderness Group: P.O. Box 1689, Greensburg, Pennsylvania 15601.

A response to the *Monongahela National Forest Plan*. This document could serve as a model for alternatives to Forest Plans throughout the country. The condensed version is printed in *Vol. 1, No. 1 of Preserve Appalachian Wilderness*.

"The best management that humans can provide is one that preserves or restores the conditions necessary for natural ecological processes to function. In many cases the best management is to simply leave it alone. Let the Forest function as it has evolved. Unfortunately human effects on the Forest [eastern U.S.] are so great that simply leaving it alone is not adequate to deal with the present crisis. Past destruction and the present level of human degradation demands a more active response. Rather than management, this response can better be described as preservation ecology. Preservation ecology deals with preserving and restoring the natural conditions necessary for the proper functioning of ecological processes."

Mountain Treasures at Risk: The Future of the Southern Appalachian National Forests
Laura Jackson. Available from: Wilderness Society Southeast Regional Office, 1819 Peachtree St. NE, Atlanta, GA 30309

A comprehensive overview and critique of the *U.S. Forest Service's Land and Resource Management Plans* for the six National Forest areas of the Southern Appalachians. The study concludes with guidelines for managing the southern Appalachian National Forests to protect wild lands and the biological diversity they harbor, meet recreational and aesthetic demands, and restore the forest habitat.

"Nitrification in Undisturbed Mixed Hardwoods and Manipulated Forests in the Southern Appalachian Mountains of North Carolina, U.S.A."
F. Montagnini, B. S. Haines, W. T. Swank and J. B. Waide. *Canadian Journal of Forestry Research.* Vol. 19: 1226-1234.

Report of the Scientific Roundtable on Biodiversity in Wisconsin's National Forests.

This 1993 report was commissioned by the Forest Service in response to a citizen appeal of one of their forest plans. The Report laments the loss of biodiversity in forest ecosystems and recommends several management changes for the Nicolet and Chequamegon National Forests in northern Wisconsin.

For copies of the report contact the Chequamegon NF Supervisor's office, 1170 4th Ave. S, Park Falls, WI 54552.

The Silviculture Book
David Smith.

A reference book for Eastern forests containing some ideas of sustainability. Latest edition is 1985. Much of it is based on practices from Europe.

Wildlands and Woodlots: The Story of New England's Forests
L.C. Irland, 1982. Univ. Press of New England: Hanover, New Hampshire.

Woodland Ecology: Environmental Forestry for the Small Owner
Leon S. Minckler, 1980. Syracuse Univ. Press: NY.

One of the best explorations thus far of restoration forestry for Eastern U.S. forests. Recommended! See Leon Minckler's article in Restoration Forestry.

Woodland Owners' Guide to Oak Management
M. J. Baughman and R. D. Jacobs, 1992. Minnesota Extension Service, Univ. of Minnesota. 8 pp.

A good resource for oak regeneration information. Oak has been in decline as a result of land management practices after white settlement. The Indians maintained open oak savannas and parklands with underburning. Grazing and fire suppression has led to a situation where hardly any oaks under 40 years of age can be found.

The Woodland Steward
James R. Fazio. 2nd edition. 211 pp. $14.95 + $3.50 s/h. Woodland Enterprises, 1049 Colt Rd, Moscow, Idaho 83843. Tel: (208) 882-4767.

A book aimed at the small woodlot owner. Hundreds of useful illustrations and references. Although it claims nationwide coverage it is mostly on eastern North America. Sections include: planting and improving the woodlot, Christmas trees, maple syrup, growing and selling firewood, woodlands for wildlife, protecting the forest, how to log, where to get help, horse logging, walnut, sample contracts, how to measure your trees and more.

Woodlands for Profit and Pleasure
Reginald D. Forbes. American Forestry Association. 1976. 253 pages.

Not a restoration forestry book. However, it does contain useful information for the small woodland owner in the eastern U.S.

Five Steps To Sustainable Forest Management of Eastern Hardwoods

Leon S. Minckler

The author, Leon S. Minckler, is a retired Forest Service researcher with 33 years of experience at four eastern forest experiment stations, researching silvicultural treatments and ecology of hardwoods.

1. **Sustainable and successful silviculture emulates nature except on a different time scale. This includes air pollution, especially acid rain.**

THE EMULATION OF NATURE means simply that we follow the ecological laws that have been established by evolution throughout the Earth's history. Since these laws vary by climate and by characteristics of the soil and topography, certain silvicultural prescriptions must be practiced within similar forest units because the forests may be quite different from place to place. This is well recognized by ecologists.

Different time scale means we harvest mature trees close to economic maturity rather than letting them die naturally as in virgin forests, though wildlife trees should be left. Diversity, stand structure, and species composition need not be basically changed, but stand improvement can take the place of the natural thinning due to mortality of weaker trees. Thinning should occur sooner than in a natural unmanaged forest.

This practice is called selection cutting of individual trees or small, naturally occurring groups of trees. Groups of trees can be sought out and cut to make small openings for intermediate, tolerant desirable species. Opening should have a diameter equal to the height of trees, emulating wind throw or natural mortality. Cull trees or other undesirable trees, except for wildlife, should be cut by individual selection if they don't fit into a group.

Pioneer species such as aspen or jack pine which form pure even-aged stands after widespread fires, can be helped to progress toward climax forests by thinning and release as well.

2. **Indiscriminate clear-cutting destroys natural ecosystems and is a crime against nature.**

Clear-cutting is almost the exact opposite of emulating nature. Even wide-spread fires do not have the same ecological effect as clear-cutting. Clear-cutting is a crime against nature because it eliminates the whole forest at one time and results in dense even aged reproduction with different species and a high proportion of stump sprouts from the smaller trees which were cut.

Stump sprouts often occur in dense clumps from one stump and are inferior as good growing stock because of frequent rot from old stumps and sweep in the first log. Very heavy thinning is required. Large trees do not produce stump sprouts so most reproduction in group or single tree selection cuts come from seedlings or seedling sprouts.

A forest which results from clear-cutting has entirely different ecological characteristics than the natural ecosystem or a forest resulting from selection cutting. The whole ecosystem, including species composition, diversity (especially vertical), water relations, soil erosion, soil life, wildlife habitat, and especially aesthetic values are altered.

Considering all values, the selection forest has by far the greatest long-term returns compared to clear-cutting each rotation. Do foresters want to maximize long term values from natural ecosystems or try and outsmart nature for ease of management and quick short term timber profits, risking soil, site, and severe water damage?

3. **With proper practices both timber and environmental values can be produced from the same forest without damaging forest ecosystems.**

This statement does not apply to designated wilderness, agro-forestry, or forests unsuitable for timber harvest because of topography or unsuitable soil-site factors. Forests of low quality potential on poor sites should not be cut at all!

In essence, if management involves the application of sound ecological factors where correct cutting of timber does not diminish watershed values, aesthetics and recreation, total wildlife habitat, natural diversity, or integrity of the ecosystem, neither does it lower long term returns from timber. If environmental dollar values are added, long term values will tend to be maximized far beyond management for timber alone.

Most foresters know this, but the objectives of quick profits and low management costs have too often been allowed to dictate clear-cutting, high grading, or diameter limit cutting. Yet we still get mostly below cost returns.

For combined single tree and group selection improvement cutting and harvest of mature trees and unwanted inferior trees, all cut trees must be marked by a forester in the woods with three objectives in mind:

1. harvest mature trees

2. cut low quality but merchantable trees

3. kill cull trees if they can't be marketed and if they are not aesthetic or wildlife trees

4. In doing this, look for places where small openings can be made for better growth of new regeneration. These factors need not be incorporated in one cutting operation. The only limit is that the cut must be operable. The forester in the woods is the king pin!

A typical example on a poor 21-acre farm woodland demonstration on the Kaskaskia Experimental Forest on the Shawnee National Forest can be cited. The original stand in 1952 had 3048 board-feet per acre of merchantable trees, 11 inches diameter at breast height (DBH) and larger, plus 67 cull trees, 5 inches DBH and larger, and 36 good growing stock trees 5-10 inches DBH. This was a poor and abused stand. As shown by a 1967 inventory, intensive group selection and tree improvement cutting in 1952 and 1959 removed 1762 board feet of the merchantable trees, per acre, eliminated all the 67 culls, and increased the good poles from 36 to 59 per acre while increasing the sawtimber volume to 3190 board feet.

The increases in saw timber and pole-sized trees was due to in-growth on trees already there. Oak and yellow poplar regeneration was also abundant in the small openings. The 1967 stand was more highly diversified, had more volume, and many more good pole trees than in 1952 and no cull trees. Compare this to what a clear-cut stand would look like after 15 years! We would have a 15-year cover of mostly stump sprouts.

4. **The public needs and desires forest products and environmental values.**

It is quite apparent that the world's forests must satisfy the needs and desires of the population in the long run. That is why we have professional foresters. This applies to both public and private lands, but often in different ways. National Forests in the U.S. are the people's forests and in the long run people can demand either the values that come from ecosystem management, especially recreation, or the quick returns from timber. The ideal is to obtain long term values from both timber and the environment.

People can require foresters to produce required environmental values and timber without site and ecosystem damage. They can also require wilderness. We are just now realizing that time is running short and that perspectives must be changed. On a world basis, population must be brought in balance with so-called renewable resources.

Commercial forest land can, to some extent, be managed as agro-forestry. This means cultivation (broad sense) and planting. However, this causes problems for water management, soil fertility, pollution, and soil erosion. Small, non-commercial private forests (most of our forests) can be managed ecologically as ecosystems.

In the long term, public attitudes influence practices and determine our ethical attitude toward our profession.

5. **An active and recognized land ethic that insures adequate productive and sustainable forests on Earth in the long term.**

We do not own the Earth, it owns us. People must cooperate ecologically with the basically fragile Earth or face dire consequences in the future. To many people this is like a religion except it depends on good will and science rather than faith alone.

In the long term, l believe it is impossible to attain sustainable and successful forest management without an understanding of the land ethic proposed by Aldo Leopold and recently emphasized by some foresters, ecologists, and many of the concerned public. What is the land ethic? It involves a moral feeling that people should maintain natural ecosystems placed on this earth by ecological laws which have developed over millions of years. We have been given a multitude of natural factors which have become harmonized and this harmony (ecosystems) must be respected by people because we too are a part of this harmony. Yet because of our mental gifts (human nature) and our greed, we have all too often disregarded natural laws and utterly destroyed, sometimes irreversibly, the natural order.

The land ethic concept is vital to maintaining sustainable forests for their great values for current forest products and for future timber and environmental values. People who do not understand the land ethic often understand greed, as if all these marvelous resources were for present use only. So the land ethic concept in its broad sense is a necessary foundation for sustainable and successful resource management.

Reprinted from Inner Voice, *December 1991.*

Selective Logging in Ontario

Delores Broten

TALKING TO A GOVERNMENT FORESTER in southern Ontario is a bizarre experience for someone accustomed to the vigorous forestry debate here in SuperNatural B.C. The foresters wax stern and eloquent over methods and principles of selection logging, fueled by a serious concern about industrial needs for quality sawlogs. It's a delightful experience to be unable to interject a word because the forester is in full spate about the way in which clear-cutting tends to reduce diversity, and destroy habitat for cavity-nesting and stick-nesting birds which are valuable components of the forest infrastructure.

Most of the forests of southern Ontario are mixed shade-tolerant hardwoods, such as maple, beech, oak and basswood. According to Martin Streit, Management Forester for Lanark County Crown Lands, Ontario selection logging used to be "high-grading" until the late 1950's, when management changed to prevent the further degrading of Ontario's valuable forests. Now, when summer students go into the woods with their paint cans to select trees for the logging contractors, they leave the better-quality trees, and remove the poor and diseased ones.

The pine forests need more sunlight than the hard woods, but the full light of a clear-cut promotes competition from other species. Further, sunlight opens White Pine to the attacks of White Pine Weevil, which damage the leaders of the young trees. Consequently, pine is managed by a uniform shelterwood method, although the Ministry is beginning to experiment with uneven-aged shelterwood systems. All over southern Ontario, on the outskirts of towns and cities, there are small unnaturally tidy young pine forests, providing green space and hiking trails in between the passes, which occur roughly every 20 years.

When asked where he learned the skills required for this selection logging, Forester Streit laughed and said, "In school. At U of T. But mostly on summer jobs, and out here, working in the forests."

Logging in Algonquin Park

One-fifth of southern Ontario's timber supply comes from the forests of Algonquin Park, where the logging of old growth While Pine started in the 1830's. Activity was intense. For example, in 1866-67, 600 men squared 30,000 pieces of pine timber for shipment to Europe. In 1893, the creation of the park was supported by logging companies, trying to protect their forest base from encroaching subsistence farming. However, by the 1960's, the conflict between logging and recreational use of the park became intense. The Ontario government acted.

In 1975, the Algonquin Forest Authority was formed, after intensive public hearings approved a detailed Master Plan which allowed strictly-controlled logging in 75% of the 750,000 hectare park and set aside wilderness preserve zones. The AFA Board of Directors is drawn from a mix of non-industry people in the surrounding communities, who report to the Ministry of Natural Resources. Clear-cutting of some species with a 40 acre maximum size is allowed in the Master Plan. However, General Manager Bill Brown states that the Authority has never considered such a large clear-cut and almost 100% of the management is selection, group selection or shelterwood cut, depending on the species.

The Park yields about 400,000 cubic meters of timber each year, which supplies all or part of the needs of 10 sawmills, 2 veneer mills, 1 pole plant, 1 pulp mill and 1 match splint mill, employing 3,500 men. Logging is done by contractors. Most of the mills had held timber licenses in the park before the creation of the Algonquin Forest Authority. According to the 1989-90 Annual Report, the $9 million worth of logs sold to the mills by the AFA created a "direct contribution by Algonquin logging and primary manufacturing to the Ontario economy of $56.5 millions in terms of 1985 value added." About half a million people also used the park for hiking, camping and canoeing.

In 1990, in the midst of the forest industry recession, the AFA paid the Ontario government $1 million in stumpage, and spent $7.5 million on logging and distribution. It covered the cost of a staff of 6 foresters, 1 chartered accountant and 9 forest technicians, as well as the seasonal employees required to do tree marking, wood measurement, maintenance of publicly used roads, a small amount of tree planting and some stand tending. In 1990, the Authority "lost" $26,000, an unusual event which, Forester Brown says, indicates that they will have to tighten up their operation and call in some accounts receivable.

Brown says that when the Authority was first established after the Master Plan was put in place, relations with industry had a "healthy tension" but that now, fifteen years later, the testiness is gone. In fact, says Brown, "Industry probably accepted the arrangement better than the provincial bureaucracy."

The conditions leading to the creation of this system which mixes and meets the needs of the forest industry and the needs for park space were unique, but Brown, who has been managing the Algonquin Forest Authority for fifteen years, sees no reason why the principles could not be applicable in other areas of Canada. He sees the role of the Algonquin Forest Authority as a third party to intervene in the forest use debate as central to a fairly peaceful compromise in these Ontario woods.

Reprinted from The Watershed Sentinel *December/January 1991 supplement.*

8

Wildlife & Woodlands

Gary Schneider

It is now clear that to maintain a rich bird fauna, conservationists in eastern North America should focus on preserving large tracts of forest—of several hundred acres or more—rather than many small tracts. And contrary to traditional wildlife management, which often seeks to create edge habitat, protected woodlands should be spared intrusion by roads, power lines and clear-cuts.

—Raymond J. O'Connor, Professor of Wildlife
at the University of Maine in Orono
and co-author of *Farming and Birds*

CONCERN OVER SONGBIRD DECLINE has grown over the past decade as research scientists and amateur birders alike report a severe drop in the number of tropical migrants nesting in forests. While we have little data from Prince Edward Island, it is reasonable to assume that chopping forests into small pieces and creating large amounts of edge has caused the same problems here. Yet there has been an ominous silence about this potentially devastating development.

Edges are those areas where one type of ecosystem meets another, such as forest to field or forest to clear-cut. The benefits of edges form the rationale for much forest management. Studies show that numbers and species of wildlife increase, notably game such as ruffed grouse and snowshoe hare. Clear-cutting patches in continuous forest creates a lot of edge, benefiting a very specific type of wildlife, usually already common, at the expense of other, rarer species. Forest fragmentation, where we create a great deal of edge and deplete the amount of continuous forest, is taking place at an increasing rate in this province. Large tracts of forest are constantly being carved up by roads, clear-cuts or developments.

In this fragmented habitat, certain predators or parasitic bird species thrive at the expense of other bird species. Blue jays, common grackles, crows, raccoons, skunks and even domestic cats and dogs are much more common along edges and can prey on eggs and nestlings.

Species most at risk are the migrant songbirds. Some, like the ovenbird and black-and-white warbler, nest on the ground where predation is especially high. Others build cup-shaped nests, more vulnerable than dome-shaped nests or tree cavities used by many year-round residents. Migrants also face the disadvantage of arriving late and leaving early. If they lose one clutch of eggs, there is not time to lay and raise another. They are usually too small to fight off predators.

Parasitic brown-headed cowbirds, which lay eggs in nests of other birds, are also prospering. A female cowbird may lay up to 40 eggs per season, one or two eggs per nest. A cowbird will replace one of the eggs in a red-eyed vireo nest, for example, with her own. The parent vireo devotes so much energy to feeding the fast-growing cowbird young that its own offspring often do not survive. The open nests of migrant warblers, thrushes, vireos and flycatchers are easy targets for cowbirds.

A Wisconsin study showed nests at the edge of a forest to be five times as likely to contain cowbird eggs as those nests more than 275 m (300 yards) from the edge. In a large area of parkland in Maryland that continues to be fragmented, there were 198 breeding pairs of migrant songbirds for every 40 hectares (100 acres) of parkland in 1948. By 1986 there were only 31 breeding pairs of migrants every 40 hectares (100 acres). Other studies have shown that birds such as the barred owl, red eyed vireo, scarlet tanager and ovenbird require large areas of unbroken forest.

Another associated problem with forest fragmentation is that the birds most affected are insect eaters—we simply do not know if the absence of these songbirds will lead to greater insect infestations in the future.

Prince Edward Island already has a lot of edges—roads, riparian zones, hedgerows dividing farm fields, even gardens and orchards. What we lack is continuous forest. To make matters worse, this is not just an isolated instance—it is happening across North America.

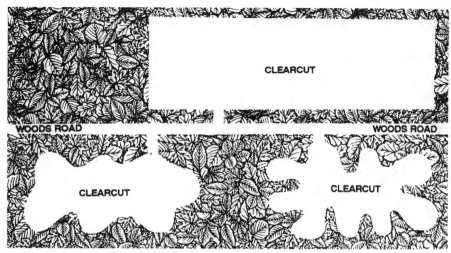

Roadways and clear-cuts create edge in woodlots—not always a good thing.

What You Can Do

1. Use natural selection harvesting systems whenever possible.

2. Refrain from splitting up long, narrow tracts of forest with wide forest roads. An 18 m (60 ft) wide road creates a lot of edge. Use narrow, curving roads wherever possible.

3. If you must clear-cut, make small patch-cuts, as few as possible, to restructure the stand into a later successional forest. A study in Illinois showed that openings less than .3 hectares (3/4 acre) did not attract edge species. In larger openings, edge species did show up, including brown-headed cowbirds. In openings .7 hectares (1 3/4 acres) and larger, cowbirds became particularly abundant.

4. Make sure there are large blocks of continuous forest in every area—whether it is publicly-owned Crown land or a group of woodlot owners getting together to address this problem. Meet with the other woodlot owners in your area to find ways to address this problem. Your forty acres of woodland may border on a piece of publicly-owned land. Cooperation between private woodlot owners and government agencies is the answer to keeping large blocks of forest intact.

5. Protect habitat for large predators, such as hawks and owls, that help control predators of songbird eggs and nestlings.

6. Make sure that your dogs and cats remain indoors or nearby your home. They should not have free range in surrounding woodlands.

This information is excerpted from Chapter 5 of Wildlife and Woodlands *by Gary Schneider, a booklet published by The Environmental Coalition of Prince Edward Island, pp. 16-18. Reprinted with permission.*

8

The Voice of Experience—Sustaining Hardwood Forests

Walton R. Smith

A STRICT—BUT VERY NARROW—DEFINITION of sustained-yield forestry implies that the land is maintained as a producing forest with removal of trees limited to the amount of growth. There are several silvicultural methods that meet such an objective through either even-aged or uneven-aged management. In my professional practice and experience in hardwood forestry over a span of 60 years, I have developed a system that I call "Continuous Production of Quality Hardwoods."

I learned this system through 33 years with the Forest Service, two years running my own lumber business, and 25 years as a practicing forest products and management consultant. Fifty of these years have included the implementation of the practices described below for Waldee Forest—150 acres of mountain hardwood land that was half forest and half open, eroded pasture and farm land.

I spent about five years on the Nantahala National Forest, dealing with timber stand improvement, fire management, and other jobs. It was during this period that I was fortunate enough to marry a local girl whose parents entrusted us with a portion of the family mountain land to put under forest management and to build our cabin there.

During my tenure with the Nantahala, I was indoctrinated into the practice of continuous-selection harvesting of mature trees and selected, low-quality trees to create openings for the regeneration of tolerant and intolerant hard woods. Logging then was primitive by today's standards, but required care to prevent erosion from roads, skidding, and other activities. Follow-up was sometimes required to mechanically release the better quality species. Highgrading wasn't condoned or practiced on the forests I worked on, although we did purchase many tracts of land that had been highgraded under the Week's Law.

Following World War II, I became a Forest Products Specialist at the Southern and (soon thereafter) the Southeastern Forest Experiment Stations. For about 25 years I

had the unique opportunity to work with industries all over the South on forest products problems. Practically every problem that develops in the wood products industry stems from the quality of the wood itself—cross grain, abnormal compression and tension wood, rate of growth, and other factors that can be tied directly to forest management issues.

Following my retirement from the Forest Service in 1969, I moved to Waldee Forest and worked as a consultant in products and management until the present, spending a small amount of time managing my own forest under the principles outlined below. I own a small circular sawmill, a farm tractor, a dehumidification dry kiln, and a fully-equipped workshop which permits me to utilize my timber, often to the finished product.

Principles of Silviculture for Quality Hardwoods

As recommended and practiced on Waldee Forest

Uneven-Aged Management with Continuous Canopy

This is a goal that sometimes takes years to attain, as was the case on Waldee Forest since half the land was open and some was eroded. We decided to plant white pine on all eroded land: Fraser fir Christmas trees on a few acres, walnut and red oak on some open cove sites (with natural seeding), and yellow poplar, ash, maple and a mixture of hardwoods on all other open land. Fraser fir was also interplanted with hardwood plantings to provide an early cash return. Now, after 50 years, all the land is forested and most sites that were formerly open have developed at least two age classes.

Adjusting Rotation to Tree Quality

A great advantage of uneven-aged management is the freedom from forced cutting because of an established rotation, which permits the development of high quality trees. Tree quality is strongly influenced by size, which in turn is usually a result of age. In selection harvesting it is possible and often feasible to allow a white oak to grow for two hundred years, whereas a scarlet oak often begins to deteriorate at 50 to 60 years and should be harvested. The forester should have the opportunity to determine each tree's rotation length by its potential for improving or increasing in value by the next cutting cycle.

Developing Diversity of Tree Species

Developing and maintaining the maximum of desirable species is highly important in hardwood or pine management for many reasons, including maintaining and improving soil fertility, insurance and protection against insects and diseases, protection against disastrous fires, providing wildlife food and habitat, and maintaining a variety of woods for different product demands. When natural reproduction lacks variety, desired hardwood species should be planted. Hardwoods can be successfully planted at a reasonable cost but require more care than softwoods. Bare-rooted hardwood seedlings are most difficult to care for, and tubelings or roots with some soil survive best. Planting with a shovel is also necessary, and tree shelters have proven helpful in lessening animal damage, increasing soil moisture, and increasing height growth, especially where undesirable sprout growth is present.

Developing Age Classes

A good, well-managed, uneven-aged forest will usually have three or more age classes depending on the combination of species, productivity of site, natural species diversity, and the owner's objective and proposed cutting cycle. I personally attempt to work toward three to four age classes with five or more species per acre (at least three of commercial value) and with a continuous selection harvest at intervals of approximately 25 years. Intermediate harvests of Christmas trees and shrubbery help with the cash flow.

A continuous selection harvest may include single tree selection, group selection, necessary thinning, or necessary salvage because of insects or disease. It usually covers all or part of a natural watershed boundary from 10 to 100 or more acres.

Special consideration should be given to riparian areas and wildlife trees. I have found no use for fires or chemicals—any necessary vegetative control is done manually.

Developing the Highest Quality Trees

Based on my experience at the Forest Products Laboratory and working with the forest products industry, I have learned that the best-quality and most valuable trees for veneer and sawlogs grow from natural seedling stock under conditions that create consistent and uniform growth. Abnormal tension wood (compression wood in softwoods) prevalent in hardwood sprouts creates longitudinal shrinkage and compression failures. This—along with tree curvature or lean from pistol-butted trees originating from sprouts—create warp, twist, rift cracks, and splits that create most problems in hardwood use and some disastrous results in construction and furniture softwoods. These conditions are very common in clear-cuts with predominant sprout growth, but less prevalent under a selection system of harvesting with small openings and minimal cutting of smaller stems which sprout prolifically.

Multiple-Use Considerations

In order of priority, Waldee Forest objectives are: protecting soil and water, encouraging abundant wildlife, providing recreation, preserving aesthetics, conducting research, and producing all types of forest products.

Currently, our biggest problems result from human-produced air pollution resulting in acid rain and from acid fog produced by nearby industrial plants. Spruce and fir on the high, eastern mountains were the first to die; oaks are dying fast in the poorer sites; the dogwoods are almost gone within the forest stands; and many other species are showing increasing mortality rates. Many practitioners and some scientists are blaming insects and disease for these mortalities, and in fact this is probably true. But surely the increased acidity and ozone, which has been documented and confirmed by research, makes these trees more susceptible to insects and disease.

The Waldee Forest has evolved from a battered piece of mountain hardwood farmland to a beautiful, continuous forest containing wild areas with wildlife including bear, turkey, grouse, fox, bobcat, raccoon, opossum, squirrel, and many others—both fish and fowl. It has been a learning place for laymen and students from many eastern universities, whose summer students learn tree, log, and lumber grading with a little sawmilling thrown in. Our gates are open to those interested in one way of managing a hardwood forest that is apparently successful. During the first 40 years of management, the sawtimber component increased about five times to a million board-feet. It has doubled to about two million during the past ten years.

As I look across the "Jim Boy" gap and the sun passes into the shadows in the late afternoon, I realize that my 83 years have taken their toll and I am a little bit of an old fogey. But I still challenge anyone to come along and show me their 150 acres that they have managed for 50 years and show better results. How I wish that my favorite past employer, the Forest Service, would return to some of the things it taught me.

Restoring Forest Diversity in the Southern Appalachian Mountains

Robert Zahner

A thing is right when it tends to preserve the integrity, stability and beauty of the biotic community. It is wrong when it tends otherwise.

—Aldo Leopold, 1949

Introduction

WE STAND AT THE THRESHOLD of redefining the importance of our mountain landscape, its natural habitats and the biota they support. Science has shown that such habitats are vital to planetary life support systems where natural communities of interdependent flora and fauna can maintain reservoirs of biological diversity.

When European man destroyed the primeval forests of the Southern Appalachian Mountains, a major component of natural diversity-habitat continuity over large areas-was lost forever. For a century between 1830 and 1930 forest clearing and burning ravaged native biotic communities. Habitats were fragmented, and surviving endemic species of the mature forest were left in isolated communities. Small reservoirs of this genetic material were preserved, unique combinations of forest interior flora and fauna.

In the first quarter of this century, with the establishment of the Southern Appalachian National Forests as watershed preserves, federal conservation policies permitted many forest habitats to begin the natural process of restoring themselves. Gradually small fragments of biota spread into larger communities. Some merged or formed ecotones (edges) with other habitats, so that a continuous forest cover developed over many tens of thousands of acres. This second generation forest was similar to the original primeval forest only in that it still contained most of the original plant and animal species. Today, after 60 to 80 years of recovery, the new forest is still maturing, still unfolding its species composition as new niches are created in the complex progression toward what modern ecologists term an "old growth forest." But

it still has a long way to go to biological maturity. We are perhaps halfway there.

There is now the potential to restore a diversity of biota that resembles the primeval forest. There is also the danger, in present National Forest management plans, of losing much of the restoration already gained. The United States Forest Service, administered by foresters who are highly competent timber managers, narrowly interprets the Congressional Multiple Use-Sustained Yield Act of 1960 with a strong bias toward harvesting commercially mature timber. The Act states implicitly, however, that all resources of the National Forest shall be managed for sustained yield. Other acts of Congress go on to define natural diversity as a vital resource of the public lands. They also mandate that this resource shall be maintained through habitat preservation. This paper is written with the intent of furthering public knowledge of this important environmental issue.

Three Levels of Diversity

In the despoilment and fragmentation of the original forest, three levels of diversity were either destroyed or placed in jeopardy:

1. genetic diversity within species

2. species diversity within habitats

3. habitat diversity within landscapes. We have no record of how many species were irretrievably lost, but we are beginning to count the numbers that today are still endangered and threatened with extinction. Let us consider how these three types of diversity are essential for a healthy bioregion, and how all three can be restored as the new forest grows toward biological maturity.

Genetic Diversity

A great many species counted as rare today can again become more abundant simply by allowing natural biotic processes to evolve unmolested. An example will help clarify this phenomenon. The mountain gentian (*Gentiana decora*) in the Southern Appalachians grows today singly or in small colonies in damp, rich wooded habitats, generally isolated from other members of the species by unsuitable habitats. Gentians are pollinated by a number of insects whose ranges are limited by terrain and plant cover. These pollinators are each able to reach several widely separated colonies of the plant. Thus, if left undisturbed by man's activities, genetic diversity will continue to increase through pollen exchanges from habitat to habitat over an ever increasing area of the mountain landscape. Such phenotypic diversity is critical to the future well being, even survival of this species, as man-caused environmental changes continue to force all biota to adapt to such stresses as atmospheric pollution and accelerated climate warming.

Similar scenarios can be made for literally thousands of species of plants and animals throughout the mountains. The endemic terrestrial mole salamander (*Plethodon nordani*) is a highly significant insectivore in the food chain of soil fauna occurring in the leaf litter under mature hardwood forest. Breeding populations of this animal disappear following removal of the forest and recover only with the forest. Viable genetic exchange cannot occur within fragments of mature habitat for this salamander, which requires contiguous forest cover for migration among populations. Forest dwelling web-building spiders do not migrate across extensive man-made disturbances, limiting their genetic diversity to small populations until such time as their mature forest habitat again becomes extensive.

Forest fragmentation, therefore, leads to inbreeding and extinction for those species of the forest interior with limited mobility for migration. Genetic diversity is essential to provide sufficient adaptability within each species to give that species the capacity to adjust and evolve to survive the accelerating environmental changes expected in the next century.

Species Diversity

The next level of diversity-species within habitats- is often misinterpreted by federal land managers to mean simply the greatest number of different species on a given unit area of land. Forest Service policy makers conclude that timber and game management activities meet the legal requirement for biodiversity. It is well known that the natural succession of weedy species occupying disturbed sites provides a wealth of diversity in terms of total numbers. The Southern Appalachian Mountains today abound with disturbed sites, the result of land clearings, road building, commercial and residential development, forest clear-cutting, agricultural practices, and wildfires. Therefore, the most common diversity is that of seral (successional) plant and animal communities, weedy annuals, biennials and perennials, with their attendant invertebrate and other animal species. Young regrowth forests abound.

But what about species diversity in habitats that were once common in the primeval forest? The one condition that managed forests do not meet is that of providing for the species diversity in critically short supply: that associated with mature old growth forests. From the biological standpoint, a typical old growth forest in the Southern Appalachians supported a mature overstory of 20 or more species of smaller trees of all ages, from reproduction saplings filling canopy gaps to very old species adapted to live out their lives under the canopy. Many tree species were more common in the ancient forest than in today's.

Because old growth stands in the southern Appalachian forests do not reach biological maturity for 200 to 400 years, and perhaps longer to be well represented in the senescence or dying categories, present-day regrowth hardwood forests must be left free of disturbance for at least another 150 years. Even then many micro-habitat niches provided by old windthrown trees, standing dead snags, and rotting logs will not become available for another century. More importantly, most of the plants and animals of our second growth forests are mid-successional and are not those which will eventually be present in climax communities. The maturing forests of today will undergo dynamic changes in species composition if left undisturbed until they reach a condition of biological old growth.

As today's forests continue to mature, the ground in many places will be carpeted with large colonies of painted trillium

(*Trillium undulatum*), baneberry (*Actaea pachypoda*), dogtooth violet (*Erythronium americanum*), umbrella-leaf (*Diphylleia cymosa*), jack-in-the-pulpit (*Arisaema triphyllum*), and many fern species. Rotting logs will provide substrate and micro-habitats for many species of fungi, mosses, liverworts, and all the attendant invertebrate and small vertebrate animals, which are unseen and generally uncounted, yet are essential to the health of the entire larger community. Add to these the many birds, including several species each of owls, warblers and woodpeckers, and other vertebrates that require a biologically mature, undisturbed mixed hardwood forest for their food, shelter, and breeding habitat. Such a biotic community is dynamic with life processes supporting a large array of life forms.

In the above example, not one of the plants or animals in itself is today exceptionally rare; although any of a number of today's threatened or endangered species, such as the small whorled pogonia (*Isotria medeoloides*) and certainly ginseng (*Panax quinquefolius*), could make a comeback in such habitats. The point is, such a combination of these species, taken together as a functioning ecosystem, is today a rare occurrence.

Thus the second level of biodiversity-species diversity within habitats-is today well represented only by the weedy and seral species common to our man-disturbed habitats. Maturing forests are evolving from these seral communities, however, with species enrichment occurring slowly in those habitats that are left undisturbed. The potential exists, therefore, for restoration of this level of diversity. Migration and dispersion of non-weedy, forest interior species into undisturbed, maturing forests will likely continue indefinitely. Biologically mature habitats, or old growth mixed hardwood forests, are again a possibility in the southern mountains within the next century.

Just as phenotypic diversity within a species is essential for evolution to adapt that species for survival in a changing environment, so is species diversity within a habitat essential for the whole community of interdependent plants and animals to adapt. When any species is extirpated from a biotic community, a strand is broken in the life support of that community, and all other species are affected. Science has not yet learned the subtleties of these connections, but the breakage in food chains and loss of shelters are obvious consequences. A fundamental law of ecology is the reciprocal relationship between the health of the ecosystem and the well being of each individual organism. The future of those species combinations best adapted to old, mature hardwood forest communities depends on the integrity of the entire habitat.

Habitat Diversity

The third level of biological diversity-habitat diversity in the regional landscape-has also been gradually emerging in the southern Appalachian Mountains throughout the second half of this century. The National Forests provide large contiguous blocks of forest area, which, if they continue to be left undisturbed, have the potential to mature into a mosaic of diverse old growth forest habitats. The key requirement for this regional diversity lies in maintaining a continuity of undisturbed habitats across the landscape. Disconnected mature habitats, left to mature as fragments ;isolated one from the other, cannot serve as more than small refugia for genetic material. As discussed in the first and second levels of diversity, such a limitation confines genetic variation to the specific environment of each habitat, leading to inbreeding, loss of species, and inability of the entire community to respond to future changes in environment.

The current policy of National Forest management to accommodate landscape diversity is to preserve fragments of old growth stands dispersed across the region.

Interspersed among these are many even-aged managed stands of younger ages and of commercially important species of trees and game animals. This concept of diversity is analogous to the preservation of species in arboretums, botanical gardens and zoological parks. Certainly a turk's cap lily (*Lilium superbum*) in a cultivated garden has lost its wild "personality," because a wildflower removed from its natural habitat is no longer serving its role as a strand in the web of life. In like manner, a fragment of old growth forest preserved in a landscape of managed young forests has lost its "old growthness." Its myriad strands are no longer connected to the regional web vital to the biological evolution of itself and of the region its genetic material serves.

The black bear (*Ursus americanus*) is an excellent example of a species requiring landscape level mature habitat. This animal is wide ranging, with adult males requiring over 30 square miles of contiguous forest habitat for food and shelter. Preferred habitat is mature hardwood forest, and quality denning sites are essential to gestational female survival. Very large, hollow living trees, dead snags, and downed logs comprise the most suitable denning sites, conditions characteristic of old growth forests. The black bear is considered by wildlife ecologists to be the best indicator of a healthy, mature forest, contiguous over large areas. Since this animal represents the top of an omnivorous food chain, a landscape that supports a viable, reproducing population of black bears contains the ingredients for fully functioning mature ecosystems.

At this highest level of biological diversity, just as at the two lower levels, the ability of an entire bioregion to adjust to and survive environmental change lies in the diversity among its natural habitats. The greater the number of mature habitat types; represented on the landscape, the more stable the entire region. With the acceleration of man-caused environmental changes, species normally adapted to ridges must migrate to midslopes, and species adapted to slopes may have to migrate to coves. Species normally found at mid-elevations may have to migrate to higher, cooler habitats.

Ecologists believe the natural ranges of species will have to shift from south to north, requiring genetic exchanges across the region. Migration of all but highly mobile, weedy species of both plants and animals occurs only on adjacent sites. During and following the advances and retreats of continental glaciers, forest communities easily migrated at a rate of a few miles per century as the climate cooled or warmed over thousands of years.

In the coming century, however, individual species and entire communities may have to migrate at a rate perhaps ten times faster, an impossible feat from isolated, fragmented old growth habitats.

Optimum regional biodiversity therefore requires continuity of habitats contiguous over the landscape in a mosaic of mature communities. As we have seen, all topographic conditions-ridges, north slopes, coves, south slopes, streams and gorges, balds and bogs-must be included. Federal protection is recently extended to many of these latter-named communities, those that support not commercially important timber resources, through Congressionally designated Wilderness Areas. But nearly all of the remainder, the large areas of contiguous second growth forests that are becoming economically mature, are allocated for harvesting, primarily by clear-cutting!

The Potential to Restore Old-Growth Diversity

Today we stand at the threshold of making one of the most important decisions about the use of our public lands since the creation of the National Forests. A land ethic, based on sound ecological principles for habitat management, is needed to protect and preserve large areas of mature forests for the future health and natural evolution of species that require forest interior habitats. The present orientation toward timber and game management is not going to maintain regional biological diversity in its broadest sense.

The United States 100th Congress stated, "The Earth's biological diversity is being rapidly depleted at a rate without precedent in human history... Most losses of biological diversity are largely avoidable consequences of human activity.... Maintaining biological diversity through habitat preservation is often less costly and more effective than efforts to save species once they become endangered." (Quote from H. R. 4335, 1988. Italics added.) The Society of American Foresters agrees, in a recent position statement, that " ....there is a compelling need to rehabilitate old growth forests throughout the United States and the world... The best way for management to create old growth is to conserve an adequate supply of present second growth forests and make the long-term commitment to leave them alone."

On the National Forests of the Southern Appalachian Mountains, we are well on our way toward restoring entire landscapes of the 150-to 200-year old forests that begin to stabilize as old growth. This rehabilitation has occurred in the 65 years since the mountain National Forests were established. I repeat, we are halfway there.

We read and hear daily the warnings of distinguished biological scientists that man-caused destruction of natural habitats is the single most serious threat to survival of life as we know it on our planet. The loss of genetic diversity and the loss of entire ecosystems are occurring at an accelerated pace from oceans, deserts, tundra, grasslands, and forestlands. Our Southern Appalachian Mountains are part of this world picture. Unbroken, naturally functioning habitats must be restored here to provide refugia for the basic life support systems crucial to carrying all forms of life through the unfolding ecological catastrophe of our times.

We come to the crucial question of our times: what is the highest and best use of our National Forests in producing the greatest benefit over the generations to come? Can we extend this beyond commodities for people to the health of the global ecosystem?

This article was previously published in Tipularia: A Botanical Magazine, *Spring, 1990. Georgia Botanical Society.*

8

8

9 Restoration Forestry in the Pacific Northwest

9

Methow Forest Watch

Restoration Forestry in the Pacific Northwest: A Resource Guide

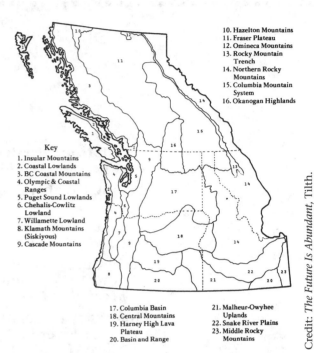

Key
1. Insular Mountains
2. Coastal Lowlands
3. BC Coastal Mountains
4. Olympic & Coastal Ranges
5. Puget Sound Lowlands
6. Chehalis-Cowlitz Lowland
7. Willamette Lowland
8. Klamath Mountains (Siskiyous)
9. Cascade Mountains

10. Hazelton Mountains
11. Fraser Plateau
12. Omineca Mountains
13. Rocky Mountain Trench
14. Northern Rocky Mountains
15. Columbia Mountain System
16. Okanogan Highlands

17. Columbia Basin
18. Central Mountains
19. Harney High Lava Plateau
20. Basin and Range

21. Malheur-Owyhee Uplands
22. Snake River Plains
23. Middle Rocky Mountains

Credit: *The Future Is Abundant*, Tilth.

Physiographic Regions of the Pacific Northwest

FORESTRY IS TUMULTUOUS in the Pacific Northwest. The battle for the region's last ancient forests has intensified into a national and international issue. The cries for the reform of forestry practices are increasingly loud and hard to ignore. The importance of the struggle for Pacific Northwest forests is in some part due to the high value of the timber versus the high value of the ecosystems as models of functioning, temperate, old-growth ecosystems.

Restoration forestry, in all its varied facets, has many promoters in the Pacific Northwest. Forest ecologists have been delivering a stream of new findings on how forests work. This research is possible because of highly-funded university and government forestry departments, and because the region still has some old-growth forests to study. Ironically, the funding for studying the old-growth has come from clearcutting most of these notable forest ecosystems.

This Pacific Northwest section is relatively large, partially because the editor is based there, and also because the region is a relative hotbed of restoration forestry. Or, perhaps we are just more vocal. At any rate, the Pacific Northwest appears to be a world leader in developing restoration forestry concepts and practices. For the past several decades, the Pacific Northwest has been a world leader in developing and exporting industrial clearcutting forestry practices and equipment. Hopefully in the future, the region will become renowned for restoration forestry instead of clearcutting.

Pacific Northwest Bioregions

The Pacific Northwest is a big place no matter where you draw the boundaries. Politically, most people include northern California, Oregon, Washington, Idaho, western Montana and British Columbia. Bioregionally, it becomes much more complex as we look at watersheds, climates, physiography and the distribution of flora and fauna. The accompanying maps can tell you something about bioregional boundaries.

Physiographic Regions of the Pacific Northwest Map

Although physiography is only one way of determining bioregional borders this map would be a good place to start, since the geographic boundaries coincide in large part with different vegetation patterns. Apologies to northern California, but the mapmaker didn't include you. (Illustration from *The Future Is Abundant*. Tilth)

Western Redcedar (*Thuja plicata*) Range Map

The map for Western redcedar (*Thuja plicata*) shows the range of the temperate rainforests of western North America. Notice the large eastern distribution of redcedar separated from the coastal forests by the dry, rainshadow area behind the Cascades and B.C. Coastal Mountains. This eastern population marks the wet forests of the northern Rocky Mountain bioregion. Even though it is on the Eastside geographically, it is a somewhat more cold-tolerant version of the coastal rainforests. These are productive forests which grow large trees. Old-growth western redcedar which hasn't been cut, shouldn't be cut.

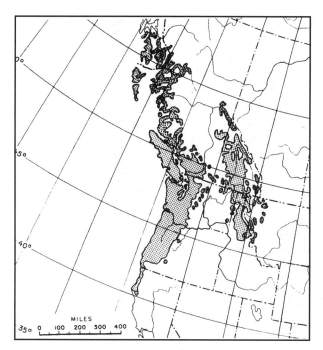

Western Redcedar (*Thuja plicata*) Range Map

Credit: Silvics of Forest Trees of the United States

Restoration Forestry Organizations in the Pacific Northwest

Association of Woodworkers Advocating Respect for the Environment (AWARE)

P.O. Box 1031
Redway, California 95560
Tel: (707) 923-3569

AWARE is an association of working people whose current and future jobs are dependent on sustainable forest resources. AWARE supports an unprejudiced analysis of how best to achieve a stable, productive, high-quality wood products industry from seedling to showroom, using Pacific Certified Ecological Forest Products or salvaged wood.

Citizens for Better Forestry

P.O. Box 1510
Hayfork, California 96041
Tel/Fax: (916) 628-5004
Contacts: Joseph and Sue Bower

Citizens for Better Forestry has put together a citizen's alternative to the forest plan for the local national forest. Through a related organization SAFE (Safe Alternatives for a Forest Environment) they are developing alternatives to the use of pesticides and herbicides in forestry.

Ecoforestry Institute

P.O. Box 12543
Portland, Oregon 97212
Tel/Fax: (503) 231-0576

Contacts: Mike Barnes, Twila Jacobson

One of the Ecoforestry Institute's goals is to put together the first eco-forestry teaching center to certify foresters. The school is scheduled to begin in the summer of 1994 at Orville Camp's Forest Farm in Selma, Oregon, and at the McMinn's Kindwood Forest on Vancouver Island, B.C. EI is also incorporated in British Columbia as the Ecoforestry Institute Society. [see B.C. section for details].

The Ecoforestry Institute practices the philosophy of Natural Selection Ecoforestry developed by Orville Camp [See Camp Forest Farm in the following section.] Natural Selection Ecoforestry (NSE) is based on the principle that Nature knows best how to manage forest ecosystems. Only Nature has a time-tested selective forest improvement process. NSE uses evolutionary natural selection indicators to reach decisions on which trees can be logged. It incorporates all other known ecological principles into its methods, and is an evolving practice. It is a flexible, landscape, ecosystem scale approach, which can be practiced at the stand level.

Ecoforestry Institute (EI) has hosted the meetings of the Pacific Cascadia Ecoforesters. (See Ecoforesters Recommendations to President Clinton.) EI publishes a newsletter.

EI's projects and programs involve seven undertakings:

1) Providing education and training programs for ecoforesters.

2) Setting up demonstration forests and research programs.

3) Developing certification systems for raw materials and secondary products.

4) Providing community education through conferences, videos and publications.

5) Helping community watershed and land trusts set up ecoforestry programs.

6) Establishing networks of ecoforesters on bioregional bases.

7) Helping groups in other countries to set up Ecoforestry Institute affiliates.

Ecotrust

1200 NW Front Ave
Portland, Oregon 97209
Tel: (503) 227-6225

EcoTrust works with local people to build ecologically and economically sound communities in the temperate rain forests of North America. Ecotrust is a branch of Conservation International, a large international NGO (non-government organization). Ecotrust is establishing a bank to provide loans to small-scale

9

forest industries, and is developing plans for sustainable resource use.

Forest Land Management Committee

8400 Rocky Lane SE
Olympia, Washington 98513
Tel: (206) 459-0946
Contact: Jean Stam

Forest Land Management Committee (FLMC) co-founder and director, Jean Stam, has single-handedly become the most important networking force for restoration forestry in Washington State. FLMC is a non-profit organization that sprung out of a desire to find a definition and method of forestry that will provide our wood needs from second growth forests.

The organization is currently a well rounded educational outreach effort. Live tours are given of excellent ecological forest practices. Over 100 people came to their tour of the Fort Lewis army base forest in February, 1993. People are interested. FLMC facilitates contact between foresters and local tribes to acknowledge and access traditional local tribal stewardship practices. FLMC does educational outreach on local, state and federal levels. A newsletter is published to update members on positive happenings in political and economic realms.

Video documentaries are being made on topics such as cutting practices, sustaining forest communities with value added and secondary manufacturing, ecoforester profiles, and Native American perspectives. FLMC has videotapes available from the first meetings of the Pacific Cascadia Ecoforesters Working Group. Membership is free.

PHOTO CREDIT: HANS LITTOOY

Jean Stam, of the Forest Land Management Committee

Old-Growth Forests and Timber Towns: Thinking about Tomorrow—A Report to Governor Mike Lowry
Melanie J. Rowland. 1993. Institute for Public Policy and Management, Univ. of Wash., Seattle. 37 pp.

A moderate, well-researched look at PNW timber communities and a range of options for sustainable development. It includes a useful set of references on the subject.

Forestcare Company

P.O. Box 38
Lorraine, Oregon 97451
Tel: (503) 942-5424
Contact: Curtin Mitchell

Forestcare Company has developed a set of forestry covenants called Forestcare Provisions. These provide legal protection for privately owned forestland in Oregon, where owners wish to insure that their land is not clearcut after ownership passes on. This provision allows the selective harvesting of timber, maintaining the forest in a healthy condition, while prohibiting clearcutting. Because this provision is attached to the deed, it should protect the land for a very long period of time. Further information available on request. They also do consulting on non-timber forest products.

Institute for Sustainable Forestry

P.O. Box 1580
Redway, California 95560
Tel: (707) 923-4719/Fax: (707) 923-4257

The Institute for Sustainable Forestry (ISF) is dedicated to promoting the ecological and economic sustainability of earth's forest resources. ISF established and administers the Pacific Certified Ecological Forest Products program to certify ecologically and economically sound forest products. They are working with other West Coast organizations to set regional certification standards. (See the wood certification section.)

A major focus at ISF has been setting up on-the-ground forestry projects and models. The Institute provides workshops for small landowners, activists and forest workers in sustainable forestry planning and practices. The Institute facilitates cooperation among people from all sides of the forestry debate to create a viable, ecologically sound regional economy and is helping develop state policy to assist small landowners in pursuing restoration forestry.

ISF is involved in organizing a major international conference on sustainable forestry in the spring of 1995. It will be held in northern California. To my knowledge, this will be the first international conference on restoration forestry.

Mendocino County Real Wood Co-op

P.O. Box 2805
Fort Bragg, California 95437
Tel: (707) 984-8354/Fax: (707) 459-0548

An organization of woodsworkers, foresters, restorationists, wood craftspersons and small mills. MCRWC promotes small-scale wood products industries.

Olympic Peninsula Foundation

1200 W. Simms Way, Suite 201
Port Townsend, Washington 98368
Tel: (206) 385-9421
Betsy Carlson, Executive Director

Olympic Peninsula Foundation began in July, 1992 with the mission of promoting a sustainable environmentally sound economy for multiple generations. They plan to purchase some forestland in east Jefferson County for an experimental forest and educational center focused on environmentally sound woodlot management. They have developed an idea for a manufacturing technology center focused on secondary wood products from composite woods, veneers, and small diameter roundwood.

Pacific Cascadia Ecoforesters Working Group

c/o Ecoforestry Institute (address earlier this section)

The Pacific Cascadia Ecoforesters Working Group consists of practitioners of ecologically responsible forestry throughout the bioregion. Some of them are elders with 20-50 years experience in restoration forestry. The Ecoforestry Institute hosted its first two meetings in 1993 and plans to facilitate two Ecoforesters gatherings in 1994. The gatherings act as a peer review process of the principles and practices of an ecocentric forestry (ecoforestry). (See "Ecoforesters Recommendations to President Clinton" article in Restoration Forestry.)

Pacific Forest Trust

P.O. Box 858
Boonville, California 95415
Tel: (707) 895-2166

Pacific Forest Trust (PFT) is committed to reforming the management of private forestlands through practical on-the-ground application of Stewardship Forestry. Stewardship Forestry is based on practices that support natural forest ecosystems and their biological requirements for healthy functioning. PFT provides a network of resource professionals actively working in the field of Stewardship Forestry and makes their services available to private landowners and their forest managers. The Trust is creating a database and bibliography of existing research on Stewardship Forestry.

Public Forestry Foundation

P.O. Box 371
Eugene, Oregon 97440
Tel: (503) 687-1993
Roy Keene, Director; Patty Keene, Administrator

Public Forest Foundation (PFF) is a not-for-profit coalition of foresters, resource professionals, and citizens dedicated to the promotion and continuance of socially responsible forestry through citizen involvement and education. PFF finds ways to sustain forests by working WITH the Forest Service, conservationists, and private timber owners. PFF is one of the most active restoration forestry organizations on the West Coast.

PFF foresters continually monitor the Pacific's public forests, seeking out good models of forest management and exposing bad forest practices. Their fully equipped research vehicle, the Forest Monitor, enables PFF foresters to travel around the West Coast teaching citizen's groups how to monitor forests through Citizen Forester Workshops. PFF actively investigates and facilitates on-the-ground solutions in forest resource disputes. PFF foresters have been consultants for a number of restoration forestry projects. PFF's magazine, *The Citizen Forester* is one of the leading periodicals on restoration forestry. See review in the following periodicals section.

Rogue Institute for Ecology and Economy

P.O. Box 3213
Ashland, Oregon 97520
Tel: (503) 482-2307
Contact: Brett KenKairn

The Rogue Institute for Ecology and Economy (RIEE) is a non-profit organization in southern Oregon whose mission is to develop, advocate, and support forest resource management which restores and sustains forest-based communities, jobs and ecosystems. RIEE promotes research and education on innovative forms of citizen participation in forest management; and provides a forum for dialogue among forest users. RIEE is one of the few organizations in the USA to develop a certification program for sustainably-produced timber and forest products.

Wood Forum

P.O. Box 2012
Bellingham, Washington 98227
Tel: (503) 856-4947
Contact: Dianne Lindsay

A network of "Wood Users Supporting Ecological Forestry." Wood Forum is mainly composed of wood

Wood Forum Directors
Cordia Sammeth (on left) and Dianne Lindsay (on right).

related business people addressing forest management in northwestern Washington. Their goal is to facilitate ecologically based, long term forest management and production of quality forest resources. Wood Forum connects local eco-forest managers and millers with markets and consumers. Wood Forum sponsors workshops, tours, and forest products marketing to bring forest ecology and economics into balance. A bi-monthly newsletter for information exchange and marketing is published. $10/yr.

WoodNet

127 E. 1st St., Suite 4-W
Port Angeles, Washington 98362
Tel: (206) 452-2134/Fax: (206) 452-7065
Contact: Gus Kostopulos

Huge amounts of logs are shipped from the Port Angeles docks to Japan and other countries. WoodNet has discovered an almost endless supply of jobs can be created by producing products locally rather than shipping the logs away. WoodNet provides a network linking Olympic Peninsula wood products manufacturers. WoodNet now has over 300 members. The organization provides business planning, sales and marketing training; helps obtain loans, and develop sales literature, along with the economies of scale that members can take advantage of because of their size. In 1993, WoodNet secured funding of $350,000 to study the feasibility of creating a Pacific Northwest Wood Products Manufacturing Technology Center. The facility would be a production center as well as a training center.

Woodworkers Alliance for Rainforest Protection (WARP)

Box 133
Coos Bay, Oregon 97420

WARP works to protect forest ecosystems for the benefit of forest inhabitants, the woodworking community and future generations, by exploring methods of sustainable timber harvest. WARP educates woodworkers to act as responsible timber consumers and encourages them to educate their clients and colleagues. Membership is $20/yr. and includes a subscription to their newsletter *Understory*, single copies $1.50 ppd.

Yuba Watershed Institute

17790 Tyler Foote Road
Nevada City, California 95959
Tel: (916) 478-0817 (message phone)

The Yuba Watershed Institute (YWI) is a group of citizens concerned with the sustainable use of natural resources and the protection of long term biological diversity within the Yuba River watershed. The Institute serves as an educational resource providing ongoing talks, seminars, publications, and walks on all aspects of the watershed.

At the core of YWI is a cooperative management agreement with the Bureau of Land Management (BLM) and the Timber Framers Guild of North America for the joint management of 1,388 acres of forest land in Nevada County. The goal of this stewardship program is to foster ancient forest ecosystems and riparian habitats while developing a timber management plan for selective and sustainable harvest of forest products. The broad intent of this agreement is to demonstrate that local citizens can become active partners in managing public lands for their intrinsic biological and landscape values as well as for the economic and cultural sustenance of the community.

The work of walking and inventorying all of the parcels for a first round overview of important biological, landscape and cultural features has been done by about twenty people. This inventory was accomplished over a year's time under the direction of retired forester, Don Harkin. This survey is an example of the kinds of inventory needed to implement restoration forestry. It also shows that implementing restoration forestry across the landscape will require substantial employment of people for inventory work.

YWI publishes *Tree Rings*, a journal which reflects the deep ecological understandings of the local people about animals, plants, birds and the web of life in the region's forests. *Tree Rings* offers a bioregional perspective of forestry. This journal is a good model for other restoration forestry groups to check out. It helps that Gary Snyder is one of the locals involved in writing for *Tree Rings*. Minimum yearly membership is $25.

The following is a listing of the research, inventory, and work projects that YWI is doing or proposing for Inimim Forest.

1) Timber inventory and survey concentrating on large trees, snags, and down logs

2) Census of cavity nesting birds and animals

3) Identification, classification and mapping of plant communities

4) Permanent vegetation and timber stand inventory

5) Census for bird and mammal use of streamside and other wildlife corridors

6) Locating, mapping, and sampling fire scarred trees and stumps

7) Develop a forest history and stand structure analysis

8) Pruning and thinning stand improvement practice plots

Restoration Forestry Periodicals in the Pacific Northwest

At this point there are only a few journals devoted to restoration forestry in the Pacific Northwest. *Forest Canada* is the most established journal to date (see British Columbia section). There are many environmental journals devoted to forest issues. Several I would particularly recommend include: *Wild Forest Review, Wild Oregon, Headwaters Journal, Northwest Conservation*, and *Transitions*. For addresses of these and others: see the Environmental Periodicals section in the USA Resource section.

International Journal of Forestry
Ecoforestry Institute
Address in preceeding section.

The first issue of this quarterly journal was in Spring 1994. Highly recommended. Subscription rates are $30 individuals, $20 students and those living lightly, $60 institutions

The Citizen Forester
Public Forestry Foundation
Address in preceding section.

This quarterly journal provides technical forestry information in a hands-on format: how to make and use forestry measurement tools; updates on "hot" forest issues; articles interpreting the most current scientific views; and opinions from progressive resource professionals. Membership/subscription is $25/yr. $15 for students and seniors. Back issues available for a small fee.

Forest Land Management Committee Newsletter
Address in preceding section.

Several newsletters a year update members on positive happenings in political and economic realms.

Inner Voice
See review in U.S. Forestry Periodicals.

The magazine of the American Association of Forest Service Employees for Environmental Ethics covers forestry around the U.S., but much of it is devoted to the PNW.

Tree Rings
See review in the Yuba Watershed Institute's entry in preceding section.

Understory
Newsletter of the Woodworkers Alliance for Rainforest Protection. Address in preceeding section.

Membership is $20/yr. and includes a subscription to the newsletter. Single copies $1.50 ppd.

Wood Forum Newsletter
Address in preceding section.

A bi-monthly newsletter for information exchange and marketing of sustainably produced timber products in northwestern Washington. $10/yr.

Restoration Forestry Models in the Pacific Northwest

Models of sustainable forestry are hard to come by in the human realm. On the other hand, Nature is full of models. Masanobu Fukuoka, of *One Straw Revolution* fame, tells us to "farm in the image of Nature." This adage can be applied to forestry. We must practice forestry in the image of Nature.

Over the three years of preparing *Restoration Forestry,* I talked to hundreds of foresters and environmentalists around the U.S. and Canada. I asked most of them the question "Do you know of any models of restoration forestry?" Few people could mention more than a few and many couldn't think of even one! In other words, long-term models outside of Nature are hard to come by. The following is an eclectic list of the more promising ones I've heard of in the Pacific Northwest.

Camp Forest Farm
2100 Thompson Creek Road
Selma, Oregon 97538
Tel: (503) 597-4313/Fax: (503) 597-4044

Orville Camp is the originator of Natural Selection Ecoforestry and one of the most famous restoration foresters in the Pacific Northwest. He was awarded The 1990 Restoration Forester of the Year Award by Friends of the Trees Society.

Orville Camp and his family have lived in Selma, Oregon for three generations, where they have mainly worked in forestry. Over the past 25 years Camp has restored his own clearcut forest land. Through observation, he has learned to work with the natural processes of the forest and work with nature in selecting trees for cutting. "Nature calls the shots, the forester listens." Camp's method of selection always leaves the best dominant trees and a forest canopy. A Natural Selection managed forest is secondarily supported by a minimum sized "contour access road system" (CARS) to get products out. Orville Camp has done innovative work with low-impact road design and road building. You can read about Camp's methods in his book *The Forest Farmers Handbook.* He is working on a new book, *The Ecoforesters' Handbook*, which will be published in 1994.

Camp is one of the few people teaching restoration forestry. He has given many tours and workshops at the Camp Forest Farm and elsewhere in the Pacific Northwest. In 1994, in conjunction with the Ecoforestry Institute, the Camp Forest Farm will be offering forestry courses leading to certification as ecoforesters. See article by Orville Camp.

Cerro Gordo Forestry Cooperative

Dorena Lake, Box 569
Cottage Grove, Oregon 97424

Cerro Gordo is a 1200-acre community near Eugene, Oregon, which bills itself as a prototype "ecovillage"—a symbiotic village, farm, and forest that allows its residents to live in harmony with the environment. The Forestry Cooperative, created in 1985, owns and manages 450 acres of forest. Using a system called Individual Tree Selection Management (see below), it can harvest enough lumber for 25 homes a year while maintaining the ecosystem.

Collins Almanor Forest

Collins Pine Co.
Chester, California 96020

"The privately owned 91,000-acre Collins Almanor forest in northeastern California has never known a clearcut. With only a few trees snaked out of the woods at a time; wildlife, clear water, and recreational opportunities abound, even on land that has just been cut. In 1941, Collins Almanor held 1.5 billion board-feet of timber, enough to build 150,000 homes. Loggers have since removed 1.7 billion board-feet, but the forest has nearly as much wood as it had when logging began—all of it still in mature forest that attracts bald eagles, ospreys, goshawks, and northern spotted owls."

—Roy Keene, Public Forestry Foundation

Fort Lewis Army Base Forest

See article in Pacific Northwest section.

Goebel-Jackson Tree Farm

62309 Wallowa Lake Hwy.
Joseph, Oregon 97846
Tel: (604) 432-2431

See article in Pacific Northwest section.

Individual Tree Selection

621 S.W. Morrison St.
Portland, Oregon 97205
Tel: (503) 222-9772
Scott Ferguson, President.

Ferguson is working with forests that have been managed under the individual tree selection method for decades. See the article by Marie Reed in the Pacific Northwest section.

Morning Song Forest Restoration Project

614 Toroda Creek Road
Wauconda, Washington 98859
Tel: (509) 486-4011
Contact: Dan Morgan
See article in Pacific Northwest section.

City of Seattle Cedar River Watershed

19901 Cedar Falls Rd. SE
North Bend, Washington 98045
Tel: (206) 888-1507
Contact: Jim Kapusinski

See article: "Bioforestry: Seattle's Cedar River Watershed" by Mark McCalmon in Pacific Northwest section.

Smilin' O Forest Farm

70417 Follett Rd.
Elgin, Oregon 97827
Tel: (503) 437-5252
Contacts: Bill and Margaret Oberteuffer

The Smilin' O is the first privately-owned forest to become a demonstration model for the Blue Mountains Natural Resources Institute. Oberteuffer practices all ages, multiple-species forest management on their 160 acres of forested land. Forestry workshops and tours are held there and visitors are welcome.

Wild Iris Forestry

Box 1423
Redway, California 95560
Tel: (707) 923-2344

Jan and Peggy Iris are pioneers in restoration forestry in second or third growth forests in northern California. Forests are typically overstocked with lots of suppressed trees, susceptible to wildfire because of fuel loading and stand density, and dominated by pioneer tree species. Their method of forest restoration involves thinning the forest, favoring desired species: late-succession species, rare species or desired market species. The thinning releases remaining trees to put on a increased growth. The forest is also less fire-prone. The thinnings supply the Wild Iris mill and kiln which turns madrone, tanoak, oaks, and other local hardwoods into beautiful lumber and flooring.

Jan and Peggy Iris of Wild Iris Forestry were much of the inspiration behind the Institute for Sustainable Forestry and Pacific Certified Ecological Forest Products.

See article by Jan Iris in the Fire section.

The Applegate Partnership

CPO Box 277
Applegate, Oregon 97530
Tel: (503) 846-6917
Contact: Jack Shipley

The Applegate River Watershed straddles the Oregon/California border and occupies approximately 300 square miles of land. In the spring of 1992, local environmentalist Jack Shipley began talking to agency scientists and others about the possibility of developing a landscape-scale management plan which would attempt to demonstrate the concepts being developed in what was loosely defined as "Ecosystem Management."

Later that fall, Jack hosted a gathering at his home in the Applegate. Over 38 people, representing a wide range of backgrounds and affiliations met that afternoon to talk about the possibility of joining together to develop a community-based solution to the timber crises. This developed into a board which started meeting 1 to 2 times per week and has done so continuously for almost a year. Early in the process of identifying its overall objectives, the partnership board identified four primary task areas necessary for developing and implementing a community-based ecosystem management plan. These task areas are: ecosystem assessment, ecological research and monitoring, community assessment, development of an effective participation program, and short-term projects designed to demonstrate the effectiveness of a collaborative approach to resource planning.

—Excerpts from "The Applegate Partnership: Ecosystem Management as Economic Re-Development," an article by Brett KenKairn in the *Inner Voice*, September/October 1993. p. 11.

A 24-page report, *The Applegate Partnership,* is available for $5. They have already distributed over 800 copies.

See also Tribal Forestry section for further restoration forestry models in the Pacific Northwest.

Some Restoration Forestry Proposals Worth Looking At

The following are proposals rather than actual models. They offer well-thought out ideas which can help inspire others. Restoration forestry proposals are proliferating in 1993; partially in response to President Clinton's Forest Plan.

USFS Peak/Stella Demonstration Project in the Rogue River National Forest in southern Oregon is a 2,200 acre site, which the Ecoforestry Institute proposes be enlarged as a landscape demonstration ecoforest. Orville Camp has been working hard on this proposal.

Clackamas Focus Partnership
Contact the Clackamas Ranger District, Mt. Hood National Forest in Washington State or Public Forestry Foundation. Address in Restoration Forestry Organizations. A forest stewardship program for Mt. Hood forest restoration; a citizen-involved landscape level management project of 5,500 acres.

The Headwaters Redwood Forest Complex in the redwood ecosystem of northern California where the local community is proposing to save the largest remaining landscape of old-growth redwood forest. See Ecoforesters' Recommendation to Clinton.

The InterTribal Wilderness Park is being proposed by the InterTribal Sinkyone Wilderness Council for 3,800 acres of forestland in the Sinkyone region of northern California. See article by Dennis Martinez.

Klamath Province Forest Training Center proposed in Hayfork, California
Contact Jim Jungwirth, Hayfork, California. The plan is for a regional watershed research and training center. Jungwirth's group envisions attracting about 200 clients at the center and about 50 teachers. The group is asking the federal government for $4 million to launch the Center. Highly skilled timber workers from northern California could be hired as teachers to pass on skills needed to practice new forestry techniques.

VISION 2020: Restoration Forestry and Ecosystem Management
Trees Foundation
P.O. Box 2202
Redway, California 95560
Tel: (707) 923-2979.

The international goal of Vision 2020 is to put a pilot project in a diverse native forest in every relevant country to begin acquiring the data on how many jobs can be created in sustainable/restoration forestry and what type of activity will be in accord with maintaining and increasing biodiversity.

The Trees Foundation has brought together US Forest Service personnel, the Karuk Tribe and practitioners of sustainable forestry to draft a long-term Ecosystem Management Strategy for the 52,000 acre Bluff Creek watershed. Bluff Creek is a tributary to the Klamath River, within the Six Rivers National Forest. The Karuk Tribe, with thousands of years of land management traditions, is integrating the Forest Service's substantial biological and geographical databases with their Geographic Information System (GIS) and combining it with their satellite imagery resources.

The Ecosystem Management Strategy requires gathering and integrating extensive biological, social and economic data. Vision 2020 is using this data, combined with a firm commitment to Native American values, to restore and maintain a healthy ecosystem.

The Trees Foundation will convene an international conference on sustainable forestry—the Vision 2020 Conference in May 1995 on the North Coast of California.

Appropriate-Scale Logging Equipment

This first edition of *Restoration Forestry* is weak on the subject of forest harvesting technology. What logging equipment is appropriate for restoration forestry? Generally, the smallest feasible which can do the job, and which will do the least damage. One of the first prerequisites of restoration forestry logging is ecologically-conscious and conscientious operators, no matter what the scale of machinery. Horses and other animal draft power should be used a lot more (see article on horse logging). Timing of the harvesting is also important to minimize damage to the forest floor. This can be during snow/frozen periods in the north, or dry periods in southern wet/dry climates.

Here are several references on logging equipment.

Institute for Sustainable Forestry

Bill Eastwood of ISF is conducting a study on small-scale logging equipment and suppliers. Contact him at ISF for results of his research. Address in Pacific Northwest Restoration Forestry Organizations section.

"Logging Systems"

Herb Hammond. 1992. Section 11 in *Community Guide to the Forest—Ecology, Planning and Use*. See B.C. book reviews.

A good article comparing the pros and cons of different logging machinery, ground skidding, cable yarding and aerial systems.

Forest Engineering, Inc.

520 SW 45th St.
Corvallis, Oregon 97333-4428
Tel: (503) 754-7558/Fax (503) 754-7559
Contacts: Ed and Steve Aulerich

This firm specializes throughout the world in small cable systems. This is also the address for the Council on Forest Engineering (COFE).

Logging Practices—Principles of Timber Harvesting Systems

Steve Conway. 1976. Published by Miller Freeman,

Some Environmental Effects of Cable Logging in Appalachian Forests

James H Patric. 1980. General Technical Report NE-55, USDA Forest Service, Northeastern Forest Exp. Stn.

Restoration Forestry Books/Articles from the Pacific Northwest

Ancient Forests of the Pacific Northwest

Elliott A. Norse. The Wilderness Society, 1990. Island Press, Washington D.C. 327 pp. $19.95

One of the most comprehensive scientific treatments of the old-growth issue. Good coverage of sustainable forestry, maintaining biological diversity and attaining environmental maturity in managed forests. It contains a large bibliography of suggested readings.

Ancient Forests of the Pacific Northwest: Protecting a Vanishing Ecosystem: A Source Book for Activists

Heather Diefenderfer, ed. 1992. Oregon Ancient Forest Alliance/Audubon Society of Portland, 5151 NW Cornell Road, Portland, Oregon 97034.
Tel: (503) 292-6726/Fax: (503) 292-1021
$30 + $5 for mailing.

A large selection of scientific and popular journal articles, backgrounders, and newspaper articles as well as contact directories, resource lists and maps relevant to the protection of ancient forests. Not a coffee-table book and the gigantic three-ring binder is somewhat clumsy to use. Still, it is a useful book with over 800 pages covering issues from ecology and logging to forest recovery and activism.

Clearcut: The Tragedy of Industrial Forestry

Bill Devall, ed. 1993. 300 pp.

Many restoration foresters from the Pacific Northwest are contributors to this recommended book. See review in U.S. Forestry Books section.

Forest Farmer's Handbook

Orville Camp. 1984. $10. Camp Forest Farm, 2100 Thompson Creek Rd, Selma, Oregon 97538.

Forest Farmer's Handbook is one of the best handbooks published on restoration forestry. This Handbook is a practical guide to the principles of Natural Selection Ecoforestry. Especially useful to the small forest land owner, but its philosophy and approach are applicable to large forestlands as well.

Camp's natural selection ecoforestry has been developed by teaching individual practitioners and crews to minimize their impacts on stand ecology and forest ecosystems. He lays down selection criteria for tree removal and for low impact access systems. It sets stringent standards for minimizing impact of access construction and equipment use. He provides key indicators which guide the selective removal of trees based on evolutionary, ecological and structural criteria, removing only trees that nature has selected for removal.

—Alan Drengson

See also Camp Forest Farm in Pacific Northwest Restoration Forestry Models section and the article by Camp further on in this section.

Forest Primeval: The Natural History of an Ancient Forest

Chris Maser. 1989. Sierra Club Books. San Francisco. 282 pp. $25.

Maser's second book is a biography of an old-growth

forest in Oregon's Cascade Mountains. Chris Maser traces the growth of the forest from its birth to its current glory as an ancient forest. Excellent ecology in a readable style.

The Forest and the Trees: A Guide to Excellent Forestry
Gordon Robinson. 1988. Island Press. 257 pp.

One of the best books on restoration forestry thus far. Gordon Robinson has been a forester for over half a century. His detailed look at the management of our forests provides a unique perspective on the principles of true multiple-use forestry and on what is wrong with forestry as it is practiced today. He describes in practical terms, "excellent forestry"—uneven-aged management for sustained yield that safeguards the rich variety of life in the forest and protects all uses simultaneously. Good coverage on the history of Forest Service and silviculture. Nearly 400 research publications are summarized, mainly dealing with the Western US.

"If logging looks bad, it is bad." That apparently simplistic but thought-provoking statement by Gordon Robinson is probably as good a slogan as any to combat the complacency among professional foresters, who are trained to respond to the demands of giant main-stream corporations.

Fragile Majesty: The Battle for North America's Last Great Forest
Keith Ervin. 1989. The Mountaineers, 306 2nd Ave. W., Seattle, Washington, 98119. 272 pp. $14.95.

One of the most up-to-date and thorough accounts of the battle for the PNW's remaining old-growth and the social and political dimensions of Pacific Northwest Forestry, with good biology as well.

Natural Selection Ecoforestry: An Alternative for the Peak/Stella Demonstration Project of the Rogue River National Forest
Orville Camp. 1992. Ecoforestry Institute.

This is an alternative plan presented to the USFS for forest management of a particular area. It is noteworthy as an ecologically-based forest plan. It contains one of the few writings by Orville Camp on his Contour Access Road System.

The Redesigned Forest
Chris Maser. 1988. R. & E. Miles, P.O. Box 1916, San Pedro, California, 90773. 234 pp. $9.95.

The Redesigned Forest is one of the most important books to emerge on restoration forestry so far. It not only explains the why but also how it can be implemented. Friends of the Trees highly recommends this book. Chris Maser is one of the most influential people articulating the concepts of a new forestry. Maser stands out as an articulate speaker and writer, who reaches our hearts as well as our minds. Maser worked as a research scientist for the U.S. Department of the Interior Bureau of Land Management for 17 years, spending the last seven years studying the old-growth forest of western Oregon. Maser has published over 170 research papers and has instructed BLM and Forest Service personnel in many parts of the country.

Although Maser has drawn heavily on his experiences with the Pacific Northwest forests, much of the book is relevant to other temperate forest regions and beyond.

Tree Talk: The People and Politics of Timber
Ray Raphael. 1981. Island Press. 287 pp.

One of the first books on restoration forestry and a good read. Especially good on community-based forest land stewardship. Raphael transcribes the most salient parts of conversations with loggers, fishermen, foresters, researchers, mill owners and others. An excellent job of articulating the concerns and viewpoints of rural people in forest communities.

Wintergreen: Listening to the Land's Heart
Robert Michael Pyle. 1988. Houghton Mifflin. 303 pp. $8.95.

The Willapa Hills in southwest Washington were once covered with magnificent old-growth forests measured as containing the highest tonnage of biomass per acre in the world. The book's subtitle—Listening to the Land's Heart—describes the journey that Pyle takes us on through the Willapa Hills, its new forests, its plant and animal communities, and communities of people. He shows us interrelationships of land and people whose fortunes are interlinked. Widely acclaimed for its catching presentation of the forest community. The intent of this work "is to assay the ability of organisms (including ourselves) to survive in the aftermath of massive resource extraction."

Books on Forest Distribution and Natural History in the Pacific Northwest

Comparative Autecological Characteristics of Northwestern Tree Species—A Literature Review
Don Minore. 1979. USDA Forest Service, Pacific Northwest For. and Rg. Exp. Station Gen. Tech. Rep. PNW-87. 72 pp.

Distribution and Ecological Characteristics of Trees and Shrubs of British Columbia
V. J. Krajina, K. Klinka and J. Worrall. 1982. Univ. of B.C., Faculty of Forestry, Vancouver, B.C.

Ecology of Forest Trees in British Columbia
V. J. Krajina. Ecol. West. North Am. Vol. 2: pp. 1-147.

Entering the Grove
Kim R. Stafford and Gary Braasch, photographer. 1990. Gibbs Smith Books.

A gorgeous coffee table book with large format photographs of old-growth forests in the Pacific Northwest. A picture is worth a thousand words (but being there is even better).

Forest Vegetation of Eastern Washington and Northern Idaho
R. Daubenmire and J. B. Daubenmire. 1968. Washington Ag. Exp. Stn. Tech. Bull. 60.

Daubenmire is a legendary ecologist for developing a system of classification of plant communities according to habitat types. One feature of the Daubenmire system is to locate and describe the species composition of the most undisturbed sites left in a region. This provides information to create a map of potential natural vegetation for the region. This serves as a bench mark to gauge changes caused by human activity. Using understory indicator plants, he was able to determine site productivity. We can learn to read the landscape and know microclimates and soil types by the plants. Daubenmire's work has been the model for habitat classification across much of the Western USA and beyond.

Forest Habitat Types of Northern Idaho: A Second Approximation
Stephen V. Cooper, Kenneth E. Neiman, and David W. Rev. Roberts. 1991. USDA Forest Service, Intermountain Research Station Gen. Tech. Rep. INT-236. 143 pp.

The addition of more than 900 plots to Daubenmire's original 181-plot database has resulted in a refinement of the potential natural vegetation of Northern Idaho.

Forest Plant Associations of the Colville National Forest
Clinton Williams, *et al.* 1990.

The Colville National Forest is located in northeast Washington State.

The Grand Fir/Blue Huckleberry Habitat Type in Central Idaho: Succession and Management
Robert Steele and Kathleen Geier-Hayes. 1987. USDA Forest Service, Intermountain Res. Stn. Gen. Tech. Rep. INT-228. 66 pp.

Indicator Plants of Coastal British Columbia
A. Klinka, V. J. Krajina, A. Ceska, and A.M. Scagel. 1989. Univ. of British Columbia Press: Vancouver, B.C. 300 pp. $36.95.

This book provides information on 419 plants found in B.C. which can be used to gauge the growth performance of reforestation sites. One method of evaluating site productivity for tree growth uses understory plants as indicators. The idea has its roots in European forest practice. Pacific Northwest field ecologists have done much work classifying habitats with indicator species.

This guide includes five introductory chapters on the conceptual and observational basis of "plant indication." Indicators are used to diagnose climatic types, soil moisture, soil nutrients, especially nitrogen, and ground surface materials. Chapter six consists mainly of ecological descriptions and color photographs of 363 indicator plant species. Although this book is focused on the coastal ranges of British Columbia, its detailed exposition of methods and concepts allow the method to be evaluated elsewhere as well. The work of Krajina, Klinka and associates are as advanced as anywhere in the world.

The Klamath Knot
David Rains Wallace. 1984. Sierra Club Books. 149 pp. $8.95.

A geological and botanical history of this diverse bioregion of Southwestern Oregon and Northern California.

Natural Vegetation of Oregon and Washington
Jerry F. Franklin and C. T. Dyrness. 1st ed. 1973. 2nd ed. 1990. USDA Forest Service Gen. Tech. Rep. PNW-8. 417 pp.

This is the definitive text on the distribution and composition of the plant communities found in Oregon and Washington.

Fascinating reading, albeit a bit dry for those with less zeal for plant ecology. The book solely uses scientific names, so unless you know the scientific names of plants this may be a frustrating book. However, there is an appendix linking scientific to common names. A must for PNW eco-foresters and bioregionalists.

Northwest Trees: Identifying and Understanding the Region's Native Trees
Stephen F. Arno and Ramona P. Hammerly. 1977. The Mountaineers, Seattle. 222 pp. $10.95.

This text is not only a helpful guide to conifer and deciduous trees in the northwest but describes each species' interaction with humans and demonstrates how essential trees are to wildlife and human life in the Northwest.

Preliminary Classification of Forest Vegetation of the Kenai Peninsula, Alaska
Keith M. Reynolds. 1990. USDA Forest Service, Pacific Northwest Res. Stn. Research Paper PNW-RP-424. 67 pp.

Preliminary Plant Associations of the Siskiyou Mountain Province
Tom Atzet and D. L. Wheele. 1984. USDA Forest Service, PNW Region.

The Sierra Club Guide to the Natural Areas of Oregon and Washington

Vorn Perry and Jane G. Perry. 1983. 335 pp.

The Sierra Club also publishes guides for other western regions.

Timberline: Mountain and Arctic Forest Frontiers

Stephen F. Arno and Ramona P. Hammerly. 1984. The Mountaineers, Seattle, 300 3rd Ave. W. , Seattle, WA 98119. (206) 284-6310. 304 pp.

While this book covers timberlines wherever they occur in North America, it has a strong emphasis on the Pacific Northwest. Excellent bed-time reading for tree enthusiasts. Take a tour of timberline forests and krummholz from your armchair. A well done, informative book on tree distribution and ecology

Visitors' Guide to Ancient Forests of Western Washington

Dittmar Family. 1989. The Wilderness Society. 79 pp.

Lists notable old-growth forests and how to get to them.

The Yew Tree: A Thousand Whispers

Hal Hartzell, Jr. 1991. Hulogosi Press, P.O. Box 1188, Eugene, OR 97440. $19.95. 320 pp.

The botany, ethnobotany, myth, legend, history, science, medicinal value, politics, forestry practice and ecology of yew are explored. The yew has recently achieved fame as the source of taxol, a newly discovered substance which might be successful for certain types of cancer. The yew species is 200,000,000 years old.

Research Centers for "Science-based" Forestry Management

The PNW's leading establishment research centers for "science-based forestry management" are COPE (Coastal Oregon Productivity Enhancement Program), the Blue Mountains Forest Research Institute, and the Olympic Natural Resources Center. These institutions are more progressive from a restoration forestry viewpoint than university forestry departments and National Forest research centers; although that is where most of their staffs are drawn from.

Although the following research institutions do have valuable, new insights to contribute to restoration forestry, readers should read their publications with critical eyes. These institutions are still strongly tied to the dominant paradigm and some of their "science" is just a cover-up for overcutting—business as usual with an ecological facade. One must be cautious about blindly accepting management practices just because they are purportedly based on science or come from universities. Our current industrial practices are supposedly based on science too.

Notwithstanding these disclaimers, these institutions have done a lot of good ecological research and do have useful publications. I have found the Blue Mountains Natural Resources Institute newsletter especially useful.

The Blue Mountains Natural Resources Institute

Forestry and Range Sciences Laboratory
1401 Gekeler Lane
La Grande, Oregon 97850
Tel: (503) 963-7122

The Blue Mountain region encompasses many forested mountain ranges in Northeast Oregon and Southeast Washington. The Blue Mountain Institute was initiated in 1990 by private citizens. It is a research/resource center and an advocate for scientific forest management. It is partially staffed and funded by the Forest Service. It currently has 75 partners from a wide range of organizations, government agencies and a few individuals. All forest user groups such as environmentalists, ranchers, timber industry, tourism, and ORV are included. NRI publishes a thought-provoking newsletter and other publications.

Coastal Oregon Productivity Enhancement Program

Adaptive COPE
Hatfield Marine Science Center, OSU
Newport, Oregon 97365
Tel: (503) 867-0220

The COPE Program is a cooperative effort between Oregon State University's College of Forestry, the USDA Forest Service, Pacific Northwest Research Station, the BLM, other federal and state agencies, forest industry, county governments, and the Oregon Small Woodland Association. The intent of the program is to provide resource managers and the public with information on the management of fish, timber, water, wildlife, and other resources of the Oregon Coast Range.

The COPE Program has two related components: Fundamental COPE is composed of OSU and PNW scientists based primarily in Corvallis; Adaptive COPE is comprised of an interdisciplinary team responsible for applying and adapting new and existing research information to solve specific management problems and also to provide education opportunities to facilitate technology transfer.

Subscription to the quarterly *COPE Report* is free upon request.

Olympic Natural Resources Center

University of Washington AR-10
Seattle, Washington 98195
Tel: (206) 543-7657

The Olympic Natural Resources Center (ONRC) is a new (1992) inter-agency forest experiment/research station. ONRC has an office at the University of Washington and a research center on the Olympic Peninsula at the logging town of Forks. They are working with New Forestry and setting up long-term experiments. Jerry Franklin and others from the University of Washington are involved. ONRC publishes a newsletter: *Update: Olympic Natural Resources Center*

Olympic Natural Resources Center

Forks, Washington 98331
Tel: (206) 374-3220

The staff is drawn from University of Washington, Oregon State University, Department of Natural Resources, and private timber companies. The politics behind ONRC reflect the struggle within forestry as a whole. Timber industry seeks to have its interests upheld in the face of increasing evidence from forest ecologists that current forest practices need reform. It remains to be seen what degree of reform ONRC will advocate. As it is a long-term research organization with a large cash-flow, we can expect a moderate and cautious voice for reform. The ecological information should be useful nonetheless.

Olympic Natural Resources Center Canopy Crane Project

David Shaw is in charge of the project at ONRC's Forks' address.

The canopy crane project entails erecting a construction crane in an old-growth stand. Researchers can ride up and down and observe canopy processes. The Olympic Center recently joined with the Smithsonian Tropical Research Institute in Panama and the Smithsonian Environmental Resource Center in Maryland to form the "International Network of Forest Canopy Research Facilities." The basis of the forest canopy network is to facilitate the exploration of how structure, function, and biodiversity of forest canopies compare at different sites around the world.

South Slough National Estuarine Reserve

P.O. Box 5417
Charleston, Oregon 97420
Tel: (503) 888-5558
Michael P. Graybill, Director

A 5,000-acre reserve established in the early 1970's as part of a national network of 23 estuarine reserves. The reserve is focusing on restoration of tidal wetlands, but is also looking at forest restoration in their 4,000 acres of buffer forest.

Long Term Ecological Research Program (LTER)

Applied Research, Forestry Sciences Lab
P.O. Box 3890
Portland, Oregon 97208
Tel: (503) 231-2030
Contact: Susan Little

In the United States, the National Science Foundation (NSF), through its Long Term Ecological Research Program (LTER), is a principal funding source for research related to ecosystem stability and implications for sustainable resource management. A primary objective of the LTER program, which encompasses 17 intensive research sites, representing virtually all significant ecosystem types from Puerto Rico to Alaska and Oregon to New Hampshire, is to search for commonalities in the way ecosystems are put together and in how they work, including how they are stabilized. The first of the LTER studies directly dealing with the influence of forest management practices on long-term productivity of forest ecosystems is on the H. J. Andrews Experimental forest in western Oregon, associated with Oregon State University, Corvallis.

Workshop On High Quality Forestry

May 11-25, 1993. Silver Falls, Oregon. Contact: Cindy Miner, USDA Pacific Northwest Experiment Station, Continuing Education, P.O. Box 3890, Portland, OR 97208. Tel. (503) 326-7135. Fax: (503) 326-2455.

This workshop is designed to explore the idea of managing forests in the Northwest on long-rotations (150-200 years) to improve the quality of wildlife habitat and wood products. The objective for this workshop is to review the current state-of-knowledge on this subject, to document this information in a single source (conference book), and to investigate and prioritize the needed research and development in this area.

U.S. Forest Service and British Columbia Forest Biologists Cross-border Conferences

Contact: Lisa Norris, Fish, Wildlife & Botany Unit, PNW Forest Service Regional Office, P.O. Box 3623, Portland, Oregon 97208.

U.S. and B.C. Forest Service biologists have been having a conference every 3 years. 200 people attended the 1992 conference. Proceedings are due out in late 1993.

Forestry Departments at Major Universities in the Pacific Northwest

The major forestry schools for each state are: University of Washington (UW) in Seattle; Oregon State University (OSU) in Corvallis; University of Idaho in Moscow; and University of Montana in Missoula. Their counterpart in British Columbia is University of British Columbia, in Vancouver.

Although traditionally biased toward the timber industry, the forest departments have always contained some biologists, ecologists and foresters who are sympathetic to, or advancing restoration forestry. Jerry Franklin at the University of Washington is well known for helping develop the concepts of New Forestry.

David Perry, from Oregon State University, has done much to advance our knowledge of forest ecological processes. There are dozens of notable people in restoration forestry who are graduates of these two schools.

A more cynical viewpoint is that universities don't turn out foresters, they turn out timber harvesters. Truth is, there are reformists versus defenders of the status quo in all university departments, including forestry.

Following are addresses of Pacific Northwest university forest departments, related institutes and publications.

University of Washington
College of Forest Resources, AR-10
Seattle, Washington 98195
Tel: (206) 543-2730

Their publication sales department is titled Institute of Forest Resources and can be reached at Tel: (206) 543-2757.

The Northwest Environmental Journal
Institute for Environmental Studies FM-12
University of Washington
Seattle, Washington 98195
Tel: (206) 543-1812

Good coverage of a wide range of topics. Some issues have been devoted to forest and watershed ecology and management.

Center for Streamside Studies
University of Washington, AR-10
Seattle, Washington 98195
Tel: (206) 543-6920

Publishes newsletter titled *Streamside Runoff.* Subscription free on request. They offer many publications on streams and riparian ecology.

Oregon State University
School of Forestry
Corvallis, Oregon 97331
Tel: 503) 737-2222/Fax (503) 737-2668

OSU is one of the USA's leading institutions in forest ecology research. OSU School of Forestry's newsletter, *Forestry Update,* is available from OSU Extension Service, Tel: (503) 754-2711.

H. J. Andrews Experimental Forest
Oregon State University.

A large-acreage OSU forest research station in the Cascade mountains for experiments on long-term productivity under different management practices.

University of British Columbia
Faculty of Forestry

2357 Main Mall
Vancouver, British Columbia
CANADA V6T 1Z4
Tel: (604) 822-2727

University of Idaho
International Forestry Program
Moscow, Idaho 83843
Tel: (208) 885-6441

Gap Analysis Bulletin
University of Idaho
College of Forest, Wildlife & Range Science.
Moscow, Idaho 83843
Fax: (208) 885-9080

Gap analysis is the process of cataloging all ecosystem types in a region and identifying which of the ecosystem types are underrepresented in present reserve systems.

University of Montana
School of Forestry
Missoula, Montana 59812-1201
Tel: (406) 243-5522

Western Wildlands
Montana Forest and Conservation Experiment Station
School of Forestry, University of Montana,
Missoula, Montana 59812-1201

A quarterly journal. Issue 17, #4, Winter 1992 is a special issue on New Forestry. 48 pages. Articles by Chris Maser and others.

Montana State University
Forestry Sciences Laboratory
Bozeman, Montana 59717
Tel: (406) 994-4548

Books/Articles by Pacific Northwest Forest Scientists

Following are some noteworthy publications by Pacific Northwest forest scientists. See also the resource guides on forest ecology, biodiversity, fire, soils, water, wildlife, restoration, reforestation and erosion control for many more Pacific Northwest references.

Alternatives for Management of Late-Successional Forests of the Pacific Northwest
K. N. Johnson, J. F. Franklin, J. W. Thomas and J. Gordon. 1991. A report to the Agriculture Committee and Merchant Marine and Fisheries Committee of the U.S. House of Representatives.

The influential, ecology-based report of the "Gang of Four" which identifies the need for late-successional reserves.

Douglas-fir: Stand Management for the Future
C.D. Oliver, D. P. Hanley and J. A. Johnson, eds.

1986. University of Washington Press: Seattle.

Forest Ecosystem Management: An Ecological, Economic and Social Assessment

Forestry Ecosystem Management Assessment Team (FEMAT). 1993. To obtain a copy of the FEMAT report, send a request to: Interagency SEIS Team, P.O. Box 3623, Portland, Oregon 97208.

Immediately following the Forest Conference in Portland, Oregon in April 1993, President Clinton formed the federal interagency Forestry Ecosystem Management Assessment Team (FEMAT). FEMAT was comprised of scientists and technical experts from the US Forest Service, BLM, EPA, and other federal agencies. FEMAT had two months to develop options for managing forest ecosystems on federal lands throughout the range of the northern spotted owl. FEMAT developed and analyzed 10 options and President Clinton selected Option 9.

This report details the 10 options that President Clinton considered. Few people will want to read through this large report, but studious restoration foresters will find interesting reading in the forest science sections of the FEMAT report.

"Focus on Old-Growth Forests of Northwestern North America"

The Northwest Environmental Journal. Vol. 6 #2, 1990. The Institute for Environmental Studies, University of Washington.

Creating A Forestry For The 21st Century

1993. Olympic Natural Resources Center.

The proceedings of a November 1993 conference held in Portland, Oregon. This conference brought together 900 forest policymakers, scientists and academics, primarily US Forest Service and other land management government agencies. The proceedings will contain a good view of what they are planning for the next several decades of forest management in the Pacific Northwest as well as an overview of the current state of knowledge of PNW forest ecology.

Forest Stand Dynamics

Chadwick D. Oliver and Bruce L. Larson. 1990. McGraw Hill. 466 pp.

Forest ecology for foresters. A state-of-the art book covering plant interactions, tree architecture and growth, disturbances and stand development, temporal and spatial patterns of plant invasion, single-cohort and multi-cohort stand dynamics, edges, gaps, clumps, silviculture, wind, fire and flood effects, forest patterns over long times and large areas, and so on. Hundreds of references.

Inventory and Value of Old-Growth in the Douglas-fir Region

Richard W. Haynes. 1896. Res. Note PNW-437. Pacific Northwest Research Station, Forestry Sciences Laboratory, P.O. Box 3890, Portland, Oregon 97208. 19 pp.

Timber inventory data for all owners in western Washington and Oregon were summarized by age classes to provide an estimate of the remaining amount of old growth timber. Although these figures are certainly inflated they do give a picture of the acreage, volume and ownership of timberland in the maritime Northwest.

Maintaining the Long-term Productivity of Pacific Northwest Forest Ecosystems

1987. Timber Press in cooperation with College of Forestry, Oregon State University, Corvallis, Oregon.

The proceedings of a symposium which contains many excellent articles by leading forest ecologists in the PNW. This is one of the most frequently cited books, I came across while researching *Restoration Forestry*.

Managing Forestlands in Washington: An Illustrated Guide for Forest Stewardship

Publication #MISC0138. $10 From Co-op Extension Bulletin Office, Cooper Pub. Bldg., WSU, Pullman, WA. 99164-4912.

This contains information for the small forest landowner, including site preparation, reforestation, harvesting, stand management, harvesting, roads, other products, and timber sale agreements. A related newsletter *Forest Stewardship Notes* is also available from the office.

"New Forestry Principles From Ecosystem Analysis of Pacific Northwest Forests"

Frederick J. Swanson and Jerry F. Franklin. *Ecological Applications* Vol. 2(3): 1992, pp. 262-274. Ecological Society of America.

"Scientific Basis for New Perspectives in Forests and Streams"

Jerry F. Franklin. Chapter 3 in the book, *Watershed Management; Balancing Sustainability and Environmental Change.* Robert J. Naiman, ed. Springer-Verlag.

Selective Timber Management in the Douglas-Fir Region

B. P. Kirtland and J. F. Brandstrom; 1936. USFS Division For. Econ.

A look at selective management in the Cascades in an earlier era, before the US Forest Service went clearcut-crazy.

Silviculture of Ponderosa Pine in the Pacific Northwest: The State of Our Knowledge

James W. Barrett. 1979. Pacific Northwest Research Station General Technical Report PNW-97. 106 pp.

Sites for Retrospective Studies: Opportunities for Research in Western Washington and Oregon

Ted B. Thomas, John F. Lehmkuhl, Martin G. Raphael and Dean S. DeBell. 1993. Gen. Tech. Rep. PNW-GTR-312. Portland, Oregon. USDA Forest Service, PNW Res. Stn. 24 pp.

176 sites were identified on publicly managed and privately owned lands in western Oregon and Washington where research or demonstration of new forestry practices could be conducted by using a retrospective approach. The stand types cataloged are characteristic of a range of structural conditions desirable for specific objectives that could be achieved with alternative forestry practices. Information from these stands will guide management in developing alternative forestry practices.

Recent Government Forestry Initiatives

Adaptive Management Areas

One aspect of President Clinton's Forest Plan is the establishment of ten "Adaptive Management Areas" (AMAs) to demonstrate Ecosystem Management on national forests in Washington, Oregon and California. These will theoretically be showcase examples, which demonstrate sustainable forestry. One aspect of the AMAs is that regulations will be stretched to allow lots of experimentation on new forestry methods.

The scale of the AMAs is too large for risky experiments. The Hayfork AMA (northern California) is 400,000 acres. The Applegate AMA (southwest Oregon) is 300,000 acres. The Cispus AMA (Gifford Pinchot National Forest in the southern Washington Cascades) is 150,000 acres. Environmentalists fear that the AMAs will get hit even harder than areas outside the AMA as a result. Time will tell. These Adaptive Management Areas are worth keeping an eye on to see if AMA management is any improvement over the current sad state of affairs.

Olympic Experimental State Forest
Department of Natural Resources—OESF
P.O. Box 47001
Olympia, Washington 98504

In Olympia: Craig Partridge, Project Manager, Tel: (206) 902-1028. Carol Lee Gallagher, Project Coordinator/Writer, Tel: (206) 902-1028. In Forks: Sue Trettevik, Olympic Region Landscape Planner, Tel: (206) 902-1046.

Washington State DNR controls one of the biggest acreages of forest land in the State. Almost all of the state-owned forestlands on the Olympic Peninsula have been designated as the Olympic Experimental State Forest. This 264,000 acres (scattered across the Peninsula) is an experimental playground and production forest where New Forestry can be applied, similar to the federal AMAs (DNR planners will collaborate with the Olympic National Forest AMA). The new practices are supposedly more

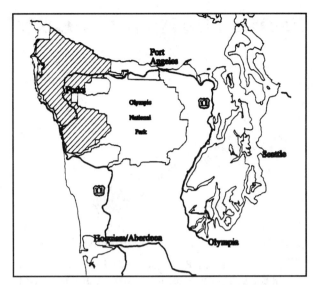

Olympic Experimental State Forest Boundaries

protective of the spotted owl, biodiversity, and heed public cries for reform. On paper it is definitely an improvement over past clearcut management, but as within the Forest Service, timber-industry yes-men (mostly men, some women) dominate Washington State's Department of Natural Resources. The legacy of decades of DNR's selling off state timber at bargain prices. Note that Washington's recent Governor, Booth Gardner, is a Weyerhauser timber heir.

New DNR head, Jennifer Belcher is a raving environmentalist compared to past DNR commissioners. The DNR is changing, and hopefully will continue to swing more toward restoration forestry practices.

A series of documents concerning the Olympic Experimental State Forest are available from the Olympia office. The comprehensive management plan has several sections. The conservation component will include a detailed research plan that focuses on discovering and integrating sound principles for commercial forest management that are sensitive to how forest ecosystems function. A new draft plan is due out in April 1994 and the final draft of the comprehensive management plan in December 1994. Periodic project updates will be printed in The Legacy, the experimental forest project's newsletter.

9

Pacific Northwest's Eastside Forests

Eastside Forests of the Pacific Northwest

THE WESTSIDE FORESTS of the Pacific Northwest get all the publicity. Most readers know about westside forests and the northern spotted owl controversy. But while all the attention is on the westside, they continue to butcher eastside forests. Here for a change is some information on eastside forests.

Semi-Arid Parts of the Pacific Northwest

The shaded areas on the map receive less than 25 inches average annual precipitation with the driest parts of the Columbia Basin receiving as low as 5 inches a year. This map was done with broad pen strokes. A detailed map would have very convoluted edges. (Illustration from *The Future Is Abundant*. Tilth.)

circling the almost treeless Columbia Basin in Eastern Washington/Oregon. It also shows that dry forests are widespread in southwest Oregon and northern California. At higher elevations, ponderosa pine gives way to more moisture-demanding trees such as western larch (*Larix occidentalis*), Douglas Fir (*Psuedotsuga menziesii*), grand fir, (*Abies grandis*), western white pine (*Pinus monticola*), and others. This map does not show the southern part of ponderosa pine's range which extends well into Mexico. (Illustration from *Silvics of Forest Trees of the United States*.)

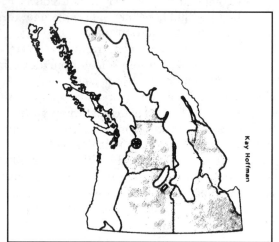

Kay Hoffman

Ponderosa Pine (*Pinus ponderosa*) Range Map

The ponderosa pine is the most drought tolerant tree over much of its range. It fringes, and interfingers with, bunch-grass and dry shrub-steppe ecosystems at lower elevations. The range of the ponderosa pine shows quite clearly where the dry eastside forests are. You can see them

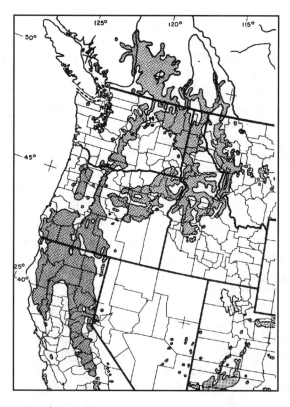

Ponderosa Pine (*Pinus ponderosa*) Range Map

Eastside Forest Health Controversy

Forest health is an important issue in the eastside Pacific Northwest. The health of many forests and tree species around the world are on the decline. There are many interacting reasons for this, including: clear-cutting, high-grading, grazing, drought, climate-change stress, air pollution, acid rain, soil compaction from logging, salination, too much fire in some systems, not enough fire in others, and insects and diseases (native and non-native). The greater the human impact, the more ecosystems become upset. Another likely factor is damage caused by increased UV (Ultraviolet radiation) rays due to thinning atmospheric ozone.

Insects and diseases are part of nature's intricate mechanisms that ensure survival of the whole. Forests can heal themselves, given the chance. The contribution of forest insects and diseases to soil fertility and biodiversity have been scarcely studied. Insect "pests" and diseases have been generally regarded as an unmitigated evil. Evidence is emerging that diseases and insects play necessary and beneficial roles in ecosystem dynamics. Insects and diseases are not the problem. The problem is overcutting and poor forest management.

Many eastside forests are having real health problems, but what measures to take to improve affairs is a matter of debate. The "establishment" pushes for salvage logging. In many cases, salvage logging will only make things worse and, in some cases, it is used as a smokescreen to log healthy stands. Salvage sales have become the timber industry's war cry. Salvage sales are presently being used in a massive way to justify logging. According to a recent article on California National Forests in the *Sacramento Bee*, over half of the timber harvest in that state comes from salvage sales. The Oregonian reported a similar trend for Oregon's eastside forests, and we see this happening in Washington's eastside forests and in the Northern Rockies.

Forest Health and Forestry?

George Wuerthner

The {Blue Mountain Forest Health} report concludes that decades of timber mining—removing the best trees from the forest—has reduced genetic diversity, hence the ability of forest ecosystems to adapt to changing conditions. In addition, little attention was paid to long term forest productivity. Livestock grazing removed understory plant communities, reducing fine fuels that would sustain small, ecologically important fires. Grazing also induced soil and watershed changes which exacerbate drought effects.

However, the report singled out fire suppression as having perhaps the single greatest impact on forest health. Removal of fire as an ecological process dramatically reduced the ability of forest ecosystems to resist drought and attacks from insects and disease, and increased the occurrence of catastrophic blazes due to higher fuel loading. Although timber companies and many foresters often imply that timber harvest is analogous to natural disturbances like wildfires, there are substantial ecological differences. For instance, smoke from fire actually kills many forest pathogens, cleansing the surrounding living forest. Fires recycle nutrients, changing them chemically into a form that is more readily available for new plant growth, while timber harvest exports nutrients from the ecosystem. Fires create numerous snags, home for cavity nesting birds, many of which are insect eaters who provide free insect protection for the forest ecosystem. Many fires do not remove all trees but thin them, thereby increasing the viability of those remaining. Fires create a random mosaic or patch disturbance which humans have thus far failed to duplicate. On the other hand, equipment used in timber harvest compacts soil, reducing water infiltration, increasing erosion, and decreasing habitat for ground dwelling insects like ants who prey on insects that attack trees.

This is not to suggest that we needn't fight some fires. There will always be a need for some fire suppression to protect homes and property, but setting up a fire line to protect a house is far different than trying to stop a fire on all sides. Fires are an important ecological process which we can not emulate with timber harvest. If we are to preserve our forests, we need to preserve the ecological forces that shaped them.

The Blue Mountain Report is the first indication that the agency is willing to publicly admit that forestry as practiced by federal foresters is killing our forests. Forests are more than trees, and up until now, foresters emphasized producing timber at the expense of ecological processes. And the results are becoming all too evident as, to quote from the report, "our forest ecosystems begin to unravel."

The Blue Mountain Forest Health Report is the first indication that the Forest Service is beginning to see the forest through the trees.

Previously published in The Networker, *Vol. 3 (3), 1991. George Wuerthner is a conservationist, writer and photographer in Livingston, Montana.*

Blue Mountains

The Blue Mountains of northeast Oregon have been at the forefront of the Eastside forest health controversy. This is partially the result of the series of reports put out by the Blue Mountains Natural Resources Institute and partially because the die-off of Douglas-fir and true firs reached epidemic proportions there before other parts of the eastside. The Blue Mountains region corresponds to the

#18 Central Mountains section on the map Physiographic Regions of the Pacific Northwest.

Even though the Blue Mountains forest health controversy has produced some relatively progressive publications, the fact remains that management has not changed all that much for the better. Much of the same destructive logging practices continue unabated, although they are now often performed under the guise of "Forest Health."

The solution to forest health problems is not to cut down the forests, the solution is to implement restoration forestry.

I have not been able to locate many people practicing or talking about restoration forestry on the eastside. A notable exception being Herb Hammond and the Silva Forest Foundation in southern Interior B.C. Other eastside models reported in Restoration Forestry are the Goebel-Jackson and Oberteufer forest farms in the Blue Mountains, Dan Morgan in north-central Washington's Okanogan and horse-logging in Idaho. Some of the environmental groups which have a particularly strong focus on eastside forestry include the Inland Empire Public Lands Council, Greater Ecosystem Alliance, Kettle Range Conservation Council, Blue Mountains Biodiversity Project, Audubon Adopt-a-Forest groups and various northern Rocky Mountain groups.

Following are some references on eastside forest health, forest management and salvage logging from various sources.

Non-Government Publications on Eastside Forest Health

Interim Protection for Late-Successional Forests, Fisheries, and Watersheds; National Forests East of the Cascade Crest, Oregon and Washington
Eastside Forests Scientific Society Panel. September, 1993. The Executive Summary is available as of December 1993. The full report will be available January 1994. Contact: Dr. James Karr, Institute for Environmental Studies, FM-12, Univ. of Wa. Seattle, WA 98195. Tel: (206) 543-1812.

This report was conducted by a panel of scientists independent of the government and sponsored by seven scientific societies including the Society for Conservation Biology and the American Fisheries Society.

The report is much stronger than the Forest Service's Eastside Ecosystem Health Assessment. If put into effect, these recommendations would be a good step towards restoration forestry. The study includes the first-ever maps showing the location and extent of eastside old-growth forests, roadless areas and key watersheds. The study reveals the tremendous destruction of the Eastside ancient forests. Only 7-13 percent of the Late Successional Old-Growth (LSOG) remains; 70-95 percent of the LSOG patches that remain on the Eastside are less than 100 acres

each. Of the seven LSOG patches larger than 5,000 acres, only one is currently protected and 20-25 percent of all the remaining LSOG is currently unprotected. Ponderosa Pine forests have been especially hard hit by logging; only 3-5 percent remains on the Deschutes National Forest (NF), 5-8 percent on the Winema NF, and 2-8 percent on the Fremont NF. Salmon production has declined to less than 5% of historic pre-settlement levels; at least 106 major species of salmon have gone extinct.

The following recommendations are from the Executive Summary of the Scientific Society report. They are designed to protect the remaining resources until a long-term strategy of protection and restoration can be developed. Further details on the recommendations can be obtained from the Executive Summary or the full Report.

Recommendations of the Eastside Forests Scientific Society Panel

1. Do not log late-successional/old-growth forests in eastern Oregon and Washington.

2. Cut no trees of any species older than 150 years or with a diameter of 20 inches or greater.

3. Do not log or build new roads in aquatic diversity management areas (ADMAs).

4. Do not construct new roads or log within:
   1) roadless regions larger than 1,000 acres; or
   2) roadless regions that are biologically significant but smaller than 1,000 acres.

5. Establish protected corridors along streams, rivers, lakes, and wetlands. Restrict timber harvest, road construction, grazing, and cutting of fuelwood within these corridors.

6. Prohibit logging of dominant or codominant ponderosa pine from Eastside forests.

7. Prohibit timber harvest in areas prone to landslides or erosion unless it can be conclusively demonstrated by peer-reviewed scientific study that no associated soil degradation or sediment input to streams results from that harvest.

8. Prevent livestock grazing in riparian areas except under strictly defined conditions that protect those riparian areas from degradation.

9. Do not log on fragile soils until it is conclusively demonstrated by peer-reviewed scientific study that soil integrity is protected and that forest regeneration after logging is assured.

10. Establish a panel with the appropriate disciplinary breadth to develop long-term management guidelines that will protect Eastside forests from drought, fire, insects, and pathogens.

11. Establish a second panel to produce a coordinated strategy for restoring the regional landscape and its component ecosystems. Emphasize protecting the health and integrity of regional biotic elements as well as the processes on which they depend.

Eastside Forests of The Old West: Issues and Solutions April 1993. National Audubon Society Adopt-a-Forest with other organizations. Available from the Ancient Forest Alliance. Address in environmental organizations section under National Grass-roots Coalition. 30 pp.

Twelve articles from leading forest-literate forest activists on management problems and possible solutions for Eastside forests. Recommended.

"Forest Health" in Eastern Oregon and Washington— Discussion Draft

National Wildlife Federation. October 12, 1992. Address in National Environmental Organizations section.

A Long-term Strategy for Eastside Forests

Natural ecosystems produce the healthiest forest. A long-term management strategy for eastside forests must emulate nature in our management and restore natural function to these forests.

+ Encourage the return of ponderosa pine and larch as the dominant tree species on sites of historical abundance.

+ Prescribe and return to fire ecology management for all applicable areas.

+ Retain all old growth ponderosa pine and western larch trees as a genetic diversity reservoir to return these species to dominance.

+ Devise ecosystem management schemes with large core areas and connecting corridors to maintain plant and animal gene pools and genetic flow across the landscape and over time.

+ Conserve and restore soil productivity.

+ Halt degradation of and provide for the restoration of watershed conditions to a stable and healthy condition.

Previously published in Methow Forest Watch Newsletter, *Summer 1993.*

Salvage Sales

There has been a lot of discussion over the possibility of using large scale salvage logging as a way to make up for timber volume lost to West Coast forest set asides. Environmentalists have grave reservations about this idea. The study of forest health has only recently emerged as an important component of forest management. A panicked approach to fixing the forest health conditions would have long lasting negative

effects on watersheds. Most of the disease and insects in our forests are a natural part of the ecosystem. They play a vital role in the succession of our forests. A healthy forest needs some unhealthy trees. The damage from large scale logging operations is much more a threat to our forests than that of the bark beetle or dwarf mistletoe.

—From *Methow Forest Watch Newsletter,* Summer 1993

"Salvage Logging: Health or Hoax"

Special issue of *Inner Voice*, March/April 1993. AFSEEE (Association of Forest Service Employees for Environmental Ethics). Address in U.S. Forestry Organizations.

This compilation of articles offers a good look at the ecology and politics of salvage logging.

Blue Mountains Biodiversity Project

HCR-82, Fossil, Oregon 97830. Tel: (503) 468-2028

This group has put together an extensive report and critique of salvage logging in the Blue Mountains.

Forest Service Publications on Eastside Forest Health

Blue Mountains Forest Health Report

Available from: Blue Mountains Natural Resources Institute, Forestry and Range Sciences Laboratory, 1401 Gekeler Lane, La Grande, OR 97850. Tel: (503) 963-7122

This report is a startling admission on the part of the Forest Service, that their past and present timber management policies have resulted in sick and dying forests. The authors of the report do not mince words when they conclude that our forests "face the probability of massively destructive forest health problems." Forestry, rather than saving our forests, is destroying them. See a more detailed review of the Blue Mountains Natural Resources Institute under "Science-Based Forestry Research Centers" in this Pacific Northwest section.

Eastside Ecosystem Health Assessment

Richard Everett et al. 1993. The Executive Summary or the full 5-volume set are available from Pacific Northwest Forest and Range Experiment Station, P.O. Box 3890, Portland, Oregon 97208. Tel: (503) 326-7128

A multi-agency scientific panel evaluated impacts of current and historic management practices on sustainability of eastside forest ecosystems. The team provided an assessment of landscape conditions on a 5.5-million-acre representative sample of the major eco-regions in eastern Oregon and Washington.

The assessment had over 70 scientists from universities, federal and state agencies, Indian nation tribes, and private firms working on the report. The team's base was the Wenatchee Forestry Sciences Laboratory in central Washington.

The report was very large, and very disappointing from a restoration forestry standpoint. Its conclusion was: there did not need to be much change in present forest management practices. It lays the groundwork for more logging in the form of salvage sales. Another expensive whitewash for "business as usual."

Forest Health in the Blue Mountains: A Management Strategy for Fire-Adapted Ecosystems
Robert W. Mutch, Sephen F. Arno, James K. Brown, Clinton E. Carlson, Roger D. Ottmar, and Janice L. Peterson. 1993. General Tech. Rep. PNW-GTR-310. Pacific Northwest Research Station. Portland, Oregon. 14 pp.

This report is a distillation of current Forest Service management recommendations for fixing eastside forest health problems. Here are some of their recommendations.

A management strategy to restore forest health will require that the seral ponderosa pine and western larch stands be managed for much lower tree densities and an open coniferous understory. Other strategies include:

1. Reducing the density of Douglas-fir and grand fir stands or understories.

2. Increasing substantially the use of prescribed fire at the landscape level.

3. Maintaining mature ponderosa pine and larch in the overstory.

4. Achieving successful regeneration of pine and larch.

5. Reducing acres burned by high-intensity wildfires.

6. Increasing available forage.

In their conclusion, the authors state that the solution to the forest health problems seems straightforward and they can fix the problem if people trust them enough to let them run the forest. While this report is a worthwhile addition to the eastside forest management debate, the public is not about to trust the Forest Service.

Eastside EIS TeamOffice
1415 SW Rose
Walla Walla, Washington 99362
Tel: (509) 522-4040
Jeff Blackwood, Eastside Strategic Manager

In August 1993, newly appointed Asst. Secretary of Agriculture for the Environment, Jim Lyons, unveiled an ambitious plan for the national forests of eastern Oregon and Washington which will culminate in a lowered timber cut, and revised Forest Plans. In preparation, the Forest Service is preparing an Environmental Impact Statement (EIS) which will cover all portions of non-spotted owl forests on the Eastside. The EIS report will be of interest to anyone concerned with forest management in the interior Northwest. A draft is scheduled to be issued by June of 1994.

Publications on Pest Ecology

"Armillaria: A Role In Long-term Stability of Native, Inland Western Forests"
Alan E. Harvey. 1991. In: *Proceedings of the 38th Annual Western International Forest Disease Work Conferenc.*; 1990 September 17-21. Redding, CA. USDA Forest Service. 6 pp.

"Pathogens and Pests—Engines that Drive Succession"
Arthur D. Partridge and Catherine L. Bertagnolli. *Inner Voice.* March/April 1993. p. 5.

An article which outlines the necessary ecological functions of insects and pathogens in forests.

"Pathogens as Agents of Diversity in Forested Landscapes"
Bart J. van der Kamp. August 1991. *The Forestry Chronicle.* Vol. 67 (4): pp. 353-354.

Abstract: It is argued that native forest pathogens may be viewed as major agents of spatial and temporal diversity, responsible for the creation of a number of special habitats, and influencing the speed and direction of succession as well as the structure of the climax forest. Although their influence is detrimental to most common purposes of management, the result of their action may occasionally be beneficial.

"To B.t. or Not to B.t.? A Question Worth Asking!"
Dr. Irene Novaczek. *Eco-News.* Summer 1992. 4 pp. Environmental Coalition of Prince Edward Island Address in Canadian Environmental Organizations.

As an organic farmer I am quite familiar with B.t. or *Bacillus thuringensis.* A bacteria which affects *Lepidoptera* larvae (i.e. caterpillars of moths and butterflies). B.t. is commonly used in gardens to control cabbage moths and other caterpillars. Over the past decade, B.t. has been aerially sprayed over large areas of forest in the Pacific Northwest, eastern Canada, and elsewhere for spruce budworm and other defoliating caterpillars. This raises some disturbing ecological questions. What are the ecological consequences of killing most moths and butterflies in the ecosystem? Here finally is a good article on the subject. Novaczek's findings cast great doubt whether the use of B.t. should continue in forest management.

For more on pest ecology, see also articles in *Restoration Forestry* by David Perry, Torolf Torgersen and Timothy Schowalter; as well as the Forest Ecology Resource Guide section.

Natural Selection Ecoforestry

Orville Camp

PHOTO CREDIT: LARRY WILLIAMS

Orville Camp

Achieving Ecoforestry Through Natural Selection Ecoforestry Concept

NATURAL SELECTION ECOFORESTRY is a management concept that has been developed to achieve sustainable "ecoforestry."

Conventionally, a "tree farm" is viewed as a "forest," those who manage them are called "foresters" and the management concept is known as "forestry."

In contrast to forestry, "ecoforestry" is a full ecosystem management program for all normal associated species and ages. "Ecoforesters" are those who practice ecoforestry.

"Natural Selection Ecoforestry" is a specific kind of ecoforestry designed to meet "Forest Ecosystem Management Goals" and "Harvest Rules for Achieving Sustainable Forestry."

What Is Natural Selection Ecoforestry?

Natural Selection Ecoforestry is a natural management and harvest selection program based on the book, "The Forest Farmer's Handbook, A Guide to Natural Selection Forest Management," by Orville Camp.

The fact is, Nature has the only time tested and proven forest ecosystem management program. Nature's key to management success has been through the natural selection process. This process is how nature has been able to continue providing plant, animal and people needs since the beginning of time.

Natural Selection Ecoforestry is based on the concept of learning how to read nature's indicators in order to allow the natural selection process to continue meeting the needs of all life.

Forest Ecosystem Management Goals

1. Conserve forest lands for forest related purposes.
2. Keep the forest ecosystem healthy for all normally associated species.
3. Maintain suitable forest climate, soil and water conditions.

4. Maintain a habitat which can meet food, shelter and reproduction needs for all normally associated species.
5. Maintain the "natural selection system of checks & balances."
6. Maintain genetic traits which are best suited for surviving ecosystem environmental extremes.
7. Use low impact equipment.
8. Locate and construct forest related dwellings and other buildings only after all forest access roads have been designed and constructed in the proposed area.
9. Have all access roads designed and constructed in accordance with "Contour Access Road System" principles in order to minimize the ecological impact of harvesting.
10. Maintain a sustainable forest ecosystem which can provide a sustainable level of commodities and other uses to serve people's needs.

Harvest Rules for Achieving Sustainable Forestry

1. View the forest ecosystem as a body of living and nonliving things and their relationships. Recognize that all living things are interconnected and dependent on one another in some way as we are upon them. Forest ecosystems are in many ways similar to the human body. Some parts are more critical than others for it's survival, but, all parts probably contribute to its well being in some way though none ever seem to be fully understood. There are no weeds in the forest.

2. Maintain the natural selection system of "checks and balances." This is the key ingredient for keeping the forest ecosystem healthy and productive. This is also the only time tested and proven management system for providing basic needs of

ecosystem life. It requires that all normally associated species be available in adequate numbers to make it work the best.

3. Address forest ecosystem needs first. In so doing you will address yours.

4. Before harvesting, learn to read the natural selection indicators. Start looking from the canopy top down to determine first which individuals are the "stronger dominants" and then which are the "weaker members" that nature has selected for removal. This may be of the same species or a different one. Some species provide an environment that through the natural selection process makes it better suited for another species. Whether the natural selection process is allowing the canopy dominant species to change or remain the same must be recognized in order to make the right decision as to which species is the stronger dominant.

5. Always leave the genetically superior "stronger dominant" trees. None of these trees should be removed. Canopy dominants are usually the stronger dominants except where past harvesting has highgraded them out. Stronger dominants may sometimes be found throughout the forest structure depending on species. They are the best ones for restocking because they have the best traits for living in that kind of environment and for surviving environmental extremes. Typically they are the fastest growing. They also have a major influence on which other species of plant and animal life can survive beneath them. Eventually all stronger dominant trees become weaker members, but, until that time they should not be removed.

6. Harvest only those weaker trees that nature has selected for removal. This will allow no more harvesting than what the forest is truly capable of producing at any given time. The forest ecosystem should then remain healthy and productive. You must be able to identify competing stronger dominants in order to identify weaker members. Before harvesting the weaker trees, however, it must first be determined whether removal will still allow other "Harvest Rules" and the "Forest Ecosystem Goals" to be met.

7. Maintain suitable climate, soil and water conditions for all normally associated species. These "Three Essentials" determine what can live in a given area. They must be kept compatible with ecosystem needs. Climate varies throughout the forest structure and is critical for determining which species of plants can live in each part. Plant life in turn determines which species of animal life can survive there. Climate also has a major influence on soil and water conditions. Before removing a single tree the effect on these three essentials must be carefully weighed. These conditions must remain favorable to all normally associated species.

8. Maintain habitat which can continue to provide food, shelter and reproduction needs for all normally associated species. Pay your wildlife workers so that they can continue to work for you and the forest. This means leaving natural-like forest habitat with some dead, dying, diseased and defective trees in order to keep forest wildlife workers healthy, happy and productive.

9. Keep the forest ecosystem healthy. Population stability year after year is a good indicator as to ecosystem health. Soaring and/or rapidly decreasing populations and extinction indicate unhealthy conditions. Though this situation typically occurs after a fire, it is usually caused by harvesting the wrong trees. It can be avoided through natural selection harvesting by meeting the Critical Elements for Sustainability and Harvest Rules.

10. Do I feel certain of my decision? The rule is: "When in doubt, don't." Here is why. Removing the wrong tree can result in hundreds or even thousands of years before the area harvested from can be brought back to its original health, value and productivity. Ask yourself this question, "If I cut the wrong tree, what will it cost and how long will it take to bring the territory that it occupied back to its original condition and value?"

How Can Natural Selection Ecoforestry Solve Environmental and Economic Problems?

I. Nature Manages:

1. Nature has the only time tested and proven forest management system.

2. Nature, through the natural selection process, has historically been the most successful at providing a suitable habitat for its wildlife. A habitat must be able to supply food, shelter and reproduction needs for all its associated life if they are to survive. No man made forest management system has ever been able to achieve this.

3. The natural selection process, either directly or indirectly, has also provided the needs of people as well. Again, no man has ever been able to even come close to equaling nature in providing those needs.

4. Natural Selection Ecoforestry uses nature's time tested and proven ecosystem management system.

II. Nature Selects for Harvest:

1. Natural Selection Ecoforestry uses nature to do the selecting of trees and other plants for removal to serve people needs.
2. Because nature does the selecting, chances of losing forest ecosystem health is near zero.
3. Natural Selection Harvesting allows only removal of those individuals that nature has selected. This means people can harvest only what the forest is truly capable of producing at any given time, not what some theory predicts. This prevents over cutting assuring a true maximum yield that is sustainable.

III. No Slash Disposal:

1. Natural Selection Harvesting has no heavy build up of slash because of smaller volumes harvested at any given time.
2. Slash is used to sustain decomposers and other wildlife needs which supports new green plant growth. Slash is used to support the forest wildlife workers.
3. No slash burning is needed.
4. No slash burning pollution.
5. No slash burning costs.

IV. No Competing Vegetation:

1. Nature controls through the natural selection process.
2. No herbicides or pesticides needed because there are no weeds.
3. No environmental costs due to use of chemicals.
4. No competing vegetation management costs.

V. More Forest Commodities and Uses:

1. Nature manages for all kinds of natural commodities, not just trees.
2. Limitless potential for recreational uses.
3. Maximum sustainable yield of all natural forest products including timber. No down time such as in clear-cuts and selective cuts such as shelter wood and regeneration.

VI. Easier to Teach and Learn:

1. Nature does the managing.
2. Nature does the selecting.

3. Management and harvesting is a relatively simple matter of learning to read nature's signs.

VII. Maintains Suitable Ecosystem Environment:

1. Far less erosion.
2. Fully stocked with vegetation at all times for holding water through drought.
3. Continuous filtering keeps water quality high at all times.

IX. Retains Soil Health:

1. Continual soil build up.
2. No fertilization costs.

X. No Reforestation Costs:

1. Nature does all the reforestation.

XI. Addresses Wildlife Needs:

1. Nature provides.
2. No wildlife management costs due to harvesting practices.

XII. Allows the Use of Smaller, Less-impacting Equipment:

1. Smaller equipment can be used because access is designed for efficiency.
2. Less impact on environment because of smaller equipment type that can be used.
3. Less capital investment in smaller sized equipment.
4. More affordable.

XIII. Reduces Fire Risk and Damage:

1. Fire fighting costs run higher each year to protect the forest. The highest risks are in the following order: clear-cuts, high removal partial cuts, and last are Nature's forest. Natural Selection Ecoforestry reduces fire damage risk by keeping a more natural like forest.
2. Special contour roads also help, plus they allow better access for fire equipment and act as fire breaks should a fire occur.

XIV. Contour Access Road Systems Are Designed for Less Impact on the Ecosystem:

1. Permanent.
2. Less maintenance.
3. Allows use of smaller equipment.
4. Far less equipment impact.
5. Far less environmental impact than typical tree farm roads.

9

6. Allows harvesting of any size or shape product.

7. Enhances aesthetics and recreational uses.

8. Costs far less per mile to construct.

9. Enables continuous annual harvesting.

10. Allows managers to quickly inventory.

11. Allows instant harvests when products are ready for removal and needed.

XV. Sustainable Employment:

1. Annual on all managed stands rather than once or twice in a lifetime.

2. Truly sustainable.

3. Limitless potential.

4. More potential jobs because the whole forest is managed for instead of only special crops at the expense of the forest.

5. Trees that nature has selected for removal are continuously harvested from seedling on to serve people's needs.

XVI. Maintains or Increases Ecosystem Net Worth:

1. The most value to man has historically been in the ancient old growth forests. Young tree plantations that people have created are very costly and have never even begun to equal the ancient old growth forests in value per acre. And ancient forests were free to people! Natural Selection Ecoforestry manages for old growth and its associated wildlife.

2. All species are considered to have value. To establish this value, one only needs to ask the question as to what it would cost, if it was possible, to replace any species population that was eliminated because of management practices. Natural Selection Ecoforestry manages for all species of plants and animals and as a result this value is not lost.

Gus diZerega

Individual Tree Selection: More than Forestry Without Chemicals

Marie Reeder

IT WAS A RARE, COOL MORNING in a southern Oregon's blazing, drought ridden summer. I was stacking firewood in a dreamy state that pleasant repetitive outdoor tasks induce.

I was stacking two kinds of wood for this winter: madrone bucked and split into hefty chunks for long burning, and mill ends for kindling and a smaller stove. Both woodpiles raised my concerns for our future, disturbing the tranquillity of stacking.

It's hard to shake nagging doubts when a task pins you to a spot for hours on end, but doesn't occupy much of your attention. If you're lucky (and the weather that morning was a fine omen), your enforced encounter results in a solution. So gradually that morning shifted my thoughts from worrying about the dangerous wounded animal of industrial forestry mangling my favorite old growth forest in its agony over continued timber supply, to remembering a day I had recently spent in the woods with Scott Ferguson and seeing what the future of forestry could be for a lot of us.

The Small Woodland Alternative

"People think that there are only two choices for their woodland acreage: devastation or preservation. A lot of what I do is just show them that alternatives exist. Scott is easing me into the cold, technical water of silvicultural management. He's the head of Individual Tree Selection Management, Inc. (ITS), a forestry consulting firm based in Portland, Oregon.

"Typically, I start with owners who don't like what they've seen happen: big clear-cuts, for example.

"If you talk to a guy who owns twenty to forty acres of forest, and tell him he should manage it commercially, he's likely to think you're pointing him into a dead end. He doesn't want to clearcut his land. So I may need to tell the owner right off that with our system he'll never need to clearcut. We work with owners to fit their needs aesthetically, emotionally, and financially. And we recognize that small woodland owners feel strongly about their land and what it looks like."

The Individual Tree Selection System is based on a couple of principles and a team of committed people. The Twin cornerstones, equal in principle, are to thin out trees in order to both promote optimum stand growth and meet the owner's needs for a steady income, sustainable over the long haul. The team consists of the landowner, who's willing to look at more than just an initial timber harvest; a forester, who will ultimately mark every tree that is ever cut, thus taking responsibility for the look and health of the forest at all stages; and the loggers, who agree to limit themselves strictly to marked trees and who can harvest skillfully enough to fall and yard without damaging the rest of the forest.

Forest considerations are the first issues we discussed. I am trying to uncover Scott's guidelines for marking trees for harvest.

"I cut for the forest, not for the product. Then I maximize the value of the product through marketing." Trees grow in groups, not in a grid pattern. I try to maximize what the group can do," he says.

As we bump along in his pickup, I piece together a lay version of what Scott Ferguson, forester, looks for in the forests he manages. In northwestern Oregon, sunlight limits the amount of growth a stand of trees can make in a year. So the most basic concept in management is to thin out trees to let in light, thus promoting growth.

So much for the easy part. The rest of the forester's decisions seem to be almost as much art as science, although a few generalizations, not rules, emerge. Scott balances sunlight with shade, for example, because shade is the tool he uses to inhibit the growth of weeds. He uses what's called "high thinning," taking out the biggest, most commercially valuable trees in order to achieve his financial goals and leave 90% of the trees untouched and growing. But "high thinning" can be a euphemism for "high grading," a logger's epithet meaning that the cream has been skimmed, leaving the worst genetic stock to replenish the forest. Again, it's a question of skill and balance.

Scott debates the scientific basis for attacking "high thinning." While he admits that his technique can be abused, he's firm about the lack of evidence that the smaller trees in a wild stand aren't genetically inferior, merely suppressed in growth by the dominant trees.

"Dick came out of forestry school in the '50s. They taught him the traditional rule of thumb: if 30% or less of the height of the tree is not in crown (needle-covered branches), it won't be released by thinning. That's bunk. He found that such trees may not respond as quickly as younger trees, but they will respond. Even 120 foot trees can be released to gain as much as an inch in girth annually."

"Bunk" is a strong word coming from Scott Ferguson. He's tall, slim, and quiet, like a reserved college professor in a field trip clothes. With a bachelor's degree from Yale and a masters in forestry from Oregon State University (OSU), he's calmly self-assured about his technical expertise. Like most foresters and wildlife experts I've met, Scott seems to detach himself from both the politics and marketing hype of the timber business, so that his iron-clad support for the radical forestry techniques developed by a Lone Ranger in the field stands in sharp contrast to his demeanor.

I probe into the root of the controversy. Since the fifteenth century, he tells me, German thought has dominated Western approaches to forestry. With an almost fanatical zeal for order, German foresters promoted the ideas of clearing out the junk and debris of wild forests. They argued that spindly-looking suppressed trees should be thinned out, even at a financial loss, to reproductively superior trees. After thinning, the commercial crop of trees would make progress in the form of a fairly uniform gain in height and girth until they crossed the zenith of the growth curve and settled into decadent old age. Like corn, the timber would then be felled in an intense, clearcut harvest cycle timed to match the top of the growth curve. It remains the model for timber as a form of industrial agriculture.

The German system so effectively shapes contemporary American thought that even our universities only studied those techniques of thinning that fit the German model. Ferguson points to the Hoshkins study, probably the most thorough in the literature, as a case in point.

"In this study, various plots on a large stand of Douglas fir were subjected to any of eight different thinning regimes, ultimately leaving, by the fourth treatment, an average of 70-225 trees per acre depending on the treatment. The un-thinned, control plots averaged 767 trees per acre.

"Conducted in Oregon by a team from Oregon State University over a twenty year period, the Hoshkins study doesn't investigate high thinning at all," Scott states.

By removing up to 50% of the smallest trees, the Hoshkins study's conventional thinning systems alter the forest environment far more dramatically than high thinning. While Scott may leave up to 400 trees per acre, thinning from below usually leaves 150 evenly-spaced trees. Since those trees are supposed to be the biggest and best, the forest is converted into a stand of even-aged trees. With the young trees and seedlings removed, Hoshkins stands are groomed for a clearcut as the final harvest operation.

This kind of study gathers no information about the release of older spindly trees into faster growth cycles. It is silent on some of the other major advantages of the high thinning system, especially eliminating the financial and environmental costs of preparing a clearcut site for tree planting.

The silence is maddening. If studies can prove that suppressed older trees will catch up with their dominant kin, we can score an enormous win for the environment by displacing the necessity of clear-cutting.

Under the ITS system, young trees grow continuously side by side with the commercial stock. Not only does this offer the potential advantage of matching the genetics of seedlings to the microsite to which their parents were adapted, but it avoids environmentally disruptive practices such as broadcast burning and herbicide applications.

The environmental problems of clear-cutting don't stop with visual blight. Silviculturists ordinarily prescribe drastic procedures to restock a clearcut with new trees. They may call for an application of alumagel, derived from the Vietnam war technology of burning enemy territory; the procedure is now used to suppress weed growth by burning clear-cuts prior to planting. After the seedlings are planted, silviculturists may find a need to further restrain competitive weeds by applying herbicides.

Never mind that the weeds are a natural part of the native ecosystem, and may contribute substantially to the health of the soil and watershed.

And hang the expense! The Forest Service often spends $400 or more per acre to prepare and stock clear-cuts with seedlings.

That $400 / acre of avoidable expenses is money left in the pocket of a landowner who hires Scott Ferguson. A tangible reason to explore alternative forestry.

Economics and the Forest Environment: Where the Rubber Meets the Road

The most important constraint facing most small woodland owners is a lack of money. As a result, most view their forest land somewhat schizophrenically. In good times, they see that it is valuable for wildlife and the family's own quality of life. But in an economic crunch, whether caused by unemployment, ill health, or sending the kids to college, the forest becomes a stand of timber, a quick influx of cash.

Steady long-term management plans can seem like pie in the sky, for a number of reasons. Woodland management can be labor intensive, and beyond the time, strength, or skill available to many landowners. Equally important, a landowner may lack an effective means of marketing.

That's where outside help is usually called in. But a hired independent logger, a gypo, may be more motivated to cut than to think about the long-term health of the stand. A contract with a large company may subject your home to the common industrial practices of clearcutting and herbicides.

That's where a forestry consultant like Scott Ferguson can make the critical difference. He or she will work with owners to develop a plan for a steady cash flow and a sustainable forest. He'll use his expertise and the skills of the best loggers he can find to take out the highest dollar-value trees with the least possible environmental damage. The whole team (owner, consultant, and loggers) is invested in the long-term process and the continued health of both forest and bank accounts.

"I've got to be frugal and put dollars to use for the owner. I want to spend money only where it counts, so that the owner winds up with a profit year after year. A good logger makes all the difference. The logger has the skill to remove the trees, knows the market at the mill, and how to get the biggest dollar for the log," states Scott.

Road costs are one place where small landowners may have a distinct advantage. While the forest Service routinely spends up to $10,000 per mile of log haul road (and as high as $250,000 per mile in the case of the Bald Mountain road in the north Kalmiopsis, a roadless area in southern Oregon), small acreages, especially those 50 acres and under, may already have all the road access they need.

The first site Scott and I visit brings the point home. It is a forty acre piece off Hugg Mill Road in Clackamas County, Oregon. Other than the country road, the roads he's used a year or two ago are now merely bands of wildflowers and grass.

Skid trails on that piece are marked only be some branches, and are half covered by berry vines and foxgloves. The benign northwest climate covers this ground with such a mat of herbs that the crash of an occasional tree seems to have negligible impact. Since I'd been concerned about compaction of the soil when harvest machinery enters a site every three to seven years, the undisturbed humus and flourishing herb layer are reassuring testimony, indeed.

Probably the most compelling evidence of the economic success of the Individual Tree Selection method comes from their case studies. The Farr tract is the one most often cited (see Table 1). After 30 years of managing 425 acres of class 3 (good, but not excellent, potential for timber production) logged over land, ITS boasts an average $4,000 net income per year from land on which the standing volume of timber has more than tripled. The owner purchased the land for $17,250; it's clear that the ITS standards for success are high.

While the Farr tract statistics can't be repeated everywhere, Ferguson says that as a rule he'll mark 2,400 to 4,000 board feet per acre for harvest every three to seven years. That's about 10% of the trees in an acre, but since they are among the largest, they equal 15% to 20% of the standing volume.

Frequency of entry is the key to small woodland owners' cash flow. Conventional thinning programs, based on the German model, call for entry only once every decade until final clear-cutting. Ten year intervals make it much harder for the landowner to maintain an even cash flow.

Another site points out the potential value to a typical small landowner. One value to a typical small landowner. One of the ITS clients is a dentist who owns 10 acres of woodland with a recreational cabin. The initial harvest netted the dentist a nest egg of $4,000 towards his son's college education. The harvest included some showplace logging techniques, including removing trees adjacent to the cabin. Not only did the loggers manage to avoid damage to the power line, cabin, and the adjacent trees, they left no ugly scars. The site remains a rustic, densely forested getaway, with the added value of producing a college trust fund. From the loggers' perspective, the challenge of such difficult tree removal was offset by the excellent country road access, which made it possible for them to log in the winter when moose industrial loggers are idle.

Scott waxes enthusiastic about these smaller acreages. "Its these forty pieces that have potential. The nonindustrial owners of 1000 acres or more have probably been contacted by one timber company or another. But for our kind of operation, efficiency is not dependent upon size. While more neighbors mean more conflicts for industrial practices, for us that's outweighed by the county road access. We may only haul out a total of ten truck loads, so it's not a steady stream of traffic for locals to contend with, I've never used herbicides on any site, so no complaints there. And almost every small acreage has one landing site already, so we really minimize our traces."

Table 1: Harvest and Cash Flow Record

Year	Board Feet	Owner's Net Timber Revenues
1955	33,660	$1,161.57
1956	444,425	10,737.21
1957	2,550	321.14
1958	33,630	957.85
1959	199,960	3,012.31
1960	40,959	747.65
1962	6,365	42.93
1963	82,140	1,641.47
1965	338,878	7,365.75
1966	197,819	3,981.62
1967	239,120	3,642.65
1968	174,530	4,677.80
1969	175,660	6,760.59
1970	192,425	6,306.28
1971	134,325	4,409.46
1972	124,030	4,860.22
1973	194,935	11,471.55
1974	87,195	5,397.23
1975	3,420	313.85
1976	72,360	5,931.00
1977	28,910	2,600.51
1978	37,030	3,810.00
1980	54,285	20,852.00
1981	18,750	5,478.10
1984	421,100	40,632.27
1985	253,080	24,430.29
1986	121,470	14,459.10
1987	397,130	33,634.06
1955-87	**4,118,140**	**$229,596.79**

Forest Inventory

1955	1,000,000
1987	3,700,000

The economic and environmental results of 32 years of Individual Tree Selection Management can be seen on the Farr Tract, a 425 acre woodland near sandy, Oregon.

The Old Growth Connection

To the wood products man an old-growth forest, with its many dead and dying trees, is an over-mature forest, a decadent forest, a forest in decline doing no human being any good. As a Reagan administration official remarked in 1984, "Old-growth forests remind me of an old folks home, just waiting to die."

He said that because when he looks at trees he sees board footage. He sees rotation cycles and allowable annual cuts, he sees lumber and houses and an ill-defined picture of progress.... But he doesn't see the slow exuberant dance the forest does through time. He doesn't see the intricate webwork of fungi that strands through the ground, drawing its food from the roots of trees and helping the roots draw food from the soil. He doesn't see the red-backed vole that eats the fungi's fruiting bodies and disperses their spores, sheltering itself in downed rotting wood. He doesn't see the spotted owl that eats the red-backed vole, hunting in the dark through thousands of acres of trees, nesting high in a standing snag and feeding her owletts, this brood and all her broods, as the Douglas firs keep growing and growing, each in its turn going down, melting into ground, sheltering the vole and feeding the fungi and holding the cold melt-water in its fragrant sponge.

—John Daniel, "The Long Dance of the Trees"

Contrary to the blindness John Daniel ascribes to the Reagan administrational official, many small woodland owners do see the noncommodity values of their forest lands. Moreover, they may have a far easier time than a federal agency's wildlife expert in balancing the need for some profit with retaining elk thermal cover, deer winter range, or a lush streambank.

Scott Ferguson shows me a large beaver pond on a forty acre piece of woodland that he's managing profitably. Stumps show that he's taken out trees right down to the water's edge. But carefully, and one at a time, over the years, A full canopy shades the creek still, maintaining an unbroken pledge to the cold water fishery. Runoff is still filtered naturally by stable soils, held in place by thick vegetation.

A short way up the path from the pond we cross over the mounds and tunnels of the mountain beaver, Aplodontia. These ancient rodents, now limited in range to small portions of the Pacific Northwest, damage enough trees to have earned the enmity of most foresters. Scott seems calm about them, though. Dick Smith had made his peace with these living relics of the Eocene when he learned to control their numbers be leaving a lot of shade. "Shade keeps down the vine maples, their preferred food. And in turn, the mountain beaver don't become too numerous," Scott says.

"But what about old-growth?" I ask. "Not a lot of non-industrial private woodland falls into that category,"

Scott says. "Woodlots have usually been entered and logged over to one extent or another before they were sold into smaller parcels."

Non-industrial management does offer some positives for those concerned about old growth protection, however. Wildlife habitat values can be protected, in many cases, under Individual Tree Selection methods. Small woodland owners can help provide the corridors that let species move among the islands of old growth that are protected on federal lands.

Another connection to old growth preservation is more utopian. The scenario goes like this:

The pressure to cut old-growth on federal lands is driven by a belief that timber supplies are inadequate to maintain the jobs in Oregon's number one industry. Small woodlands in Oregon comprise the largest untouched new source of logs, since over 90% of small woodland owners don't manage their lands at all. Theoretically, if more timber were to flow from small ownerships into millyards, the pressure to cut federal lands would be reduced.

Exporting logs, mill automation, and subsidies paid from federal timber receipts to local governments attenuate the linkage between old-growth left on federal lands and the intensified management of woodlots, But there's no doubt that increasing the amount of management of non-industrial private woodlands would have a positive effect on another environmental issue, land use planning.

Implications for Land Use

Public interest groups like 1000 Friends of Oregon, (a group that watchdogs Oregon's land use planning process) claim that local governments are permitting the suburbanization of forest lands by failing to adequately enforce Oregon's land use planning laws. They fear that sprawl will take woodlands out of timber production, increase air pollution from wood stoves and auto emissions, and will lead to the loss of the open spaces of Oregon's countryside.

For example, 1000 Friends successfully appealed Land County's plan, which would have permitted housing on 150,000 acres of forest lands. but lawsuits and minimum lot size requirements are usually seen as all stick and no carrot. Whatever the laws may say, there's little political momentum to conserve land by saying "no" to development.

Recognizing that, Henry Richmond, Executive Director of 1000 Friends, has proposed that the state government explore a new system to encourage the active management to woodlands.

Some government, private, or cooperative agency would arrange annual payments to landowners in ex-change for receiving the timber revenue when the landowners harvest their trees. This kind of arrangement could add millions of acres to Oregon's timber base and slow the pattern of chopping forest lands into smaller, suburban parcels. Assuming that many small woodland owners would choose to manage along the lines of Individual Tree Selection's system, it could also help to break down the hidebound notion that forestry in the Pacific Northwest must follow the German model. It's a daring, new idea that will depend as much upon the goodwill of many of the 19,000 owners of non-industrial private woodlands as much as it depends upon a change in law or a source of funding.

Community

After we talk about the big picture, especially the future as seen through the 1000 Friends' proposal, Scott and I focus more on forestry as a human activity. I ask him why he has chosen this line of work.

"It's a challenge, to work in it all the time and still enjoy it. but I knew that I wouldn't like the life of an industrial forester. In the winter, they stand and watch the planting, then they burn in the summer, repeating the same thing every year on a huge territory. I think I have a much more satisfying relationship with the land.

"Dick knew some of our tracts for 35 years. He told me that it would take me five years before I'd even know if I'd like the work well enough to keep at it.

"When he died last February, about half of our clients phoned me just to see if I was okay. It's not only a money arrangement for them either.

"They really opened my eyes. Now I know that my number one job is to communicate enthusiasm for what we can do with their land. We have to show owners that it can be profitable, enjoyable, and that they can do what they want for their land.

"Most owners don't know what they have. Its our job to educate them. I try to talk with everyone at least twice a year, not just to plan harvests."

I ask him about how closely he works with his clients, and how he finds new ones.

"It's almost 100% referral by word of mouth. The owners usually can't work along side of us, but we're still a team. Dick found that it took so many hours to try to teach owners how to mark trees that it wasn't profitable for them to pay him by the hour. And as for logging, it takes a lot of skill and the right equipment to take out an individual tree without damaging others.

"My loggers, especially George and Larry baker, are my best salespeople. I've found the owners down there just watching them work, seeing their skill firsthand. And the loggers are great to talk with. George, Larry's father, has been working with Individual Tree Selec-

9

tion for thirty years now. He knows his stuff."

A laden log truck passes us. Scott cranes his neck to get a last look as it goes over the hill, into town. He estimates that the truck holds about 15 logs, worth about $1,300.00

The load is part of the 200,000 board feet George and Larry are currently taking off a 60 acre site near Molalla.

"George and Larry are shopping for a new skidder. It will cost them about $54,000 if they have to buy a new one. With equipment costs like that, I take seriously the task of keeping them in timber to cut, and I try to keep them working year round."

By now we've caught up with the loggers, who are finishing up a day's work in the heat of mid-afternoon. The log truck has made its last haul of the day, and the men seem willing to visit with us a while.

"They kid Scott for bringing me to this site which is still recovering from an industrial thinning job arranged by a prior owner, rather than to the Farr tract or one of their other showcases. It was obvious that they look at the individuality of their harvest areas with as much regard as Scott does.

They want to know a little of my background, so we talk about southern Oregon forests and the continuing struggle over herbicides. Larry is warm in his skepticism about the safety of forest chemicals.

They seem genuinely interested in what I have seen and how it compares to my home turf. Logging techniques will always have to change with the site, and southern Oregon can seem like a different world to a woodlot owner or manager from the lusher north. I tell them about the importance of hardwoods as a year to year firewood income for many southern woodland owners. I talk about the generally lower timber productivity, since natural regenerative potential is hampered by summer drought.

George and Larry talk about traveling to Canada to search of a skidder, and how different the forests are.

Shop talk, I've always liked it. You get some feel for the personalities of the workers through their discussion of tools and techniques. I am a little sorry to leave.

But you've always got to wrap up a job. George and Larry skid the last logs down to the landing, buck them to length for the mill, sharpen their tools, and pack up. I shoot my remaining film and Scott figures out when he can schedule them for another site. And we all joke about whether Larry's dog is working or still on his break.

It was that image, the day's end in the woods, that cheered me up as I stacked my firewood. You've got to take some stuff on faith, that we'll bungle through well enough millwork and some native hardwoods over the long haul. but it bolsters my confidence to shift focus back from the big lands and the impersonal federal forest policies maneuvered in Congress to the more human scale of a few people working on their dreams in somebody's backyard.

A forester I know down here told me all the good stuff was really about people to people.

Remembering Richard Smith

Whether you swore by him or at him, Dick Smith stood for something. When he died in February, 1988, he heft a legacy to the forests of the Pacific Northwest in the style of management he called "Individual Tree Selection." In stark contrast to the tenets of industrial foresters, Dick Smith built his career around keeping the forest environment intact while pursuing a profitable business in timber harvest. He often stood alone, and always outside the mainstream of professional foresters.

He wasn't necessarily a loner by choice. He didn't claim credit for "discovering" the tenets of his management style. In press interviews, he often cited the work of others, A Danish forester, C.D.F. Reventlow, who argued against clear-cutting in the 1700s, was his most frequent reference.

In an article he wrote in 1978, Smith chose the words of an American forester, Bernhard E. Fernow, to summarize his modest sense of what drives and limits his chosen field. "Forestry is an art born of necessity, as opposed to arts of convenience and of pleasure. Only when a reduction in the natural supplies of forest products under the demands of civilization necessitates a husbanding of supplies... or when unfavorable conditions of soil or climate induced by forest destruction make themselves felt does the art of forestry make its appearance."

While death caught Dick Smith before he could finish the book he was drafting to compile his philosophy and craft, his thoughts are published in occasional papers and articles. Read in the context of the warm support he earned from Scott Ferguson, the loggers he employed and retained as friends, and the landowners who became believers and remain ITS clients, Smith's words are probably his best verbal memorial:

"The owner of a small woodland tree farm should realize he is only a caretaker of this natural resource, and should have as a goal the conservation of the forest plus a profitable income.

"As foresters, we are concerned with growing and harvesting trees. As stewards of the land, we are also keenly aware of the need to protect the beauty of the forest, as well as wildlife, soil, watershed and recreational aspects."

There remains, of course, another memorial that Smith would appreciate; the verdant hills of the Farr tract and the other acres he knew and in which he worked.

From Journal of Pesticide Reform, *Vol. 8, No. 3*

Bioforestry on Seattle Water Department's Cedar River Watershed

Marc McCalmon and Jerry Franklin

THE SEATTLE WATER DEPARTMENT manages three water sheds for the production of drinking water for over one and a half million people in the Puget Sound area. One of the historic secondary uses of the watersheds, for almost 100 years, has been timber harvest. However, in 1985 a public involvement process began that culminated with a new set of policy guidelines. These policies place a greater emphasis on non-consumptive use of watershed forest resources. The Cedar River Watershed is the largest watershed and was the primary focus during the public process. Only about 16 percent of the 90,000 acre watershed has late successional forest cover. The policies call for placing all remaining old growth and 50 to 65 percent of the younger forests into a reserve status and managing for water quality and wildlife habitat objectives. The remaining area of the watershed will provide a land base for developing a long-term timber harvest program. During 1990 the Water Department developed harvesting plans for balancing values of pending land and timber exchanges within the Cedar River Watershed. These exchanges provided an opportunity to develop silvicultural and harvest unit design strategies for contributing to structural and biological diversity on a stand level. The large reserve area on the watershed will likely meet landscape level needs for wildlife habitats and ecosystem processes; however, the Department believes that organisms will also benefit from actions taken to retain structural diversity in harvested stands.

As we began discussing how we should develop new forestry practices, we soon coined the term "Bioforestry" to describe Department efforts to blend biodiversity with forest management. We felt this term reminded us that forestry is a form of biology and that there is more to the forest than trees.

We began our planning process by establishing objectives for addressing stand level processes. We intended to address landscape level processes and patterns through a comprehensive management plan for the entire watershed. Fundamental to our objectives was the notion of providing a structural legacy that would carry forward through time and benefit species typically impacted by intensive even-aged management. In the simplest of terms this called for developing harvest prescription that retained green trees and coarse woody debris. Harvesting has been completed on 360 acres using a variety of strategies and designs.

Three distinctly different designs are illustrated in this article. The first example is an aggregated peninsular cutting pattern (Figure 1), the second is a dispersed green tree retention system (Figure 2), and the third is a modified group selection (Figure 3). The unit designs and prescriptions responded to existing stand structures and desired future conditions (see Table 1).

Figure 1

Diagram of peninsular aggregated design (for details, see Table 1).

Figure 2

Diagram for dispersed green tree retention system (for details, see Table 1).

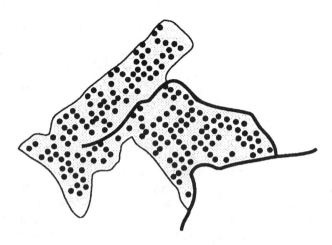

Figure 3

Diagram for modified group selection with high density dispersed retention (for details, see Table 1).

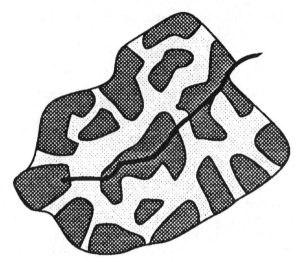

To begin the process we examined the stands to develop an understanding of species composition, stand structure, the location and abundance of snags and downed woody debris, and any other attributes that would contribute to meeting treatment objectives. The stand examinations provided the framework for identifying potential concerns for blowdown, regeneration, safety, and future growth and yields. The desired future condition for all three stands was to contribute to vertical diversity by creating conditions for development of two or more canopy layers within treated stands. Vertical diversity objectives also included provisions for maintaining or recruiting snags, cavity trees, and trees with branching characteristics or forms that could be used by various species. Horizontal diversity was also a part of the desired future condition. We tried to create spatial variability within stands to develop various light regimes with resulting understory composition and development.

All units are in second growth stands that ranged from 55 to 70 years in age at the start of the experiment. Elevations range from 1,100 feet to 1,500 feet above sea level. The topography is generally flat and the areas were logged using ground-based equipment. We primarily focused on retaining dominant Douglas fir as the preferred leave tree. These dominants have been more exposed to the wind over time and may have a lower susceptibility for blow down. These trees will be retained through the next rotation. At that time, enough balance may be restored to the landscape to allow that some of these large, high-quality trees to be harvested.

The units will be planted with a mixture of species that correspond to microsite conditions within the units. Areas with greater crown closure or shading will be planted with shade-tolerant species; open areas will receive shade intolerant species.

We have begun monitoring effects of blowdown, change in tree geometry, understory vegetation development, and regeneration. A wildlife-monitoring plan will be developed this winter. Unfortunately, because of time constraints, we were unable to conduct preharvest surveys to estimate wild life usage or populations. We do intend to develop a plan for monitoring and recording usage of the harvest units by key species. There have been at least three storms with winds around 50 miles per hour within the units. Only about 15 trees have been lost to windthrow over the 360 acres.

We have seen that it is operationally feasible to create a legacy that will provide short-term benefits to some species and possibly provide future stand structures that will benefit other species in the coming years. By adopting bioforestry on the Seattle city watershed, we are attempting to learn new information through a willingness to set aside our old paradigms and try something new.

We are in the process of summarizing harvest activities and anticipate having copies available for distribution in early 1993. Anyone interested in receiving a copy can write to the Seattle Water Department, Attention: Marc McCalmon, 19901 Cedar Falls Rd. SE, North Bend, WA 98045.

Reprinted with permission from COPE Report, *Vol. 5, No. 4, Fall 1992.*

Table 1
Stand characteristics for Cedar River Watershed bioforestry harvest units

Stand information for each stand	Peninsular aggregated design	Dispersal green tree retention	Modified group selection
Primary Spp— % composition BA/Acre	DF—67%	DF—71%	WH—52%
Secondary Spp— % composition BA/Acre	WH—20%	RC—16%	DF—34%
Tertiary SPP— % composition BA/Acre	RC—11 %	WH—12%	RC—11 %
Acreage	40	60	44 acres in gaps (39 acres in retention)
Net volume per acre	50,000	43,000	32,000
Basal area per acre	261	269	327
Trees per acre	162	172	363
Relative density	26	65	91
Crown competition factor	295	316	418
Site index (50 year)	138 DF	129 DF	110 DF
Percent retention	14% of Vol. (20% of area)	20% of Vol. (12 Trees/acre)	16% of Vol. (50 TPA retained)
Falling, bucking, and yarding costs/MBF (As reported by contractor)	$58	$43	$44

The Forest We All Want

Mark Wigg

PLANNERS CAN USE FORECASTING in two ways. The passive way currently used by the forest service timber planners is leading toward disaster. The forest which will result from the proposed forest plans will be composed of small trees averaging less than 10 inches in diameter, timber harvests will be dominated by knotty, low quality wood with a very high percentage of juvenile wood fiber, and the forest will be dominated by clear-cuts. The alternative is to identify our goals for timber management, which we have done. Our goals are to produce high revenues, high employment, and high timber volumes. After identifying our goals, we look for alternatives which will best meet these goals. This method of planning to meet our goals is not even considered by Forest Service plans. The forest we all want is one managed for larger, older, higher quality trees and a wide diversity of species. Whether or not this is the forest we want is easy to establish. Just ask:

- Ask sawmill owners which forest produces the trees they want.
- Ask plywood producers which forest produces the trees they want.
- Ask the Japanese which forest produces the lumber they want to import.
- Ask pulp and paper manufacturers which forest produces the highest quality fiber.
- Ask carpenters which forest produces the lumber they want to use in construction.
- Ask counties which forest produces the most revenues for their roads and schools.
- Ask hydrologists which forest produces the highest quality water.
- Ask ecologists which forest is more ecologically stable.
- Ask fire control specialists which forest will withstand fires.

- Ask window, door, and molding manufacturers which forest produces the wood they want.
- Ask the cedar industry which forest produces the wood they want.
- Ask tourists which forest they want to see.
- Ask environmentalists which forest they want.
- Ask loggers which forest is more profitable for them.
- Ask economists which forest will provide the most jobs.
- Ask economists which forest offers the most economic stability.
- Ask wildlife biologists which forest offers the most diverse habitat.
- Ask yourself if you want a forest of small saplings, poles, and clear-cuts, or one dominated by majestic trees with few clear-cuts.

We know what type of forest we want. We have identified our goals for timber management.

From a paper written by Mark Wigg, a forest economist, based in Corvallis, Oregon. Reprinted with permission.

Restoration Thinning

Headwaters

The Thinning Debate: Restoration Thinning Elucidated

THINNING PRESCRIPTIONS in restoration forestry must be done on a site by site basis. Thinning prescriptions need to take forest health into account first and foremost, and, secondly, provide products for human use. The concept of forest health can be interpreted in many different ways. Unscrupulous forest managers and loggers (and even well-meaning ones) can use "thinning" as a pretext to high-grade stands or remove most of the merchantable volume. Ecologists should be making thinning plans rather than timber sales people.

One environmental group that has given some attention to thinning in a restoration forestry context is Headwaters in southwest Oregon.

Headwaters' Alternative for the Draft Resource Management Plan for the Bureau of Land Management: Medford District lays out some of the best rationale and guidelines for restoration thinning to date. Integrating protection and management across the forest landscape with reserves and restoration thinning.

The proposal developed by Headwaters recommends thinning thick young stands and overstocked understories to improve owl habitat. Such thinning would also help fireproof late seral/old-growth stands by reducing the fire fuels in adjacent stands. Thinnings would occur on an experimental basis in the previously managed landscape outside of owl reserves.

The following article is excerpted from: "Headwaters' Alternative for the Draft Resource Management Plan for the Bureau of Land Management Medford District: Integrating Protection and Management Across the Forest Landscape with Reserves and Restoration Thinning." Reprinted with permission.

Logging systems need to be scaled down. Lighter, smaller equipment is needed for ground-based yarding, including rubber-tired skidders and horses. The smaller yarders, tractors, etc. that were prevalent 40 years ago before the advent of mass clear-cutting need to be reintroduced. Small tractors by Kubota, and rubber-tired skidders are available. Conventional cable yarding systems may not often be suitable for restoration thinning operations, and cable yarding set-ups appropriate for restoration thinning need to be developed. More information is needed on suitability and availability of cable systems. Helicopters can be used for stands not accessible by existing roads. Thinning with helicopters has not often been attempted, but preliminary results seem positive (e.g. the Deadhorse Sale on the Lowell District of the Willamette National Forest).

Draft Guidelines for Restoration Thinning

Headwaters has been engaged in dialogue with forest scientists and other conservation groups since December 1992 in an effort to define an experimental method of thinning that might assist in the restoration of forest ecosystem functions. This type of "restoration thinning" is intended to serve three main purposes:

1. To reduce stress from overstocking where wildfires have been suppressed;

2. To improve foraging habitat for spotted owls in dense young stands;

3. To encourage the more rapid development of late seral/old-growth forests that serve as nesting habitat for spotted owls and critical habitat for the 480+ other species.

Definitions and Goals

Restoration thinning modifies conventional thinning techniques to favor biodiversity.

"Thinning" is a means of taking trees from the forest

that focuses primarily on what is left, rather than on what is removed. Traditional silviculture classifies thinning as a method for "stand improvement," where some trees are removed in order to stimulate the growth rates, health, and vigor of the remaining trees.

In "restoration thinning," the goals of conventional thinning are supplemented to enhance forest ecosystem health and restore wildlife habitat by promoting:

1. **Structural diversity**
    All the existing components of the forest's diversity should be retained after thinning, such as remnant older trees, so-called "wolf trees" with unusual genetic characteristics, snags, hardwoods, and down logs.

2. **Minimized ground disturbance**
    Damage to the duff layer and compaction should be avoided. However, some ground disturbances may be beneficial on some sites.

3. **Species diversity**
    Where fire suppression has resulted in an overabundance of certain species on a site (e.g. white fir), then thinning should be designed to selectively remove these species, in order to move the stand towards the species composition that it possessed prior to the suppression of wildfires. Hardwood species should be retained as a natural component of the stand.

4. **Down woody debris**
    Forest sites vary greatly in the amount of down woody debris. On some sites where this is sparse or absent, thinning may be used to increase down material by leaving cut trees to rot on the forest floor. The need to contribute to future woody material by retaining unburned slash from thinning must be balanced with the need to decrease fuel loading.

5. **Decreased fuel loading**
    Thinning operations should reduce fuels. Excess material (slash) remaining after thinning may be treated in various ways, such as lop-and-scatter or pile-and-burn. Prescribed broadcast burning after thinning may also be desirable on many sites, to simulate the effects of a natural ground-fire.

6. **Windfirmness**
    Care should be taken not to increase the risk of blowdown in thinned stands. Some even-aged plantations may need to be thinned in two stages, in order to gradually increase the root strength and windfirmness of the remaining trees. This will be especially true for young so-called "pinhead" stands where the ratio of live crown to total height is less than 10 percent.

Criteria To Control Thinning Prescriptions

The criteria for restoration thinning (described below) must vary according to forest type, such as Douglas-fir, mixed conifer, true fir, and ponderosa pine. The numerical thresholds are subject to change based on further research.

1. Retain a defined percent of canopy closure.
    The canopy closure after thinning shall be at least 60 percent for pine stands and 75 percent for other stands. This restriction on canopy closure will protect adequate habitat for dispersing juvenile spotted owls and is larger than the 40 percent minimum required by the Interagency Scientific Committee's 50-11-40 rule.

2. Provide relatively even spacing for the remaining trees, while at the same time respecting the natural variability of the site.
    Full site utilization (even spacing) must be balanced with the need to retain the stand's structural diversity. Do not create "park-like" stands. Keep some unthinned clumps and thickets.

3. Retain more than half of the basal area of the current stand.
    The exact percent of basal area to be retained will vary according to the productivity of the site (as measured by site class), and by the ecotype.

4. Restrict the diameter of trees to only thin the smaller size classes.
    Limiting the diameter will protect residual old trees, thereby enhancing stand structure and reducing fire hazards.

    a) In uneven-aged stands, trees larger than the quadratic mean diameter should be retained, so that the understory will be thinned rather than the overstory.

    b) In even-aged stands, trees larger than a certain percent over the quadratic mean diameter should be retained. This percentage should be determined specific to each site and will vary by eco-type and region.

Note: Detailed discussions of the goals and landscape context of restoration thinning can be found in *Headwaters' Alternative for the Medford BLM's Draft Resource Management Plan*, "Integrating Protection and Management Across the Forest Landscape with Reserves and Restoration Thinning." Applications for the northern spotted owl are also discussed in a paper prepared for the Western Ancient Forest Activists Conference, entitled "The Role of Forestry in Ecosystem Restoration."

A Woodlot Management Plan Utilizing Horses

Rosemary LaVernier

MANAGING A WOODLOT PROPERLY can be a baffling business for those who aren't sure of how to go about it. One northern Idaho horse-logger shared his methods in this interview.

Cliff Stansell lives near the small town of Priest River. He has devised and implemented a management plan for his 15-acre woodlot, where he is slowly improving the appearance of a neglected, overgrown plot of land.

Stansell, a skilled horseman and a saddle-maker by trade, uses his Percheron-cross horses for the job. In addition to working his own woodlot, he hires himself out to others who lack the time or expertise to manage their forested lands.

Stansell has definite ideas about why a woodlot should be managed. "As the nation's overall timber supply is depleted, the price of lumber per board-foot rises," he said. "With the increasing demand for sawlogs and lumber products, it's wise and even necessary for owners of timbered acreage to manage their land." If the trees are not managed, and they become unhealthy and die, they are no better than firewood, according to Stansell. Then, the owner has lost not only money, but one of his most valuable resources.

The Sustained-Yield Woodlot Management Plan

"In order to get maximum production of every species of tree, the woodlot must have a sustainable growth of healthy, disease-resistant trees that are constantly propagating seed and can be harvested at an even rate," Stansell said.

"The common operation of timber companies and government lands is to harvest the largest, select trees and leave the scabs," he added. This practice is referred to as Forest Liquidation, and leaves very little for the future, according to Stansell.

Stansell's method is the opposite. Called Future Planning for a Sustained Yield, it involves removing the unhealthy, diseased, and overcrowded trees, and leaving the healthy ones to grow at their maximum rate, reproduce, and be thinned later.

Benefits of the Sustained Yield Plan

The initial monetary gain in this method is minimum compared to Forest Liquidation. As opposed to marketing only the prime trees, the smaller, diseased, and unhealthy trees which don't bring high market prices must be dealt with.

"The woodlot manager must keep in mind that this is a long-term investment, as compared to the fast buck acquired when liquidating," Stansell pointed out. "Looked at from a long-term standpoint, it will actually yield a greater gain; a forest that can be continuously harvested, is beneficial to our earth and atmosphere, and is a pleasure to look at and walk through."

He explained that healthy trees gain more board feet when the forest is open, as they have access to plenty of sunshine. "In the long run, a Sustained Yield program is more profitable financially." Profitable not only in monetary terms, but in usable harvests as well. "I always have an abundant supply of firewood and post and rail material to be utilized or sold," Stansell said.

Stansell's Methodology

"Over the past several years, I have been managing my own woodlot in a way to maximize growth in the native trees and produce a healthy forest," Stansell said.

He starts in one corner of his land and works his way through, first creating skid trails in the area where he will be working. He removes the diseased and overcrowded trees first, harvesting one species at a time so that he can take advantage of the current market.

When cutting, he drops the larger trees towards the trails, though a tree doesn't always fall in the direction intended. Then he takes his horses in to skid. When he has enough for a full truckload of one species, he calls in the logging truck.

Overcrowding was a major problem on Stansell's land.

The rule of thumb he used in thinning was to provide 15 feet of space between maturing trees. "If you have younger trees, you might want to leave some," he added, "in order to keep a steady stream for harvesting."

Thinning of younger trees is performed after the larger diseased and unhealthy trees have been removed. That way, he can harvest any that are damaged when the larger ones fall.

If the soil is rocky, sandy, or devoid of organic matter, Stansell suggests scattering the brush, which eventually breaks down and adds duff to the forest floor.

"On my place," he said, "the duff and undergrowth is so thick that it isn't feasible to scatter the brush." Instead, he piles and either burns it or leaves it to break down over time. "I'm piling brush all the time," he said. While thinning, he takes out the smaller, harvestable trees, which can be sold to the mills for pulpwood or used for posts and rails.

One 20-acre plot Stansell logged involved removing diseased and unhealthy white pine only. White pine was priced high at the time, and almost all of his client's white pine had been infected by blister rust. Two 16-foot loads were sold, and after paying Stansell and the hauler, the owners made a profit of about $1700 on trees that would have died within a few years.

Assessing A Woodlot and Implementing A Plan

"Because every woodlot is different in species, terrain, forest condition, and access, it's impossible to make a determination as to the best management method without cruising the area," Stansell said. "Cruising involves looking at desired species, tree spacing, individual tree health, and assessing the amount of board feet."
Stansell looks at the species of trees present, and learns what the market for each is. If one species appears healthy and disease-free, and is not too crowded, it need not be logged. Stansell prefers to concentrate first on those species having the most disease.

For non-diseased trees that are overcrowded, look at the roots and crown for determining which ones to remove. Assess straightness, scars, and markings, and aim for 10-20 feet of space between mature trees.

Leave saplings to grow and be harvested later. With the Sustained Yield plan, the idea is to keep a steady stream for harvesting. Some trees of each species should also be left behind for seed trees.

"I don't always take the biggest trees," said Stansell. "I try to leave the big, healthy ones unless they're crowded."

For those who know little or nothing about the health of trees and their identification, a forester can be called upon to help. Local mills employ foresters, "but they may not have the same mind-set as the small

woodlot manager," Stansell warned. "Mill foresters may try to buy your trees."

In many states, the Department of Lands or the State Forest Service have established woodlot forestry programs aimed at helping private woodlot owners. State foresters will assess a private woodlot free of charge, educate in tree identification, health, and disease, and advise the owners as to the best management plan.

In Stansell's case, a forester took core samples of his trees to determine their age and found that some trees were over 100 years old. They were so crowded that they had grown at a much slower rate than normal.

Using Horses for the Job

Stansell uses his Percheron-cross horses for skidding and decking the logs. He has chosen to do this work with horses because of the minimal damage and the low mortality rate to young trees compared to machinery operations. "Simply put," he said, "horses can't pull as much, therefore the damage they cause is less."

Stansell has worked concurrently on the same piece of land with a skidder. "I was appalled at the mortality rate where the skidder worked," he said. He estimated that 70-80 percent of the trees near the skidder's path were damaged. Many of the damaged trees were white fir and hemlock, which die easily once damaged. Stansell cites several reasons for using horses over machines. For one, skid trails can be narrower. And, because horse are easier to maneuver in the woods than skidders, less devastation to remaining trees is caused, both of which translate to more trees for later harvest as well as a more natural-looking forest once the job is finished.

Horses are better for the environment than machinery. Their hooves cause less soil compaction and seedling damage than large tires or tracks, and instead of the atmosphere polluting exhaust from machinery, horses' waste fertilizes the soil.

Logging with horses is not without drawbacks, however. Using horses to log on hilly land may be impractical. Factors such as steepness, the size of the load being skidded, and the direction of the grade must be considered. Often though, there are ways around such problems. Building a road downhill from the logged area, reducing the size of the load, or using two horses instead of one, are all possible solutions to working in a hilly area.

Horse logging requires patience, as it is slower than high-production skidders. Many factors are involved when comparing the two method's relative speeds, but Stansell estimates roughly that a skidder can remove five times as much in a day as a horse can.

"You have to take care of your horses," Stansell said, "their teeth, their feet, their health. I rest my horses about every 300 feet."

Cost comparisons involve multiple factors also. If a horse logger is hired for the job, he generally charges more than a skidder would. Stansell charges $50 per 1000 feet to skid, pile brush, and deck with his horses. A skidder in the Priest River area charges about $100 per 1000 feet for skidding and decking (some will pile brush by pushing it into piles, but machines do a far less neat and effective job than Stansell).

"A person has to decide if he wants money up front, or later, " said Stansell, who noted that using horses is more of an investment.

Training the Horses

Using horses for wood lot management requires special training. Stansell trained his own horses for the job. "The most important thing, " he said, "is to train them to stop immediately when you say 'Whoa.' If they don't, serious injury can result to both the horse and logger."

Stansell uses a round training corral. He gets the horse into a lunge, then trains it to stop, walk, trot or lope by voice commands. He also teaches the horse to turn using lines he controls from behind, but when logging, uses these only as a precaution and depends mainly on the voice commands.

For load pulling, he starts each horse with a light load, such a firewood or a small tree. He works the load size up until the horse is able to pull a load as heavy as its own weight. (This depends on the ground conditions, though.) After each horse is trained separately, Stansell puts two horses together, usually a young horse with an older, more experienced one.

When working in the woods, Stansell always allows the horses to look at the load before they pull it. "They can tell if it's heavy," he said. "They get smart about it. If two people are working together, the horses can be trained to skid the logs out of the woods to where the second person is waiting, and walk back to the logger after the load is unhooked. "When they start logging, they know nothing," Stansell said. "They learn over the years."

Stansell keeps his horses in shape for pulling when he's not logging by having them pull a sleigh, snow plow, or mower.

His horses also deck the logs. They can do it in one of several ways. Stansell's method is to roll the logs together side by side, hook one log to the horses, position them so the log is even with the deck, then have them walk around the deck pulling the log up and over the end. The horses stop, and Stansell uses a peavey to swing the other end of the log around.

The first time Stansell decked a load of logs, the trucker, who had expressed dismay when he learned he would be picking up a load decked with horses, was amazed at how neat and tight the pile was.

Another decking method using horses is to make a long string of logs and let the truck pick them up a few at a time. Most truckers don't like to see this, though, because it involves moving the truck several times while loading.

Stansell mentioned a gin pull, which he has never used himself. A gin pull consists of a pulley coming off of two poles. A log is hooked, the horses pull a rope attached to the pulley and the log, and the log is lifted and placed on top of the pile.

Utilizing the Harvests

There are many uses for the timber harvested using the Sustained Yield plan, the most obvious of which is selling it to a mill.

Stansell sometimes hires a band saw mill to cut lumber, which he uses for building at a much lower cost than he could purchase retail. He occasionally sells some of it. He was quick to point out though, that for cutting lumber to sell, one must have a storage area and a market for it. "You get better money milling it yourself than you would selling it to the mills," he said. According to Stansell, when the mill buys a 1000-foot load, their common overrun is 100 percent, meaning they will obtain 2000 feet of cut lumber.

Diseased trees that aren' t suitable for saw logs, as well as smaller trees, can be sold to some mills as pulp wood. However, some species, such as cedar, won't be accepted for pulp wood.

Stansell saves the larger cedar trees which can't be used as saw logs for posts. He has built a bin where he stores trees suitable for rails and posts, and either uses them himself or sells them. If the wood isn't good enough for any of the above uses, it can be used for firewood.

Conclusion

Stansell points to the quick liquidation schemes used by big timber companies as the cause of many of today's problems: low timber prices, over-stocked mills, and clearcut patches of land that allow soil erosion and watershed pollution and induce environmental appeals.

He summed up the Sustained Yield plan by saying, "This type of forest management is geared toward the small woodlot owner who understands what is happening to our forests and has the foresight to appropriately take care of the land deeded to him."

Reprinted with permission from Small Farmer's Journal, *Winter 1993.*

Morning Song Forest Restoration Project

Michael Pilarski

DAN MORGAN AND FAMILY have been working quietly for 14 years on 500 acres of forested countryside in the Okanogan Highlands of north-central Washington. His land lies between 3,000' and 4,000' elevation, and with only 30 miles to the Canadian border, the snow cover doesn't disappear until May.

Morgan has been applying what he calls "forest restoration" to his acreage, with good results. In 1992, when he felt he had something to show, the project went public with a well-received workshop for local foresters and forest workers.

The Morgans have planted many trees over the years to fill in gaps in the forest. Another major effort includes a case by case approach to mistletoe control, in which mistletoe is usually pruned out of the tree. Only occasionally is the whole tree taken out. Mistletoe is a major problem in Okanogan forests, so this is an important experiment in mistletoe control. In some stands mistletoe can affect over half of the trees, and prescribed sanitation cuts may remove most of the forest canopy.

Much of the project's efforts have gone into cleaning up logging slash from the 214 acres which were logged in 1950. One million board feet were taken off and the owner received $100,000 in stumpage fees.

The Morgans estimate that the loggers left behind 2000 cords of slash on the ground and that it is costing them $72,000 to clean up the slash. They have 14 years of work into the job and have 6 more to finish. They figure the cost of cleaning up the loggers' mess is close to the total the land owner received from the loggers, and that is not counting the lost productivity.

The Morgans' main reason for cleaning up slash is to reduce the high fire hazard. The slash is piled and burned. Morgan prefers to burn when there are several inches of snow on the ground, a heavy snow falling, and no wind. He aims to be real safe not to start forest fires. Morgan believes in stringent precautions, since there are hundreds of forest fires started each year in the Pacific Northwest from burning slash piles.

MSRFP land is in trust so it will be managed for restoration and sustainability for generations to come. Starting in 2020, the plan calls for 50,000 board feet to be harvested each year. At that rate the forest should be able to sustain that level of harvesting and still increase volume. The funds generated will be reinvested in further forest improvement. The end goal is not making money, says Morgan, the end goal is a healthy, natural forest.

Update: Unfortunately, Morgan is now going to court to try to save 120 acres of his forest from logging by a local timber mill which bought "timber rights" in the 1940's for $1/acre. The mill notified Morgan in July, 1993 that they are coming for the third harvest. The mill also has recently offered the "timber rights" for sale at $1,400/acre. If Morgan can't stop the logging, he will see a lot of his work undone, crop trees taken, regeneration killed, and another giant accumulation of slash created. Many neighbors are also fighting the legality of these "perpetual timber rights". Anyone with helpful legal information is invited to contact the Morgans.

Morning Song Forest Restoration Project
Dan Morgan
614 Toroda Creek Road
Wauconda, Washington 98859
Tel: (509) 486-4011

Editor's Note

A permaculture perspective leads me to think of ways to make use of the productivity/value the slash represents. At 40 years of age, much of it is well-rotted and would take relatively little energy to turn into mulch. Slash can also be concentrated in the landscape at safe points, which still achieves the aim of reducing wildfire risk. Tightly-piled slash fills part of the beneficial, ecological functions of large logs in the ecosystem. Piles of organic matter are sites of productivity for trees, wildlife, and soil microorganisms. The carbon "fuel" the biomass represents spreads out into the surrounding landscape through many pathways, enriching the ecosystem.

The Goebel-Jackson Tree Farm

Michael Pilarski

LEO GOEBEL'S FATHER was a rancher and logger. Leo is following in his father's footsteps, only he is using a small crawler tractor instead of horses. Goebel's partner, Bob Jackson is a consulting forester. The 160 acre forest they manage has become a notable forest model in northeastern Oregon. Leo's wife and five children have been active in the management of the tree farm and virtually all of the work has been done by family members. They have received the Oregon State Tree Farmer of the Year award twice and in 1992 were named the Western Regional Tree Farmer of the Year.(16 western states)

When they bought the 160 acres in 1970, it had an estimated 1,900,000 board feet of timber. Over the last 22 years, they have harvested every year(total harvested so far is 1,500,000 board feet) and still have an estimated 2,000,000 board feet of standing timber. Today, the average tree in their forest is bigger, of better quality, and is twenty feet taller. Goebel believes in always leaving the best trees no matter what the size. He harvests three to four percent of the total volume each year. Leo knows his forest intimately since he goes over the forest every year with an eye to culling the weak, injured or diseased trees. Goebel believes that with their present management techniques, they can rotate the volume of timber in their forest in 30 years while maintaining a complete, fully-stocked forest. If the land were clearcut, it would take at least 100 years or more to grow this same volume.

High-pruning is Goebel's special project. About 700 trees have been pruned 50-80 feet up from the ground. Almost all of the limbs pruned are dead as he does not want to slow tree growth by cutting green limbs. If the dead limbs remain on the tree, it grows around them and leaves knots which may become holes when cut into boards. After pruning, the wood put on by the tree is clear, knot-free, high quality wood which will fetch a premium price. Goebel estimates that if an 18~ DBH(diameter breast high) tree is high pruned, the wood created by the time it reaches 30" DBH would produce 500-600 sheets of clear plywood veneer 1/8 inch thick.

Goebel believes other benefits of high pruning include increased light penetration into the forest and less damage to other trees when falling the tree. Leo high prunes the ponderosa pine, Douglas fir and western larch, but not the spruce or white fir since they will sprout new limbs. Goebel does not plan to harvest the high pruned trees in his lifetime unless an individual tree dies or loses it's place in the stand. He feels there is no reason to harvest a tree that is healthy and has room to grow. The high pruned trees (in fact most trees on the tree farm) may have another 200-300 years in their life span and their harvest will be left to generations not yet born. In addition to high pruning, they have pruned the lower limbs off of most of the trees up to head height to reduce the chance of a ground fire climbing into the crowns of the trees.

Goebel feels that it is important to maintain the forest habitat for the full range of life from the soil bacteria to the mice and voles to the largest native mammals. He is proud of the fact that his tree farm is inhabited by pileated woodpeckers, goshawks, deer, elk, bear, and cougar. (68 species of birds, 16+ species of mammals)

Goebel believes in tighter tree spacing in the forest than promoted by the Forest Service. He wants his trees to grow at a slower pace to make tight-grained wood. The more open spacing advocated by industry means faster-growing individual trees which put on wide growth rings and consequently produce less structurally sound lumber.

Goebel compares the Forest Service and industry taking too much timber out at once to a rancher who sells almost the whole herd and keeps only the lowest quality animals. "With that kind of treatment, how long is it going to take to build up to a productive herd again?" When you clearcut a forest or take out most of the trees with a seed tree or shelterwood cut, you lose much of the photosynthesis capacity of the forest and biomass production. Those seedling trees planted in clear-cuts do not put wood on like his 150 year old trees. Leo's forest is always fully stocked with all sizes of trees and putting on quality wood. He estimates that his forest drops between a ton to a ton and a half of needles per acre per year. That is fertilizer!

Goebel disagrees with the Forest Service on their assessment and recommendations on how to handle the highly-publicized insect epidemics in Eastern Oregon. The main reason for the problem has been decades of a lack of forest management by industry, government, and private landowners. Decades of high-grading, over cutting and a lack of stocking control and precommercial thinning have left many forests overly stocked (too dense). If they had thinned the young forests to obtain better stocking density, the remaining trees would be less water and nutrient stressed and more resistant to insects and other diseases. The trend toward even-aged timber stands in recent decades has also taken many acres of land out of active timber production and decreased the volume of timber managed on a sustained basis. Heavy harvesting opens up the forest floor to drying sunlight. Goebel claims one reason his stands are so productive is that full stocking allows for a moister micro climate on the forest floor.

Besides managing his own 160 acre tree farm, Goebel manages and does the logging on several thousand acres of forestland for other landowners. Leo has a Master of Science degree in Geology and taught math and science at the high school level for 17 years. The last seven of those years he started and taught a forestry class to teach the students hands-on forestry including how to splice cables, set chokers, fell trees, drive the skidder, climb and prune trees and to observe life in the forest. Between his teaching and his carefully managed forest, Goebel is creating a forest heritage which will last for generations. Bob Jackson is now retired, but still spends much of his time on the property helping with odd jobs and assisting with his expertise as a consulting forester.

Leo Goebel
> 62309 Wallowa Lake Hwy.
> Joseph, OR 97846
> (503) 432-2431

10 Restoration Forestry in British Columbia and Canada

10

Restoration Forestry In British Columbia and Canada: A Resource Guide

Western Canada has much of the high quality, long-fibre old growth timber left in the world. We can liquidate it and sell it cheaply as we are currently doing, or we can cut it on a sustainable basis, make high quality wood products, and name our price. From an economic standpoint, we have scarcity on our side. Because of world demand for high quality old growth wood, we could recover the costs of careful stewardship and labour-intensive practices. However, as we have seen, this is not the agenda of major timber corporations that control forests of Canada.

—*Herb Hammond*

Canada—Brazil of the North

CANADA HAS BECOME KNOWN as the "Brazil of the North" because of the speed with which its forests are being felled. One acre is cut every 12 seconds in Canada compared to one acre every 9 seconds in the Amazon. Across Canada, from the expansive boreal forests of the north to the hardwoods of southeastern Canada, to British Columbia's temperate rainforests, clearcuts are expanding at an alarming pace.

Boreal forest covers 34% of Canada. It is largely an evergreen forest dominated by spruce, fir and pine, with poplar and birch the prevalent deciduous trees. Roughly 65% of Canada's boreal forest (almost 100% of the most productive forests) are scheduled for logging.

The temperate rainforests of the Northwest coast of North America were one of the largest reservoirs of biomass on Earth. We do not know the impact of eliminating this biomass reservoir on regional and global climate. Will Canada's citizens and government wake up in time to save the remaining fragments of this precious heritage and valuable component of the Earth's climate stabilization system?

Industry pours millions into marketing campaigns to assure the public that everything is just fine with current forest practices; and spends millions funding the pro-resource exploitation "Share Groups." Canada's version of the "Wise-use Movement." In spite of the propaganda, throughout Canada, more and more people are getting fed up with the desecration deforestry practices of the multi-national forest industry and their government sympathizers. The desire for restoration forestry and the need for restoration forestry grows with every year.

British Columbia, Canada

Perhaps it makes sense that in British Columbia, which has some of the largest clearcuts on the planet, there has been a pendulum swing by some people towards restoration forestry practices. In this British Columbia section, we report on a few people and places who have models or publications which fit into the broad category of restoration forestry. "Restoration Forestry" is not a term in common usage in British Columbia. Herb Hammond has popularized the term "Holistic Forestry." The term "Ecoforestry" has also received some publicity. Regardless of the labels, there is a growing interest and understanding of restoration forestry in B.C.

British Columbia (B.C.) is a big place, 366,253 sq. miles (948,596 sq. km.), most of B.C. is mountainous and about half of the province is covered by forests. There may not be much old-growth left, but British Columbia is still a magnificent part of the planet.

British Columbia's population is only 3 million people living on a huge land and natural resource base. After decades of cashing in one of the biggest supplies of high-quality, fine-grained timber in the world, B.C.'s government has gone into debt, unemployment is high, and B.C.'s economy is in crisis. Most of the easily accessible old-growth in the valley bottoms is gone and the timber wealth has flowed into corporate bank accounts.

British Columbia forest industry practices devastation forestry

The British Columbia forest industry has the dubious distinction of having the world's lowest rate of employment per volume of wood cut. The September/October, 1990 issue of Forest Planning Canada has some astounding figures on how fast British Columbia's forests are being clearcut. In 1988-1989, 75.6 million cubic metres of timber were logged on British Columbia Public (Crown) Lands (official government figures). Contrast this with the 54.2 million cubic metres logged in all U.S. National Forests combined during the same period. In the state of Washington we are appalled with the 5.5 million cubic metres cut in Washington State's National Forests. We should be happy that our forests are not being managed by the B.C. Ministry of Forests!

Half of all timber cut in the public forests of British Columbia since 1911 has been liquidated in the last 13 years (at a large loss to the B.C. treasury). There is little old-growth forest left on Vancouver Island and lower coastal B.C. Two large timber corporations, MacMillan Bloedel and Fletcher Challenge, are behind much of the B.C. logging and work hand in glove with the B.C. Forest Ministry. Now that the forests in the lower maritime B.C. are stripped, emphasis is switching to the interior B.C. forests, northern B.C. coastal forests, and boreal forests of other provinces.

Facts About British Columbia's Forests

1. The regulated timber cut was increased 380% from 1960 to 1987 (20.5 million cubic meters to 76 million cubic meters).

2. The public's forests have been highgraded and the remaining timber supplies are of increasingly lower quality and greater expense to access and extract.

3. Employment in timber extraction industries has decreased by 22% from a high in 1978 of 94,778 people to current levels of approximately 76,000. Capital is replacing labour in corporate forestry. In 1950, approximately 2.6 people were employed for every 1,000 cubic meter logged in British Columbia. Statistics in 1986 revealed that only 0.8 persons were employed for every 1,000 cubic meters logged. In other words, approximately 3 times as much timber must be cut in 1986 than in 1950 to provide one job in the forest industry.

4. In 1987-1988 British Columbia planted 169,000 hectares, site prepared 124,434 hectares, brushed and weeded 26,269 hectares, and applied intensive silviculture to another 75,076 hectares for a total number of 394,779 hectares treated (Ministry of Forestry Annual Report, 1988). This represents a ratio of a .52 hectares treated silviculturally to every hectare harvested.

British Columbia's current logging rates are 650,000 acres yearly. 70 percent of the profits from B.C. logging do not go back into B.C.'s economy, and 43 percent leaves Canada altogether. The B.C. Provincial government has protected only 2 percent of the temperate rainforests on Vancouver Island. Over 90 percent of B.C. logging is done by clearcutting, 100 percent of coastal logging is clearcut. B.C. has the largest clearcut in the world at 50,000 hectares (125,000 acres).

Because of public pressure, the B.C. government has been making some improvements in the forest practices code, timber supply review, lowering of the Annual Allotted Cut, and adding protected areas. Nevertheless, the provincial government's 1993 decision to log most of Clayoquot Sound shows it still dances largely to the tune of multinational timber companies. The forests of B.C. will continue to go downhill until this changes. Hopefully, someday local control and restoration forestry will replace multinational clearcuts.

Restoration Forestry Resources in Canada

Contact Catalog of Alternative Forestry Practitioners
CUSO c/o Bill Wells
P.O. Box 5, Johnson's Landing,
Kaslo, British Columbia, V0G 1M0, CANADA
Tel/Fax: (604) 366-4482

In 1993, CUSO embarked on a project to catalog examples of sustainable forestry in Canada and throughout the world. CUSO is a Canadian NGO doing international development. The first part of the project is to identify the best examples of sustainable forestry. Stage two of the project is to help establish communication links between existing projects and new projects getting underway. Bill Wells is coordinating this CUSO project.

Citizen's Guide to Timber Management Practices
1993. 100 pp. $12. Available from Tim Gray—forestry coordinator, Wildlands League, 160 Bloor St. E., Suite 1335, Toronto, Ontario, M4W 1B9, CANADA

Community Forum for the Forests in Canada
Community Forum for the Forests in Canada has been proposed as a local to nationwide process to build broad-based community consensus on sustainable forestry practices. The forum concept was initiated by B.C. forester, Herb Hammond. (See Silva Forest Foundation in Organizations for address.)

Restoration Forestry Models in British Columbia

Wildwood Forest
Merv Wilkinson
R.R. 3
Ladysmith, British Columbia, V0R 2E0, CANADA
Tel: (604) 722-2853

Merv Wilkinson has one of the longest-term and most outstanding examples of restoration forestry in B.C. Merv has lived and worked for more than 50 years at Wildwood, his 55-hectare forest near Ladysmith on Vancouver Island. Since 1935, Merv has selectively logged his land nine times, removing about 1.25 million board feet of timber; and Wildwood is still a diverse forest, with nearly the same volume of standing timber (1.5 million board feet) as in 1935. He estimates that 250 acres of coastal forest like Wildwood would keep two people working and financially solvent, permanently. "Based on this formula, the 40.9 million hectares of available forest land in B.C. could furnish 320,000 jobs," says forester Herb Hammond. "Wildwood style forestry could probably easily provide five to six times the number of jobs currently furnished by timber companies."

His work is featured in the book *Wildwood* and in the video, "Thinking Like a Forest." Merv and Wildwood have been featured on television and in major newspapers. He receives visitors from around the world. In 1990, Merv was awarded the "Restoration Forester of the Year Award" by Friends of the Trees Society.

The Kindwood Foundation
499 Millstream Lake Road
RR 6, Victoria, British Columbia, V9B 5T9, CANADA
Tel: (604) 478-4403, R. G. McMinn

The Kindwood Foundation is dedicated to the promotion of sustainable forestry and sustainable agriculture. Kindwood, which is located on 340 acres of forest and farmland, some 12 miles from downtown Victoria, the capital of British Columbia, is ideally suited as a demonstration and teaching area. Kindwood is teaching horse logging methodology and 250 acres is being developed as a demonstration of Ecoforestry. Orville Camp has been involved in developing their forestry plan and has put in 1/2 miles of his Contour Access Road System.

Wavehill Farm
230 Bridgeman Road
Fulford Harbour, Saltspring Island, British Columbia, V0S 1C0, CANADA
Tel: (604) 653-4121

The owners are practicing Natural Selection Ecoforestry on 250 acres of woodland plus an additional 250 acres are in preserve. Orville Camp has been involved in developing their forestry plan and has put in 3 miles of his Contour Access Road System. Wavehill Farm offers Earth Education workshops in forestry, agriculture, self-sufficiency and permaculture as well as nature walks.

Restoration Forestry Organizations in British Columbia

Ecoforestry Institute Society
P.O. Box 5783, Station B
Victoria, British Columbia, V8R 6S8, CANADA

Tel/Fax: (604) 598-2363

The first Ecoforestry Institute, under the leadership of Orville Camp, was incorporated in Oregon in 1991. In the spring of 1992, a second affiliated organization, the Ecosystem Institute Society (EIS) was incorporated as a non-profit society in British Columbia, Canada. The organizations' objectives include: setting up demonstration forests; providing information; establishing certification systems and educational programs for forest products derived from ecological responsible practices; developing ecoforestry land-trusts for communities and watershed alliances and forming links with other organizations.

Alan Drengson has been the leading person behind the Ecosystem Institute Society. Drengson is Professor of Philosophy at the University of Victoria, and is the editor of *The Trumpeter*, a leading Deep Ecology magazine. Doug Patterson is the society's executive director.

EIS hosted the second meeting of the Pacific Cascadia Ecoforestry Working Group in September 1993. The primary purpose of the meeting was to bring together practicing ecological foresters and facilitators for peer review of the hypothesis of Natural Selection Ecoforestry. In this method, one cuts only the trees nature has already selected out. Thus nature, not humans, decides the forest's future condition. This is the ecological practice upon which the Ecoforestry Institute Society is based.

The meeting also included tours to three forest properties: Merv Wilkinson's Wildwood, Nancy and Bob McMinn's demonstration forest, and the Wavehill Farm. The working group ended with a statement called the Wavehill Statement which enumerates the consensus reached during the weekend. This statement is available from the Ecoforestry Institute Society.

New Perspectives Forestry Society
158 Joseph St.
Victoria, British Columbia, V8S 3H5, CANADA
Tel: (604) 383-9959
Jim Pine, Publicity Chair

Pulp, Paper and Woodworkers of Canada
201—1184 West 6th Ave.
Vancouver, British Columbia
CANADA V6H 1A4
Tel: (604) 731-1909/Fax: (604) 731-6448

The Pulp, Paper and Woodworkers of Canada is a democratic Canadian union founded in 1963. Most of the 7,500 members are employed in pulp and paper mills. The PPWC is a union which has not swallowed the industry line of jobs vs. forests. PPWC believes if B.C.'s forest industry was managed properly, there would be plenty of both. PPWC's Forest policy paper "Jobs, Trees & Us" discusses restoration forestry.

Silva Forest Foundation

P.O. Box 9
Slocan Park, British Columbia
CANADA V0G 2E0
Tel: (604) 226-7222/Fax: (604) 226-7446

The Silva Forest Foundation (SFF) is a Canadian non-profit society whose major goal is to empower individuals and communities with the skills and knowledge to carry out or to continue the work of protecting, maintaining, and restoring the forest they are part of. Building on the philosophy and practice of holistic forest use, the SFF seeks to develop and implement practical solutions to forest use problems.

SFF is coordinated by Herb and Susan Hammond. Herb is a registered professional forester with a Masters of Forestry in silviculture and forest ecology. Since 1977, they have specialized in holistic forest use particularly for community groups and Native bands. Herb has become a well-known figure in B.C. for his stand against current industrial forestry practices. He is author of *Seeing the Forest Among the Trees: The Case for Holistic Forest Use*; Susan and Herb co-authored the *B.C. Community guide to the Forest*. Both are excellent contributions to restoration forestry (see reviews in this section).

SFF has developed some initial certification standards for ecologically responsible forest uses that maintain fully functioning forests. Eventually SFF hopes to provide a certification system for non-timber forest uses such as eco-tourism and mushroom picking.

SFF helps private land owners place forest land in trust to be managed by long-term forest stewardship agreements.

Silva Forest Foundation offers practical workshops in holistic forest use planning and holistic timber management. The science of landscape ecology is used as an important part of holistic forest use planning. These 3- to 5-day workshops are hands-on and interactive. Led by forest ecologist and forester Herb Hammond, workshops will include presentations by others practicing alternatives in using forests. Location: Silva Forest Foundation forest reserve and other forests near Salmo, B.C.

Students for Forestry Awareness

c/o Faculty of Forestry,
2357 Main Mall, University of British Columbia
Vancouver, British Columbia
CANADA V6T 1Z4
Tel: (604) 822-2727
Contact: Rick Walters

The Students for Forestry Awareness represent the progressive wing of UBC forestry students. Their Speaker Series every noon hour on Thursday features a wide range of speakers, including ecologists, foresters, industry and government. They have held several sym-posiums, including one on "The Role of Forests in Community Stability." Proceedings from symposia are available.

Restoration Forestry Periodicals in British Columbia

Forest Planning Canada

P.O. Box 6234, Stn. C
Victoria, British Columbia
CANADA V8P 5L5

Canada's Community Forestry Forum. This is Canada's top forestry periodical from a restoration forestry perspective and one of the best in North America. It is a good source of information on the management practices for "New Forestry." It is a professional quality publication which reports on forest developments in the environmental community, professional foresters, government, industry, woodsworkers, unions, ecology, science, politics, organizing, watersheds, legalities, resource boards, mills, etc. Indispensable to restoration foresters in Canada. Useful in the Pacific Northwest states and worth looking at as a model by restoration forestry networkers elsewhere. $28 Canadian/year.

International Journal of Ecoforestry

Ecoforestry Institute Society
PO Box 5783, Station B
Victoria, British Columbia, V8R 6S8, Canada
Tel:/Fax: (604) 598-2363

A new journal with the first issue published in Spring, 1994. The journal will be produced by the Ecoforestry Institute Society's staff working with Bob Nixon, the editor of Forest Planning Canada.

Watershed Sentinel

Friends of Cortes Island (address and review in Gulf Islands section following). C$12 in Canada. C$16 international.

Gulf Islands Build Models of Community Control of Forest Practices

B.C.'s Gulf Islands are found scattered along the southern and eastern edge of Vancouver Island. Only small patches of old-growth remain on the Gulf Islands, but second growth is currently being harvested. While major logging corporations who own large pieces of land in the Islands prefer to clearcut, island residents have formed forest committees to do research, education and planning about sustainable forest management. Many of the islands are now in the process of forming island-wide forestry practices guidelines. None of the islands have achieved community control over forest practices yet, but they are gaining ground.

The Gulf Islands offer some of the Pacific Northwest's

10

best examples of local community consensus on the management of forests. Canada is more advanced in community forest management than the U.S., perhaps because there are less regulations regarding timber practices. Since, the B.C. government would do nothing to curb the timber industry, local people are forced to organize as a community. Lasqueti Island is one of the leaders in this movement. Contact Doug Hopwood (604) 333-8876.

State of the Islands
Box 986, Station A
Nanaimo, British Columbia
CANADA V9R 5N2

The various Island organizations listed here (and others) make up the Islands Alliance. State of the Islands held a conference at Beban Park, Nanaimo, in October, 1989. Many issues were covered, including the relative state or condition of Vancouver Island and its adjoining islands, state of the area's forests and creatures, and sustainable resource management concepts. The conference produced an 11-point *Recommendations for Change* addressed to the B.C. government.

Green Islands
Box 254
Ganges, Saltspring Island, British Columbia
CANADA V0S 1E0
Tel: (604) 537-4471 or 537-4653

Cortes Island Forest Committee
Box 177
Manson's Landing
Cortes Island, British Columbia
CANADA V0P 1K0
Tel: (604) 935-6417—David Shipway

The Cortes Island Forest Committee (CIFC) was formed in 1988. The purposes are to develop ecologically responsible and balanced forest use of Cortes Island forests, to develop a sustainable forest-based economy, to educate ourselves and the public regarding appropriate use of Cortes Island forests, and to work towards a broad based public consensus for the use of these forests.

With these purposes in mind, the committee has negotiated with MacMillan Bloedel Ltd., Raven Forest Products Ltd., and the Ministry of Forests to improve timber management practices on the island. In addition to these negotiations, CIFC has carried out and published an extensive questionnaire covering the use of island forests, published a regular public newsletter (now carried in the *Watershed Sentinel*), sponsored a conference on sustainable community forestry, conducted numerous public meetings, and written a variety of briefs and papers related to forest use. A member of the Islands Alliance.

Friends of Cortes Island
Box 105
Whaletown, British Columbia
CANADA V0P1Z0
Tel: (604) 935-6992

In a 1990 survey, 75% of Cortes landowners supported a moratorium on clearcutting. This grass-roots citizens group was formed to influence forest and aquaculture management on Cortes Island (located about halfway up the east side of Vancouver Island). They have been negotiating with multinational timber companies and the B.C. Ministry of Forests. Six issues per year of their publication, *Watershed Sentinel*, is available for C$12 in Canada. C$16 international.

Friends of Cortes Island has also produced a set of forestry flyers (December, 1991) which can be used by community forestry organizations as posters or as bulk mail flyers. These are 8.5"x14" two-sided flyers titled, *Logging Without Clearcutting, There's More to the Forest Than the Trees; Natural Regeneration,* and *Selection Logging Speakers' Bureau.* See list later this section.

Denman Island Forestry Committee
Sandy Kennedy
Denman Island, British Columbia
CANADA V0R 1T0
Tel: (604) 335-0400

The Denman Island residents are close to reaching a consensus on forestry practices after two years of discussion. The Forestry Committee also holds educational workshops with knowledgeable local and off-island people.

Galiano Conservancy Association
R.R. 1
Galiano Island, British Columbia
CANADA V0N 1P0
Tel/Fax: (604) 539-2424

"Multinational Timber Company Negotiates with Quadra Island Community Forest Group"

The Quadra Island Forest Resources Committee has agreed to a five-year plan for logging on Quadra Island after two years of negotiations with transnational forest company Fletcher Challenge (FC). FC holds about two-thirds of the island, 17,000 hectares. Fletcher Challenge, is a multinational timber company with its headquarters in New Zealand, where it got its start cutting New Zealand's old-growth.

The agreement allows for FC to harvest 1,140 truckloads of timber annually on the northern third of Quadra, for a total of 300 hectares of clear-cuts in the first five years of the agreement. Clear-cuts in the southern island may be a maximum of 5 hectares, (vs. 35 hectares in the north).

Also logging of several view watersheds will be deferred for twenty years. In the southern part of the island, FC will experiment with different harvesting methods including individual tree selection, two methods of green tree retention harvesting, and European strip harvesting.

Reprinted with permission from The Watershed Sentinel, *Vol. 1 (4), Aug.-Sept. 1991. pp. 5-6.*

Tin-Wis Coalition

c/o Kathryn Cholette
1938 Parker St.
Vancouver, British Columbia
CANADA V5L 2L3
Tel: (604) 253-7628 or 299-9532

The Tin-Wis Coalition is a hopeful sign of community consensus. Created in 1988, the alliance of Native, labour, and environmental organizations formed in response to conflicts about the use of Strathcona Park lands on Vancouver Island.

According to the Tin-Wis Coalition, "Native peoples require control of their lands for their economies and cultures. Workers need to protect the resource bases which sustain their jobs and cultures. Everyone needs to protect global and local ecosystems in order to survive, so that we can have viable economies and culture—today and tomorrow. The focus of the coalition is to promote awareness of each others' interests, and to develop alternatives to existing social structures."

Books on Ecologically-Responsible Forest Use in British Columbia

Community Guide to the Forest: Ecology, Planning and Use

Susan Hammond and Herb Hammond. 1992. Slocan Valley Watershed Alliance, PO Box 139, Winlaw, B.C. VOG 2J0. A fat, 3-ring binder. C$50.

This publication is a major contribution to restoration forestry. It should be in the hands of every serious forester, environmentalist and forest community. The Hammonds have identified and referenced key books and articles on many aspects of restoration forestry. Best of all, Susan Hammond has synthesized the state-of-the-knowledge findings on many aspects of forest ecology with literature reviews on old-growth, mountain pine beetle, root rot, spruce budworm, landscape ecology, biodiversity and so forth. Herb Hammond contributes many articles on community control and silviculture. The Handbook also contains articles by other restoration forestry authors.

This Handbook's extensive writings and reference sections rivals *Restoration Forestry*. It is an excellent complement to *Restoration Forestry* and does an even better job on forest ecology and forest management. Highly recommended!

Cut and Run: The Assault on Canada's Forests

Jamie Swift. 1983. Published by Between the Lines. Distributed by Univ. of Toronto Press, 5201 Dufferin St., Downsiew, Ontario M3H 5G8. Tel: 416-667-7791, or 1-800-565-9523.

This book provides a well-written history of Canadian logging practices.

The Ecoforesters' Way: Oath of Ecologically-Responsible Forest Use

Alan Drengson, Ecoforestry Institute Society, Victoria, B.C. Canada. (Address in B.C. Organizations section).

This Ecoforester's oath is an impressive document which offers much food for thought. The Oath was synthesized by Drengson from the work of deep ecologists Bill Devall, George Sessions and Arne Naess, and restoration foresters Orville Camp, Herb Hammond, Chris Maser, Merv Wilkinson, Gordon Robinson and others. For a copy of the document write Alan Drengson.

Ecoforestry

Ruth Loomis. Reflections Press [see address in *Wildwood* book review].

Ruth Loomis is writing a book on ecoforestry practices and ecoforestry practitioners. Loomis has already authored *Wildwood* with Merv Wilkinson and written the text for the video "Thinking Like a Forest." We can expect her new book will be a good addition to the restoration forestry bookshelf.

"Environmental Health—Democratic Health: An Examination of Proposals for Decentralization of Forest Management in British Columbia"

Duncan Taylor and Jeremy Wilson. *Forest Planning Canada.* Vol. 9 (2).

This paper examines a set of reform proposals which have the potential to bring together those opposed to "business as usual" management of the forests. It considers the idea that the responsibility for forest management should be with local communities.

Forests of British Columbia

Cameron Young. 1985. Whitecap: North Vancouver, B.C.

A well-written book emphasizing the beauty and diversity of the forests of B.C.

Forests—Wild and Managed: Differences and Consequences, Symposium Proceedings

Students of Forestry, UBC, 270-2357 Main Mall, Vancouver, B.C., V6T 1W5. Tel: (604) 228-2727

The Proceedings contain a number of papers pertaining to restoration forestry. Available for $15.

10

Framework for Watershed Stewardship
> Prepared by the Village of Hazelton, 1991. Send $2 to P.O. Box 40, Hazelton, BC. V0J 1Y0.

Seeing the Forest Among the Trees: The Case for Holistic Forest Use
> Herb Hammond. 1992. Polestar Press. 309 pp. C$46.95.

Herb Hammond is one of restoration forestry's most knowledgeable and articulate spokespersons, although Hammond calls it "Holistic Forestry." Seeing the Forest among the Trees is one of restoration forestry's premier textbooks and the most beautifully done. Hundreds of color and B&W photographs and many illustrations make the presentation beautiful as well as educational. The quality makes it a high price tag, but the book is well worth the price.

Includes sections on: what are the forests, how we currently use forests, what are the impacts of traditional use, the politics of forestry, and the solution—holistic forest use.

> "Hammond's work has developed forms of community participation and education; it incorporates and explains conservation biology and landscape ecology to large audiences...Hammond's holistic forestry is especially good for comprehensive zoning of land use patterns which preserve from 25-35 percent of the land base, including all riparian and critical areas. It identifies forest stands in which ecoforestry can be practiced."
>
> —Alan Drengson

Slocan Valley Community Forest Management Project Final Report
> 1975.

This is a unique, comprehensive study of the natural and human resources of the Slocan Valley. The Slocan Valley is one of the first Pacific Northwest communities to put together their own forest plan. (Address in B.C. Environmental section.)

The State of Forestry in Canada
> 1990. Report to parliament by Forestry Canada. Copies available free of charge from Forestry Canada, Corporate and Public Affairs, Ottawa, Ont. K1A 1G5. 80 pp. Tel: (819) 953-2312

You won't find much about restoration forestry in here, but facts, figures, and charts about industrial forestry.

Three Men and A Forester
> Ian Mahood and Ken Drushka. 1990. Harvour Publishing: Madeira Park, British Columbia.

One of B.C.'s top foresters, and a former confidant of H. R. MacMillan, (of MacMillan-Bloedel) gives a biting analysis of forest management gone wrong. Written by a career forester in B.C. forest industry, this book is strong criticism of B.C.'s forest practices. An honest view from inside the forest industry.

Tree Planning—A Guide to Public Involvement in Forest Stewardship
> Joan E. Vance. 1990. Available from: B.C. Public Advocacy Centre, #701-744 W. Hastings St. Vancouver, B.C. V6C 1A5 and the Western Canada Wilderness Committee. 148 pp. $12.00 ppd.

How the public can influence decisions. An invaluable tool for every forest activist in the province and a useful model for elsewhere.

Touch Wood: B.C. Forests at the Crossroads
> Bob Nixon, ed. 1993. Harbour. $16.95 paper.

This collection of essays is a cornerstone in the current round of debate in making forest policy decisions that integrate social, economic, and environmental concerns. Some of the topics are forest ownership, democratic public participation in forest decisions, corporate ownership of forest lands, environmental assessment principles, directions in small-scale forestry, moving toward holistic forest practices, the role of the First Nations in aboriginal forestry, and rhetoric and reality of forest policies.

Wildwood
> Merv Wilkinson and Ruth Loomis. 1990. Reflection :Press, Box 178, Gabriola Island, B.C., Canada V0R 1X0.
> Tel: (604) 247-8685

Not a large book, but a close look at Merv Wilkinson, his silviculture and philosophy. [See Merv Wilkinson review in Forest Models in B.C. and also excerpts from Wildwood in this section].

Videos/Films

"Battle for the Trees"
> Canadian National Film Board.

This film on B.C.'s ancient forests has been shown extensively throughout Europe with rave reviews.

"Ecology and New Forestry" (26 min.)
> Open Learning Agency, P.O. Box 82080, Burnaby, B.C. V5C 6J8. Tel: (604) 431-3000/Fax: (604) 431-3333

"Ecology and Woodlot Management" (26 min.)

"Ecology and Development" (28.5 min.)
> Trevor Chandler, director, 1992. Canadian Ecology Series; Open Learning Agency. British Columbia.

These three videos are directed at educating the general public about ecological forestry.

"Still Life for Woodpecker?"
> Francis Paynter, Producer/ Director. 1992. THA

Media Dist., 100 Homer St., Vancouver, B.C. V6B 2X6. Tel: (800) 661-4919. Available in the U.S. from Bullfrog Films, Oley, PA 19547. Tel: (215) 779-8226

An exceptional film incorporating an ancient native myth that shows the importance of preserving old growth forests by focusing on the pileated woodpecker and its critical role in the ecological chain. The pileated woodpecker plays a role of forest health indicator for eastside PNW forests similar to that of the northern spotted owl in the westside forests. A moving presentation with good messages on forest ecology for children and adults. 28 minutes.

Thinking Like a Forest: A Case for Sustainable Selective Forestry

Seymour Trieger. Available from: All-About-Us, R.R. 3, Ladysmith, B.C., V0R 2E0. Tel: (604) 722-3349

This positive-minded film shows how work in the woods can be done without destroying the forest. It provides teachers with an alternative viewpoint. The film focuses on Merv Wilkinson and his Wildwood Forest. The half-hour video ($35), is accompanied by a "Teacher's Manual" ($5) and the book "Wildwood" ($10). The whole packet is $50. 20% off for environmental organizations.

All-About-Us has plans for seven more films in a series on restoration forestry.

(Also, Sierra Club of Western Canada, and Western Canada Wilderness Committee have both produced videos on B.C.'s forests. See addresses in BC Environmental Organizations section.)

British Columbia Selection Logging Speakers Bureau

The following people are willing to speak to forestry committees and community groups in B.C. Time and fee scheduling are at the speakers' discretion. All speakers require at least a few weeks advance notice. R.P.F. = Registered Professional Forester.

This list was compiled by Friends of Cortes Island and is by no means complete. There are many dedicated people in British Columbia who are qualified and interesting speakers on forestry matters. For future editions contact: Friends of Cortes Island, Box 3333, Manson's Landing B.C., V0P 1K0, CANADA. Tel: (604) 935-6500 or 935- 6992.

Jim Cooperman

RR 1, S 10, C 2
Chase, British Columbia
CANADA VOG IMO
Tel: (604) 679-3693/Fax: (604) 679-8248

Forest policy, planning practices, use of Landsat photos.

Herb Hammond, R.P.F.

Silva Forest Foundation (see address in B.C. Organizations).

Holistic forest use, design of alternative forestry systems, evaluation of conventional timber management plans and practices.

Dave Neads

Box 3419
Anaheim Lake, British Columbia
CANADA V8N 1P2
Tel: (604)742-3222

Community Resource Boards.

Ray Travers, R.P.F.

1790 Carnegie Crescent
Victoria, British Columbia
CANADA V8N 1P2
Tel: (604) 477-8479

Forest policy, forest planning, old growth, forest economics, ecology, history, and community forestry.

Mickey Udal

Site 20 A, R.R. 2,
Gabriola Island, British Columbia
CANADA V0R 1XO
Tel: (604) 247-9657

Selection forest management and logging with horses.

Leonard Vanderstar, R.P.F.

R.R. 2, Site 67, Comp.11
Smithers, British Columbia
CANADA
Tel: (604) 847-9729

Public involvement in resource management planning, policy and legislation, forest ecology, soils and hydrology, fish and wildlife, tourism and recreation.

Lynn Wallace

R.B. 71, R.R. 4
Nanaimo, British Columbia
CANADA
Tel: (604) 722-2460

Reforestation.

Mark Wareing, R.P.F.

c/o Western Canada Wilderness Committee
20 Water St.
Vancouver, British Columbia
CANADA V6B 1A4
Tel: (604) 683-8220

Forest watch workshop, selection logging techniques.

Merv Wilkinson

(see address in B.C. restoration forestry models).

Selection forestry, *Wildwood*, forest management.

10

Conventional Forestry Organizations in Canada

Algonquin Forest Authority

Ontario Ministry of Natural Resources
P.O. Box 1138
Brace Bridge, Ontario
CANADA P1L 1V3
Tel: (705) 645-8747/Fax: (705) 645-7379
Contact: David Dugo

The Ontario Ministry of Natural Resources forestry department in the Algonquin Region forestry department has a reputation for progressive forestry practices (relative to other Ministry departments). They are moving away from highgrading, and towards restoration forestry practices.

Dan Galley has been working with how to regenerate red oak which is becoming scarce due to its poor regeneration in single-tree selection systems. They are experimenting with prescribed underburning in spring to aid red oak regeneration.

Two Districts are now run out of the one office. The Perry Sound District has been working with the uniform shelterwood system. The Brace Bridge District (run out of the same office) has been especially working with eastern white pine regeneration and management.

Association of British Columbia Professional Foresters (ABCPF)

404 789 West Pender St.
Vancouver, British Columbia
CANADA V6H 1H2
Tel: (604) 687-8027/Fax: (604) 687-3264

1993 the ABCPF established a new Code of Ethics. Good stewardship based on sound ecological principles that do not cause environmental damage is the overriding principle. The B.C. Environmental Coalition says it sounds good on paper.

B.C. Forestry Continuing Studies Network

UBC Faculty of forestry
270—2357 Main Mall
Vancouver, British Columbia V6T 1Z4, CANADA
Tel: (604) 822-5874/Fax: (604) 822-3106
Contact: Shirley Sato

The B.C. Forestry Continuing Studies Network (FCS Network) has compiled a Forestry Educational Resource People Database which has over 300 listings. The FCS Network is a non-profit organization that coordinates adult education in sustainable forest resource management. The education resource database includes information about companies and individuals with experience in developing, designing, producing and/or delivering adult forestry education activities.

The FCS Network is an independent, non-profit organization committed to quality adult education in sustainable forest resource management. Their Catalogue of Activities for September 1993-April 1994 was an impressive publication (52 pages) with information on about 150 courses along with contact addresses and phone numbers. The courses are mainly in B.C. but also elsewhere in Canada and the U.S. Most of it is conventional.

British Columbia Forest Service

1450 Government St.
Victoria, British Columbia
CANADA V8W 3E7

Canadian Forestry Service

Pacific & Yukon Region
506 W. Burnside Rd.
Victoria, British Columbia
CANADA V8Z 1M5

Centre de Foresterie des Laurentides

Forets Canada
C.P. 3800
Ste-Foy, Quebec
CANADA G1V 4C7
Tel: (418) 648-3957

CORE—Commission of Resources and the Economy

7th Floor, 1802 Douglas St.
Victoria, British Columbia
CANADA V8V 1X4
Tel: (604) 387-1210/Fax (604) 356-6385

The Commission on Resources and Environment (CORE) is the government's attempt to end confrontation in B.C. forests by asking companies, workers, environmentalists, native people, government officials and others to sit down together and negotiate agreements about land use. CORE does not have much binding power and some environmental groups quit in disgust and protest over the provincial government's decision to log most of Clayaquot sound. Some have since returned. The progress of CORE is well worth watching as a lesson in participatory land use planning on a regional scale.

From Ideas to Action: Monitoring Progress towards Sustainability, a forthcoming publication outlining the progress of CORE so far and assessing the province's progress towards sustainability. For more information phone the Round Table's toll free line 1-800-665-7002.

Forestry Canada

Place Vincent Massey, 351 St. Joseph Blvd.
Hull, Quebec
CANADA K1A 1G4
Tel: (819) 997-1107/Fax (819) 997-8697

Maritimes Forest Research Center

P.O. Box 4000
Frederickton, New Brunswick, E3B 5P7 CANADA
Tel: (506) 452-3175

They publish a newsletter Recent Publications.

Ministry of Forests Research Branch

31 Bastion Square
Victoria, British Columbia
CANADA V8W 3E7

Northern Forestry Center

Forestry Canada
5320 122 St.
Edmonton, Alberta
CANADA T6H 3S5
Tel: (403) 435-7210

Pacific Forestry Center

Forestry Canada
506 West Burnside Road
Victoria, British Columbia
CANADA V8Z 1M5
Tel: (604) 388-0600/Fax (604) 388-0775

A major government forestry research institution.

Model Forest Network

John Hall, Secretary
Forestry Canada—Headquarters
Place Vincent Massey, 351 St. Joseph Blvd.
Hull, Quebec
CANADA K1A 1G5
Tel: (819) 997-1107/Fax: (819 994-7022

Forestry Canada has recently created the Model Forest Program, a five-year, $54 million federal initiative to establish working models of sustainable forestry in each of Canada's 10 major forest regions. These Model Forests are supposedly more ecological and allow for more involvement of local communities. We'll see, but I doubt it will look much like restoration forestry. For one thing, the scale is wrong. The model forests are hundreds of thousands or millions of acres in size and management is heavily dominated by giant timber corporations and Forestry Canada officials.

The initiative is young, however, and should be given the benefit of a doubt. The program might come up with something useful to restoration forestry. I'll guarantee that $54 million spent on subsidizing many, small, private forest models would accomplish a whole lot more.

Conference on Old Growth Forests

A conference held January 20, 1990, which was sponsored by the Faculty of Forestry and the School of Continuing Studies, University of Toronto and the Ontario Ministry of Natural Resources.

Conventional Forestry Journals in Canada

Canadian Journal of Forest Research

National Research Council of Canada
100 Sussex Dr.
Ottawa, Ontario
CANADA K1A 0R6
Tel: (613) 993-2054

Journal available for $98.00/year.

The Forestry Chronicle

Canadian Institute of Forestry
Suite 1005, 151 Slater St.
Ottawa, Ontario
CANADA K2J 1W1

Forestry Forum

Forestry Canada
Place Vincent Massey
351 St. Joseph Blvd.
Hull, Quebec
CANADA K1A 1G4
Tel: (819) 997-1107/Fax: (819) 997-8697

Forestry Newsletter

Great Lakes Forestry Center
P.O. Box 490
1219 Auuen St. E.
Sault St. Marie, Ontario
CANADA P6A 5M7,
Tel: (705) 949-9461

Foret Conservation

915, Blvd. Saint-Cyrille ouest, Bur. 110
Sillery, Quebec, G1S IT8, CANADA
Tel: (418) 681-3588 or (800) 463-4538

Le magazine de la Foret, de L'Environment et des Sciences Naturelles. French language C$2.75 each.

Global Biodiversity

P.O. Box 3443, Station D,
Ottawa, Ontario
K1P 6P4, CANADA

This magazine changed its name from *Canadian Biodiversity* in 1993.

10

The Environmental Movement in British Columbia & Canada: A Resource Guide

RESTORATION FORESTRY is at its infancy in British Columbia. The environmental movement is helping to define what restoration forestry will look like in B.C.'s conditions. Their major concerns now are:

1. wilderness preservation
2. improved forest practices
3. community control
4. watershed protection

Clayoquot Sound

Clayoquot Sound is the last, major, unlogged watershed of western Vancouver Island's lowland coastal temperate rainforest. Clayoquot Sound is one of the most hard-fought battles for old-growth thus far in B.C. The struggle, which has gained international recognition, is still ongoing. A broad-based coalition of activists have been non-violently protesting every day since July 5, 1993 following the decision by the BC government to allow 75% of the remaining temperate rainforest on Clayoquot Sound to be logged. Over 800 concerned citizens have been arrested for blocking logging roads to halt the destruction of Clayoquot Sound. Thousands of people assisted those who did the actual blockade. The civil disobedience and publicity raised public awareness, but did not actually stop business-as-usual logging. The blockade camp was voluntarily closed down in October. It will most likely reconvene in 1994, unless the provincial government finally heeds province-wide and international opinion to stop Clayoquot logging.

Canadian Environmental Directories

British Columbia Environmental Directory
1992 edition is 3rd ed. Available from: British Columbia Environmental Network. $25 + $3 postage.

The most comprehensive B.C. directory with over 100 pages covering over 500 of B.C.'s environmental, peace, native, and labor organizations. Updated annually. Indexed by subject, alphabetical and region. Lists address, phone, persons to contact, purpose and primary activities.

The Canadian Environmental Education Catalogue
The Pembina Institute (address in Canadian environmental organizations). Large format, binder, printed Version $55.00. Computer Version $120.00.

A comprehensive guide to 1600 references, books, periodicals, organizations, videos, etc. Compiled especially for school and community educators, but useful to anyone researching environmental issues. An international guide. About 60% Canadian, 35% USA, and 5% other countries.

The Green List: A Guide To Canadian Environmental Organizations and Agencies
Available from: British Columbia Environmental Network.

It lists 1500 resources around Canada including hundreds of grassroots organizations and persons.

British Columbia Environmental Periodicals

British Columbia Environmental Report
1672 E. 10th Ave.
Vancouver, British Columbia
CANADA V5N 1X5

The quarterly newsletter of the British Columbia Environmental Network offers the best province-wide reporting on forest and environmental issues. Subscriptions are C $15/year in Canada. $20/yr. outside Canada.

The New Catalyst
P.O. Box 189
Gabriola Island, British Columbia
CANADA V0R 1X0
Tel: (604) 247-9737/Fax (604) 247-7471

Since 1985, the New Catalyst has been one of the better bioregional magazines in North America. Often has articles on forestry. Quarterly. Free subscription upon request. They also publish two books a year in their Bioregional Series.

The Trumpeter
P.O. Box 5833, Stn. B.
Victoria, British Columbia
CANADA V8R 6S8

A quarterly, transdisciplinary journal, in its 10th year dedicated to exploration of ecosophy (ecological wisdom and harmony). A journal of "Deep Ecology." I regard it as one of the best sources for the philosophical underpinnings for restoration forestry. Editor, Alan Drengson is a founder of the Ecoforestry Institute of B.C.

Volume 7, No. 2 (Spring 1990), is dedicated to Ecoforestry. Subscriptions are $20 Can/$20 US a year and overseas surface. Back issues are $4.

British Columbia Environmental Organizations

British Columbia Environmental Network (BCEN)
1672 E. 10th Ave.
Vancouver, British Columbia
CANADA V5N 1X5
Tel: (604) 879-2279/Fax (604) 879-2272

BCEN is the major environmental coalition in B.C. The BCEN's participants include approximately 550 environmental organizations, churches, native councils, unions, and professional associations. BCEN facilitates communication and interaction among non-government organizations and individuals who share a concern for the protection and enhancement of the quality of our environment.

British Columbia Environmental Network
Forest Caucus
Jim Cooperman
R.R. #1, Site 10
Chase, British Columbia
VOE 1MO, CANADA
Tel: (604) 679-3693/Fax: (604) 679-8248

B.C. Public Interest Advocacy Center
#701, 744 W. Hasting St.
Vancouver, British Columbia
CANADA V6C 1A5

Canada's Future Forest Alliance
Box 224
New Denver, British Columbia
CANADA V0G 1S0
Tel: (604) 358-2660/Fax: (604) 358-7950

CFFA's Colleen McCrory is a leader in the struggle to save the ancient forests and boreal forests of Canada. CFFA is the Canadian contact point for the international Taiga Rescue Network and also the office for the Valhalla Society.

Canadian Earth Care Society
Box 1810, Stn. A
Kelowna, British Columbia
CANADA V1Y 8P2
Tel: (604) 861-4788
On line modem: (604) 769-5097

Their EarthNet/EEMS system is a computer, database-searching service and environmental networking service. EarthNet has various databases including VISIT (Vendor Information System of Innovative Technology), a database of suppliers of technological solutions to environmental problems.

Carmanah Forestry Society
1131 Richardson St.
Victoria, British Columbia
CANADA V8S 1R1
Tel: (604) 381-1141

Carmanah Forestry Society is a registered society formed in 1990, which has been active in the Walbran and Carmanah Valleys in all aspects of forestry reform including: critiquing logging plans, arranging public meetings, arranging tours, lobbying government, media work, map making, etc. We have built 30 km. of trail in the Walbran and Carmanah Valleys as well as successfully lobbied to have forest set aside in the Nahmint Valley, all of which are on Vancouver Island.

Clearcut Alternatives
RR #2
Galiano Island, British Columbia
CANADA V0N 1P0

Member of the Islands Alliance.

East Cariboo Environmental Group
Richard Case
Box 34
Big Lake Ranch, British Columbia
CANADA V0L 1G0

Addressing forest issues.

East Kootenay Environmental Society (EKES)
Box 8
Kimberley, British Columbia
CANADA V1A 2Y5
Tel/Fax: (604) 427-2535

EKES is a coalition of many small, local groups around the east Kootenays. A beautiful mountainous region in the southeast part of the province, including parts of the Purcells, the Rockies and the Rocky Mountain Trench. EKES has forestry committees which review logging practices in the Kootenays and promote sustainable forestry practices. Monthly newsletter. Membership is $15/year.

10

Friends of Clayoquot Sound
Box 489
Tofino, British Columbia
CANADA VOR 2ZO
Tel: (604) 725-4218

A main force behind the massive logging protests during the summer of 1993 which drew over 8000 people to Clayoquot Sound to help stop the clearcutting. They support a complete moratorium on clearcut logging, native land title struggles, ecological restoration of damaged watersheds and a bioregional vision.

Friends of the Tsitika
479 4th St., 2nd Floor
Courtenay, British Columbia
CANADA V9N 1G9
Tel: (604) 338-9242

The Tsitika is the last major river system on Vancouver Island's east coast which hasn't been damaged by logging or other industrial activity. It drains into Robson Bight, one of the few Orca whale rubbing beaches in Canada.

Grand Forks Watershed Council
P.O. Box 1706
Grand Forks, British Columbia
VOH 1H0, CANADA
Tel: (604) 442-8342

Greenpeace Canada
1726 Commercial Drive
Vancouver, British Columbia
CANADA V5N 4A3
Tel: (604) 253-7701

Sierra Club of Western Canada
620 View St., Rm. 314
Victoria, British Columbia
CANADA V8W 2K1
Tel: (604) 386-5255

Slocan Valley Watershed Alliance
P.O. Box 139
Winlaw, British Columbia
CANADA VOG 2J0

One of the best models in B.C. of a citizen's group articulating a sustainable vision for their West Kootenay watershed. Instrumental is protecting the Valhalla Wilderness. Herb and Susan Hammond live in this watershed and work closely with SVWA.

Tatshenshini Wild
843-810 West Broadway
Vancouver, British Columbia
CANADA V52 4C9

Works to protect North America's wildest rivers—the Tatshenshini and the Alsek. Their larger goal is to protect some 25 million acres of wilderness as part of the largest contiguous wilderness ecosystem of its type in the world. They achieved a major victory in late 1993 when the B.C. provincial government declared the Tatshenshini a protected wilderness over the objections of the mining industry.

Temperate Rainforest Action Coalition
c/o Box 489
Tofino, British Columbia
CANADA VOR 2ZO
Tel: (604) 725-4218

This organization is a coalition of environmental groups, mainly on Vancouver Island.

Temperate Rainforest Education Center
P.O. Box 381
Tofino, British Columbia
CANADA VOR 2ZO
Tel: (604) 725-2001

Their Clayoquot Biosphere project has developed study areas within the Clayoquot Valley.

Three Rivers Environmental Education Society (TREES)
Box 52, Site M, RR #1
Hazelton, British Columbia
CANADA VOJ 1YO

They must be doing a good job, since the town of Hazelton has published a very forward-looking plan for sustainable forest development.

Valhalla Society
(address: c/o Canada's Future Forest Alliance)

During the last 5 years, the Valhalla Society has been working on the development of a comprehensive proposal for completing B.C.'s system of protected park and wilderness areas. The Valhalla proposal calls for the preservation of approximately 14% of the province. They have available an Endangered Wilderness Map and Proposal.

Western Canada Wilderness Committee
20 Water St.
Vancouver, British Columbia
CANADA V6B 1A4
Tel: (604)683-8220/Fax: (604) 683-8229

One of the largest and most effective forest conservation groups in Canada. British Columbia's only province-wide, big-budget wilderness protection group. Famous for its colorful, information packed educational newspapers on selected threatened areas.

WILD Campaign (WCWC)
340 West Cordoba, Suite 710
Vancouver, British Columbia
CANADA V6B 2V3
Tel: (604) 683-1254 or 669-9453

WCWC's international project, the WILD Mapping Project, is an ambitious global campaign to map and protect the earth's remaining wildernesses of which less than 5% are presently protected. WILD has sponsored several international conferences.

Yalakom Ecological Society
Box 486
Lillooet, British Columbia
CANADA V0K 1V0

Publications on Canada's Forests

Brazil of the North: The National and Global Crisis in Canada's Forests
Canada's Future Forest Alliance. 36 pp. $2.00.

A scathing review of Canada's forest practices. Includes articles on the destruction of boreal forests for paper pulp, the problems with pulp mills, the impacts of hydroelectric projects on forests, the use of herbicides in forestry, the elimination of indigenous cultures through forest practices, and more. Covers every province in detail. A very important publication with information on Canada's ecological disasters which will disturb even the most cynical and hardened environmentalist.

Old Growth Temperate Forest on Vancouver Island: A Disappearing Heritage
Available from The Sierra Club of Western Canada (address in B.C. Environmental Organizations).

Canadian Environmental Organizations and Periodicals Outside of B.C.

Alberta Forest Caucus
Bob Cameron and Lorraine Vetch
3743 48th Street
Edmonton, Alberta
CANADA T6L 3T2
Tel: (403) 463-9245

Biosphere
Canadian Wildlife Federation
1673 Carling Ave.
Ottawa, Ontario
CANADA K2A 3Z1

Canadian Environmental Network (CEN)
251 Laurier Ave., Suite 1004
Ottawa, Ontario
CANADA K1P 5S6
Tel: (613) 563-2078/Fax (613) 563-7236

CEN includes regional networks (such as British Columbia Environmental Network) across Canada. As in the USA, Canadian local grassroots forest groups form into regional coalitions and they in turn, link up into national coalitions.

CEN's Forestry Caucus chairperson is Craig Boljkovac, who can be contacted at CEN's office.

Canadian Forest Caucus
Lucie Lavoie and Henri Jacob (Co-Chairpersons)
121 Banning Street
Thunder Bay, Ontario
CANADA P7B 3J1
Tel: (807) 344-2356/Fax: (807) 343-8023

Conservation Council of New Brunswick
Peter Hardie
180 St. John Street
Fredericton, New Brunswick
CANADA E3B 4A9

EarthKeeper: Canada's Environmental Magazine
P.O. Box 1649
Guelph, Ontario
CANADA N1H 6R7
Tel: (519) 763-9357

One year subscription (6 issues) C$24. Scott Black, editor.

Ecology North
Box 2888
Yellowknife, Northwest Territories
CANADA X1A 2R2
Tel: (403) 873-6019

Environmental Coalition of Prince Edward Island (ECOPEI)
Gary Schneider
R.R. #2
Cardigan, Prince Edward Island
CANADA C0A 1G0
Tel: (902) 838-2678

Also:

ECOPEI Forest Committee
Bruno Peripoli
126 Richmond St., Rm. 1
Charlottetown, Prince Edward Island
CANADA CIA 1H9
Tel: (902) 566-4696 or 583-2917

ECOPEI has set up a special "sister relationship" with Jamaica environmentalists. They have found this to be a mutually enriching experience and encourage other environmental groups to link up with counterparts in other parts of the world. Contact ECOPEI for pointers.

Macphail Woods Ecological Forestry Project

Sponsored by the Friends of Macphail and Environmental Coalition of Prince Edward Island, the Macphail Woods Ecological Forestry Project is taking place on a 140-acre property in Orwell. The project combines protection of a natural riparian area, wildlife enhancement, and examples of good forest stewardship.

Federation des Societies de Conservation du Quebec

3700 rue du Campanile
Ste-Foy, Quebec
CANADA G1X 4GB
Tel: (418) 653-1475/Fax: (418) 653-1983

Forests for Tomorrow

355 Lesmill Road
Don Mills, Ontario
CANADA N0B 1B0

A coalition of environmental groups that intervene to ensure the continuing health of forests on crown lands in Ontario.

The Green Web

RR #3, Saltsprings
Pictou County, Nova Scotia
CANADA B0K 1P0
Tel: (902) 925-2514

The Green Web is a small independent research group which serves the needs of the environmental and green movements at local, provincial, national and international levels. Major areas of focus are forestry, sustainable development, pesticides and pulp mills. A literature list of 40 bulletins and other resources can be requested.

Humber Environment Action Group

11 Montgomerie Street
Cornerbrook, Newfoundland, CANADA
Tel: (709) 634-0371/Fax: (709) 753-5768

Northwatch

Box 282
North Bay, Ontario
CANADA P1B 8H2
Tel: (705) 497-0373

A regional coalition concerned with forestry, mining and other natural resource issues. Brennain Lloyd.

Nova Scotia Coalition for Alternatives to Pesticides

Charles Restino
R.R. #1
Baddeck, Nova Scotia
CANADA B0E 1B0
Tel/ Fax: (902) 295-3053

Charles Restino knows of a few, small, private operations which would qualify for restoration forestry models in the Canadian provinces of Nova Scotia and New Brunswick. Nothing he can recommend in government or industry.

The Pembina Institute

P.O. Box 7558
Drayton Valley, Alberta
CANADA T0E 0M0
Tel: (403) 542-6272/Fax (403) 542-6464

Services and publications for Canadian environmentalists. For restoration forestry practices contact Richard Chant. Pembina Institute has worked with Yukon First Nations people to prepare a Community Resource Management Program. For a photocopy of the program report send C$10 to the Pembina Institute: Attn. Richard Chant.

Saskatchewan Forest Conservation Network

c/o PO Box 1372
Saskatoon, Saskatchewan
CANADA S7K 3N9
Tel: (306) 665-1915

TREE/Friends of Nopoming

Box 3125
Winnipeg, Manitoba
CANADA R3C 4E6
Tel: (204) 269-7477/Fax: (204) 261-3767

Tree Watch

Box 77
Ariss, Ontario
CANADA N0B 1B0

A network of people concerned with the death of trees from atmospheric toxins and pollution.

Western Canada Wilderness Committee

Alberta Branch
9526 Jasper Ave. #6
Edmonton, Alberta
CANADA T5H 3V3
Tel: (403) 487-7616

A good source of information on Canada's boreal forests.

Wildlands League

160 Bloor St. E, Suite 1335
Toronto, Ontario
CANADA M4W 1B9
Tel: (416) 324-9760

A chapter of Canadian Parks and Wilderness Society. Tim Gray is their forestry coordinator. Wildlands League has prepared a Citizen's Guide to Timber Management Practices (See Canada Forestry section).

Yukon Conservation Society

Box 4163
Whitehorse, Yukon
CANADA Y1A 3T3
Tel: (403) 668-5678/Fax: (403) 399-4319

Wildwood, A Forest for the Future

Merv Wilkinson

The Seedling

THE NATURAL GROWTH of Wildwood is managed, yet reseeding is left to nature. The planning of parent seed-trees has been a fascinating process. Why have I chosen certain trees for regenerating the land? How did I know it would work? Why not cut the lofty parent trees for their wood products and replant with commercially prepared seedlings? Here I am back to my number one rule: Work with nature! Invariably "nature knows best," and my instinct says nature's ways are vastly superior to human ways. Since I do not clearcut, there is no need for mass replanting. I have staggered my parent trees throughout Wildwood in prime positioning for regeneration. I am managing a forest, not a plantation.

The cones of the evergreens start to dry in the fall and scatter with the equinox winds. Cedar and balsam cones don't open until they have a good frost—then the seeds fly with a little weather vane. After an early snowfall, such prizes may be seen lying on the surface of the snow, food for the hungry birds and chipmunks. A tree 150 feet tall experiencing a 5 to 10 mile per hour wind will seed an area a thousand feet in diameter. A moderate wind of 15 to 20 mph will extend this to half a mile, and a strong wind will double that!

Some of my best trees are parent trees. They are the ones that show strong growth, free of genetic defects with good quality cone production. A tree needs to be observed over several seasons before it is selected, to see that the cones are abundant, well-developed and not misshapen. Undeveloped cones signal that an aging tree has lost vigor. I have chosen the best possible type of each species, located in suitable soil conditions: fir on drier locations and cedar where it's wet and moist.

Trees start naturally by finding their own habitat, doing it very well through a process of elimination. Wind, rainfall and weather help to regulate the growth. There are early signs if the growth of the seedling is not vigorous. Then I step in and manage by eliminating the real "strugglers" or deformed trees.

Natural seedling always takes place under a canopy. The "canopy" is the overhead branches and crowns of the growing trees through which light is filtered. Trees 40 to 50 years old (approximately 75 feet in height) make excellent canopy. To be successful in natural growing, there has to be the correct amount of light. To avoid becoming bushy, the trees need to reach for the light. This encourages long, straight trunks, with healthy crowns and minimum size limbs. A safe rule is half light, or half the light a tree would have standing by itself in the open. This varies according to species.

A good forester manipulates the canopy, opening up and letting light in when necessary. A suppressed tree, one not growing vigorously because of insufficient light, will release (gain a good growing pattern) when sufficient light is returned. There is no reason to remove a "light suppressed" tree, and lose the advantage of its early growth period just before the volume gain. Let the tree "release" by thinning neighboring crowns or selecting the mature trees near it for removal in the rotating cut.

A canopy also protects the seedlings, diffusing heavy snowfalls and hard, early frosts. I know the normal rate of growth for this area and know, by simple observation, whether a tree is suppressed (not enough light) or forced (too much light). Enough light to make the tree grow, enough shade to make it reach for the light, is the rule. This is key to the success in Wildwood's regeneration.

In the case of clearcutting, where there is no canopy at all, seedlings that survive look like Christmas trees. They are bushy and as they get older, crown off too soon. These trees are shorter, with heavy butts, short taper and lots of knots. This kind of growth is for pulp wood, not timber.

A tree that has been transplanted needs eight to ten years to be completely clear of shock. I have seen plantations where the seedlings seemed to have survived the first shock of transplanting, but eight years later the small trees go into another shock which eventually kills them. This is not due to salal or insects, but often because of

10

intolerable light and soil conditions. To show how trees grown under a protective canopy reach for the light, I did an experiment. I grew seedlings on a strip that had been clearcut and other seedlings under canopy adjacent to the clearcut. The seedlings that were protected showed 15 percent more growth, at the same age, over those in the clearcut. It makes one wonder, doesn't it, about our future "forests," plantations, fraught with problems. The idea that regeneration cannot happen under canopy is a total myth perpetuated by those who want all mature trees cut for economic gains. Has nature been wrong for thousands of years by regenerating under the protection of parent trees?

In fact, nature is so determined in her regeneration that trees grow out of stumps and can be manipulated to do so. This is called "coppicing." A tree stump is kept alive by leaving its root system intact in order to produce more trees. A tree is cut high enough to leave intact one or two good limbs, preferably on the north side of the stump. I've seen eight or ten trees produced off the same stump. It is a way of keeping a healthy root producing for many years. If the parent tree is cut at a fairly young age, there is a good growth of branches nearer the ground and each of these branches are trained into trees. The process may be repeated when the tree that had been formed from the original branch is cut, leaving another branch which in turn grows into a tree...and so on. The root system is growing bigger and bigger and enough coppicing is done to take up that energy. I have produced some very high quality Christmas trees coppicing in selected areas.

The best coniferous species for coppicing are balsam, fir and spruce. Hemlock does not seem to respond well and pine is questionable as it reacts quickly to any cut or wound. Coppicing is also very appropriate with deciduous trees. Maple, arbutus, and birch will sprout from the root (another form of coppicing) if the parent tree is felled when the sap is down. I keep the best sprout or two to form the new trees, a marvelous way of utilizing a well-established root. I have an arbutus that I have coppiced three times, each cut is used for choice firewood. Alder is the one deciduous tree that does not respond well to coppicing, but reseeds itself naturally. The diversity of the forest safeguards the future of Wildwood. I see the conifers and deciduous growth above ground contributing to the cycle that happens below ground. Nature equips these trees with the genetic ability to adapt and survive. I am not interested in planting genetically manipulated stock which jeopardizes the resiliency of Wildwood's forest.

Soil: The Real Resource

A forest depends on the quality of its soil. The soil consists of many things: the organic matter and plant nutrients; the sub-soils underneath which provide the trees with anchorage and mineral intake; the bacteria and micro-organisms; the fungi and the bugs and critters that aerate the soil. It is a balanced entity, so that if you destroy that balance, you're going to be in trouble. In assessing Wildwood's soil, I analyzed it for three major factors: texture, drainage and organic material.

There is little likelihood of improving soil by a short process. Chemical fertilizer is only a stimulant at best. It is like a shot in the arm to a drug addict. The effect of chemical fertilizers is very minimal and can have the disastrous result of stimulating a tree, then retarding it. If fertilizing is continued, the soil will be damaged and the result will be poor quality timber. Fertilizer might be used only in very special situations where there is temporary stress on the trees. It will keep them on "hold" during a disruptive project. Even in that case, the value of chemical fertilizer is questionable because the soil can become further damaged by the killing off of micro-organisms.

The size of particles beneath the composting, organic layer gives texture to the soil. The largest particle size is sand, which is gritty; next in size is silt, and then clay. Most species of trees are tolerant of a wide range of soil types. Here are some general observations:

Douglas-fir, pines and cottonwood are most suited to sandy or gravelly soils. True firs, (amabilis, grand, sub-alpine) and cedars love soils with sand and silt.

Spruce is happy with a base of silt and clay mixed.

Hemlock wants a well-drained soil with a top layer of organic matter. Humus is a necessary ingredient of good quality soil, just as it is in a garden. I never discourage "unwanted" species on the land. In fact, contrary to many forester's way of thinking, I don't consider much as unwanted species. Alder, maple or willow add humus, through the annual shedding of leaves. By protecting soil from evaporation, more moisture is saved than the trees use. The willow produces a great deal of compost with the dropping of its leaves. It doesn't suppress the growth of the young evergreens. Its foliage is not dense, nor does it grow very tall.

"Soiling" plants are plants which add nitrogen to the soil, particularly alder and broom. Broom grows on very poor soil converting the nitrogen (which is "fixed" with the help of bacterial action) so that other plants can absorb it, leaving much improved soil.

One notices that bush alder comes back first on many slide areas, holding the soil so that trees have a place to grow. Alder can make a good cover crop, and as a tree it has commercial value. If allowed to become too dense, it can retard the growth of seedlings. Alder, however, dies off quickly. Thinned and spaced, it can provide an ideal protective cover and speed up the growing of the seedlings. The question here is, under that type of management, is the soil ready to bring the conifers to maturity?

With the help of a friend on Saltspring Island who is using alder in a rotation to conifers, I am studying this question.

Leaving biodegradable waste on the forest floor is the most effective way for improving soil. The best biodegradable waste is that which comes from the trees themselves thereby ensuring that nothing is introduced which will upset the ecosystem. Branches, leaves, needles and leg sections should be left to rot. After a cut, I care for the soil by allowing forest litter (branches, unusable parts of the trunk, rotten wood) to go back to the forest floor. Organic material on the surface indicates how quickly decomposition is happening. However, if there is more than 10 cm. of organic materials (often true in swampy sites) tree growth will be slow.

The burning of slash is the worst crime perpetuated against the forest soil. The average soil building rate in North America is one eight of an inch every hundred years. If a man-set fire is burned over this, it destroys the accumulation of many centuries of topsoil. It is the topsoil that grows the trees. The subsoil provides the anchorage. If the topsoil is destroyed by fire or scarifying with heavy equipment, causing erosive water run-off, the potential for growing a new forest is lost. Retrogression then takes place and only the primitive forms of plant life grow, such as mosses and lichens. The damage of man-set fires is very great.

A natural fire, such as one started by lightning, usually happens in a forest that has not been cut. The soil in that forest retains much more moisture than the soil in an area which has been stripped. A wild fire, in a mature forest, is never as devastating to the soils as a fire set in a logging slash. The wild fire will not kill all the main trees. It does kill a lot of the undergrowth, but often only the part above ground. While the bush looks ugly, frequently the root systems are not dead. The fire forms the basis for a terrific downfall of organic substances. With the help of bacterial action still alive in the soil, fallen needles, singed leaves and bushes will rot. This is a platform, a compost, for new seedlings. Because there is the added impetus of potash, phosphorous and nitrogen, and there is still growth to hold the soil, the new seedlings often appear within a year and thrive. People traveling this province have seen the terrible examples of erosion due to careless, thoughtless logging practices. Clearcutting, burning, stripping, and exploitative road-building all contribute to the loss of topsoil by erosion. In order to get the water to percolate instead of running (which carries the topsoil with it), a good forester will have trees and underbrush left, even after he has logged. This is what selective sustainable logging is all about.

Plant and tree roots hold the soil in place by draining it of water. Roots (tubular conductors of water), insects and small animals create pores in the soil which hold air and water. Our current logging practices reduce or remove most of the natural biology of the forest and uses heavy equipment which compacts the soil. Excessive run-off and erosion are the consequences. The roots of plant growth in poorly drained soils, become water-logged, shallow and stunted. Dry, fast draining soils leach out nutrients quickly, also affecting the tree growth.

In working Wildwood's forest, I planned the roads to protect the soil. Road planning is as important to the woodlot as a foundation is to a house. If the roads are well constructed and not over-used, damage is minimal and accessibility a real asset.

Roads are necessary to extract forest products, but if built incorrectly, the drainage and erosion caused by fast-tracking water completely alters the nature of the forest area. For example cedar, which desires a considerable amount of moisture, could find its roots too dry because of altered drainage; Douglas-fir, in the way of a large amount of run-off, could "drown." The combination of clearcutting and road building contribute enormously to the erosion of the soil.

My first task in planning the road network was to do some paperwork, following these guidelines:

1. Make use of old road grades

2. Follow contour lines wherever possible

3. Identify sites for decking (log storage for truck loading

4. Keep curves on minimum grades

5. Avoid areas that may catch and hold water

6. Avoid unstable soil conditions

Selective sustainable forestry results in a tremendous saving in road costs. Due to repeated use of the same roads, the amortization goes down with every cut. By the end of my ninth cut, the 1.25 miles of main lead has cost 29 cents per foot. Future cuts will further reduce this cost.

Since it is unnecessary to bring in large equipment to Wildwood, the dimensions of my roads can be minimal: a 10-12 foot wide main road with good shoulders, an avoidance of sharp curves (each curve needs a 4- or 5-foot clearance back from the road so the end of the logs can swing) and no grades over 10 degrees. Skidder trails, which connect to the main road are only 6 to 7 feet wide. If I ever found an area unsuitable for skidder machinery, I would use horses. They need only a width of 4 to 5 feet, can pull out anything that a small skidder can manage, yet are very maneuverable. There is now a tremendous interest in horse logging which avoids the destruction of heavy machinery.

I have tried to keep my roads to a minimum. I even vary the skidder trails, sometimes letting the ones used in the last cut grow over if the erosion is evident. One can see that selective, sustainable management allows for such variables. A new skidder trail made for another cut is fine if I can utilize the wood that is removed.

In one place on my main road I had to cross a swampy area. I used a method known as "punching." I pushed down into the swamp some junk cedar and ran equipment over to pack it down, then put dirt on top. I have two feet of cedar slabs under the dirt and the road will last for many years as long as the wood stays wet. Punching is very economical. Roads going across muskeg were built this way. Another name for it is "corduroy road." Good roads are built in the spring. By fall everything is settled and packed. A good road grade is not over 10 degrees and slants toward the bank, avoiding valleys or draws by passing the end or mouth of them. Every road made destroys the productivity of that part of the forest, so of course, the less road making the better. A canopy overhead diffuses the rain and protects the surface of the roads. Driving into Wildwood, one feels the protection of the forest which thrives on its natural soil conditions.

The Essential Ingredient

The essential ingredient in effective woodlot management is time—a long-term perspective and a day-to-day participation in a living landscape that evolves over decades and even centuries. Good woodlot management demonstrates viable alternatives to the devastation of the current forestry practices in British Columbia where timber management has been for short term economic benefits based on the dogma of clearcut and replant.

The North American forestry industry, for over half a century, has followed the German approach of using timber as a form of industrial agriculture. This model was fastidious in the cleaning of the forest of all debris. Fallen trees, branches and other residue were carefully removed.

Spindly, suppressed looking trees were thinned out of the stand, the assumption being that these suppressed trees could not be released into a growing pattern. This left evenly-spaced, even-aged reproductively superior trees, a commercial crop which gained height and girth uniformly until it reached the top of the growth curve and became (that unholy term) "decadent." At this point, the timber was cut, like any other agricultural crop, in an intense, clearcut harvest cycle timed to match "ripening." North American industry "improved" German technology by "cleaning up" debris with slash burning which removed the problems of converting waste into useful products.

One of the first things woodlot foresters discovered was that many suppressed trees to respond to release thinning (taking out other growth to let in additional light), perhaps not as quickly as younger trees, but they responded—120 foot trees could be released to gain as much as an inch in girth annually. Conventional thinning practices, which alter the forest environment dramatically by taking out the younger trees and grooming and nurturing only those of the same age category, is based on an incorrect assumption. Many foresters using alternative methods have proven that suppressed, older trees will catch up with their dominant kin, displacing one economic argument for clearcutting and subsequent monocropping.

Slash burning is a further brutalization of forest soil. After clearcutting and slash burning there is no longer a forest, only the skeletal remains of degraded soil unable to support the living, breathing ecosystem of a forest. Alternative woodlot management, as conducted at Wildwood, challenges ingrained ideas. The telescoping of forest productivity into a time frame for boardroom economics is replaced with a continual growing forest. The boardroom's cut and plant mandate is threatening not only the life of our forests, but also our social and economic well-being. Businesses judge success by "net worth." Clearcutting reduces the net worth of a forest to zero. If that forest was old growth, it will be several hundred years at best before the original value can be obtained, several hundred years not considered on the balance sheet of the company boardroom. Alternative woodlot management understands the time-frame of a forest.

…This more sensitive, more sensible forestry, as practiced at Wildwood, will be the forestry of the future, bridging areas that must now be restored to health after being brutalized, and areas of old growth that must remain untouched laboratories for restoration, heritage for all life on this planet. This bridge will involve human activity, forest productivity, and a caring for its life system. The forestry of the future holds the essential ingredients, time and patience with nature's design, a new way of thinking about one of the oldest living species on earth, the tree.

Excerpts from Wildwood. *Written by Merv Wilkinson with Ruth Loomis, 1990. Published by Reflections, Gabriola, B.C. 55 pages. Reprinted with permission.*

PHOTO CREDIT: JEAN STAM

Merv Wilkinson speaking to group

Standards for Ecologically-Responsible Forest Use

Herb Hammond

Silva Forest Foundation
Working to protect, maintain, and restore forests.

Stand Level Standards

The stand level is the scale closest to human scales. Human plans for modification generally focus on the visible stand level, but have effects on both the stand level at invisible or microscopic scales and on landscape levels. Required stand level standards for ecologically responsible forest use include:

1. Protect and maintain composition and structures to support fully functioning forests at all scales. Important forest structures such as large old trees, snags, and large fallen trees are maintained by requiring that a minimum of 20-30% of overstory trees (well distributed spatially and by species) are permitted to grow old and die.

2. Use ecological rotation periods—for example, 150-250+ years.

3. Prohibit clearcutting as currently practiced and utilize ecologically appropriate partial cutting methods that maintain the canopy structure, age distribution, and species mixtures found in healthy, natural forests in a particular ecosystem type.

4. Prohibit slash burning.

5. Maintain/restore fire where necessary for ecosystem functioning.

6. Allow the forest to regenerate trees through seeds from trees in the logged area. Tree planting will generally not be required because a diverse, fully functioning forest is always maintained.

7. Maintain ecological succession to protect biological diversity.
   The practice of "brush" control will be avoided.

8. Prohibit pesticide use.

9. Minimize soil degradation by:
   a) minimizing road impacts (including skid roads) by minimizing width, disruption to drainage, and frequency
   b) avoiding use of roads (including skid roads) wherever possible.

10. Protect water by:
    a) protecting riparian ecosystems
    b) minimizing impacts on drainage patterns
    c) deactivating old roads (including skid roads) to reestablish dispersed water movement patterns

Restoration Standards

As with other forms of ecologically responsible stewardship, we must learn, in the process of restoration, to solve problems with finesse and ingenuity, rather than with force. Soft approaches that protect all the parts of the ecosystem must be used rather than aggressive approaches that label some parts as valuable and other parts as worthless or harmful. Careful restoration includes five important principles:

1. Restore the forest at the stand level while making sure that these activities rebuild landscape connections.

2. Mimic historical ecological processes.

3. Restore whole watersheds/large landscapes.

4. Prepare restoration plans and carry out restoration activities with local people, ideally those who inhabit the forest.

5. Treat the causes of degradation, not just the symptoms.

People experienced in agricultural restoration have found that degrading land use activities have often been designed by specialists and accomplished by powerful technologies, such as large machines and pesticides. In contrast, effective restoration requires all kinds of people with all kinds of skills. People with shovels will be as important as people with machines. Restoration must be more than a swift afterthought or hopeful solution to a single problem, no matter how commendable the impulse.

10

Some of the important activities that might comprise an adequate restoration plan include:

- restoration of soil health, including breaking up compacted soil surfaces
- introducing vegetation to stabilize soil, build soil nutrient levels, and restore water holding capacity
- establishment of natural drainage patterns
- encouragement of natural diversity by reseeding (instead of replanting) naturally occurring tree species
- planting trees and shrubs where required for stabilization and diversification of a degraded forest community
- carefully reintroducing animal and micro-organism species
- restoration of riparian zones by re-establishing streamside vegetation
- stabilizing stream banks and diversifying stream channels by reintroducing large logs (until natural large fallen trees are available)
- careful reintroduction of natural and human-induced fire by limiting the practice of fire suppression to specified areas (near human dwellings and in holistic timber management zones)

Conclusion

Ecologically responsible forest use must begin from the humble understanding that the forest is an interconnected web that focuses on sustaining the whole, not on the production of any one part or commodity. All of the standards summarized in this paper—protecting and maintaining composition, structure, and functioning; respecting biological limits; and limiting the scale of our activities—apply to every kind of human use, whether we are building a wilderness lodge, grazing cattle, or cutting timber. Ecologically responsible practices accept the control of natural processes—nature is at the wheel—and mimic the subtlety, diversity, and unpredictability of natural changes, while using the forest carefully in a variety of ways. Ecologically responsible forest use focuses on what to leave—fully functioning forests—not on what to take.

Of all the components of the forest web, the only one we know to be completely optional is human life. The forest sustains us, we do not sustain the forest.

This piece by Herb Hammond is excerpted from a larger paper published by the Silva Forest Foundation. Reprinted with permission.

Forest Trusts

Citizen Involvement in Forest Stewardship

Tyhson Banighen

Why Forest Stewardship?

THERE IS A BASIC PARADOX inherent in the private ownership of forest resources: If you own the forest, you can exploit it for short term profits; If you don't own the forest, why should you care enough about the forest's future to wisely manage it in the long term?

The concept of forest stewardship is an attempt to bypass this paradox. Forest stewardship is making land use decisions that nurture the health of the natural ecology, while fulfilling the goals of those stewarding the land's resources. The Land Stewardship Trust (LST) model is a legal agreement(s) that ensures that the steward of the forest does not have the ability to exploit the forest resource in a way that will damage the forest ecosystem, yet at the same time the model provides incentives for the steward to act in his own behalf, while simultaneously acting in the best interests of the future forest (Concept adapted from Raphael: 1981, p235).

The Need for a Land Ethic

Aldo Leopold (1987-1948), who was also a professional forester as well as the founder of the Wilderness Society, wrote in 1949:

> There is as yet no ethic dealing with man's relationship to land and the animals and plants which grow upon it...The land relation is still strictly economic, entailing privileges, but no obligations...Obligations have no meaning without conscience, and the problem we face is the extension of the social consciousness from people to land. All ethics so far evolved rest upon a single premise: that the individual is a member of the community of interdependent parts... The land ethic simply enlarges the boundaries of the community to include soils, waters, plants, animals, or collectively: the land.
>
> (Leopold: 1966 p. 239)

It has been forty years since Leopold wrote those words. Now the need for a "land ethic with obligations" is even greater, as we realize there are limits to progress based on our utilitarian ethic of unlimited growth.

Turtle Island Earth Stewards (TIES)

Turtle Island Earth Stewards (TIES) is a non-profit charitable society incorporated in Canada in 1972 and in the U.S.A. in 1982. One of TIES objectives as a society is, "to research, develop and teach stewardship of the land and its resources within an ecological context."

The Implementation of a Land Ethic

In order to implement the concept of stewardship as a "land ethic with obligations, "TIES developed the Land Stewardship Trust (LST) model.

Using the LST model TIES assists citizens and non-profit organizations to place their lands in public trust, or use conservancy and stewardship principles to protect and manage land. Lands presently in LSTs in B.C., Washington, Oregon and California are stewarded by non-profit charitable societies doing a variety of social service and land stewardship activities.

The LST model is now being broadened by TIES to include the stewardship of forests on Cortes and Lasqueti Island, agricultural lands in Armstrong, Black Creek, Cortes Island and the Kettle Valley, an urban community garden in White Rock, and the incorporation of land conservancy and stewardship principles as components of a comprehensive land use plan for Burns Bog. The conservancy principles will protect Burns Bog ecosystem, while the stewardship principles will allow for sustainable development to take place within clearly defined ecological perimeters.

What is a Land Stewardship Trust?

The LST model is a whole systems design approach to land use planning using land conservancy and land stewardship principles. The LST model integrates elements from other land trust models into one comprehensive LST agreement. The various land trust models that LST model integrates are as follows.

Conservation Land Trusts

The conservation land trust creates Nature preserves that protect unique and special ecologies. The Nature Conservancy, Nature Trust and the Ecological Reserve Branch of B.C. specialize in this kind of trust activity to protect endangered species of plant and animal communities. The LST model sets aside ecologically protected areas or buffer zones as part of a comprehensive land use plan.

Community Land Trusts

The Community Land Trust (CST) is a private non-profit corporation created to acquire and hold land for the benefit of a community and provide secure affordable access to land and housing for community residents. In particular, CLTs attempt to meet the needs of residents least served by the prevailing market. CLTs prohibit speculation and absentee ownership of land and housing, promote ecologically sound land use practices and preserve the long-term affordability of housing (ISCE:1988). LSTs have similar goals in providing access to land for those who could not otherwise afford to buy the land, and the implementation of ecologically sound land-use practices is a necessary condition for residency on trusted lands.

Agricultural Land Trusts

An agricultural land trust uses land conservancy techniques, such as conservation easements and estate planning devices to maintain the farm land virtually in its present natural condition and to prevent the decline of agriculture and the family farm. Similarly agricultural lands in a LST are stewarded according to set of clearly defined ecologically sound principles.

Forest Land Trusts

A Forest Land Trust consists of a group of farmers (or land owners) donating the "development rights" of their forested land to a Land Trust and receiving a tax credit for doing so. The farmers (or land owners) would then form a partnership and pool the value of their trees in a long range forestry program managed by the partnership and/or the Land Trust. Such a plan can increase the value of the trees several fold and bring an additional income to farmers and land owners (ISCE:1980). Then LST has similar goals in stewarding forested lands, but in addition the use-rights to forested lands are conditional on the stewards fulfilling a clearly defined set of ecological principles that protect the forest ecosystem.

How the LST Model Differs From Other Land Trust Models

In addition to incorporating aspects of the other Land Trust models, as mentioned, the LST model has the following additional purposes:

To ensure that a whole systems design approach to comprehensive land use planning incorporated the values of ecosystem preservation as well as land stewardship.

To ensure that use-rights to land and its resources are dependent on the application of a stewardship ethic with obligations.

To ensure that the legal framework supports mutually nurturing, long term relationships between people and land so that the stewards can realize their own personal dreams, while at the same time foster a thriving natural ecology.

To provide community control of land and its resources as the basis for community based and ecologically sound, sustainable development.

The LST Model as Applied to Linnaea Farm

Linnaea Farm, a 311 acre farm on Cortes Island B.C. is a good example of how the LST model uniquely blends concepts from the other Land Trust models.

The Conservation Land Trust aspect of Linnaea includes two ecological reserves: one a high bluff and the other forest lands bordering Gunflint Lake, which is a designated volunteer bird sanctuary.

The Community Land Trust aspect allows the members of the community of Linnaea as stewards access the land they could not afford to buy.

The LST aspect insures occupancy of the land by the stewards is dependent on the wise stewardship of the agricultural and forest lands, according to a set of ecological conditions that protects the heart of the farm and its surrounding ecosystem.

At present, TIES as the Land Trust is negotiating a Land Stewardship Trust Agreement (LST Agreement) with the present stewards of Linnaea farm which will include both an Agricultural and forest Management Plan based on sound stewardship principles.

To date TIES has completed a number of LST Agreements with various groups of stewards living on lands placed in trust.

Why Place Lands in Trust?

Because lands in trust cease to be commodities that can be bought and sold for speculative gain, nor encumbered or used in anyway except as outlined in the trust agreement, the value of agricultural or forest land drops and then stabilizes. For example, the value of agricultural or forest land stabilizes because it can no longer be sold for development purposes. Essentially a landowner trades short term speculative gains for long term private and social benefits. These benefits are derived from land conservancy and/or the wise stewardship of resources in perpetuity.

If the owner does not want to give up ownership rights then conservation easements can be placed on the land or the development rights sold, donated, or bequeathed to a Land Trust in order to protect the ecological integrity of the land, or to implement wise stewardship practices. Essentially the main issue is not who owns land and resources, but how the land and its resources are managed ecologically and in a sustainable manner for present and future generations.

Advantages of Using the LST Model

While LSTs provide for local community control over the "ownership rights" to lands and resources by placing them in public trust, the real advantage for the community is to be able to ensure that the "use-rights" to lands and resources are conditional on their wise use. The important issue then is how to implement and monitor a stewardship ethic with obligations at the community level, whether the lands are owned privately, cooperatively, or by the Crown.

For example, both Crown land and lands in trust are held as "commons" for the common good of society. A commons is an economic resource like forest lands that are subject to individual use but not to individual possession.

The essential difference is that Crown lands can suffer resource depletion or degradation degraduation like the forests of B.C.—an eventuality characterized by Hardin (1968) as the "tragedy of the commons," in that ownership by all managed by a distant government can be as indifferent in consequence as no ownership at all. In contrast, lands in a LST are managed locally and are used according to an underlying ethic of responsibility.

The LST Model and Sustainable Development

The goal of a land stewardship ethic is to protect a sustainable ecologic system as the necessary underpinning for both sustainable social systems and sustainable economic development whether at the community, bioregional, provincial, national international or global level.

Sustainable development requires decisions to be made in three areas; biologic, economic, social. For biologic systems the goal of sustainable development is: maintenance of genetic diversity, resilience, and biological productivity through the recognition of ecological thresholds and the need to merge human activities with natural replenishment cycles. For economic systems the goals are: satisfying basic needs,

achievement of equity, and increasing useful goods and services. For social systems the goals are: maintenance of cultural diversity, provision for participation and self-determination, social justice, and institutional adaptability (Barbier: 1987, pp. 101-102).

The World Commission on Environment and Development's 1987 report titled, Our Common Future, defines sustainable development as "development that meets the needs of the present without compromising the ability of future generations to meet their own needs" (WCED: 1987, p. 43).

All development, whether sustainable or not, is dependent on a sustainable ecological system as the necessary underpinning for a sustainable socio-economic system, and if there is not, there will be an inevitable socio-environmental systems crash. While the LST model is designed to protect ecological sustainability and to manage lands and resources held in public trust, the same stewardship principles could be applied, if there were sufficient political will, to manage Crown Lands, or for that matter the Global Commons.

Once the sustainability of the ecological system is protected, then the LST model can be used to operationalize sustainable socio-economic development at the community level by using the principles of Community Economic Development (CED).

The LST Model and Community Economic Development

Local ownership and control is the basis for both LST's and Community Economic Development (CED). The Social Planning and Research Council (SPARC) states:

Community Economic Development is concerned with fostering the social, economic and environmental well-being of communities and regions through initiatives, taken by citizens in collaboration with their governments, community agencies and other public and private organizations, that strengthen local decision-making and self-reliance, cooperative endeavors and broad participation in community affairs (Claque: 1986, p. 6).

According to this definition, CED is sustainable development by and for a local community, and LST is a technique for implementing CED.

For example, when private forest lands are placed into an LST, communities can practice self-governance through forest stewardship that provides for both sustainable CED, and environmentally sound, integrated forest management. Forests managed in trust incorporate the following CED principles, to name a few: local ownership and control of enterprise, local permanent employment creation, worker / employee participation, equality, cooperation, interdependence of economic, social, and environmental factors and opportunities for all citizens to participate fully as contributors and consumers.

How to Place Forest Lands in Trust

There are number of ways in which lands and forests can be placed in trust and / or managed by stewardship principles: by outright purchase, by donation, or by bequests of land, or alternatively by acquiring conservation easements or development natively by acquiring conservation easements or development rights to forests lands either by purchase, donation or bequest. To understand conservation easements, or purchasing development rights, think of owning land as holding a bundle of rights. A landowner can sell or give away the whole bundle, or just one or two of these rights—the right, for example, to manage the timber on the land. To give up certain rights, while retaining most of them, the landowner deeds an easement which may apply to the entire parcel or a portion of it. Exactly what the landowner gives up, and what he or she gets in return, is spelled out in terms of each easement's legal document. By granting conservation easements or development rights forest landowners can be ensured that their forests will be protected and / or wisely stewarded in perpetuity without giving up their ownership rights. Conservation easements can also be tailored to the specific ecological concerns of each land owner.

A community can also use the same principles to obtain the development rights to land and its resources, in order to protect the ecological and scenic integrity of the community and its surrounding environs.

Why Use the LST Model to Manage Land and Resources?

An LST ensures that the use rights to lands and resources are held in public trust and are conditional on the application of a land stewardship ethic, which both protects the ecological integrity of the land and its resources, while allowing stewards to derive income from them.

Stewardship of the Forest

The LST model applied to lands with forests can provide for the preservation and conservation of old-growth forests, as well as the "wise use" of forest resources not just for economic gain but for recreation, education, or spiritual nourishment.

How Does an LST Manage the Forest?

A committee of forester(s) familiar with the principles of holistic forestry would assist the Land Stewardship Trust to draft a set of ecological management principles—sort of an operationalized "land ethic"—that would outline the conditions necessary for forest stewardship and forest harvesting based on the principles of holistic forestry.

The ecological use conditions of the forest would be "site-specific" as to geography, soil type, tree species, rate of growth, etc., and would be designed to ensure the long term viability of the forest ecosystem. Forest companies would submit Five Year Forest-Management Plans to the Forest Land Trust. Each company would outline how they intend to steward the forest in compliance with the ecological conditions placed on the forest lands in trust.

If a forest company's plan is accepted by the LST then a fifteen-year lease is negotiated. The LST's function as lessor is to ensure the Forest Management Plan will guarantee a healthy forest in perpetuity, while the forest company's function, as Lessee or steward, is to manage the forest according to the ecological conditions and the Five Year Forest Management Plan.

As long as the forest company stewards the forests appropriately, then the lease is renewable in its last year for another 15 year period. In this way the forest company has use rights in perpetuity for as long as they meet the ecological conditions of stewardship

How to Create an LST in Managed Forest Lands

TIES works carefully with each community group to design an LST model that fits their particular needs. There are many creative ways in which lands and resources can be placed in trust to be protected, or wisely stewarded— the only limiting factor being what is possible within the present context of Canadian and Provincial law, or U.S. and State law.

Two models have been used so far by TIES to place lands in trust. The first model is that lands, or money to purchase land, are donated to TIES. In this case all donations to TEIS are tax deductible. Tax advantages include the possibility that if the present owner is willing to sell the land at less than the market price, then the difference between the appraised value and the selling price is tax deductible.

The second LST model is that TIES, or another non-profit society, holds a Reversionary Interest (RI) on the land title of the lands placed in trust, while the group of stewards retains actual ownership. The Reversionary Interest consists of a $1.00 option to purchase that can only be exercised by the Reversionary Interest Holder (RIH) if the steward violates the LST agreement, refuses to rectify the situation, and after due process is found to negligible. The stewards are then given thirty days to rectify the situation and if non-compliance still occurs then the Committee would notify the forest company to rectify the situation or the lease would be terminated, and new stewards found.

Why Use the LST Model to Manage Forest Lands?

Using the LST model to manage forested lands has a number of economic, social and political advantages. Economic advantages include: decreased land taxes, economy of scale, Government funding, long term planning, as well as being a technique to apply CED or sustainable development at the local level. Other reasons are political in nature such as community control of resources and being able to set an example to government. Finally, some are social, such as collective ownership of resources or providing right livelihood in the community.

Decreased Taxes

Timber on residentially zoned lands can be costly to the landowners, as Lasqueti Island residents discovered, when they received their 19989-90 tax assessments. The B.C. Assessment Authority added timber values to their previous property values. As a result the land values jumped significantly if the majority of trees on their land were greater than 13 inches in diameter, the minimum size mills accept as merchantable timber (Rusland: 1989 The Parksville-Qualicum Beach News). However, if these timber stands were placed in trust or under conservation easements the lands could be reclassified as Forest Lands, Accordingly to a Port Alberni assessment authority," Forest Land isn't assessed until the timber is cut" (Rusland: 1989 The Parksville-Qualicum Beach News).

Economy of Scale

All the timber on private lands can be stewarded by an LST under one management and harvesting plan. To increase the economy of scale the LST could also apply to manage other timber on Crown Land under a Woodlot License. If sufficient timber is managed by the LST, about 2000 acres, then the economy of scale permits hiring a part—or full-time resident forester to manage the forested lands.

Funding Availability

Individual land owners usually do not have sufficient lands in forests to qualify for funding from the Canadian Forestry Service under the Private Forest Lands Program, whereas the LST as "trustees" of the collective forests lands would qualify.

Forest lands under the direst jurisdiction of Municipal or Regional governments can obtain funding from the Ministry of forestry as part of their Community Forestry Program. There may be ways in which an LST could collaborate with local governments or in the future qualify for these funds.

Long-Term Planning

A LST provides the secure long term land tenure necessary for holistic forestry based on all age management, selective logging and a sustained yield cut, which in turn ensures a permanent forest cover for wildlife and recreational use.

Long term generational planning creates a balance between short term and long term profits, and allows for a steady forest income—profits that stay within the local community—replacing the boom and bust cycles common to clearcut logging practices.

Right Livelihood

Forests in trust provide secure long-term work, a "right livelihood" that promotes a form of living which also enlarges the spirit. Trees planted today become a community forest for tomorrow.

Community Control

When private forest lands are placed in public trust or protected by conservation easements the community begins to gain control over a local resource. Presently there are no controls over how forests are managed or harvested on private land. Usually, developers and logging companies simply clearcut and subdivide.

Community Planning

A considerable amount of community planning is necessary to place forest lands in trust and in the process local citizens will develop a deeper personal relationship with the forest as a complete ecosystem which not only grows timber, but serves the recreational needs of human.

Setting an Example for Government and Industry

By placing forests in trust a strong message is sent to government and the forest industry that the public sector can manage forests in perpetuity, not only ecologically, but economically for the benefit of the whole community. While at the same time as long as the lease agreement is upheld then the integrity of the forest ecosystem as well as the forest company's use rights are protected in perpetuity.

If citizens want to change the way forestry is done in B.C., then a good way to start is to create a local LST as a demonstration forest project that can show citizens, forest companies, and government that there are viable alternatives to clearcutting. In the process the community will become familiar with the long term economics of holistic forestry, and be able to present a strong case to the forest industry and the Government of B.C. that stewardship obligations monitored by local citizens are a prudent way to manage all of B.C.'s forests.

Conclusion

In summary, land trusting techniques and conservation easements are a set of legal tools that can be used by a community in many creative ways to implement sustainable development plans at the community level. The implications of managing forests in trust are economic, social and ecological and could include the following:

- New jobs
- Increased productive use of the forest by polling small tracts of forest land to managed collectively
- Tax incentives for land owners
- Strengthen local economy by increased revenue to land owners and the community
- New possibilities for value added forest products
- Resource profits that are dependent on the wise stewardship of the ecosystem
- Establish Community economic development in the forestry sector by and for local residents—not just for this generation but for future generations
- Create conservation zones or ecological reserves to include old growth forests, wildlife preserves, wildlife corridors, watershed buffer zones, etc.
- Protect the integrity of ecosystems or watersheds
- Maintain a community's ecological integrity through the conservation of wildlife habitants and/or wilderness
- Protect agricultural lands for agricultural purposes
- Provide access to land for low income people, which they can not otherwise afford to buy, in order to establish cooperative community ventures
- Provide for appropriate development by keeping the ecological impact of the development to a minimum.

Ecologically sustainable development at the community level cannot happen overnight as Aldo Leopold said:

"We shall never achieve harmony with land, any more than we shall achieve justice or liberty for people. In these higher aspirations the important thing is not to achieve, but to strive...."

Managing a forest according to the concepts of a LST model is one way of a community can strive towards a "land ethic" or as Aldo Leopold says," yet another search for a durable scale of values"—an environmental ethic that can endure from generation to generation, not to each other, the planet, and to all of life.

For further information or technical advice please contact:

Tyhson Banighen, Executive Director
Turtle Island Earth Stewards
Box 39077 Point Grey RPO
Vancouver, BC
CANADA VGR4P1
Tel: (604) 736-9221/Fax: (604) 736-9218
(604) 432-9473 evenings

References

Barbier, Edward. "The concept of Sustainable Economic Development," *Environmental Conservation*, Vol. 14, no. 2 (Summer 1987), pp. 101-110.

Claque, Michael. *Community Economic Development in British Columbia*. Vancouver: SPARC Status Report IV, August 1986.

Hardin, G., "The Tragedy of the Commons," *Science*, 162, 1968, pp. 1234-1248.

Leopold, Aldo. *A Sand Country Almanac*, New York: Ballantine Books, 1966.

Raphal, Ray. *Tree Talk: The People and Politics of Timber*, Island press, 1981, p. 235.

Rusland, Peter." Lasqueti Feuds Tax," *The Parksville-Qualicum Beach News*, Tues., Apr. 18, 1989.

World Commission on Environment and Development (WCED), Our Common Future, Oxford: Oxford University Press, 1987.

This is the second of a two-article series on Land Trusts; the first article was in the Winter 1990 issue of The Trumpeter. *The second part reprinted here with permission is from* The Trumpeter *7:2, Spring 1990, pp. 80-85.*

11 Native Americans and Forests

11

Native Americans and Forests: A Resource Guide

Native Americans: Gardeners of the Landscape

Message from Walking Buffalo

We were called a lawless people, but we were on pretty good terms with the Great Spirit, creator and ruler of all. You whites assumed we were savages. You didn't understand our prayers. You didn't try to understand. When we sang our praises to the sun or moon or wind, you said we were worshipping idols. Without understanding, you condemned us as lost souls just because our form of worship was different from yours.

We saw the Great Spirit's work in everything: sun, moon, trees, wind and mountains. Sometimes we approached him through these things. Was that so bad? I think we have a true belief in the supreme being, a stronger faith than that of most whites who have called us pagans...living in darkness.

Did you know that trees talk? Well they do. They talk to each other, and they'll talk to you if you listen. Trouble is, white people don't listen. They never learned to listen to the Indians so I don't suppose they'll listen to other voices in nature. But I have learned a lot from trees: sometimes about the weather, sometimes about animals, sometimes about the Great Spirit.

—Walking Buffalo, a Canadian Stoney Indian

Native American Ecosystem Interactions

Michael Pilarski

After 500 years of repression of Native Americans, it is about time that the descendants of the colonists and immigrants take a close look at traditional Native American land management to see what can be learned. To address this issue in Restoration Forestry we include several articles on Native American land management and a bibliography of references. This is the tip of the iceberg. Much of the knowledge is not recorded in writing, but is held in the oral traditions and memories of (mostly) elder Native Americans around Turtle Island.

Integrating a blend of Native American traditional land management practices and modern disciplines such as restoration ecology and permaculture, allows us the insight to work with nature's healing processes to restore ecosystem biodiversity, function and health, while at the same time yielding a stream of products for human use.

Native Americans have a lot to offer in sustainable land management. After all, the Native Americans have at least ten thousand years of experience in managing the American landscape as compared to the several hundreds of years of experience (mostly disastrous) of European settlers and their descendants. In some areas, population densities of Native Americans were historically greater then present-day rural populations, including some parts of California.

Dennis Martinez points out that the Native Americans had no word for wilderness in their vocabulary. To one degree or another, almost all of the North and South American continents had been affected by humans before European arrival. Interventions included: hunting, the use of fire, and the deliberate planting of preferred plant species to increase their abundance and extend their range. Early hunters might have been responsible for the large-scale extinction of megafauna in the America's about 10,000 years ago such as giant sloth, mastodon, saber-tooth tiger, giant beaver and others.

The Use of Fire by Native Americans

Fire was the Native Americans' most effective means of managing ecosystems. Fire was widely employed in the Americas, particularly in its drier climates. It is well-known that many grasslands were fire created and maintained by native peoples. While there is debate on whether Native American management was always favorable or benign to specific ecosystems there is no doubt that when Europeans arrived they found a land rich in soil, clean waters, wildlife and awe-inspiring forests.

Huge portions of the Western States were managed by Native People with fire, particularly the dryer forest zones. Generally fire management created open, park-like forests of large, old trees of thick-barked fire-resistant species such as Ponderosa pine. Few of these forests remain. They have largely been cut over and replaced with agriculture or younger forests with a higher percentage of fire-intolerant species.

The Native peoples generally practiced cool burns set in the early spring or late fall when moisture/humidity conditions largely prevented the outbreak of "hot" stand-destroying fires. These cool burns crept among the big trees. In today's parlance they are also called "underburns." Cool fires do not volatilize as many of the nutrients as "hot" fires. Thus more of the fertility is cycled within the system. Nutrient loss through streamflow is higher in "hot" fires as erosion is often accelerated by the increased amount of bare ground.

Conversely, fires set by miners and settlers during European colonization were often set in the summer when fuel was dry and humidity was low. European settlement in the US was accompanied by a great increase in catastrophic hot fires. Fire suppression policy at the Federal Level, which began in the 1930's within the burnt-over and cut-over forest lands of the USA, has led to a vastly increased threat of catastrophic stand-destroying fires when compared to Native people's fire management. Fire suppression and logging have resulted in large accumulations of fuel in forests which in the past had been used to periodic light burns which did not allow fuel to accumulate.

It may be prudent to begin to practice the Native American methods of fire management in some of our forests.

Traditional Knowledge

Centuries of trial and error taught Native Americans how to harvest sustainably. They were good at it. They would carry seeds, bulbs and plant starts to new locations to expand sources of useful plants. The modern popularization of a wild plant for food, medicinal or ornamental use can result in over-harvesting and its decline or even extinction. A case in point is the decimation of ginseng in the Eastern United States. For this reason regulations are needed on native plant harvesting. A careful study of native peoples harvesting techniques would help to develop non-destructive harvesting practices.

By and large, the early Europeans did not see how much the landscape was a result of human interaction. So, rather then learn from the Natives, the settlers largely ignored the knowledge in front of them, and pursued genocidal policies toward the peoples who were then living in harmony with nature.

In his talk, Martinez emphasized that much of the remaining traditional knowledge held by the elders is within a finger's breadth of being lost. At this juncture in history there are increasing numbers of Native American youth, qualified and willing to receive this knowledge. This transfer is to be encouraged. Native Americans are still being persecuted in many ways by dominant society. It is time for society to give them the respect and the rights they deserve. This includes honoring broken treaties and satisfying land claims.

The practical knowledge and wisdom of indigenous cultures are a source of stability and adaptiveness in the world. There are many reasons to learn from indigenous peoples about how to live from what nature has to provide locally on a renewable basis. It is of utmost import that help be obtained in answering questions such as: What are the uses of each of the plants around us? What is edible, medicinal, or has other uses? There are myriad ways to assist in recording answers to these questions. Oral interviews and videos of knowledgeable native people are two ways to preserve knowledge.

Some Ethical Questions

What is the ethical way to proceed in this 'capturing' of traditional knowledge for possible commercialization? Whose knowledge is it? How is it to be used? Patent rights and reciprocity with regard to traditional peoples knowledge of such things as plant genetics and knowledge is a hot topic in international development circles. What of the rights of Native Americans today? Some may ask if this search for traditional knowledge is just another wave of exploitation and disenfranchisement.

Mechanisms need to be put in place to ensure Native Americans are compensated for their knowledge. Many fortunes have been made based on their knowledge. Seldom have they got anything in return. This includes monetary compensation, but even more important would be respect, greater autonomy and larger land bases.

It is not surprising that some native peoples do not want to talk about their surviving traditional knowledge. This is particularly the case where spiritual practices or sacred plants are involved. After all, it was only in the past several decades that they could practice their religions above-ground. It was illegal for native Americans to practice their own religion in the USA! In the land of religious tolerance?! This is a strong issue for Native Americans and there is a wide range of opinion. Some share knowledge if their trust can be gained. Others feel it is wrong to share spiritual or other traditional knowledge with non-Indians.

How can society enable traditional people's knowledge to be kept alive? It is a difficult task to "rescue" traditional knowledge. Few, if any, of the world's dominant societies allow the indigenous people to live in peace and freedom. From the United States, to Brazil to Indonesia, Thailand, and India, minorities and tribal peoples are economically and militarily oppressed and their forests and traditional ways disrupted. Guatemala, for instance, is infamous for its slaughter of tens of thousands of Mayans in the past two decades. Some people say we have been experiencing World War III, fought against indigenous people on hundreds of fronts around the globe. Indeed, it is but an extension of a war waged for centuries against non-Western cultures.

Just as it is almost certainly futile to keep wild animals from going extinct by keeping them in zoos, it is ethically unsound to keep traditional knowledge alive in books. It has to be part of an alive culture—it has to be lived. Indigenous cultures need our respect and judicious support where they wish. It is we modern people who have to learn to live indigenously and not that indigenous traditional cultures need to become modern. Modern cultures are destroying the Earth, each other and themselves. There is some hope that we can learn how to live more appropriately from traditional cultures. Let us reach out for indigenous knowledge, but in a way that is respectful and with reciprocity and fairness. There are many debts to pay and many wounds to heal.

Just as restoration forestry's best management for many forests is to simply pull out and let nature do her thing, so too should dominant societies pull their tentacles back and let other cultures run themselves.

Ethnobotany

Ethnobotany is the study of aboriginal peoples utilization of plants for food, medicine, tools, trade and other uses. Methods of harvesting, preparation and storage are usually included. Less common but still present to some degree or another in these studies are how different tribes manipulated ecosystems. Taken as a whole, the ethnobotanical studies of Native Americans offer one of the most extensive accounts of Native American land management.

How many ethnobotanical texts have been written? How much traditional knowledge has been lost and never recorded? How many ethnobotanical texts touch on ecosystem management practices?

Native plants can provide a wide range of food as well as many other useful products. In modern-day language these useful plants are called "secondary forest products," timber being considered the primary product. A careful study of ethnobotany can reveal a bountiful livelihood from our wild lands.

The more energy we put into caring for the forests and ecosystems the more they can give us. So-called secondary products and wildcrafting can become primary products in some forests and timber can play a reduced role.

The preceding article is based partially on comments Dennis Martinez made at a workshop on traditional Indian land management.

Dennis Martinez, Native American Restorationist

Dennis Martinez
American Indian Cultural Center
2122 S. Pacific Hwy.
Talent, Oregon 97540
Tel: (503) 535-6031

Dennis Martinez is a West Coast authority on restoration ecology and the regional representative for the Society for Ecosystem Restoration.

See Martinez's article reprinted in Restoration Forestry, "The Sinkyone Intertribal Park Project." A proposal to have part of the Sinkyone region in northern California become a biosphere reserve where traditional land management can be practiced by Native Americans.

Ethnobotany: A Bibliography

California Indian Horticulture: Management and Use of Redbud by the Southern Sierra Miwok
M. Kat Anderson. 1991. Journal of Ethnobiology 11(1):145-157 Summer.

The Desert Smells Like Rain
Gary Nabhan.

Nabhan is one of the most knowledgeable and respected researchers and writers on ethnobotany and native land management in the southwest states and adjacent Mexico. His many books and writings show a good a good grasp of native culture as well as plant lore.

Ethnobotany of Western Washington
Erna Gunther. 1973 revised edition. Univ. of Washington Press: Seattle. 71 pp.

Food Plants of British Columbia Indians
Nancy J. Turner. British Columbia Provincial Museum.
Part 1–Coastal Peoples. Handbook #34. 1975. 264 pp.
Part 2–Interior Peoples. Natural History Handbook #36. 1978. 260 pp.

Nancy Turner is one of the foremost ethnobotanists in British Columbia. She has spent many years working closely with individuals from many tribes in British Columbia. Turner is enabling tribal elders to pass on generations of knowledge to those who are willing to listen. Her work has given her a strong acquaintance with native land management. Both of the above books cover the habitat, distribution, Indian use of hundreds of plants. Good ID guides also with many color and B&W photos and plant descriptions.

Ethnobotany of the Okanagan-Colville Indians of British Columbia and Washington
Nancy Turner, Randy Bouchard, Dorothy I.D. Kennedy. 1980. British Columbia Provincial Museum. Occasional Paper Series No. 21. 179 pp.

The authors worked closely with Okanagan and Colville elders to record the gathering, preparation, storage and other uses of plants. A well-done and thorough guide. Indian names and pronunciations are given and places where the plants were traditionally harvested.

Plants in British Columbian Indian Technology
N. J. Turner. 1979. British Columbia Provincial Museum Handbook No. 38, Victoria, B.C. 304 pp.

Handbook of Indian Foods and Fibers of Arid America
Walter Ebeling. 1986. University of California Press: Berkeley. 971 pp.

The economic botany of prehistoric and historic desert peoples. One of the most ambitious syntheses of western North American ethnobotany texts. Ebeling lists 1,367 species. Coverage varies widely. Some plants have pages devoted to them, others are briefly mentioned. Ebeling's writing is easily understood. 75 pages of references make it one of the more complete bibliographies on the subject.

The book gives many details of Indian cultures and history as well as plant knowledge. The book describes agricultural methods, livestock, and hunting practices. Although there is cursory mention given to land management there is no 'pointed look' at the subject.

Indian Uses of Native Plants
Edith Van Allen Murphey. 1959. Mendocino County Historical Society. 81 pp.

The result of consulting Native Americans around the Great Basin. A cursory treatment.

Lost Crops of the Incas
National Research Council. 1989, 406 pp. $24.95 Available from: agAccess, P.O. Box 2008, Davis, CA 95617.

A fascinating, well researched look at many little-known fruit, tuber, grains, legumes, vegetables and crops domesticated by the indigenous cultures of South and Central America. More than 600 contributors discuss ethnobotany, agronomy, use, and future potential of major and minor crops native to the Andes.

Plants used by the Indians of Mendocino County, California

V. K. Chesnut. 1974. Mendocino County Historical Soc. 127 pp.

Uses of Plants by the Indians of the Missouri River Region
Melvin R. Gilmore. 1977. Univ. of Nebraska Press: Lincoln. 108 pp.

Uses of Plants for the Past 500 Years
Charlotte Erichsen-Brown. 1979. Breezy Creek Press: Box 104, Aurora, Ont. CANADA L4G 3H1. 511 pp.

Erichsen-Brown draws from virtually all the enthnobotanical accounts in eastern Canada and North-eastern United States since European settlement to produce this compilation. She does not synthesize the accounts, but prints them verbatim. Thus the reader has to interpret ancient English language, and take some information with a grain of salt. This is not easy reading nor is it a field guide. Only the serious student of ethnobotany will want to wade through the ages to find the gems of knowledge. Several hundred sources are cited.

Books on Native Use of Fire

Burning Mountain Sides for Better Crops: Aboriginal Landscape Burning in British Columbia
Nancy J. Turner. 30 pages plus appendices.

Ecological Effects and Management Implications of Indian Fires
S. F. Arno. 1985. USDA Forest Service, General Technical Report INT-182: pp. 81-86.

Effect of Natural Fires and Aboriginal burning upon the Forests of the Central Sierra Nevada
R. D. Reynolds. 1959. M.A. Thesis (Unpublished), Univ. of California, Berkeley.

"Fire as the First Great Force Employed by Man"
Omer C. Stewart. In: *Man's Role in Changing the Face of the Earth.* W. L. Thomas, Ed. 1956. University of Chicago Press. pp. 115-133.

Fire in the Boreal Forests
Henry Lewis. Univ. of Alberta Press.

Henry T. Lewis, of the Department of Anthropology , University of Alberta, Canada, is one of North America's authorities on traditional Indian land use management.

"Fire Yards, Fire Corridors and Fire Mosaics: How to Burn a Boreal Forest"
Henry T. Lewis. and T. Ferguson. 1988. *Human Ecology.* 16:57-77.

"The History of Aboriginal Firing"
S. J. Hallam. In: *Fire Ecology and Management in Western Australia Ecosystems.* J. R. Ford (Editor). 1985. WAIT Environmental Studies Group Report No. 14: Perth, W.A. Western Australian Institute of

11

Technology.

"Maskuta: The Ecology of Indian Fires in Northern Alberta"
Henry T. Lewis. 1977. *Western Canadian Journal of Anthropology* 7:15-52.

Patterns of Indian Burning in California: Ecology and Ethnohistory
Henry T. Lewis. 1973. Ballena Press: Ramona, California.

Reconstructing Patterns of Indian Burning in Southwestern Oregon
Henry T. Lewis.

"Strategies of Indian Burning in the Willamette Valley"
R. J. Boyd. 1986. *Canadian Journal of Anthropology* 5:65-86.

"That Place Needs a Good Fire"
Hector Franco. 1993. In: *News from Native California.* Vol. 7, #2, Spring. pps. 17-20.

Excellent article on Natives' interaction with the land. Reprinted in *Restoration Forestry.*

"Why Indians Burned: Specific Versus General Reasons"
Henry T. Lewis. 1985. In: *Proceedings, Symposium and Workshop on Wilderness Fire.* Intermountain Forest and Range Experimental Station, Forestry Service: Missoula, Montana.

Walpole Island

Walpole Island, situated in the province of Ontario in one of the Great Lakes, is one of the few remaining places in North America where native peoples never stopped their traditional grassland burning. In the island's grasslands can be found healthy stands of many of Ontario's endangered plant species.

Books on Indigenous Land Management in North America

For related references see the following section: Books & Articles on Indigenous Land Management in Central America, South America, Asia and Africa.

Aboriginal Resource Use in Canada: Historical and Legal Aspects
Kerry Abel and Jean Friesen, Editors. 1991. University of Manitoba Press. 341 pages.

Ancient Alternatives: Archaeological Solutions to Environmental Problems
M. Leland Stilson. 1986.

American Indian Ecology

D. Hughes. 1983. Texas Western Press: El Paso.

Before the Wilderness: Environmental Management by Native Californians
Thomas K. Blackburn and Kat Anderson, eds. 1993. Ballena Press: 823 Valparaiso Ave., Menlo Park, CA 94025. Tel: (415) 323-9261. $31.50.

This recent book is one of the largest and best compilations of writings on indigenous land management. Californians especially, can learn from this book, but it is fascinating reading for anyone in the western USA, or beyond, who is interested in this subject. It includes articles by Henry T. Lewis and others on native burning, much on managing the environment for food crops such as acorns, pine nuts, and bulbs; basketry, bow staves, and much else. Recommended.

"California Indians and the Environment"
Malcolm Margolin and Jeannine Gendar (Editors). 1992. *News from Native California Special Reports #1:* Vol. 6 No. 2, Spring, 1992. $4.95. See *News from Native California* address in Periodicals this section.

A variety of articles which support the ". . . important realization that the former abundant landscape of California did not exist despite the presence of Indians, but because of them. Far from being passive hunters and gathers, the Indians of California managed the landscape on a grand scale. By burning the land regularly, by the coppicing of basketry plants, by regulating the fishing and hunting resources, Indians altered the California landscape profoundly. And by altering it they made it more productive, more fertile."

Changes In The Land: Indians, Colonists, and the Ecology of New England
William Cronon. 1983. Putnam. $9.95/ 241 pp.

A comparison of how New England Indians and early English colonists used the land.

"Gift of our Ancestors"
A video documentary
Available from Video Landscape, 307 Mead Street, Ashland, Oregon 97520. 30 minutes.
$20 + shipping.

Agnes Baker 'Tao-Why-Wee' Pilgrim and other traditional native people living in the Rogue River Valley of Southern Oregon are the subject of a video documentary "Gift of our Ancestors." Agnes Pilgrim is the granddaughter of Chief George Harney, the last chief before the Takelma Tribe were either forced from their land or killed in the late 1860's. Agnes is an articulate, powerful speaker. Her messages and prayers come from the heart to the Great Spirit. Agnes Pilgrim symbolizes the revival of the Native Spirit on the land. This moving presentation gives us a glimpse of the life of past and present Native Americans.

In the Absence of the Sacred: The Failure of Technology and the Survival of the Indian Nations
Jerry Mander. 1991. $25.00. 446 pp.

A very perceptive book of two world views in conflict. The technological world is failing and it is time that we listened to the native peoples of the planet for world views that will enable us to find our way back from the brink. Manders' country-by-country overview of the indigenous peoples situation is one of the best global overviews inside of one book cover.

Indigenous Peoples and Tropical Forests: Models of Land Use and Management from Latin America
Jason W. Clay. 1988. Cultural Survival: Cambridge, MA. $8.00. 116 pp.

This book summarizes the research undertaken to date on activities used by indigenous peoples to sustain their populations and the environment: gathering forest products, hunting, aquaculture, shifting agriculture, permanent agriculture, and upgrading of the natural resource base. Although this slim volume can only scratch the surface, it is a welcome general overview. It includes a bibliography of more than 400 works on resource management in tropical forests.

Love, Justice, Truth, Spirituality: Indigenous Women of North America
Common Ground, 1017 Abington Pike, Richmond, IN 47374. $7.

North American indigenous women's views on seeing beyond domination and resistance.

Manitoba Studies In Native History VI Aboriginal Resource Use in Canada: Historical and Legal Aspects
Kerry Abel and Jean Friesen, eds. 1991. University of Manitoba Press: Winnipeg, Manitoba, CANADA R3T 2N2.

Resource Managers: North American and Australian Hunter-Gatherers
N. M. Williams and Eugene S. Hunn, eds. 1980, Australian Institute of Aboriginal Studies. PO Box 553, Canberra, ACT 2601, Australia. Published by Westview Press in the USA. Boulder, Colorado. AAAS Selected Symposium #67.

Knowledge of aboriginal burning practices benefits from international exchange. This book reflects some noteworthy cooperation between researchers in Australia and the Western USA.

Shadows of Our Ancestors
Jerry Gorsline.

The chapter entitled "Cultural Transformation in Sequim Prairies" gives an account of the traditional ecosystem management practices of the Native peoples of the Sequim area (in northeast Olympic Peninsula), and the sequence of changes after white settlement.

To the American Indian. Reminiscences of a Yurok Woman
First published in 1916 and published in 1991 by Heyday Books, P.O. Box 9145, Berkeley, CA 94709. Available for $12.95 postpaid.

Native management in the Klamath region including their use of fires. Also discusses taboos and penalties for harming food resources such as pine seed crop trees.

Wisdom of the Elders
David Suzuki and Peter Knudtson. 1992. Bantam Books: NY.

Wisdom of the Elders is organized mainly as a series of vignettes, short insights into the minds and life ways of a number of different indigenous or "first people." Cultures from Asia, Australia, Africa, and North and South America are explored.

11

Indigenous Forest People: A Resource Guide

Indigenous People—A Definition

...a cultural group in an ecological area that developed a successful subsistence base from the natural resources available in that area.

—Kuhnlein and Turner, 1991

THE REMOTE PLACES where the world's old-growth forests still survive are often places where tribal cultures still survive. The fight for tribal peoples' survival has become increasingly linked with the battle for the world's most intact forests. Forest dwelling people in Malaysia, India, Brazil and British Columbia have much in common as they face dominant societies' liquidation of their forests and ways of life. Even the creation of National Parks or biological reserves often results in the relocation of the tribal peoples living there. Much better are plans for Biosphere Reserves in which indigenous people are allowed to continue traditional activities and their way of life.

There are between 300,000,000 and 500,000,000 indigenous people in the world, depending on various people's definitions. Just about anywhere you go, you will find these people discriminated against and the object of racism. Most are poor in material possessions. At the same time we generally find a richness in spirit, strong family and community ties, cooperation, humor and laughter. The knowledge and wisdom of tribal people is of great value at this time as we strive to extricate ourselves from our world wide dilemmas and crises.

There is an international resurgence of support for tribal peoples, but unfortunately the positions of most tribal peoples is still precarious at best. In many countries (including the United State), they are still being subjected to murder, torture, hunger and repression.

The voices of traditional people have been getting stronger in spite of this, or perhaps because of it. The tribal peoples of the world are forging stronger and more vocal coalitions within countries, continents and internationally. They are aided by progressive people from 'overdeveloped' countries and by worldwide communication networks.

As well as erosion of seed genetic stock, erosion of soil, and depletion of forests, the world is also seeing the erosion of knowledge of traditional land-management systems worked out over hundreds and thousands of years by indigenous peoples around the world.

The study of indigenous agricultural systems and hunter/gatherer ways is a hot topic these days. More and more people are beginning to realize the immense value of this traditional knowledge. Unfortunately, not all of this interest is enlightened beneficence. Multi-national companies have sent out agents over the past three decades to the far corners of the world to collect germplasm for large seed banks in industrialized countries. Now they are turning their attention to farming systems. What kind of ethics is it for the overdeveloped world to catalog these traditional farming methods while continuing the policies of consumption and exploitation that condemn the indigenous peoples of the world to impoverishment, disenfranchisement and genocide?

It is time that humanity take a stand against injustice, oppression, war, racism, hatred, bigotism, and apathy. It is time to choose a path of love, cooperation, friendship, tolerance, compassion, service, and self-reliance. Time to choose an environmentally-friendly lifestyle. Time to honor and respect indigenous peoples.

Indigenous People's Gatherings

Over a thousand Indians from many tribes of the Bolivian Amazon marched 650 km to La Paz in summer 1990 to protest the destruction of their forest homes. Their cause generated a huge groundswell of public sympathy. Faced with this level of popular support the government had no choice but to negotiate, and in a series of Presidential decrees, the government recognized all the three areas in question. As is so often the case, however, the recognition of their rights on paper has not been applied on the ground.

The First Continental Encounter of Indigenous Nations and Organizations

On July 17-21, 1990, nearly 400 Indian people representing 120 nations, tribes and organizations of the Western hemisphere met for the first time in Quito, Ecuador to discuss their peoples' struggles for self-determination and strategize for a unified response to the 1992 Jubilee celebrations. A detailed outline of the Encounter can be obtained from: SAIIC [see address in this section].

The indigenous peoples marched on Quito to demand sacred land rights for Ecuador's Indian people. The well-publicized march engendered so much support nationally and internationally that Ecuador's President came out to welcome them and acquiesce to many of their demands. It remains to be seen how much will result later on, but the gathering and march definitely helped the cause of the Ecuadorian Indians and the cause of Indian land rights elsewhere in the Amazon basin.

Their declaration included:

> Despite the offensive denial of truth in the official histories, we choose instead to use this symbolic date to reflect upon what the invasion has meant to us, to work with a renewed effort for our autonomy, to educate the people of the world, to celebrate that we are still here and our cultures are still alive thanks to 500 years of resisting, and to formulate alternatives for a better life, in harmony with Mother Earth.

The Second Continental Encounter of Indigenous Nations and Organizations, 8th to the 13th of October, 1993

A significant step towards the search for unity amongst Indigenous peoples—a unity which respects our diversity—is manifested in the many representative organizations which have been created on regional and national levels, organizations that seek to affirm our mutual solidarity and strengthen our common positions. Many of us share the vision of a strong movement of Indigenous Unity on a Continental level. The formation of the Continental Commission of Indigenous nations and Organizations (CONIC) can be an instrument for developing and strengthening that unity.

The First National Encounter of Indigenous Women of Bolivia

Held from June 21-23, 1993 in Tiwanaku.

This encounter was the culmination of two years of grass roots community organizing by Bolivian women. The Coordinating Commission of Indigenous Women of Bolivia is a member of the Coordinating Commission of Women of South and Meso America and of CONIC. For more information contact:

Coordinadora de Mujeres Indigenas de Bolivia
Casilla 2315
La Paz, BOLIVIA
Tel: (592)(2) 36 99 63/Fax: (592)(2) 39 13 65

The World Conference of the Indigenous and Tribal Peoples of Tropical Forests

Held in Malaysia in February, 1993. The second meeting is expected to take place in May, possibly in Peru.

The Third Inter-American Indigenous Congress on the Environment and Economic Development

Held September 25-19, 1993 in Vancouver, British Columbia, Canada and attended by delegates from North, Central, and South America.

The conference was organized, in part, by the British Columbia Aboriginal Forestry Association. Contact Alex Hamer: Tel: (604) 769-4433/ Fax: (604) 769-4866.

Directories/Resources to Indigenous Peoples

Amazonia: Voices from the Rainforest

Rainforest Action Network (RAN) and Amazonia Film Project. 1990. Available in Spanish or English for $8.50 plus $1.75 shipping. Order from RAN.

A resource and action guide, sponsored by SAIIC and the International Rivers Network with a comprehensive listing of international rainforest and Amazonian Indian organizations.

SAIIC 1992 International Directory and Resource Guide

(for address see SAIIC in organizations)

An annotated directory of over 600 international organizations who participated in 500 Years of Resistance projects. Includes declarations from Indigenous conferences and organizations and information on curriculum resources, speakers bureaus, computer networks, audio-visual resources and printed resources. $10 plus $1.75 shipping.

Indigenous Peoples' Organizations

These organizations were selected with an eye towards those who are Indigenous rights activists and/or protecting and restoring Mother Earth. They range in size from local tribal organizations to national and international coalitions of indigenous peoples. Also are included some indigenous people's support organizations.

See also the Resource Guides to Central and South America, Asia/Pacific and Africa for additional resources covering indigenous peoples in those parts of the world.

Alliance for Cultural Democracy

P.O. Box 7591
Minneapolis, Minnesota 55407 USA
Tel: (612) 724-6795

11

A networking group working on indigenous cultural issues. Have a newsletter called Huracan.

Aukin Wallamapu Ngulam (The Council of All Land)
Casilla 448
Temuco, CHILE
Fax: (56) (45) 21 30 64

CIKARD: Center for Indigenous Knowledge for Agriculture and Rural Development
318B Curtis Hall
Iowa State University
Ames, Iowa 50011

Traditional land management, ancient crops, swidden agriculture, and hunter gatherers are the subject of increased study by NGOs and academia. CIKARD is a primary network in this international effort. CIKARD published a newsletter for several years which was one of the best early newsletters in the subject. CIKARD publishes books and monographs and maintains a collection of documents on indigenous knowledge. They have been hampered by lack of funding and in 1992, transferred most of their functions to CIRAN in The Netherlands (see review this section).

COICA (Coordinating Body for the Indigenous Peoples' Organizations of the Amazon Basin)
Calle Alemania No. 832 y
Av. Mariana de Jesus
Casilla Postal 17-21-7531
Quito, ECUADOR
Tel/Fax: 553 297

CONAIE
Casilla Postal No. 92-C, Sucursal 15,
Los Granados 2553 y de Diciembre (Batan),
Quito, ECUADOR

National Confederation of Indigenous of Ecuador. This is the South American contact for information in Spanish.

Cultural Conservancy
P.O. Box 5124
Mill Valley, California 94942
Tel: (415) 491-1948

A native organization working to preserve traditional cultures. They attempt to save land through acquisition, cultural conservation easements or land trusts.

Honey Bee
Professor Anil K. Gupta, Honey Bee Center for Management in Agriculture
Indian Institute of Management
Ahmedabad-380 015
INDIA
Fax: +91-272-427896/e-mail: anilg@iimahd.ernet.in.

Honey Bee is not about beekeeping. *Honey Bee* is a global network for documenting, testing and exchanging information about indigenous ecological and technological innovation. A crucial aspect of the network is that it and its members are accountable to the people whose knowledge can provide sustainable alternatives for future agriculture. The membership fee is $30.00 for people from the developed world and from NGO's supported by foreign donors. People from developing countries may contribute in kind, i.e. with material describing local innovations or by sending their own publications on an exchange basis.

Indian Liberation Movement
Lil'Wat Nation
P.O. Box 155
Mt. Currie, British Columbia
CANADA V0N 2K0
Tel: (604) 894-6635/Fax: (604) 498-6846

The Indian Liberation Movement hosted the "First World Eco-development Congress: Indigenous Development Now 93-1." This Congress took place July 24 to August 1, 1993 to support the social and economic advancement of the Lil'Wat Indian Nation and to discuss and learn about eco-development which is defined as that which "respects cultural and environmental heritage and sustains quality family life." Native leaders from Hawaii, Fiji and Pueblos of the Southwestern US also participated.

Indigenous People's Center for Documentation, Research and Information
Case Postale 101
CH-1211 Geneva, SWITZERLAND
Fax: 41-22 735-4047

Provides technical assistance to indigenous delegates to UN forums in order to help them defend their rights without intermediaries. Their newsletter, *Update*, is available free to indigenous organizations.

Indigenous People's Support Network
356 Queens Ave.
London, Ontario
CANADA N6B 1X6

They co-published with OXFAM-Canada a book with an overview of major indigenous struggles in the Americas: *1992 and Beyond: An Indigenous Activists Resource Kit.* $20.

Indigenous Women's Network
Winona La Duke
P.O. Box 174
Lake Elmo, Minnesota 55042
Tel: (612) 777-3629

A group of indigenous women from around the world who are working to strengthen their communities and introduce some of the knowledge and wisdom from their ancient traditions into the larger culture.

The International Indian Press Agency (AIPIN)

Calle Madero 67-611
Colonia Centro Mexico
Mexico, DF 06000, MEXICO
Tel: 576-50-99/Fax: 761-85-73

AIPIN is the first continental attempt to present an accurate image of Indigenous people and to professionally report on the Indigenous issues from an Indigenous perspective. AIPIN is now inviting open participation of Indigenous people who have been practicing journalism in various media: radio, video, newspaper, electronic mail.

International Indian Treaty Council

710 Clayton St. #1
San Francisco, California 94117
Tel: (415) 5466-0442

They network with the indigenous peoples from Alaska to Central and South America, the Caribbean and the Pacific Islands. Their newsletter *Treaty Council News*, is $15 per year.

Inter-Tribal Sinkyone Wilderness Council

190 Ford Rd. #333
Ukiah, California 95482
Tel: (707) 485-8744

The InterTribal Sinkyone Wilderness Council is a nonprofit consortium of ten federally-recognized California Indian Tribes in the historic process of establishing the nation's first InterTribal Wilderness park area, to be located within the aboriginal Sinkyone homelands of northwest Mendocino county. The InterTribal Park will re-establish the model of sustainable land stewardship guided by the Native American land ethic, and will be open to the public.

Our work has successfully concentrated upon education, cultural preservation, bioregional restoration, forestland watershed rehabilitation, and the establishment of an appropriate level of economy for our diverse community.

Innu Nation

P.O. Box 119
Sheshatshiu, Labrador, Newfoundland
CANADA A0P 1M0
Tel: (709) 497-8390

Instituto Qheshwa "Jujuymanta"

Alvear 966, Local 6
Codiga Postal 4600
San Salvador de Jujuy, ARGENTINA

Mother Earth Healing Society

8631-109 Street, Suite 211
Edmonton, Alberta
CANADA T6G 1EB
Tel: (403) 439-6132

Native Americans for a Clean Environment

P.O. Box 1671
Tahlequah, Oklahoma 74465
Tel: (918) 458-4322

Nucleo di Cultura Indigena

PRACA—Doutor Enio Arbato
S; N
Dairro do Caxingui 05517, South Sao Paulo, SP,
BRASIL
Tel: 55-11-813 1754/Fax 55-11-211-9996

Address for Ailton Krenak, Director of Union of Indigenous Nations.

People of the Land Gathering

David Lujan or Laurie Weahkee
P.O. Box 40182
Albuquerque, New Mexico 87196-0182
Tel: (505) 256-0097

An association of over 50 land-based groups and communities from the Four Corner states of New Mexico, Colorado, Arizona, and Utah. The Association reflects the multi-ethnic mix of the border area. An ecotone between cultures.

Pikuni Traditionalists Association

Box 611
Browning, Montana 59417
Tel: (406) 338-5801

PTA is an organization of traditional Blackfeet (Pikuni) spiritual leaders, formed as an official group in 1986.

Currently, they are trying to protect the Badger-Two Medicine area of the Rockies Front Range, bordering their reservation, which is threatened by USA Forest Service plans for extensive road building and oil and gas development. They seek your help.

SAIIC (South and Meso American Indian Information Center)

P.O. Box 28703
Oakland, California 94604
Tel: (510) 834-4263/Fax: (510) 834-4264
Peacenet E-mail: saiic@igc.org.

SAIIC serves as a liaison between Indigenous people of the South and North, and educates the general public about what the past 500 years have meant to Indigenous people and their strategies for change. They publish an excellent newsletter, resource guides, and sell books.

Saskatoon Indigenous Coalition
824 Broadway Avenue
Saskatoon, Saskatchewan
CANADA S7N 1B6
Tel: (306) 665-5962/Fax: (306) 933-4346

Shuswap Environmental Action Society
Box 1021
Salmon Arm, British Columbia
CANADA V1E 4P2

Survival International
310 Edgeware Rd.
London, W2 1DY
UNITED KINGDOM
Tel: (071) 723-5535/Fax: (071) 723-4059

A worldwide movement to support tribal peoples, SI stands for their right to decide their own future and helps them protect their lands, environment and way of life. They publish many bulletins and a newsletter, *Survival*. Today, it is one of the largest and most effective organizations of its kind.

Indigenous People's Periodicals

Agriculture and Human Values Journal
Agriculture and Human Value Society
1001 McCarty Hall
University of Florida
Gainesville, Florida 32611

Although the journal focuses on agriculture, it is a good source of information on indigenous people's relationships with the forests and ecosystems. The Summer, 1989 (Vol. VI #3) issue's focus was "Building on Local Agricultural Knowledge". The ten articles comprise an excellent treatment of the subject. Each article is well referenced. Subscriptions are $20/students, $25/individuals, $35/institutions. Back issues $7/copy.

Akwesasne Notes
Box 196, Mohawk Nation
Rooseveltown, New York 13655

Mohawk and national Native American news. One of the longest running, radical Indian magazines (over 20 years). 6 issues/yr. $15/yr.

Akwe:kon Journal
300 Caldwell Hall
Cornell University
Ithaca, New York 14853
Tel: (607) 255-1923

A scholarly quarterly about Native Americans by Native Americans. Formerly the *Northeast Indian Quarterly*. The Summer 1992 issue, "Indigenous Economics: Toward a Natural World Order," is on the impact of indigenous knowledge on economic development and environmen-

tal protection. $12.

The Calling—Women of Spirit
c/o Janet Cutting
410 W. 24th St.—PHA
New York, New York 10011 USA

The journal of a Global Women's Network. Each edition is produced from a different place in the world. the Winter 1992 edition was produced in Costa Rica at the Global Women's Center.

Common Ground
1017 Abington Pike
Richmond, Indiana 47374

Lilith Quinlan, editor. An annual grassroots women's journal on peace, justice, women, Native Peoples, and spirituality.

Common Property Resource Digest
1994 Buford Avenue
St. Paul, Minnesota 55108
Tel: (612) 625-7019/Fax: (612) 625-6245

This newsletter covers management of common property, especially in Africa and Latin America. Forests, fisheries, grazing. Subscriptions: $20.00/yr.; income below $15,000: $5.00/yr. Six issues/yr.

Cultural Survival Quarterly
53-A Church St.
Cambridge, Massachusetts 02138 USA
Tel: (617) 495-2562/Fax: 495-1396

This quarterly gives the most consistent in-depth news and analysis of indigenous people around the world. Frequent articles about ecotourism and other development projects as they affect native peoples. The Spring 1993 issue focuses on Indigenous people and the forests of the Americas, including a good resource directory to Indigenous forestry organizations. Sub: US$45/yr.; back issues US$5.

Etnoecologica
Apdo. 41-H, Sta. Ma.
Guido Morelia, Michoacan 58090
MEXICO

A new periodical addressing issues of ethnoecology and the conservation of diversity. Includes discussion among scientists, environmentalists and indigenous peoples on the status and perspectives of the conservation of biological and cultural diversity and intellectual property rights. Articles are in Spanish and English. $30 for US subscribers.

Fourth World Bulletin
Fourth World Center for the Study of Indigenous Law and Politics
Dept. of Political Science, CU—Denver

Campus Box 190, P.O. Box 173364
Denver, Colorado 80217-3364
Tel: (303) 556-2850/Fax: (303) 556-4822

The *Bulletin*, published three times a year disseminates news and analysis of the legal and political affairs of indigenous peoples.

Indian Rights + Human Rights

Indian Law Resource Center
601 E St. SE
Washington, DC 20003
Tel: (202) 547-2800

A new quarterly publication concerned with legal efforts to protect indigenous rights and resources around the world. Free subscription.

Indigenous Woman

See Indigenous Women's Network for address

News, issues and voice of indigenous women in the Americas and the Pacific. Two issues/yr. $10.

New World Times

625 Ashbury Street #14
San Francisco, California 94117
Tel: (415) 864-0487/Fax: (415) 864-0455
$10.00/6 issues/yr.

Perspectives from North American Indians. Some of the most perceptive and progressive solutions to world problems are being proposed by grass-roots people from Third World countries. *New World Times* is another demonstration that North American Indians, as part of the Third World, have very useful ideas for all people to consider.

News from Native California

P.O. Box 9145
Berkeley, California 94709
Tel: (510) 549-3564/Fax: (510) 549-1889

A quality journal with an inside view of the California Indian World. It frequently features articles on native land management, restoration, and land use. $17.50/yr. Single copies $4.50. Foreign rates $27/yr.

Turtle Quarterly

Friends of Turtle Island
25 Rainbow Blvd. S.
Niagara, New York 14303

U.N.P.O. News

Postbox 85878
2508 CN, The Hague
NETHERLANDS

A new quarterly publication of the Unrepresented Nations and People Organization. $30 a year. The US address is Friends of UNPO, 347 Dolores St., Suite 206, San Francisco, CA 94110.

Books on Indigenous Land Management

For related references see the previous section: Books & Articles on Indigenous Land Management in North America.

Analysis and Typology of Indigenous Forest Management in Humid Tropics of Asia

Dr. L.H.M. Umans. Werkdocument IKC/NBLF nr. 26

This study contains a general overview and analysis of existing knowledge on indigenous forest management in humid Asia. For further information contact: Foundation BOS, The Netherlands.

Ancient Futures: Learning from Ladakh

Helena Norberg-Hodge. Rider Press.

A classic example of a society that really worked, ecologically and socially, and how it was changed by "development." Also available as a video.

An Emergency Call to Action for the Forests, Their Peoples and Life on Earth

Declaration of the World Rainforest Movement
Penang, Malaysia, April 17, 1989.

The statement drafted by participants of the World Rainforest Movement Meeting in Penang, Malaysia is a clear message from indigenous people for saving the forests. Available from: World Rainforest Movement, 87 Cantonment Rd., Penang, MALAYSIA.

Ethics of Environment and Development. Global Challenge: International Response

J. Ronald Engel and Joan Gibb Engel, Editors. Univ. of Ariz. Press. $14.95.

A treatise on applying traditional, indigenous environmental ethics in today's world. Learning from Pre-invasion land ethics.

The Gaia Atlas of 1st Peoples: A Future for the Indigenous World

Julian Burger. 1990. Robertson McCarta. £ 8.95. 190 pp.

Brief descriptions of a very wide variety of different peoples and their cultures.

Good Farmers: Traditional Agricultural Resource Management in Mexico and Central America

Gene C. Wilken. 1987. University of California Press: Berkeley. 303 pp. $55. (Available from agAccess, see Food Sources section.)

One of the best books on traditional agriculture in Central America. Wilken draws on agricultural systems from many parts of Mexico and Central America that have been used over the past several thousand years.

Wilin relied on archeology, records, and present-day systems. Includes many references.

Land Management in Amazonia: Indigenous and Folk Strategies
D. A. Posey, ed. Advances in Economic Botany, Vol. 7. Scientific Pub. Dept.: New York Botanical Garden, Bronx, NY 10458. $62.65. 287 pp.

Managing Africa's Tropical Dry Forests: a Review of Indigenous Methods
G. Sheperd. 1992. 117 pp. £9.95 from Overseas Development Institute: Regent's College, Inner Circle, Regent's Park, London NW1 4NS, UK.

This book suggests that local people be allowed to make resource management decisions, since they are the ones who suffer the consequences of poor decisions. Includes 111 abstracts of related documents.

Natives of Sarawak: Survival in Borneo's Vanishing Forests
A book on the indigenous peoples' fight for survival against timber and development in Borneo's tropical forests. An in-depth analysis of the problems faced by the native peoples of Sarawak and how their traditional way of life is increasingly threatened by the forces of 'modernization.' Available from *The Ecologist*.

The Once and Future Resource Managers
A Report on the Native Peoples of Latin America and Their Roles in Modern Resource Management; Background and Strategy for Training; 1980, 58 pp.; Final Report to: WWF-US; AMARU IV Cooperative Inc., West End Station Box 57155, Washington DC 20037. Tel: (202) 387-8668.

A good overview of the ethnobiology and native agriculture of indigenous peoples throughout Central and S. America.

People of the Tropical Rain Forest
J. Denslow and C. Padoch, Editors. 1988. Univ. California Press. $19.95. 230 pp.

Slash and Burn Farming in the Third World Forest
William J. Peters, and Leon F. Neuenschwander. 1988. University of Idaho Press: Moscow, ID 83843. 113 pp.

Also called swidden or shifting cultivation, slash & burn agriculture is widely decried in some circles as a leading cause of the loss of tropical forest. Closer examination of swidden agriculturists shows that with low population densities of the past, the impact on forest ecosystems was sustainable. This short book deals especially with the role of fire in swidden systems. Over 100 references.

Taking Care of Sibo's Gifts: An Environmental Treatise from Costa Rica's Kekoldi Indigenous Reserve
Paula Palmer, Junaita Sanchez and Gloria Mayorga. Editorama, S.A., San Jose, Costa Rica. 96 pp.

An account of how one tribe is adjusting to live in the 21st Century while protecting their environment. Available for $10.00, plus $2.50 postage, from Cultural Survival, 53 Church St., Cambridge MA 02138.

The Vanishing Forest
Report for the Independent Commission on International Humanitarian Issues. 1986. Zed Books: London and New Jersey.

The study concentrates on the human consequences of deforestation—the health, malnutrition, and migration of tribal peoples. It also discusses the environmental management of tropical forests for tribal peoples, as genetic reservoirs and for climate regulation.

Indigenous Knowledge

Center for International Research and Advisory Networks (CIRAN)
Gadhuisweg 251
P.O. Box 90734
2509 LS The Hague
THE NETHERLANDS
Tel: (70 3510574/Fax 70 3510513

During 1992, CIRAN took over many of the activities of CIKARD, based in Ames City, Iowa. This puts CIRAN at the forefront of scientific international networking on Indigenous Knowledge. CIRAN publishes *Indigenous Knowledge & Development Monitor*. Volume 1, No. 1, 1993 lists the addresses of 11 indigenous knowledge resource centers around the world.

TEK Talk
135 Hawthorne Ave.
Ottawa, Ontario
CANADA K1S 0B2

A quarterly newsletter on traditional ecological knowledge (TEK). $18/yr.

Indigenous Agricultural Knowledge Systems and Development
Special double issue of *Agriculture and Human Values*, Vol. 8 Nos. 1 and 2, 1991. $18.00. 184 pp.

Indigenous Technical Knowledge of Private Tree Management: A Bibliographic Report
Evelyn Mathias-Mundy, Olivia Muchena, Gerard McKiernan, and Paul Mundy. 1992. Bibliographies in Technology and Social Change No. 7. $18.00. 175 pp. Available from CIKARD.

Contemporary Tribal Forest Management

IN THIS SECTION we have looked at traditional North American land management. What about current forest management on tribal forest lands in the United States? How traditional is management today?

Current forest practices on tribal lands varies from tribe to tribe. Some tribes have atrocious reputations, while others, such as the Menominee (Wisconsin),the Yakima (Washington), and Flathead (Montana), have good reputations in restoration forestry circles. Single tree selection has been practiced on Southwest reservations for a long time, such as on the White Mountain Apache Reservation, the Taos, and the Zuni. The Taos tribe in New Mexico has 8,000 acres of designated wilderness.

The biggest problem tribal forests have faced is the Federal government's Bureau of Indian Affairs (BIA), which has controlled forestry on many reservations for the past century. The BIA has decimated many tribal forests. It has been said that the BIA makes the Forest Service look good. Some tribal forestry departments are still dominated by the Bureau of Indian Affairs.

The "Compact" tribes have been able to take over control of forestry operations from the Bureau of Indian Affairs (mostly in the past decade). The BIA still has most tribal forestlands in trust and the tribes are contracting out to do the BIA's previous work. This gives tribal forest managers more room to move and explore new kinds of forestry. A change in forestry practices is underway in reservation forestry departments as it is is through much of the forestry world. For instance, the Flathead tribe in Montana has notified the BIA that they will not allow clearcutting on their forests anymore and logging must leave a good-looking forest behind.

Bad logging practices have damaged or wiped out most salmon runs. The legal rights of Native American fisheries continues to grow. Some Pacific Northwest tribes have been major opponents of the timber industry and the US Forest Service over watershed and salmon issues.

Politics on Indian reservations can be complicated. In many tribes, traditional people have been pushed into the background and tribal leadership is dominated by BIA-leaning lackeys. As traditional influences grow, forestry managers are pushed toward restoration forestry.

Under President Clinton's Forest Plan Option 9, Federal subsidies are allocated to increase cutting on reservations by 400 million board feet. An increase of 40% from 1 billion board feet to 1.4 billion board feet. According to the BIA Washington DC office, this proposed increase in cut would come only from Pacific Northwest tribal forestlands, and these harvest levels are already approved in tribal plans, but which have not been met due to lack of staffing. The plan calls for a transferal of funds and staff from BLM and USFS to work under tribal management.

Sounds like a new attack on Native American's forests to make up for spotted owl set-asides. Given the present political climate on reservations it remains to be seen if the Federal government can make this proposed increase in cut happen. Let's hope not.

—Michael Pilarski

The following is an excerpt from "Foundation for the Future: The National Indian Forest Resources Management Act" by Gary S. Morishima in Indian Forest Management: Foundation for the Future. *1990-1991. Intertribal Timber Council. Reprinted with permission.*

The vital importance of Indian forests to tribal economies and cultures can be readily illustrated by a few simple statistics. Indian forests are found on 115 Indian reservations located in 23 states; of a total of 52 million acres of Indian land, some 16.5 million acres are forested. The annual sustained yield from 5.85 million acres of commercial forest land exceeds a billion board feet, provides in excess of $56 million in stumpage payments and supports some 12,000 person years of employment and over $156 million in employment income. Additionally, substantial economic benefits are generated from 9.0 million acres of Indian woodlands. Indian forest resources also provide habitat for fish and wildlife, native medicines and foods, recreational opportunities, and sanctuaries for worship and religious ceremonies.

Despite the central significance of Indian forests, the legislative and policy framework for management remained woefully inadequate until enactment of the National Indian Forest Resources Management Act (NIFRMA) in October 1990. Until that time, federal policy objectives were barely reflected in four statutes and appropriations authority was limited to the Snyder Act. The lack of standards and a solid legislative foundation no doubt contributed to large variations in management of Indian forest lands, huge losses in income suffered by generations of Indian people, and virtually no management for woodland resources. Several lawsuits have been brought alleging mismanagement by the Bureau of Indian Affairs. In a 1983 landmark case involving the Quinault Reservation, United States v. Mitchell (463 U.S. 206), the Supreme Court found that the United States had a federal trust responsibility for the management of Indian forest resources.

Statistics gathered by the Society of American Foresters for the 1987-89 academic years, reported that, on the average, only 12 out of 3,100 baccalaureate degrees in forestry are awarded to Indian students annually.

Tomorrow's tribal leaders and enterprise managers will confront higher stumpage prices, less timber and more appeals to stop timber harvesting.

Reservation forests are not tree farms, nor are they parks; they are the Native people's backyards. A place to harvest wild plants, and other forms of sustenance. A place to feel at home.

Resources on Tribal Forestry

"Resource and Sanctuary. Indigenous Peoples, Ancestral Rights and the forests of the Americas"
A special issue of *Cultural Survival* magazine. Spring 1993. $5.00.

One of the most up-to-date and thorough looks at current forest management on Native forest land in North and South America. Many excellent articles and resources. It contains an extensive listing of Native American tribes with forestry operations in Canada, the US, Mexico, Central and South America.

Indigenous Agendas for Conservation

A directory to 117 Native American projects in sustainable development and restoration. One-page is devoted to each project. Produced by *Cultural Survival* and the Dine Nation. Copies are available from *Cultural Survival* for $10.

Bureau of Indian Affairs—Division of Forestry
U.S. Department of the Interior
230 Room 4545 MIB
1849 "C" St. NW
Penobscot, DC 20240
Tel: (202) 208-3962
Chief Forester: Jim Howe

The BIA has available a list of "Timber Reservations" which lists 83 reservations in the USA with significant forestland. Their Biannual Report offers information on tribal forestry.

100 Years of Trust Management

A BIA publication on the history of the BIA and tribal forest management. A limited number were published several years ago. It was reprinted by a university press in 1993.

Inter-tribal Organizations Concerned with Forest Management

Intertribal Timber Council
4370 N.E. Halsey St.
Portland, Oregon 97213
Tel: (503) 282-4296/Fax: (503) 282-1274

Each tribe is a government within itself. Tribal forestry departments participate in the Intertribal Timber Council to facilitate interchange and learning between tribes. The council maintains a central office in Portland, Oregon. The quarterly newsletter is available to non-tribal subscribers for $10 a year.

Established in 1976 to provide a forum for communication between tribes and the Bureau of Indian Affairs (BIA), some primary purposes of the Intertribal Timber Council are:

1. Promoting sound, economic management of Indian timber resources.

2. Providing information concerning state and federal policies affecting Indian timber interests.

3. Facilitating communication among members on matters relevant to the management of Indian timber lands and forest products.

4. Assisting the establishment of Indian business enterprises.

5. Encouraging the training and development of Indian foresters.

The Intertribal Timber Council also conducts the Annual National Indian Timber Symposium. The Eighteenth Annual National Indian Timber Symposium will be held April 25-29, 1994 in Polson, Montana.

Northwest Indian Fisheries Commission

Timber, Fish & Wildlife, TFW Coordinator
6730 Martin Way E.
Olympia, Washington 98506
Tel: (206) 438-1180

The Northwest Indian Fish Commission is a coalition of 20 western Washington tribes. TFW also works as a coordinating agency for East side tribes. The Tribes have made an agreement with State agencies, industry and environment groups for improved management of watersheds which the tribes utilize for salmon harvest. The idea being to prevent continued degradation of fisheries resources. Each tribe has a TFW biologist who watchdogs logging activities in drainages affecting tribal fisheries.

Columbia Inter-Tribal Fish Commission

729 NE Oregon #200
Portland, Oregon 97232
Tel: (503) 238-0667. Fax: (503) 235-4228.

Native American Fish and Wildlife Society

750 Burbank St.
Broomfield, Colorado 80020
Tel: (303) 466-1725

An inter-tribal organization.

Intertribal Agriculture Council

100 N. 27th St., Suite 450
Billings, Montana 59101
Tel: (406) 259-3524

An inter-tribal organization concerned with agriculture, crops, livestock and rangeland management.

Some Tribal Forest Departments

Disclaimer: These are just a few of the tribes with forestry operations. To the best of my knowledge, I have endeavored to point out those which are closest to restoration forestry, but not all of these listed here are necessarily practicing restoration forestry. Undoubtedly there are other tribes who are practicing restoration forestry besides those listed here.

Hoopa Tribal Forestry

P.O. Box 368
Hoopa, California 95546
Tel: (916) 625-4284
Contact: Greg Bloomstrom

Of the USA's 106 timber reservations, the Hoopa would be rated in the top 20 in terms of sustainable forestry management. The reservation contains 76,000 acres of timberland of which 35,000 acres remains in old growth. There is a dialogue going on within the tribe on how much of the remaining old-growth should be set aside from timber harvest. Most of the best has been clearcut. Much of the remainder is difficult to access and/

or low volume sites. In 1982, most of the clearcuts were in the 20 to 40 acre range. The size of the clearcuts has since been reduced and now average 7 acres .

Lac Du Flambeau Tribal Forestry

P.O. Box 67
Lac Du Flambeau, Wisconsin 54538
Tel: (715) 588-3303/Fax: (715) 588-7930

The Lac Du Flambeau practice sustained forest management employing tribal members. Also developing non-timber products such as wild rice, sweetgrass and birch bark for basketry.

Lummi Nation

2616 Kwina Road
Bellingham, Washington 98226
Tel: (206) 734-8180/Fax: (206) 384-4737

The Lummi Nation is a leader in promoting restoration forestry practices on their own land and in Puget Sound watersheds which impact their salmon fisheries. On their own land they have comprehensive plans for forest management including restoring native conifer forests and a moratorium on clearcutting. In 1979, they led an effort by 14 tribes that identified over 400,000 acres of traditional religious and ceremonial sites in the Mt. Baker-Snoqualmie National Forest. The Lummi have developed international networks among native peoples and provide support to the Mayan Lacandones, seeking to protect 500,000 acres of rain forest in Mexico.

Macah Forestry

P.O. Box 116
Neah Bay, Washington 98357
Tel: (206) 645-2229

The first industrial logging began on the Macah reservation in the 1930's. Their forests are managed for sustained yield.

Menominee Tribal Enterprises

Forestry Division. Marshall Pecore
Box 10
Neopit, Wisconsin 54135
Tel: (715) 799-3896

One of the most publicized examples of Native sustainable forest management. They were awarded an international award for their forestry and are Green Cross certified. Large volume wholesale only. Conducting sustainable-yield forestry on their 218,000 acres of tribal land since 1854.

Recent articles on Menominee forest management can be found in *Cultural Survival*, Spring 1993. In the December, 1993 issue of *Harrowsmith Country Life*. In the *Journal of Forestry*, July, 1993. In a recent issue of *Turtle Quarterly*.

Port Gamble/S'Klallam Tribe

Steve Moddemeyer
Environmental Resources/Forestry
P.O. Box 280
Kingston, Washington 98346
Tel: (206) 297-2646/Fax (206) 297-7097

The S'Klallam tribe has been developing a 10-year forest restoration plan which will be completed in Fall of 1993. It will be one of the first tribal forestry plans focusing on restoration.

The tribe's land is found on the Kitsap Peninsula in Puget Sound. The reservation's 1,000 acres of timberland was clearcut in the 1920's and never replanted. Most of it has grown back in alder. About half of the second growth was clearcut in the 1980's. In the late 1980's the tribe stopped clearcutting due to concerns about the depletion of resources.

Gathering of shellfish, berries and traditional plants is still very much a part of the culture and they wish to manage the forest for a continuing supply of traditional forest products. For instance, it has become harder for the tribe to locate cedars suitable for canoes. The tribe has replanted riparian corridors with cedar and sitka spruce to provide basketry materials and cedar for canoes.

Surveys of tribal members, including elders and youth, were recently carried out and long-term goals synthesized from the survey. These goals include managing the forest for the greatest number of uses, including traditional products, cultural values, wildlife, water, and healthy freshwater and marine ecosystems. The goals include multi-species, all-aged forests.

The tribal forestry budget was tripled to meet the goals of forest restoration. The restoration work is done solely by tribal members and provides employment for five families. Many of the tribal members work in the forest products industry, which has been experiencing cutbacks due to loss of resource base in the area. The restoration work keeps tribal members working and at the same time enhances present and future productivity.

Skokomish River Estuary Restoration

Margie Schirato
N. 541 Tribal Center Rd., Skokomish Fisheries Office
Shelton, Washington 98584
Tel: (206) 426-4232

The current major project is the removal of dikes and restoration of a 600-acre area.

Skokomish Tribe Forestry

Floradell Wiazcek
Tel: (206) 426-4232

Most of the Skokomish's forest was clearcut in the late 1980's at the BIA's urging to cash in on the big income the forest represented.

Umatilla Tribal Forestry

The Umatilla Tribe of northeast Oregon is rapidly turning to restoration forestry practices after years of BIA management. In October 1993, The Umatilla tribe rejected a BIA plan to log 5,288 acres and said they would rather keep the forest intact for traditional activities such as hunting and gathering. The BIA proposal would supposedly had netted the tribe $3 million. The tribe hired the Public Forestry Foundation, a restoration forestry consulting firm in Eugene to assess the BIA logging plan.

Yakima Nation Forestry Department

Box 632
Toppenish, Washington 98948
Tel: (509) 865-2373/Fax (509) 865-5522

Contact tribal forester, Glen Lyle. The Yakima Nations signed a treaty in the 1850s which allowed them to retain part of their territory. From the top of their sacred mountain (Mount Adams) to the Yakima River. It is one of the largest reservations in the Pacific Northwest (1.3 million acres) and includes much timberland. The Yakima tribe has one of the better reputations in the region for good forest management. The tribal forests are still mostly under BIA management. They have a strong wildlife department who work closely with the forestry department to insure good wildlife habitat. 90% of their harvesting is individual tree selection. the other 10% are in group tree selection, and small clearcuts. The forests standing volume has remained steady since logging stared in 1946. Many managed stands have been entered three or four times since. 60,000 acres were sprayed with B.T in 1990 to combat spruce budworm. Most tribal members don't like clearcuts, They want an aesthetic forest and lots of wildlife. Lyle says their management has created some outstanding spotted owl habitat.

Zuni Sustainable Resource Development Plan

P.O. Box 339
Zuni, New Mexico 87327
Tel: (505) 782-5852/Fax: (505) 782-2726

They are developing on their lands, a rehabilitation program for degraded lands, and a training component so Zuni can implement the plan themselves.

Canadian Aboriginal Forestry

What is Aboriginal Forestry?

ABORIGINAL FORESTRY is not necessarily different in practice than other forms of forestry, but one generalization that can be made is that it will usually be different than an industrial timber company's version of forestry. The fundamental differences lie in different land ethics and value systems.

A land ethic can be defined as an individual's or group's understanding of and value placed upon their relationship to the land. Everyone has a land ethic, whether it be indifferent, dependent, superior, humble and/or spiritual.

In most Aboriginal communities, the land ethic is very spiritual and rooted in traditional cultural beliefs. This ethic is an integral part of every aspect of society and the fundamental essence of the people's understanding of who they are as life forms, individuals, families and/or communities. The people see themselves as a small and very dependent piece of a larger web. With this perspective, one quickly develops a direct understanding of action and consequences with respect to land use and a strong respect and reverence for life and the land. From this understanding and respect comes an overriding social responsibility to care for the land and life as it cares for you; thus, the land is commonly referred to as "Mother Earth."

Other practices, beliefs and values that stem from this understanding, which help to shape the nature of a land management regime, include:

- respect for wisdom (elders)
- consensus decision-making
- respect for individual freedom of choice
- humility in the face of natural processes
- commitment to fit within your natural place and to achieve a balance with the world around you
- respect for relationships with family, society and other life in general

Excerpts from: Aboriginal Forestry Training and Employment Review. Final Report—Phase I. *Prepared for the National Aboriginal Forestry Association. Reprinted with permission.*

National Aboriginal Forestry Association—NAFA
875 Bank Street
Ottawa, Ontario, K1S 3W4, CANADA
Tel: (613) 233-5563/Fax: (613) 233-4329
Harry Bombay, Director/Sheila Walinski, staff

NAFA is a grass roots initiative backed by Aboriginal groups and organizations. The creation of NAFA was called for at the landmark conference National Native Forestry Symposium: Ethic To Reality, held in Vancouver, November 22-24, 1989, and attended by some 450 Native delegates (proceedings are available from NAFA). The delegates' consensus favored establishing a national organization to promote forestry as necessary for Aboriginal economic development, repair of environment degradation, and restoration of cultural and community spiritual health for Aboriginal people across the country.

NAFA is to promotes and supports increased Aboriginal involvement in forest management and related commercial opportunities. NAFA is committed to holistic or forestry, which implies rebuilding and sustainably developing forest resources to serve a multitude of community needs: protecting fur bearers, clean and adequate water supplies; establishing areas for recreation and tourism, traditional cultural and spiritual use; and producing fiber for timber, pulp, paper and other wood by-products. Community based strategies are the key to transforming this resource ethic into reality.

Over the past year and a half, NAFA and other organizations have been working on legislation to enable First Nations to manage their own forest resources according to their community needs and aspirations.

NAFA produces a quarterly newsletter. Other publications are available.

NAFA completed a "First Native Forest Practices

Code" in late 1993, providing a guide for ethical forestry that allows Native peoples full involvement in forest management, planning, and economic development.

What is the Present Situation?

(On Aboriginal Forest Lands in Canada)

The forests on Indian lands are in deplorable condition. Historically, stands of timber have been treated like mines. Intensive logging has occurred with little, if any, attention to wildlife or other values or to the fact that forests are renewable. The productive capacity of land for sustainable forestry was ignored. No attention was given to reforestation of areas cutover or damaged by fire, insects and diseases. It has been estimated that the volumes harvested from Indian lands have decreased by half over the last two decades. ...total expenditure per hectare of productive forests on Indian lands is about half the average for Canada—NAFA.

Canadian Tribal Forestry Organizations

Intertribal Forestry Association of British Columbia
#201–515 Highway 97
South Kelowna, British Columbia
CANADA V1Z 3J2
Tel: (604) 769-443

Harold Derickson: President. They promote economic opportunities, obtain funding for tribal forest projects, distribute information on forest management, education and training. A subscription to their newsletter *Bush News* is presently free.

Alliance Tribal Council
130 N. Tsawwassen Dr.
Delta, British Columbia
CANADA V4K 3N2
Tel: (604) 943-6712

Coastal Native bands.

Algonquin of Barriere Lake
Rapid Lake Indian Reserve, Quebec
CANADA J0W 2C0
Tel: (613) 729-9491

They have developed an integrated resource management plan, outlining cultural and environmental areas for protection and limits on the way wood can be harvested.

Carrier Chilcotin Tribal Council
59 S. First Ave
Williams Lake, British Columbia
CANADA V2G 2V4
Tel: (604) 398-7033/Fax: (604) 398-6329

The Ulkatcho and Kluskus bands are developing holis-tic forest-use plans the emphasize diversified products from timber.

Mid-Island Tribal Council
P.O. Box 720
Chemainus, British Columbia
CANADA V0R 1K0
Tel: (604) 245-5674/Fax: (604) 246-2347

The Council is negotiating a co-management agreement for holistic forest management practice.

Nuu-chah-nulth Tribal Council
P.O. Box 1383
Port Alberni, British Columbia
CANADA V9Y 7M2
Tel: (604) 742-8570

They've worked closely with environmental groups in their area to achieve holistic forestry practices.

Tanizul Timber Ltd.
PO Box 988
Fort St. James, British Columbia
CANADA V0J 1P0
Tel: (604) 648-3221/Fax: (604) 648-3266

A company of the Tl'azt'en Nations and the first First Nation band to obtain a 25-year Tree Farm License from the BC government, extending their land base to 124,000 acres.

Teme-Augama Anishnabai TEMAGAMI
Group Box 46
Bear Island, Ontario
CANADA P0H 2H0
Tel: (705) 237-8933/Fax: (705) 237-8908

In 1990, the TEMAGAMI signed an agreement with Ontario to co-manage almost 100,000 acres, emphasizing culturally and environmentally sensitive forest use.

Educational Institutions Offering Resource Management Courses with an Aboriginal Emphasis

Described in *NAFA Newsletter* Vol. 2, No. 1.

Meadow Lake Tribal Council—Integrated Resource Management Program
Student Services Co-ordinator
P.O. Box 2138
Meadow Lake, Saskatchewan
CANADA S0M 1V0
Tel: (306) 236-4448/Fax: (306) 236-4818

Nicola Valley Institute of Technology—Natural Resource Programs
Attn: Gordon Prest
Merritt, British Columbia
CANADA V0K 2B0
Tel: (604) 378-2251

"The Earth's Blanket:" Traditional Aboriginal Attitudes Towards Nature

Nancy J. Turner

...flowers, plants, and grass, especially the latter, are the covering or blanket of the earth. If too much plucked or ruthlessly destroyed earth sorry and weeps. It rains or is angry and makes rain, fog and bad weather.

—James Teit, ethnographer, unpublished notes on Nlaka'pamx, or Thompson, plant knowledge, ca. 1900, cited from Turner, *et al.* 1990: 54

UNDERSTANDING AND LIVING SUSTAINABLY within a particular environment has been a matter of survival for the Aboriginal Peoples of Canada, as it has for Indigenous Peoples the world over. A definition of Indigenous People, as "...a cultural group in an ecological area that developed a successful subsistence base from the natural resources available in that area" (Kuhnlei and Turner 1991:2) reflects the close relationship Aboriginal People have had with their environment, a relationship that embodies dependence, familiarity, awe, respect, and kinship. This article focuses on Aboriginal Peoples of western Canada in the examples used, but the concepts expressed are widespread in Aboriginal teachings.

Despite, or perhaps because of, their detailed knowledge of the natural world, Aboriginal Peoples have regarded many aspects of Nature as powerful, or magical. There is a spiritual side of Nature, addressed in traditional ceremonies, prayers and stories, going far beyond its modern role solely as a resource to be exploited by people in their quest for survival and the acquisition of wealth. The philosophy expressed in the introductory quotation, reflecting the power and persona of nature, and the necessity to use it carefully and not to abuse it, was widely taught to Aboriginal children and young adults by their elders.

"Never waste anything." Everything has a purpose, people were taught, even those things frequently regarded as useless by most people today. The sinew from a whale's back made the strongest kind of rope for the Nuuchah nulth people of the West Coast of Vancouver Island; fine powder from sharpening giant mussel shells for chisels was used by the Ditidaht of Vancouver Island as a lubricant for the skin when people spun nettle fibre into string on their bare legs; salmon heads were used all along the Pacific Coast to make a rich, delicious and highly nutritious soup; the eyeballs of a bison were used for glue by the Blackfoot of Alberta; the ribs of a deer were softened, split into slivers and used for awls by the Secwepemc, or Shuswap, and other peoples. The bark of trees, generally removed and discarded in modern sawmilling, was used traditionally as a source of fibre, basket materials, medicine and even food (Turner and Hebda, 1990; Gottesfeld, 1992).

Red alder (*Alnus rubra*) is a plant species that epitomizes the contrasting attitudes people have towards Nature. It is a tree of western North America, regarded by industrial foresters of the Pacific coastal region as a noxious weed that competes with commercial fibre species such as Douglas-fir (*Pseudotsuga menziesii*). Alder is variously sprayed with herbicides, such as Roundup, girdled with special circular saws to kill it, or removed by cutting. Among Northwestern Aboriginal Peoples, however, it was, and still is, highly valued. In some mythical traditions, Alder was formerly a woman with red skin, transformed to her present state long ago as a gift for other humans.

Its soft, even-grained wood is an ideal fuel for smoking fish and meat, and for carving bowls, masks, and rattles. Its bark, which turns bright orange or red with exposure to air, was a major source of dye. It was used for coloring fishnets to make them invisible to fish, and for red-cedar bark (*Thuja plicata*) used in clothing, mats and ceremonial neck rings, providing a contrasting hue with the natural brown.

The cambium and inner bark tissues of red alder were eaten in spring by the Saanich and other Coast Salish Peoples of Vancouver Island. Alder bark is also the source of important medicines, used by Aboriginal Peoples for treating a variety of ailments from tuberculosis and internal hemorrhaging to skin infections. Preliminary screening for antibiotic properties at the Department of Botany of The University of British Columbia showed it to be effective against a wide range of bacterial pathogens. One need only look at the story of western yew (*Taxus brevifolia*) (see McAllister and Haber, 1991 in Canadian Biodiversity) to find an example of a tree hitherto regarded as useless whose commercial value has sky-rocketed following the discovery of a promising anti-cancer compound, taxol, in its bark. Red alder may well become another "yew story." Aboriginal People have known, used, and valued both of these species for centuries.

Among the Kwakwaka'wakw (Kwakwala-speaking People, formerly Kwakiutl) of coastal British Columbia, everything used was honored with a prayer, acknowledging its healing or nurturing role and its power to help. The following prayer, recorded by ethnographer Franz Boas (translated from Kwakwala), is addressed by a medicine gatherer to an alder tree along a river bank. The man wishes to use the alder's bark to treat his wife, who is spitting blood (from tuberculosis):

> I have come to ask you to take mercy, Supernatural-Power of-the-River-Bank, that you may, please, make well with your healing power my poor wife who is spitting blood. Go on, please, pity me for I am troubled and please, make her well, you, Healing-Woman, ...and, please, stop up the source of blood, you Causing-to-Heal-Woman, and, please, heal up the cause of trouble of my poor wife, please, you, great Supernatural One....
>
> (Boas 1932:237-238)

Four pieces of the bark were carefully removed, taken home, and administered with additional prayers to the "Healing-Woman" alder. All medicine harvested must be used; if it is thrown away or wasted, the person could suffer hardship in some way, because of the disrespect shown. The practices of careful harvesting and use of such materials allowed for their continued utilization over many generations—in other words, sustainability.

What does all this mean for protection of Biodiversity? Aboriginal Peoples need to use their environment, and the other living things in their ecosystems, for survival, just as all of us do. However, the attitude of respect, gratitude and honor, and the spiritual relationship humans have had with Nature in traditional cultures, is important in determining how they used their environment. Religious attitudes in traditional societies may be metaphorical guidelines for sustainable living. Prayers, stories and ceremonies abound in the Aboriginal societies of Canada and elsewhere that teach people the principles of sustainability: Take only what you need, and do not

waste what you take. Harvest with care. Honor and appreciate everything you get and everything around you. Share with others: do not hoard. Observe carefully for signs of scarcity or overuse, and if you find them, change your use patterns. Remember. Nature can affect your life, for good or for bad, depending on how you treat it.

If Society at Large were to uphold these principles, and follow them, doubtless we would all be more successful at living sustainably and preserving the other life forms of the planet.

Acknowledgments

My sincere gratitude goes to the many wise and knowledgeable Aboriginal People who have taught me about traditional plant use. I would especially like to acknowledge the late Annie York (*Nlaka'pamux*), the late Edith O'Donaghey (*Stl'atl'imx*), the late John Thomas (*Ditidaht*), Mary Thomas (*Secwepemc*), Kenneth Eaglespeaker (Blackfoot) and Kim Recalma-Clutesi (*Kwakwaka'wakw*) for the information contained here. Robert D. Turner, Alison Davis and David Bosnich provided helpful editorial council.

References

Boas, Franz. 1930. Religion of the Kwakiutl Indians. *Columbia University Contributions to Anthropology*, Vol. 10, Part l, Texts; Part 2, Translations. Columbia University Press, New York.

Gottesfeld, Leslie M. Johnson. 1992. The Importance of Bark Products in the Aboriginal Economies of Northwestern British Columbia, Canada. *Economic Botany* 46(2): 148-157.

Kuhnlein, Harriet V. and Nancy J. Turner. 1991. Traditional Plant Foods of Canadian Indigenous Peoples. Nutrition, Botany and Use. Volume 8. In: *Food and Nutrition in History and Anthropology*, edited by Solomon Katz. Gordon and Breach Science Publishers, Philadelphia, Pennsylvania.

McAllister, Don E. and Erich Haber. 1991. Western Yew—Precious Medicine. *Canadian Biodiversity* 1(2):2-4.

Turner, Nancy J. and Richard J. Hebda. 1990. Contemporary Use of Bark for Medicine by Two Salishan Native Elders of Southeast Vancouver Island, Canada. *Journal of Ethnopharmacology* 29: 59-72.

Turner, Nancy J., Laurence C. Thompson, M. Terry Thompson, and Annie Z. York. 1990. Thompson Ethnobotany: Knowledge and Usage of Plants by the Thompson [Nlaka'pamux] Indians of British Columbia. *Royal British Columbia Museum Memoir* No. 3, Victoria.

That Place Could Use A Good Fire

Hector Franco

THIS INTERVIEW WITH HECTOR FRANCO about the traditional use of fire as a forest management tool among Wukchumni and other Yokuts people was conducted by Kat Anderson, a Ph.D. candidate in ethnobotany at UC Berkeley. Fire was one of the primary tools used by the native people who tended the giant forests of the Kings Canyon and Sequoia National Park areas, believing their role in nature was to take care of the land and keep it clean. Our thanks go to the people at the LEF Foundation, who contributed funds for this and several other projects designed to give native scholarship its due.

A few years back a gentleman contacted me and said that he was trying to get people through out the state to come together and talk about what's happening to the Giant Forest—how the burn policies, 75 years of the Smokey the Bear policy, have ruined the forest. I told him I would get involved in this and I would help him as much as I could, because as it is right now we as Indian people can't get a word in edgewise to talk about our land.

They've done a lot of damage up there, not just to the Giant Forest, but to the whole ecosystem. The animals have suffered, all the plant life has suffered. The different pines—the smaller pines that are right next to the large ones—the digger pines, white firs, incense cedar, they've all suffered. There's been overcrowding. There's been a lot of diseases in the root systems and in the bark. A tremendous population of creatures and organisms has developed in the ground. We've all been told this for years and years by some of the biologists, so we know that.

Fire is one of the things that will give the soil some type of balance again—the ash itself, the chemicals in the ash. That's what the fire does in general. It will create life again and it will also correct some of the imbalance.

The easternmost village of the Wukchumni people was up in Patwisha, the Hospital Rock area. From there we would venture out into the high country. We went clear over to a place called Denizen Peak and over to the Blue Ridge area. There's stands of huge trees and forests up in there. Some of our people would go clear up into Slate Mountain before they'd go up in the Kern Valley, and there's a huge stand of redwoods up in the Kern River area, a place called Peppermint Ridge.

I remember what the old people told us, and this has to do with our religious beliefs I heard this many times from our spiritual people, the elders—my grandmother especially. We Indian people have a responsibility to take care of the earth; to take care of it and maintain it the way it was given to us and to take care of the animals. When they burned the Giant Forest—and they burned even the lowlands and the foothill areas—it would benefit all the animals, all the creatures, all the plants. And we have not been able to do that. We haven't been able to take care of the earth.

I heard several stories from my grandmother, Jenny Franco. She lives on the Tule River Indian Reservation. And I heard lots of stories from my own dad. His name was Leo Franco. And from some of the old timers, some of the old people we knew that lived both on the Reservation at Tule [River] and down in this area here, in Visalia and up over in Fresno—different areas. These things have stuck with me over the years and I just remember bits and pieces of different things that people told us.

The last old man that we were told that still practiced fire burning up here in the Giant Forest was old man Topna. He's mentioned in *Latta [Handbook of the Yokuts,* by Frank Latta]. Topna remembered when he was a boy in the early 1900s, no later than the 1920s, accompanying the old-timers when they would burn up there. He remembers when they got into trouble. They were run off and there was a big manhunt for them. They made it down to Three Rivers, and they hid at a ranch. They had been up in the high country and burned a section of forest that had a lot of black oak and golden oak.

This was done for a reason. Fire will stimulate the trees to become healthier, to produce more roots and consequently more mass, and more acorns will come the following year and more food. And you see all of these galls on these oak trees—if you had a good fire go through here you would not have all these galls. They occur naturally on oaks, but they'll kill a tree— fire will help reduce those parasites.

The old people knew which trees were healthy and which trees were unhealthy. They knew that fires were going to help get rid of a tree because if too many bugs or woodpeckers mess with this tree, it's going to cause harm to other trees. Fire was a cleanser.

When we helped the forest by cleaning all the old brush out and burning every thing it would help the animals also. There would be more animals—deer, bears, birds, squirrels—and they'd be able to live in peace. The animals would find more food when the land was cleaner.

I know that down in the low country in Yokohl Valley the Indian people would burn that whole valley. It produced grass seeds—that type of rye that looks like wild rice. They would burn every year down in the lower country for saltgrass. A lot of grass-producing seeds—those real hard little red ones you would call flannel seeds, the wild rye, the grass, the mushrooms, the chawkish would grow quicker.

And there were the finer plants, like the coyote thistle. You can eat those when they're little—the new shoots. When it gets big it's too thorny. Those areas were burned and those plants were gathered. Now the coyote thistle is on the endangered species list. It only occurs in two parks in California, a refuge in Los Banos and here in Dry Creek.

Tules, the bulrushes—whole forests of tules were burned. In the Kaweah Oak Preserve there are bulrushes and roots that we know they burned and you can see what I'm talking about—the congestion, what it does to the plants. It does not let them grow healthy.

Clover patches were burned. In Squaw Valley the Indian people burned clover patches right by the mission. My dad said there's not that much clover left now because of all the buildings, the houses—they've destroyed a lot of the clover. There used to be sloping meadows of clover. They would burn for clover late in the year, because the clover was gathered early, in March, April. When it got older, it got tougher and it didn't taste good. I remember the people wouldn't uproot the whole plant. They would pinch it off. My dad said that they burned it after it produced seeds and after the seeds fell—fire also stimulates different seeds. They probably burned it at the end of the year when they burned everything else—in the cool time, anywhere from October to November.

If you look at the berry bushes, they can become really congested. There's berries in the center, but you can't get to them be cause it's so congested. When fire would go through these areas the plants weren't as congested. The brush wouldn't be as full or thick. You'd be able to reach in the bush and grab berries.

Chaparral pea was eaten. It is really hard to find. The chaparrals are good to eat. They're blood medicines, medicines to cleanse the blood. It's mostly distributed sparsely in foothills, from Butte to Mariposa County. It's more indigenous to the north. Chia was one of the plants that benefited from the fire. The old people would soak the seeds—two real hard, dark red seeds off of a shrub and then crush them. The bracken fern were burned too. I don't know how often those were burned. Some other plants that benefited from the fire were the yerba santa, the elderberry, the chokecherry, the buckbrush, the mountain ash, and also the tobacco.

They burned every year under the black oaks—they produce a lot of leaves. They said they would burn to help the acorn. But there's so much land. I don't see how they would be able to burn every single area. Maybe they burned some areas that were more accessible more often than others. Up in Drum Valley and up in the higher country, they would burn the oaks in that area because there was a lot of open sloping country. Acorns were easy to gather. As you go up higher, the terrain is too rough.

Over on the other side of the range where the pinon trees would come up from the Isabellas area, that whole area was burned to stimulate the growth of the pinon trees.

They would only burn once every two or three years in the giant sequoias, but there were some areas that had more plants. The sourberry grows up high. They would burn every year in the areas where there were the most sourberries, to stimulate growth for the following year, for the berries and for the basketry material.

Up at a place called Delilah Lookout [Mount Sampson] there's an old village site there, and that's where we go pick our sourberries. Right intermixed with the sourberries in little clumps was a lot of mountain mahogany. It's all mangled and twisted, and my dad would tell us that in the olden days they would burn this area. They wouldn't let trees get this bad—mangled like this. When a fire came through it would stimulate strong shoots that would come up from the bottom rather than high in the tree. Those were used for the digging sticks. The bark from mountain mahogany is medicine for the liver. The leaves were also used to produce a tea. When you use the bark and the leaves, it turns the tea a reddish color. It is really a good-tasting tea. Also we would trade with the Indian people in the lower country. I imagine they used some of the mountain mahogany for spears at Tulare Lake, because they used to have long hard wood spears.

We've gone to get mountain mahogany sticks and bark and leaves for medicinal purposes. We were told the best time to pick the medicine is in the springtime—right when the sap is starting to come back up. I've also gone and gotten mahogany for walking sticks. Some of the old-timers used them for walking sticks. I really don't know how long after a fire they would wait to harvest it. The way they let the sticks harden was they wouldn't put them out in the sun. They'd let the mountain mahogany sticks dry in the shade, wrapped to keep from drying too quick because then they will crack.

One of the plants that I heard about from the old people that really benefited from fire was manzanita. The manzanita sticks were used for digging sticks also, and for ceremonies, like a baton or staff. Small stems were used for pipes. They made cider out of the berries, and the leaves and bark were used for medicinal purposes. You can't have a lot of manzanitas all cluttered. The tree has to be free. When they're not all cluttered, they get really, really big and that's when they are really beneficial. The people had to keep the small manzanitas under control.

Dogwood was used also for stems for pipes. I've seen a lot of mangled dogwood and hazelnut in the high country and it just doesn't look natural. More than likely they probably burned those areas there to get them back into shape.

I've noticed that after a fire the redbud would produce straight sticks, real pretty ones. It seems to make the tree healthier. I've heard it mentioned before. Another basketry material they burned for is the white root. My grandmother said they would go and they would clean out areas and they would leave roots. In other words, they would thin them out and they would burn in the fall—that would keep the bunchgrass from getting intertwined. When they'd go back the following spring they'd dig up those roots and then they'd grow longer—they'd be more manageable. They would burn every year for white root, in the same spots.

There's another plant that my dad said benefited a lot by fire—the Indian hemp. It could get really knurled up. They used that for rope—they needed those straight long stems so they could crack them open and get their fiber out of there. The whole plant would burn all the way down to the roots, but then it would come up the next year straight.

How did they know where to burn? Indian people would go out walking in the forest and they knew that an area just didn't look right, or they could tell because it didn't produce enough of the materials or foods and they knew that a fire would be beneficial. There were mangled groves of trees, areas that were overgrown, areas that had too many pine needles. The people knew that if there were too many pine needles collecting in an area it would hurt the trees when they'd burn. The fire has to be a gentle fire—it can't be a type of fire that's going to be real destructive. But at the same time, the fire has to be such that it is going to do some good.

When I go up there now it disturbs me to see these huge scars, and from talking to some of our people I know that's the result a fire that's too hot. The scars never used to be there. A lightning bolt might come down and practically cut a tree in half and I'm sure that would leave a nasty scar, but there's just too many of them up there— too many trees that were burned. That's not healthy for them if they're burned all the way through that way, it's going to shorten their life span.

Oftentimes my dad and I would walk up in the Giant Forest and different areas, up until the time that he got real, real sick. We were still going and doing ceremonies up at the Giant Forest. No one would know about them because, once again, the old people were very careful. The trees for us are living creatures that we have to take care of. Oftentimes I'd walk over to my dad and he'd say, "That place needs a good fire." And then I'd look over there and it was real overgrown. There were no animals in the area. Everything just looks unhealthy.

The old people, they knew where to burn. They could feel it. It's just like any farmer nowadays. He goes walking out on his field and he can tell by looking at his plants whether they need water. After a while you develop an eye. You can train yourself and you know the needs of your particular plant—like the grape growers. The grape growers say, "Look at these grapes, in a couple more days it's going to have just the right sugar." They'll come out in the fall. They'll look at their plants. They'll prune their plants. Men, whether they're white men or Indian men. People that work with plants, when they're close to nature they know.

They knew exactly when it was time. We would consult with the spiritual people, the tribal elders, and usually they did most of the burning in the fall, right after the harvest of the acorns. And of course a lot of other things were also harvested at that time to prepare for the winter. And then we'd have our fall ceremonies, almost when Thanksgiving is celebrated now, maybe the latter part of October, the first part of November.

I can only tell you what our family said, but I heard that there were other people that burned earlier in the year, in the spring. But whether it was late or early it was always cool. They never did it in the summertime because it was too hot. Fires were hard to control then. They'd burn when there wasn't a whole lot of wind. Moisture in the air was important—it wasn't going to be a fire that was going to rage out of control and be real hot.

If you go up above Denizen Peak, there's a giant forest up there. They would burn down below and the fire would go up. I know where they burned there, and it would go up. Over at Lodgepole and then down below on the western side of the foothills going down the Pinehurst area—I know where they burned there. I don't know if they were burning to make a back fire or burning for it to go up.

The people would gather plant materials, shrubs, herbs, make offerings of tobacco and make a little pile. One in the north, one in the south, one in the east, and one in the west, and then they would stand in the middle and say prayers and do this ceremony to help clean the land. In the prayer the people would always talk to the animals and all the plants to tell them what they were doing. It's just our way of respecting them. Like asking permission because it was their land before it was our land.

When they burned they wanted it to spread in four directions. It's ceremony—this is all part of their religious beliefs. They didn't just go out there with a road flare and set fire like I've seen done with controlled burns. We, Indian people, we talk to the fire. We've learned through religious teachings that fire lives inside of us also. That would be the electrons that course through your body. Fire was thought of in a very reverent manner. It wasn't taken lightly at all.

Reprinted with permission from News from Native California, *Spring 1993.*

11

The Sinkyone Intertribal Park Project

by Dennis Rogers-Martinez

A coalition of Indian people is working to realize a vision of ecological and cultural restoration in redwood country.

The first restorationist was the Creator of the earth. The Sinkyone Indian people of the northern California coast called him Nagaicho. One of the last fullbloods, Jack Woodman, told of a dream-encounter with Nagaicho:

Nagaicho came over Elk ridge and he saw where white man had peeled tanbark. He said to me, "It looks like my people lying around, lying around with all their skin cut off." He looked, he looked, he looked once more and he hung his head. He was sad, sad, and he would not look again, he felt so grieved. Tanbark has great power and it all belongs to Nagaicho. He saw men breaking rocks and plowing up grass. He saw all things leaving and going back where they came from. He felt worst about the tanbark. Then Nagaicho told me that he wanted to make another freshet from the ocean—make everybody die so the world would come back as it used to be... You know this is the third time he wanted to make a freshet because the people are so bad.

—Nomland, 1935

TODAY, SOME 120 YEARS LATER, the forests of the Sinkyone country south of Eureka on the California coast still show the scars of more than a century of exploitation, and the timber industry threatens those forests that remain. Recently, however, the ancient Indian vision of land-healing has given life to a new plan for the future of the forest—not through the apocalyptic destruction of the human inhabitants, but through a coalition of tribes working with non-Indians and with state and local governments to acquire a sizeable tract of land in the area once occupied by the To-cho-be-keah (Shelter Cove) Sinkyone people in order to restore it to its historic, pre-contact condition. Created for this purpose in 1987, the Intertribal Sinkyone Wilderness Council (ITSWC) has fostered a vision of both ecological and cultural restoration for the area and has begun to realize this vision in its plan for a 2,800-ha (7,100-acre) Sinkyone Intertribal Park.

The park would serve as a meeting ground for Indian people and as a place to carry on traditional ceremonies, and traditional hunting, fishing and gathering. It would also serve as an educational center, providing Indians and non-Indians with information about Indian cultures and traditional Indian ways. Above all, Sinkyone would become a place to teach our children about the Indian way, a place to experience the forest directly and to learn how to relate to it in respectful ways, a place in which to experience the sacred. Sinkyone will provide an opportunity for Indians and non-Indians to work together on hands-on land restoration work and to learn traditional Indian land management methods.

In this way, the project offers an ideal opportunity for the Earthkeeping program being developed by the Society for Ecological Restoration and the University of Wisconsin-Madison Arboretum to provide opportunities for people to participate in restoration projects at selected sites as a way of learning about natural ecosystems and their history. As a result Earthkeeping is now part of the developing vision for the future of the Sinkyone. What follows is a brief account of the project from my perspective as consulting restorationist for ITSWC and as an American Indian.

The area known as the Sinkyone is in rugged, mountainous country (often exceeding 80 percent slopes), along the coast between Usal and Whale Gulch in northern California. Visitors driving up the coast on Highway I or 101 skirt the area—its ruggedness discourages road building and is one reason the area still retains at least some of its natural character. Here unpaved Mendocino County Road 431 (formerly a haul-road for logging) follows the first main ridge paralleling the sea through thick second growth brush, Douglas-fir, tan oak, redwood, madrone and chinquapin, and provides excellent views of the Pacific from elevations of around 1,200 to 1,500 feet straight up from the ocean. Three small groves of old-growth red woods are all that remain of the historic redwood forest in the only known stretch of coast where both redwoods and mountains come down together to the sea.

Spectacular as it is, the Sinkyone has changed dramatically since the time of European contact, most of the changes having occurred since World War II when intensive logging of the upland redwood forest began. In Indian times the area was a patchwork of well-spaced old-growth temperate rainforests dominated by redwood with Douglas-fir and tan oak. Secondary, with bunchgrass prairies on the ridges and on the coastal bluffs, supporting, according to reports of early travelers, almost unbelievable numbers of animals, fish and birds. This abundant landscape, however, was no wilderness—at least not in the modern sense of nature without people (there is no word in any Indian language for "wilderness"). In fact, Indian populations were considerable. Population estimates by anthropologists are typically very low, not taking into account losses of up to 80 percent or higher from European diseases in the late 18th and early 19th centuries (even before actual contact). Nevertheless, according to these conservative estimates, northern California had the largest population of aboriginal people north of the Valley of Mexico. More over, their attitude was not that of the modern-day preservationist. "When people don't use the plants, they get scarce," an elder of the Makahmo Pomo once said. "You must use them so they will come up again. All plants are like that. If they're not gathered from, or talked to and cared about, they'll die." Accordingly, the people used the resources available to them, and the landscape in which they lived was shaped by their activities including hunting and gathering, both intensive and extensive forms of agriculture, and—especially—burning. Fires deliberately set by Indian women created the park-like look written about by early California travelers. Land health was directly linked to the health of the people, and the health of the land depended on fire. Competence in prescribed burning, therefore, was critical to survival, and the burning maintained a relatively open landscape made up of a mosaic of trees, shrubs, bunchgrasses and forbs. This rich complex of ecological communities ensured a high level of biodiversity and ensured the Indians a variety of animal and vegetable foods. All levels of succession were represented in the same forest— from the pioneer to the climax stage.

Whites referred contemptuously to the Indians of this area as "Diggers"—a reference to the digging sticks the women always carried and used to harvest various under ground plant parts. Anthropologists still refer to Indians like the Sinkyone as "hunter-gatherers." But there is no hard and fast line between hunting and gathering and what Europeans called agriculture. Sinkyone Indians employed both extensive and intensive resource management techniques, including pruning, cultivation, weeding and clearing, selective harvesting and planting, game inventory and management—and of course controlled burning. What they practiced was a kind of agro-ecology.

The Indians kept collecting areas clean by weeding and removing debris. They also cultivated fields of "Indian potatoes" (a catch-phrase that refers to a variety of plants exploited for their tubers and roots, including Brodiaea, Calochortus and Allium, basket sedges (*Carex barbarae*), and medicinal plants—an activity that interrupted the natural process of plant succession and ensured the persistence of a variety of early-successional species. They pruned trees and shrubs such as gray willow (*Salix Hindsiana*), elderberry (*Sambucus glauca*), and hazelnut (*Corylus cornuta*) regularly to ensure strong, straight shoots for baskets and flutes.

By carrying seeds from one camp to another, they expanded the range of many species; some of these crossed with native stock to form hybrids; others developed into new species (we believe we were here much longer than the anthropologists say). For example, coast live oak (*Quercus agrifolia*) may have developed into interior live oak (*Quercus wislizenii*) as acorns were planted in interior places (Personal communication from David Peri, Coast Miwok Indian and professor of anthropology, Sonoma State University, Cotati, Califomia). Coast live oak produces a bitter acorn but makes abundant crops every season. The preferred acorns from tan oak or black oak make good crops only intermittently. Therefore, the coast live oak provided a valuable back-up source—an incentive for Indians to plant them inland, expanding their range. There is reason to believe that activities such as these strongly influenced both the vegetation and the distribution of species in the landscape. In fact, Peri has suggested that large tracts of ethnobotanically important species in northern California are largely the result of Indian planting and harvesting activities over thousands of years.

These activities were, however, regulated by a complex system of social sanctions and religious taboos. Among the well-developed ceremonial traditions were rituals of world renewal, which were carried out periodically to renew and revitalize the earth through ceremonial contact with the spirit world, realm of Natural Law. These traditions, implicitly acknowledging effects of people on the landscape and life forms dwelling there, and seeking to reverse or compensate for it, are common to many indigenous cultures. Today these are being revived by some tribes, and provide a ceremonial and cultural tradition that closely parallels at a spiritual and emotional level what the restorationist seeks to achieve in the landscape itself.

The Indians of the Sinkyone area lived for at least 8,000

years in traditional ways, little influenced by European culture until the middle of the 19th century. The landscape, too, remained largely as it had been for thousands of years. This changed abruptly, however, with contact with Whites during the 1860s. Major ecological changes occurred following contact with the development of cattle and sheep grazing, tan oak bark peeling for the tanning industry, and redwood logging. This violent exploitation of the landscape was accompanied by a systematic assault on the indigenous people—a program of genocide that was a part of one of the most shameful chapters in the history of our nation.

By the 1870s most of the Sinkyone Indian people had been massacred. They were shot down like deer for sport, shot down and scalped for bounties—25 cents for children, 50 cents for women and one dollar for men. And then the earth itself was peeled of her hair, her beautiful green skin of forest trees. Even the sacred redwood trees were cut down and sold.

Major clearcutting of the redwood forest began in the 1890s and continued until after the turn of the century, mostly near the sea, in the more accessible alluvial flats and stream mouths. Following World War II, the upland forest was logged as well.   The last cutting was made in 1985 by Georgia-Pacific under timber harvesting plans approved by the California Department of Forestry. Three pitiful groves of old-growth redwood remained—islands of a few hectares in a sea of thousands of hectares of clearcut devastation on the Lost Coast of Mendocino.

Ecologically, the results have been catastrophic. Researchers have described the North Coast watershed as the "most rapidly eroding, non-glaciated basin of comparable size in North America." The Sinkyone is a land of precipitous cliffs dropping hundreds of feet into the sea. The fragile, fragmented Franciscan sandstone and melange of metamorphic rocks are always falling into the sea. But the luxuriant vegetation has historically slowed erosion. Now the scalped land unravels westward to the sea at an ever increasing rate.

Today, even on the old skid roads, the Sinkyone is so choked with second-growth forest that in many areas it is difficult to walk cross-country. Douglas-fir is coming up in thickets of buckbrush (*Ceanothus* sp.) which earlier had invaded redwood groves following clearcutting and in tense slash fires. The ridges, where the people lived, are choked with manzanita (*Arctostaphylos* spp.), buckbrush and exotic and native pioneer species such as pampas grass (*Cortaderia selloana*), and coast cut-leaf fireweed (*Erechtites arguta*). Indian burial grounds and artifacts and the old Indian trails, which once linked forest openings maintained by Indians and led inland from the coast, have been obliterated by skidroads. And many of the plants once used by the Sinkyone people for food, for medicines, and for materials are either gone or rare. Native clovers were once abundant and widely used for food. At least five species are never seen now. And the native coho salmon, trout, and many species of frogs and salamanders are extinct or nearly so as a result of sediments washed down to the stream from the eroding slopes. Many Indians from the area still go to the Sinkyone to gather seaweed, mussels, surf-fish and abalone, but it is a pitiful harvest compared to former times.

Thoughts of restoration, of bringing back the forests and grasslands of the Sinkyone and making it once again a suitable place for its people began in 1985 when a coalition of local environmentalists and Indians (among whom were Richard Gienger, a non-Indian riparian and fisheries restorationist, and Fred "Coyote" Downing, a Wailaki Indian elder, who are still working with ITSWC) sued the California Department of Forestry and the Georgia Pacific Corporation for failure to consider the cumulative impacts of clearcut logging and failure to protect Sinkyone Indian burial sites. They won their suit in 1985, and Georgia Pacific quickly sold the 2,800 hectares that comprise the area now targeted for acquisition and restoration by ITSWC. A bit over half went to the Trust for Public Lands, the remainder to California Department of Parks and Recreation.

Encouraged by this stay of execution, Bill Wahpepah and Ricardo Tapia of the International Indian Treaty Council formed a coalition with local environmentalists to stop further cutting, protect burial sites and gain access by Indian people to traditional hunting, gathering and fishing places. This initiative led to the formation of ITSWC, which currently operates out of the tribal offices on the Coyote Valley Reservation (Pomo) near Ukiah. Priscilla Hunter, Coyote tribal administrator and then chair of the California State Indian Heritage Commission, lent her considerable authority to the struggle to protect burial sites. In 1988 the Treaty Council requested me to work with the Sinkyone Council as restoration consultant.

What do we mean by "restoration"? In the January/February 1989 issue of *z* I was quoted as follows:

> Restoration is not reforestation. It may include reforestation, but it is much more… Restoration is the bringing back together of people and land in a close working relationship to ensure the health and survival of both. It includes the restoration of respect for Natural Law. But to get to that point of harmony, we are forced to grope in the present darkness—in our ignorance of natural processes—with poorly-defined Euro-American management tools and limited scientific concepts. We must seek out elders who have some memory of what the old-

growth Redwood Forest was like, who remember the plants that were used for medicine, baskets, food, who remember which plants, animals, birds, fish, insects are no longer with us, where they lived, how many, etc. Above all, we need to seek guidance from the Creator in our restoration efforts. We need to ask our elders how to pray to the Spirits that inhabit the Sinkyone, the Spirits that live in the trees, streams, springs, rocks for guidance and understanding.

We must use as best we can the newer management tools of Euro-America, which are appropriate to the new destruction—the scale of which no indigenous people has had to deal with before modem times. As we work on long-term forest restoration, we must bring together our own indigenous knowledge, spiritual heritage, respect for Natural Law, with those Euro-American management tools which conform most closely with natural systems and Natural Laws.

What do we want to restore? We want to restore life. We want to restore the living and sacred relationship between the people and the earth. We want to restore our spirits as we restore the land. We want to restore our culture, our songs, our myths and stories, and the Indian names for creeks and springs. We want to restore our selves. This is what we want to restore at Sinkyone.

Our model for this work will be traditional Indian land stewardship. For knowledge of this we will depend in part on descendants of the Sinkyone people and closely-related tribes. Anthropologists say the Sinkyone are extinct. We know better. The ITSWC has interviewed forty individuals, many of whom have direct genealogical and historic connections with the people called Sinkyone. The native peoples of the area know better than anyone what is going on with the land—where the deer are fawning, how many good soil and water indicator plants are left, which exotic plants and animals are invading, and so forth.

In developing our restoration plan we've used word lists from now-extinct Indian languages to find out what plants and animals were there in pre-Columbian times. From this information we're developing our own endangered species list—plants and animals that may not be on the official lists but that are locally missing or present only in greatly reduced numbers. These include many plants used for medicine, food and fiber, as well as spiritually important animals and birds. Deer, bear, coyote, mountain lion and many species of native rodents and seed-eating birds—all species characteristic of the early- to mid-successional communities common in the area today, are abundant. Animals characteristic of old-growth forests—martens and fish, salamanders, insectivorous birds and the notorious spotted owl—are missing or present only in much reduced relic populations. Salmon and steelhead are nearly gone.

What we are seeing in the Sinkyone is the first phase of classic desertification, a pattern evident not only here, but in many areas of the mountainous West as old-growth forest is removed, reducing both humidity and, in coastal areas, collection of moisture from sea fogs. The bird most sacred to the Sinkyone people, the American condor, may be extinct. Eagles and ravens—powerful medicine birds—are seldom seen, but still exist in the Sinkyone and might be brought back in greater numbers.

Early records show that the temperate rainforests of the Sinkyone were dominated by redwoods, with Douglas-fir as a secondary co-dominant. My survey in 1990 documented a clear shift in favor of the more xerophytic Douglas-fir and tan oak. Among understory plants I also found evidence that the more moisture-demanding species are declining. Members of the lily family were especially hard to find. (This reflects a general pattern in the western mountains. More than a fifth of the species officially listed as "sensitive" by BLM and the Forest Service are members of the Liliaceae that are dependent on moist, fertile soils.) Of the native bunchgrasses once abundant in the area, only Nootka reedgrass (*Calamagrostis nootkanensis*) is still common. Others, notably species of Stipa, Poa, Agrostis, Danthonia, and Festuca are very rare.

In grassland areas on the bluffs above the sea the major influences have been overgrazing by cattle, the introduction of exotic plant species, and the absence of the pre scribed fires of the pre-contact era. Coastal grasslands have been replaced almost completely by exotic perennials like Australian hairy oatgrass (*Danthonia pilosa*) and German velvetgrass (*Holcus lanatus*) and, in the absence of fire, are being invaded by coastal scrub and salt-tolerant Douglas-fir. Native forbs are also scarce. Something conservationists tend to forget: Grassland restoration is not just for the Midwest!

The reason we say that restoration must precede sustained logging (assuming that is even possible at Sinkyone) is that Sinkyone is a marginal site for redwood regeneration. We've documented the beginning stages of desertification in the shift from mesic to more xeric species, which reflects the loss of topsoil, as well as the loss of the tall old-growth humidity-trapping canopy. A climatic anomaly, called by Paul Zinke of UC Berkeley (in *Terrestrial Vegetation of California*, Barbour & Majors) the Mattole Backeddy, begins just north of Sinkyone and includes all of Cape Mendocino. This is where the red wood forest retreats inland to the Eel River, being replaced by extensive coastal grasslands and scrub, brush, Douglas-fir and hardwoods. The King Range (the highest rise in elevation known on the Pacific perimeter in this hemisphere) is whipped by fierce winds which create desiccating down-drafts of warm air. On a smaller scale the steep Sinkyone mountains create the same drying effect. There is just enough sea-fog to nurture redwoods, but because of the downdrafts it doesn't stay long enough to provide the moisture needed for good regeneration in the absence of a forest canopy and undisturbed soils. This regional climatic drying due to deforestation may erase what little margin is left, and the process would only be accelerated by global warming.

The Indian people of the North Coast knew that the redwood trees guarded the water. Countless genera-tions of Indians saw the giant trees capture sea fog, saw it drip down to the ground, saw it come out again in springs on the ridges where the people lived. This knowledge was expressed in the stories the elders told to the children—deep metaphors of the Sacred con-taining life-sustaining, ecological information. When we retrieve these stories we are restoring that deep ecological knowledge for future generations.

Restoration of the water is our main goal at Sinkyone. Everything else will follow from that. Our first job will be thinning and fuel load reduction. The management plan we currently are developing will help in determining our site-specific priorities. We will work within a long time frame. Hand-thinning will provide employment for the Indian and non-Indian communities. Marketing strate-gies for both redwood and Douglas-fir saplings and hard-woods will need to be developed. Earthkeeping volun-teers will be an important complement to our restoration efforts. The California Department of Forestry could pay up to 90 percent of the thinning costs.

The next task will be to start the slow process of bringing back the tall, moisture-trapping forest canopy. We plan to thin redwood stump sprouts in logged areas from 7–15 to only one or two per stump. Where the redwood stumps have failed to regenerate due to dam-age by intense slash fires or equipment, and where Ceanothus thickets (especially on south and west slopes) are now nursing Douglas-fir seedlings, we will hand-plant nursery-grown redwood seedlings. (A native plant nursery is another possible source of support for the restoration work.)

The way we will do this may serve as a model of holistic planning and implementation—a model the agencies simply are not able to provide. For example: instead of cutting the young Ceanothus to make way for redwoods, we will simply allow the short-lived (15–25 years) Ceanothus to begin to die before planting. The nitrogen-fixing Ceanothus will start the slow process of rebuilding the forest soils, check erosion and provide shading for the young redwoods. As the brush dies and collapses (further protecting and rebuilding soil), exotic grasses will begin to

invade, competing with the young trees for nutrients and water. To prevent this we may seed the native biennial or short-lived perennial meadow barley (*Hordeum brachyantherum*) at the time of redwood planting. It is a poor competitor and will not overrun the young trees. It will also act as a buffer to slow down more serious competitors. After two or three years we would then seed a long-lived native bunchgrass like purple needlegrass (*Stipa pulchra*), which takes two or three years to become well-established. By the time the Stipa is a serious com-petitor (five or six years after the tree planting), the red wood root system would be deep enough and extensive enough to withstand grass. We know from our historical model something managers have tended to forget—that Nagaicho meant grass and trees to grow together. Nagaicho also intended that the grass should carry reju-venating fires. When the redwoods are large enough (around 20 years), we will be able to burn. This, along with the formidable root system (root-to-shoot ratio of 10:1), will retard brush re-invasion, which is a principal reason for regeneration failures in western mountains. The de-composition of the bunchgrass root systems will do the main job of soil rebuilding until around 100 years when the litter from the large reedwoods will permanently replenish the soil. The grasses in the meantime will gradually be shaded out in some places, but will remain permanently in other places as little meadows between well-spaced redwoods. Native forbs will be introduced with the bunchgrasses at initial seeding and reintroduced, as necessary, following burning. Native shrubs and ferns will also be introduced following the burns (probably on eight-year or longer cycles), and periodic light fires will be reintroduced. As the vegetation recovers, hydrological processes will recover as well, and springs will once again flow year-round, as in pre-contact times.

If water is the blood of the Mother Earth, then the streams are her blood vessels. The great floods of 1955 and 1964 devastated streambeds, undercutting banks and widening channels to as much as ten times their previous width. Now efforts by organizations such as the Civilian Conservation Corps, the California Fish & Game Depart-ment and private contractors working with ITSWC to construct fish ladders, remove obstacles, and stabilize banks have begun to pay off. In February, 1992, we heard the thump-thump of many spawning steelhead at Sinkyone's Jackass Creek for the first time in years. Much work, however, remains to be done.

Another project will involve planting of redwood seedlings in groves of red alder (*Alnus oregana*) that line the lower reaches of the Sinkyone streams. These origi-nally served as nurseries for redwood regeneration, but no redwoods have appeared in the thickets since the nearby redwood groves were cut and the streams began silting up (sediment loads are now up to 85 times what they were prior to 1955).

A distinctive feature of the project will be its ecological and cultural integration. Upland restoration will proceed hand-in-hand with restoration of waterways and wetlands, and cultural recovery will accompany recovery of the land. In the past ecological restoration projects have been defined almost entirely in landscape terms, but the Sinkyone project will be different in that it will also involve the restoration of indigenous cultures, which we recognize as a major factor in the ecology of the systems we aim to restore. In other words, what we aim to restore is not only the land, but our relationship with it. The project rests on our understanding that the landscape and the people, nature and culture, are ultimately inseparable. The land reflects culture, just as culture reflects the land. Hence restoration of the historic landscape of the Sinkyone depends as much on restoration of the historic Indian cultures that helped shape that landscape as on restoration of old growth forest and bunchgrass prairie.

In this way the Sinkyone project represents a vision for a renewal of the human relationship with nature—and also for the achievement of a healthy relationship between cultures, for the success of a project like the Sinkyone restoration will depend ultimately on cultures working together, and on the European culture now dominant in the area recognizing the indigenous Indian cultures as part of its own heritage.

As an Indian, in this 1992 Quincentennial year, I want to express my conviction that the continuance of this traditional Indian heritage is essential to land restoration. Restorationists, by restoring ecosystems, also restore medicine plants, birds and animals that Indian people need in order to perform world-renewing ceremonies. In turn, these Indian ceremonies help renew the world. This simple truth has been ignored by the dominant culture for 500 years. We are hanging on by just a thin thread. But this thread is the last living link between the native past of all of us in this global village and the future of our children. That is why we must work together.

People from both cultures have a crucial role to play in the restoration of the Sinkyone. Already two or three times each year local Indians gather at Usal Beach in the Sinkyone to perform traditional dances and feast on local traditional foods like surf-fish, salmon, seaweed, abalone, tan oak acorn soup, mussels and deer. Many non-Indians support and attend these gatherings.

Last year the Tule River people brought to the Sinkyone their Bear Dance, the first time a Bear Dance had been performed at Sinkyone in 140 years.

And the old people said:

Nagaicho made the world and patted it down so everything would stay in place. But bad men were not satisfied and tore it down, tore up the ocean banks, tore up the trees, tore down the mountains. Since that time we have had to sing and dance every year to make it right again.

Reference

Nomland, G. A. 1935. *Sinkyone Notes*. University of California Publications in American Archeology and Ethnology, Berkeley, CA. p. 167.

Reprinted with permission from Restoration Management Notes *10:1, Summer 1992.*

The California World-Renewal Tradition

Our story starts at the beginning of time. Our knowledge stems from a race of Spirit Beings whose job at the beginning of time was to unravel the mystery, to discover the ideal way of life on the newly created Earth. By trial and error, intuition and feeling, they unlocked the mysteries one by one. The Spirit Beings were followed by, and their divinely wrought knowledge passed onto us, the Indian people of the Klamath River. In exchange, we assumed responsibility to Fix the Earth each year: to make the world over, through ceremonial re-enactment of the Spirit Beings' first successful World Renewal; to set the world back on its axis. Many of us today still subscribe to this belief. For us the vision of the future is grounded in the responsibility of annually fixing the world. We cannot conceive of a time when stabilizing the world will become an irrelevant act.

—Julian Lang, Klamath Tribe
Introduction to *To the American Indian*
by Lucy Thompson

Gus diZerega

Burning Mountainsides for Better Crops:
Aboriginal Landscape Burning in British Columbia

Nancy J. Turner

Controlled Burning Techniques

TECHNIQUES OF CONTROLLED BURNING are little known, since most of the elders who recall the practice remember only observing it from their younger days, not actually participating in it. From available evidence, mainly the accounts cited earlier, specific sites were preselected for burning over, and from all indications, the times for burning, and the conditions were also selected, as they were by other peoples such as the Slavey of northern Alberta (Lewis, 1978, 1982) and the Salishan and Kootenai peoples of western Montana (Barrett, 1980). Annie York's recollections of her uncle waiting until huckleberry berry picking was finished, then choosing a time just before a rainfall to carry out the burning is in keeping with this suggestion. Suttles (1951a) noted that on southern Vancouver Island burning was carried out in the summer, after the camas harvest. This would have been a dry period, but since, at least in historic times burning was carried out mainly on small islets, it would have been easier to control.

Factors determining the nature of landscape burning for indigenous peoples of Montana and Alberta include: seasonality (fires were usually set in fall or early spring when the ground was wet and hence control better); time of day; relative humidity of certain fuel types; knowledge of winds; slope; size of areas burned; and frequency of burning. To further control set fires, the Slavey employed natural and man-made fire breaks, backfires, and active use of wetted conifer boughs to extinguish or direct the fire (Barrett, 1980; Lewis, 1978, 1982). It can be assumed that these factors were also important to indigenous peoples of British Columbia.

Controlled landscape burning required a detailed and in-depth knowledge of natural systems, especially the ecological characteristics of vegetation, and the successional nature of plant communities, as well as of various geographical and climatic features of the landscape. This knowledge, acquired through centuries and generations of careful observation and experimentation, has seldom been acknowledged by non-Native people. In fact, foresters and rangers have often regarded aboriginal landscape burning as nothing more than "carelessness" (cf. Hunn, 1990: 130).

Resource Species Enhanced by Burning

Seventeen plant species (within two general categories) were reported by indigenous peoples to be enhanced by periodic landscape burning (Table 2). Of the species mentioned, eleven are shrubby fruiting species, and the remaining six are herbaceous plants with edible underground parts. All of the species have the capacity to regenerate from underground rhizomes or subterranean storage organs. Hamilton and Yearsley (1987), in a study of repopulation strategies of plants after clearcutting and burning on moist sites in the Sub Boreal Spruce Zone of central British Columbia, note that fruiting shrub species such as *Sambucus racemosa* (red elderberry), *Ribes laxiflorum* (white flowered currant), *Ribes lacustre* (swamp gooseberry), and *Rubus parviflorus* (thimbleberry) readily re-establish through resprouting from underground rhizomes, although they found that *Vaccinium membranaceum* (black mountain huckleberry) was slow to re-grow after burning.

In general, it appears that many the species whose growth and productivity are increased following landscape burning are successional species requiring clearings or open canopy for optimum growth, or at least somewhat tolerant of open conditions. For example, Minore (1972) summarizes the situation for huckleberries and blueberries:

Most huckleberry fields originated from the uncontrolled wildfires that were common in the Northwest before modern fire protection and control techniques were applied. Ecologically, these fields are seral—temporary stages in the natural succession from treeless burn to climax forest. Without fire or other radical disturbance, huckleberries gradually are crowded out by invading trees and brush. A few years after establish-

11

ment they produce a maximum amount of berries; then production gradually declines as other shrubs and trees dominate the site.... The acreage occupied by thin-leaved huckleberry fields is declining rapidly as old burns become reforested and new burns become increasingly rare. Many formerly productive huckleberry areas now produce no berries at all. Others are shrinking as trees and brush invade along their edges.

From the testimonies of the native elders, such as Baptiste Ritchie and the late Julia Kilroy of Coldwater in the Nicola Valley, regrowth of the "root" plants after burning is accompanied by a notable increase in the size of the edible portion. Julia Kilroy, for example, recalled having seen some bulbs of tiger lily (*Lilium columbianum*) the size of tennis balls from a place where the area had been burned over the previous year, and attributed the immense size to the burning (Turner *et al.* 1990:127). Possibly increased growth would result from an increased supply of available nutrients near the surface of the ground following burning (cf. Minore, 1972). Connor and Cannon (in this volume) provide further evidence for this, noting that fire increases the pH of the soil through release of alkaline ions such as phosphorus, potassium, calcium and magnesium, and cite studies showing that these nutrients are more readily accessible to plants after a fire. The amount of nutrients released varies with the type of soil and intensity of the burn. Burning would also be expected to reduce competition from fire intolerant species (Joe Antos, personal communication, 1991).

Landscape Burning Today

Many aboriginal people in British Columbia still rely on wild foods for substantial portion of their diet. The use of wild foods and traditional medicines, considered an important part of the cultural heritage of First Peoples, is being promoted in native communities (cf. 'Ksan, People of 1980, Coqualeetza Education Training Center 1981, Port Simpson, The People of and School District No. 52, 1983, Secwepemc Cultural Education Society 1986). In general, the traditional diet of Indigenous Peoples of Canada is considered to be a healthy one, and continuing and increasing use of wild foods is desirable from many perspectives (Kuhnlein and Turner, 1991). Given this situation, the enhancement of habitat for the growth of wild plant and animal foods should be given priority.

Fire ecologists and wildlife biologists in western North America are rethinking the strategy of total forest fire suppression which has dominated forest management practices in the present century. For example, Parminter (1978) notes that, as well as fire control, "...the skilled application of fire as a forest land management tool" may be undertaken in some situations (Parminter 1978:3).

It might be argued that the present forest management

policies of extensive clearcutting followed by slashburning in both coastal and interior forests is imitative of previous aboriginal landscape burning in the province. Indeed, several of the elders quoted in this study, including Alec Peters of Mount Currie and Hilda Austin of Lytton, said that logged areas were where people now went to gather berries, and also to hunt. Hilda Austin (personal communication, 1982) discussed going to pick huckleberries on Thompson Mountain, about 20 km south of Spences Bridge, on Nicomen Creek:

We were climbing, right to the other side of the mountain. The guys logs it, cuts, that, and c'elc'ala (Vaccinium membranaceum) grows on hat, that's where we were picking it... I guess there's lots of snow when he logs it, and that's why the stumps are long. Yes, that's where we were picking the huckleberries.... But it's just starting to grow, I guess. It's short. ...I see the boys, he went and hunts over there. They didn't cut the whole thing, you know, just certain places. Still, there're deer....

On the other hand, others do not consider these areas to be as good for berries as the traditionally burned places. Annie York (personal communication, January, 1991) said, "They [berries] do come after logging but it's not the right kind; it's not as good." Intensive burning can be detrimental because it can result in decreased organic matter in the soil and increased erosion (cf. Connor and Cannon, this volume). Furthermore, aboriginal people say that access is often cut off to them when they try to go into logged areas or powerline rights-of-way. Additionally, with many areas now being sprayed with Roundup and other herbicides to eliminate brush and species such as alder (*Alnus rubra*) that might compete with commercial forest trees, people fear contamination. In 1986, for example, the Lillooet Tribal Council appealed six permits authorizing the forests ministry to apply Roundup in the Cayoosh, Texas and Lillooet drainages, and a highways permit for application of Tordon 22K on a spot basis (Pynn, 1986). The Haida have also expressed grave concerns about pesticides and other pollutants contaminating their wild foods and medicines (Bohn, 1987).

There is another problem complicating the picture of traditional landscape burning and aboriginal resource use. Many aggressive exotic species have been introduced within the past century and before. Some of these, such as Scotch broom (*Cytisus scoparius*) on southern Vancouver Island, invade large tracts of land formerly occupied by indigenous plants. Broom and other weedy species do not seem to be harmed by burning, and can become quickly established in burned or logged areas once the original cover is removed (see Figures 7 and 8). [Plant ecologist Joe Antos (personal communication, 1991), however, believes that annual burning of an area would reduce or eliminate broom.] Introduced species such as thistles (*Cirsium vulgare* and *C. arvense*), burdock (*Arctium minus*), knapweed (*Centaurea diffusa* and *C. maculosa*), mustards (*Brassica* spp., *Sisymbrium* spp. and related species) and foxglove (*Digitalis purpurea*) are taking over large tracts of logged, burned, or otherwise disturbed lands in British Columbia. These species, and the livestock they often accompany on range and meadow lands both in coastal and interior areas, pose an increasing threat to the productivity of traditional resource species. Trampling and overgrazing of pigs and sheep on southern Vancouver Island and the small islands of Haro and Rosario Straits, and undoubtedly the weedy species which accompanied them, spoiled the once productive camas beds of the Straits Salish people in many places (cf. Suttles, 1951:59). Botanie Valley, by historical account one of the most productive traditional root-digging grounds of the entire province, has been changed irrevocably by trampling, grazing livestock, and the weedy plants accompanying them (cf. Turner, et al., 1990).

Mary Thomas, Secwepemc (Shuswap) elder from the Salmon Arm area has observed, during the course of her own lifetime, a marked deterioration in the size and abundance of traditional root vegetables such as yellow avalanche lily (*Erythronium grandiflorum*), and she believes this is due to the invasion of couch grass (*Agropyron repens*), knapweed and other weeds, and to trampling and overgrazing by livestock (Mary Thomas, personal communication, October and December, 1991). In one intentionally burned area of grazing land on the Skeetchestn Reserve (Secwepemc) in Deadman's Creek valley near Savona, there was a dramatic reduction of knapweed in the first year following the burn, but instead, the entire area was populated by a dense growth of another weed, hedge mustard (*Sisymbrium loeselii*) (personal observation, 1990, 1991).

Thus, even if aboriginal landscape burning practices were reinstated, the resulting vegetation would not have the same composition as it would have prehistorically. The situation is similar in California and elsewhere. Timbrook, et al. (1982:165) note for California, "...the effects and frequency of grass fires today are not necessarily comparable with those in aboriginal times before introduced weeds and heavy grazing destroyed native grasslands...."

If landscape burning to increase production of traditional plant resources were to be reincorporated into forest management strategies of the future, it would have to be done with caution and with careful monitoring of effects on native plant communities. Simple mimicking of past burning techniques may not produce the same enhancement of resource species. Minimal soil distur-

bance is obviously desirable to avoid damage to the underground reproductive parts of berry and other resource plants, and to avoid creating areas that are easily invaded by weeds. Soil temperatures that are too hot may imperil the survivability of some resource species. Much on the variable effects of burning is already known to forest ecologists, who have been accumulating data on ecological effects of fire for the past quarter century (cf. Walstad, et al., 1990). Additionally, as stressed by Phillips (1985), different landscape burning strategies were used by aboriginal peoples for different objectives and on different sites. Furthermore, the effects of fire on each ecosystem and site can vary significantly; some sites might be detrimentally affected by fire (Arno, 1985). Nevertheless, with caution, it may well be worthwhile to attempt burning over certain restricted sites in the traditional way. Careful attention to season, weather and other factors can reduce potentially adverse effects traditionally associated with fire (Little, 1990). Hand pruning and mechanical brush-cutting might also be investigated as alternatives to landscape burning.

Conclusions

Aural accounts by contemporary indigenous people in British Columbia, especially those of the grandparent generation, provide many records of the practice of intentional landscape burning. Although this has not been done for many years, because of government fire suppression policies dominant in the present century, records indicate the practice was once widespread. The main purpose of landscape burning was to enhance the growth and production of plant food resources, especially certain types of berries and root vegetables, as well as to create good forage for deer and other game.

Burning was generally done at the end of the harvest season, and optimum productivity of berries and root crops was said to occur after about three years. Rotation of burning areas was practiced, to achieve continual production in an overall area.

The importance of wild plant resources which are noncommercial and therefore do not feature in the mainstream economy has also been generally overlooked in resource planning and management in British Columbia and elsewhere. Perhaps it is time to reevaluate the directions of forest management. New forestry should both be more accommodating of the needs and traditional practices of Indigenous Peoples, and give more recognition to the values of traditional resources.

The foregoing is excerpted from a larger paper by Nancy J. Turner. Reprinted with permission.

11

Gardeners in Eden

Kat Anderson and Gary Paul Nabhan

The first people of America not only revered the wilderness, they managed it with loving attention to the needs of diversity and abundance.

We might consider doing likewise.

A NATIVE AMERICAN ELDER sets a fire under the oaks to destroy duff infested with acorn weevil in Yosemite Valley. Edging a nearby stream, a dull-brown, gnarled, big-leaf maple is pruned by a basket maker, so that it will produce straight, sienna-hued sprouts for her next season's weaving. The sticky rhizomes of a bracken fern are dug up by Miwok Indian women over by Mirror Lake, loosening the soil and transforming the patch into a garden....

These Yosemite landscapes, shaped by centuries of Indian burning, pruning, sowing, weeding, coppicing, tillage, and selective harvesting, were the same ones early Europeans and later generations of nature-lovers were wont to view as unmarked by human manipulation. Few whites could recognize the ingenuity of indigenous management practices that encouraged the growth and maintenance of a variety of wild resources—not even John Muir, who spent more time rambling though the region than any other person of his time (and most since). Muir exemplified the Euro-American urge to fully experience the wildness of the Sierra. Yet not only the Yosemite trails he walked upon but the vegetation mosaic he walked through were the legacy of Miwok subsistence ecology; he simply missed all but the most blatant signs of indigenous land management. "How many centuries Indians have roamed these woods nobody knows," he wrote on one occasion, "but it seems strange that heavier marks have not been made....Indians walked softly and hurt the landscape hardly more than the birds and squirrels, and their brush and bark huts last hardly longer than those of wood rats, while their enduring monuments, excepting those wrought on the forests by fires they made to improve their hunting grounds, vanish in a few centuries."

The selective vision of Muir and the other early preservationists influenced an environmental movement that ever since has generally perpetuated the myth of pre-Columbian America as virgin, nearly uninhabited wilderness. The tradition was echoed in the famous 1963 "Leopold Report" to the National Park Service, which declared that each large national park should maintain or recreate a "vignette of primitive America," seeking to restore "conditions that prevailed when the area was first visited by the white man"—this in spite of the fact that as many as twenty million indigenous people were hunting, gathering, burning, tilling, and otherwise managing North America when Columbus appeared to them. And, for the most part, doing a better job of it than we have since.

When Hernan DeSoto and his soldiers entered what is now South Carolina in 1540, the chronicler of their adventures noted that they "journeyed a full league in garden-like lands where there were many trees, both those which bore fruit and others; and among these trees one could travel on horseback without any difficulty, for they were so far apart that they appeared to have been planted by hand." Some probably were, as it happened. Careful reconstructions of historic landscape ecology made by ethnohistorian Julia Hammett have demonstrated that South eastern Indians managed such landscapes by burning, clearing, and subsequently replanting useful trees into park-like patches. "Apparently," she says, "Native Americans initiated and maintained park lands extending perhaps several miles beyond the obvious limits of their towns." Ethnobiologist Eugene Hunn believes that enough fragments of these traditions have become known that we can now "firmly reject the stereotype of hunter-gatherers as passive food collectors in opposition to active, food producing agriculturists." In some scholarly circles, there are those who would go even further, contending that native peoples commonly depleted the most highly valued local fuel wood and wildlife resources before moving on to ravage another area; only when their population densities remained low and their technologies primitive could they escape the consequences of their destructive habits.

This interpretation—that which holds that the Indians had virtually no impact at all—ignores the vast terrain between the two extremes. If either of these stereotypes were generally true, we would not see the development of the sophisticated taxonomies, taboos, and management practices for key wild resources that were so widespread among Native communities. It is more likely that indigenous cultures developed conservation practices when it became clear that important resources were getting scarce.; the more crucial the resource, the stronger the practice became. The Paiute in western Nevada, for example, otherwise would have had no reason to cut bow staves from juniper trees as they did—in a manner that did not kill the trees but instead ensured the continued production of straight-grained wood from the same trees. Other Paiute would not have gone to the effort of irrigating stands of wild hyacinth and yellow nutgrass in the Owens Valley of California, increasing their yields severalfold. Likewise, the Ojibway along Lake Superior's marshlands would have had no reason to replant about a third of their wild-rice harvest to ensure a yearly increase, or to have sown additional stands where they did not formerly exist.

Centuries before the United States Congress passed the Sustained Yield and Multiple Use Act of 1960, the harvesting techniques employed by many Native Americans allowed for the sustained-yield production of wild plants. Rhizomes of bracken ferns used in Pomo basketry and sweet flags used for Pawnee medicines were dug in ways that stimulated new rhizomes to grow into spur plants. Mushrooms were gathered in a way that did not disturb the mycelia in order to ensure future production. Subterranean foods, such as groundnuts, yampah, tiger lilies, and Indian celeries, were harvested in quantity, but many bulblet, cormlet, and tuber fragments were purposely left in the loosened earth with less competition to deter their growth the following season. For many curative plants, Navajo medicine men still refrain from harvesting from the same stand two years running, granting periods of rest and regrowth between those of tillage and extraction.

From experimental ecological and horticultural studies on key resource plants, it has become clear that certain traditional gathering methods stimulated and sustained yields much as pruning and fertilizing aid orchard crops. What is intriguing is that the historic levels of production common to well-known subsistence grounds may have been achieved by human mediation. Today, Indian elders across the country remember a more abundant America, before the disruption of their traditional management strategies.

In the absence of human-set fires, for example, the berry bushes of Oregon no longer produce the thick crops of huckleberries recorded in oral histories. The hazelnut and beargrass of northwestern California's forests are regarded by Native basket makers to be of poorer quality today. In the Sonoran Desert's dunes, an underground parasitic plant called sandfood is now considered endangered in two states, yet it was historically encountered year-round over a large area where Sand O'odham Indians once migrated. The few remaining Sand Indians claim that it has decreased in abundance and quality since their people were no longer able to gather it on a regular basis, which stimulated the branching of sweeter, more tender tissue—though others say it is because of the decline in the O'odham rainmaking traditions. "There was plenty of rain in those days," Sand Indian elder Alonso Puffer remembered, "and the desert yielded lots of food. The Sand Indians dug up a sweet potato-like plant with long roots that grows in the sand, and they ate it raw. Now these same plants are very bitter. They don't taste the same."

Conservation biologists have recently come to appreciate the fact that Native Americans not only were stewards of major food resources, they also protected certain plants and animals that were too rare to have ever been valued on utilitarian grounds alone. In New Mexico, prehistoric Indians apparently safeguarded a chance hybrid between two cholla cacti that are seldom found together today. The hybrid cactus, known as Opuntia viridiflora, now persists only around ancient pueblo sites in the Upper Rio Grande watershed, where urbanization and other non-Indian land uses currently threaten it.

Similarly, over twenty species of threatened Arizona desert cacti and herbs are known, named, and nursed along by the Tohono O'odham, desert people who protect in natural habitat or in their home gardens some of the few remaining populations of these rarities. Although some of these plants continue to be used occasionally, the O'odham cite reasons other than pure economics for being concerned about the survival of the species; their importance to cultural identity and history is demonstrated by their association with sacred places and stories.

Indigenous peoples have managed their surroundings on many levels. Often, a woodland was manipulated to encourage the growth of selected species: oaks to produce acorns, mock orange trees to produce arrows, or elderberries to produce flutes. Throughout the Sierra Nevada today, there remain a handful of Maidu, Miwok, and Mono elders who carefully prune individual redbuds to stimulate the production of long, blood-red sprouts, cherished for basketry designs. Old, crooked, insect-infested branches are snipped away. When the women return the following season, each shrub has been miraculously transformed into a storehouse of straight, supple, deep-colored suckers suitable for basket weaving. "It's like pruning an apple tree to increase your apple supply," one weaver said when interviewed. "Before these tools came along," said another, referring to her pruning shears, "my grandmother used to pile brush onto redbuds, willows, and sourberries, and light them on fire to get the nice sprouts."

While redbud frequently grows singly or in small patches, plants such as sedge, sawgrass, and bracken fern flourish in dense stands that demand another kind of management to sustain their productivity. If you walk with Pomo women into their favorite sedge populations along central California rivers, you will see rigorously weeded gardens of evenly spaced plants that have been carefully tended for the white root—a rhizome prized in basketry. These small, single-crop edge fields are managed to produce a continuous supply of long, straight rhizomes with no subsequent branching. Elders of the tribe assert that pruning the white root exposes the plants to no more disturbance than they can tolerate naturally; the impact is not unlike that of periodic flooding or rodent burrowing. "And if we don't use these plants," one Pomo woman said, "they'll die."

The comment was no mere rationalization. It was supported by observation of sedge patches that have not been worked in years. Tangled masses of weedy annuals are mixed with sedges "that are no good"—their white roots are short, with kinks, knots and bends that render them unsuitable for weaving. In contrast, when rhizomes are dug up and pruned off a mother plant, this process reinitiates production of appropriately shaped white root. Pomo Indians are considered among the best basket makers in the world, but the quality of their work results from tending plants in the wild quite as much as from meticulous preparation and the actual weaving.

Many indigenous cultures know forests as well as they know individual trees. Certain American cultures are cognizant of species guilds, associations of flora and fauna that they sometimes manage to their benefit. Indians throughout the arid subtropics and tropics not only know where wild chiles grow, for example, but under what shrubs the peppers grow and which birds disperse the seeds of both. The Chontal Maya of Tabasco, Mexico, conceptually associate the Great Kiskadee with wild peppers, and intentionally open up small patches in the forest to which these birds disperse the chile seeds—which the Mayans can later harvest.

Traditional managers of wildlands also classify and manipulate habitat mixes much as they do plant populations. Some of the habitat mosaics are anthropogenically maintained; that is to say, Native managers keep vegetation communities in different stages of succession, in clear proximity to one another, to maintain the heterogeneity of plants and animals that can be gathered there. Through burning or clearing to create ecotones or habitat edges, these people have hit upon the same processes that some professional foresters have discovered to increase wildlife abundance or diversity. (There are, however, key differences: the logging industry often uses wildlife habitat enhancement as its obfuscation for simply eliminating old growth and planting uniform stands in its stead.)

Environmental historians Stephen Pyne and Henry Lewis have demonstrated that burning to sustain habitat for animal populations critical to tribal subsistence was a widespread tradition in America. On the prairie/woodland edge, fire enhanced buffalo habitat; in the tules of the Colorado River watershed, it favored wood rats and cottontail rabbits; in the Great Basin, deer and antelope increased following burns, and in California, hunters gleaned grasshoppers, hares, and deer from recently burned woodland edges.

The best-known examples of such Indian-created habitat are the twin Sonoran Desert oases of Quitovac and Quitobaquito, the latter in Organpipe Cactus National Monument, Arizona. Through burning, flood-irrigating, transplanting, and seed-sowing to create different contiguous patches of vegetation, O'odham families have nurtured a diversity of plant and bird species far greater than that for any areas of comparable size in the Sonoran Desert.

Yet after the last O'odham left Quitobaquito in the 1950's, a park superintendent decided to deepen the oasis pond, eliminate burning and irrigation for pastures and orchards, and halt any replanting of cottonwoods, willows, or other wild plants, native or nonnative. As the oasis lost its dynamic nature, biologists began to notice declines in the endangered pupfish and mud turtle populations there. Fortunately, subsequent park managers and biologists became concerned and began to look for management options that might reverse the process. Ironically, they independently came upon some of the same management practices that the O'odham had used there in previous decades (and are still used at Quitovac): the periodic flooding of tree stands; diversifying water depths to encourage a wider mix of semi-aquatic plants; transplanting mesquite and other natives; and cleaning out deadfall in microhabitats where it inhibits sprouting of other plants. Quitobaquito is now "recovering"—if not to its pre-human condition at least to the dynamic commingling of natural and cultural processes that encouraged high biodiversity. The National Park Service recently received the Arizona Regis-Tree Award from a coalition of conservation groups, Native American heritage projects, and sustainable agriculture organizations in gratitude for reversing the loss of plant genetic resources at Quitobaquito.

The Quitobaquito management history is but one example of recent scientific investigations validating the conservation benefits of traditional wildland practices based in indigenous science. Whereas disturbance was once categorically considered a dirty word to most conservation biologists and wilderness advocates, it is now recognized that some wild plants and animals require a certain level of exposure to fires, floods, or loosened soils to rejuvenate their populations. For centuries, indigenous cultures provided low- to medium-level disturbance in small patches, and in the absence of this, it is probable that a number of disturbance-adapted species have declined. In the Indiana Dunes National Lakeshore, for instance, biologists have confirmed that a large portion of the area's endangered plants require anthropogenic disturbance to persist. Without periodic fires and newly-formed blowouts in the dunes, these plants would be locally extirpated.

Western scientists have found several reasons for deferring to the folk science of indigenous peoples. In the Sonoran Desert, only about one fifth of all the endangered plant species have been adequately studied. Government agencies seldom provide more than 55,000 per species for a year of data-gathering required to locate, protect, or rescue a threatened plant. In contrast, well over a quarter of this endangered desert flora is intimately known by Native American dwellers, who have detailed knowledge of changes in the distribution and abundance of the these species. By working with elderly Indian residents, Navajo biologist Donna House has tracked down a number of additional populations of rare desert plants formerly unknown to conservation biologists. Assistance from such Native American consultants can help endangered plant surveys go much further on the little resources available to them.

Indigenous knowledge and management can also help with the reintroduction of wildlife and the restoration of habitats. In central Australia, where a third of all desert mammals have disappeared in the last fifty years, zoologists Ken Johnson and Andrew Burbridge requested assistance from aborigines in reversing this trend. Cognizant that the few mammologists who had preceded them in the Tanami Desert had left little in the way of distributional records to go by, they began to talk with aboriginal elders who had spent decades in the bush observing wildlife. These elders helped Burbridge and Johnson target microhabitats suitable for translocations of rufous hare-wallabies and bilbies from remnant populations and then offered suggestions about fire management of the vegetation.

Indigenous people of North America have initiated several of their own efforts to better conserve and manage wildlands. The Salish-Kutenai tribes of the Northwest have designated the Mission Mountain wilderness area on reservation lands to protect grizzly bear habitat. Likewise, on the Yakima and Warm Springs reservations, considerable land has been set aside for wildlife reserves,

where tribal law forbids hunting. The Navajo Nation has collaborated with the Nature Conservancy on a Natural Heritage program to inventory rare plants, animals, and habitats on the largest reservation in the United States. And recently, the Tohono O'odham Nation followed the lead of their Cila River Pima relatives and has worked to strengthen its native-plant protection laws to preserve both cultural and natural resources. And in reviewing their tribal regulations, Natural Resources committee members discovered that the first act ever passed through their founding Tribal Council a half century ago sought to prohibit the destruction or removal of native cacti from the Tohono O'odham reservation.

We see such efforts as a returning to sources, and it is worth reflecting on the root meaning of the word resource. That root is not "an economic commodity" or "raw material," but the Old French resoudre, "to rise again," or "to recover." It is often noted that wilderness is the ultimate wellspring of life, and for that reason we must revive its significance in our modern society. We may also want to recover a sense of how ancient place-based cultures studied, used, managed, and protected wildlands, for those diverse traditions may offer us some options for the future not presently contained in Western schemes for the scientific management of wilderness.

And perhaps there remains the possibility of regaining something still larger: the capacity for future generations to behave as natives once more, to belong to particular landscapes, instead of being endlessly adrift in a cosmopolitan sea where each place is treated just like any other. When such a sensibility reemerges among modern cultures, they will have begun restoring their ability to coexist with wild creatures, and wilderness with, "not man apart" from it will become more than just another slogan.

Reprinted from Wilderness, *Fall 1991.*

11

California Indian Horticulture

M. Kat Anderson

FOR MILLENNIA, native people have used the vast diversity of California's flora as a source of food, medicine, basketry, weapons, tools, games, shelters, and ceremonial items. Plants were integral to every facet of Indian culture, accompanying people in major rituals and life events such as childbirth, puberty rites, burial practices and religious festivals. Plants were talked to, prayed for, and thanked with offerings. Deference to the living spirit of plants, as well as continual use of plant parts, was believed to be essential to ensure a sustained yield and diversity of plants to meet Indians' cultural needs. This ancient relationship that Indians maintained with plants included the protecting and tending of favored plant species using an array of horticultural techniques. Through coppicing, pruning, sowing, weeding, burning, digging, and selective harvesting, California Indians encouraged desired characteristics of individual plants such as larger leaf size, branch elongation, bark color, flowering stalk strength and number, and straighter rhizomes. On a larger scale, Indians managed plant mosaics, to attract wild game, eliminate brush for increased visibility and ease of movement, and encourage a diversity of food crops. Today California Indians often refer to this horticulture as "caring about" the plant. It involves activities such as pruning diseased parts of favored plants, weeding around plants to decrease competition and aerate the soil, replanting the smaller bulblets of harvested plants, and scattering seed. Modern Indian people of tribes such as the Yurok, the Southern Sierra Miwok, the Hupa, the Pomo, the Chuckchansi Yokuts, and others still continue a tradition of indigenous horticulture. Although missionaries, anthropologists and settlers provide us with the earliest written records of California Indian cultures, their perception is that thousands of years of Indian plant harvesting had little influence on the shaping of California plant communities. The degree of influence has recently gained increasing attention among anthropologists, ecolo-gists and resource managers and it is changing the image of the California Indian from one of a hunter-gatherer to that of horticulturist.

Contemporary Uses of Native Plants

According to the 1980 U.S. Census, the state's American Indian population is 201,311 persons and twenty-five percent of this figure or 50,000 people are California Indians. Many of the native tribes are governed by tribal councils and at least 25 tribes have petitioned the Bureau of Indian Affairs for federal acknowledgment, a process by which the government recognizes the group as having sovereign status and enters into a government-to-government relationship with it. California Indian tribes have spent a century and a half resisting Anglo appropriation and restriction of their plant resources. Today Indian descendants of different tribes still gather plants on California wild lands and on private property to meet cultural needs. Their present plant knowledge has grown out of a blending of inherited memory of old knowledge with a revitalized interest in their cultural heritage. Major California Indian plant use categories include basketry, ceremonial items, and foods. Grasses, sedges, vines, ferns, herbs, shrubs and trees all contribute suitable plant material for California Indians' cultural needs. Plant parts still harvested include: bark, berries, branches, bulbs, rhizomes, corms, tubers, cones, flowers, leaves, pitch, roots, seeds and stems. For example, the branches of willows (*Salix* spp.), the flower stalks of deergrass (*Muhlenbergia rigens*), the roots of ponderosa pine (*Pinus ponderosa*), the fronds of the five finger fern (*Adiantum pedatum*) and the rhizomes of bracken fern (*Pteridium aquilinum* var. *pubescens*) are still gathered for basketry material. The variety of plant foods still harvested demonstrate the tremendous diversity of the traditional Indian diet. The berries of manzanita (*Arctostaphylos* spp.) and sourberry (*Rhus trilobata*) are made in to refreshing beverages such as manzanita cider and sourberry fizzies. A variety of mushrooms are collected under ponderosa pine trees, or on the trunks of willows or alders at the borders of foothill streams, and are used in stews and gravies. Some individuals still collect Ephedra species and make hot beverages, Indian tea. Gooseberries (*Ribes roezlii*), huckleberries (*Vaccinium* spp.), salmonberries (*Rubus spectabilis*) and raspberries (*Rubus leucodermis*) provide after noon snacks and berries such as elderberry (*Sambucus caerulea*) are gathered in late summer and used in pies and jellies. Indian potatoes, the underground stems of various herbaceous plants, (*Sanicula* spp., *Brodiaea* spp., *Lilium* spp.) are dug and eaten raw or boiled. Seeds include acorns from different oak (*Quercus* spp.) species, chinquapin (*Castanopsis* spp.) nuts, and pine nuts of one or more kinds (*Pinus sabiniana, Pinus monophylla, Pinus lambertiana*).

California Indian Horticulture

Recent evidence suggests that for the California Indian the harvesting of plant materials required rigorous, patient work, long before the weaving of an Indian basket, the making of a weapon, or the eating of a meal could begin. Indians chose their harvesting sites carefully with respect to environmental factors such as soil type, light, and moisture in order to provide the best conditions for growth of preferred plants. Initial management of the selected sites was often necessary before a sufficient quantity of any of these plant materials could be harvested. California Indians practiced a variety of vegetation management methods the most prevalent of which were coppicing, soil and weed management, tillage, and burning. These horticultural techniques were applied to plant communities for the purposes of improving wild life habitat, facilitating seed gathering, and increasing forest visibility. Techniques were also applied to individual plants to assure the availability of some useful plant part, either edible or utilitarian, and/or to change the plant's morphological characteristics, usually for utilitarian purposes.

Coppicing

Many cultural products made by California Indian tribes for domestic use required special types of branches such as looped stirring sticks, rods for baskets, and arrows. The best plant materials were long, straight, slender switches with inconspicuous leaf scars, and no lateral branching. Called "withes" or "sprouts" in the literature, these types of branches seldom occurred naturally on mature plants, and therefore, to obtain a sufficient supply, shrubs were coppiced (cut to almost ground level) at least one full growing season before harvest. A shrub that had never been harvested or coppiced before, in most cases, con-

tained very few "usable" shoots (defined as twelve inches or longer with no lateral branching). Interviews with North Fork Mono, Chukchansi Yokuts, Central and Southern Miwok individuals reveal that the severe pruning (coppicing) of plants is still conducted today with pruning shears or a hand or power saw. The technique is mainly applied to shrubs for the collection of branches for basketry materials. Some of the species still coppiced include: redbud (*Cercis occidentalis*), deerbrush (*Ceanothus integerrimus*), buckbrush (*Ceanothus cuneatus*), sourberry (*Rhus trilobata*), red willow (*Salix melanopsis*) and sandbar willow (*Salix hindsiana*). Each of these plant species responds to pruning by vigorously sprouting new shoots from dormant or adventitious buds. The result is increased numbers of long, straight, slender switches with inconspicuous leaf scars, and no lateral branching. These are the characteristics most valued by basket makers. This contrasts with a wild shrub which has a mottled, cracked bark and twisted branches that are forked and often brittle. Where the twig or branch joins a larger branch or fork there is a notably more fragile area, making this section unsuitable for basketry. Consistent, frequent pruning produces a plant of smaller stature, with many small-diameter boles that are easy to reach and cut, saving the basket weaver harvesting effort and time.

Soil and Weed Management

The roots of species such as sawgrass (*Cladium mariscus var. californicum*) the rhizomes of sedge (*Carex barbarae*) and the rhizomes of bracken fern were harvested by California Indians to provide the structural and design elements in baskets. Roots and rhizomes were generally dug in the fall or winter after sufficient rains and before the ground froze, although all times of the year have been documented, depending on the plant species. The preferred digging implement of most California Indian tribes was a sharpened digging stick made of mountain mahogany, buckbrush or some other hard wood, because it allowed economical harvesting without breaking the length of the plant part. Native Americans dug down till they hit the rhizome or root and then delicately followed along it length, moving back the dirt with their hands. The rhizome or root was then torn or cut from the parent plant. Roots of ponderosa pine and gray pine (*Pinus sabiniana*) were harvested with a small obsidian ax or by slowly burning through the green root with a small fire. Long straight roots or rhizomes, free of branching, with few or no kinks, unimpeded by rocky soils, or weed competition were preferred by basket weavers. Again, these types of underground plant parts seldom occurred naturally. Therefore, areas were carefully selected and managed to create suitable growing conditions to promote the desired characteristics. Conifer roots, fern rhizomes, and sedge rhizomes are very much affected by the types and conditions of the soil in which they grow. When the growth of a root or rhizome is not restricted by soil compaction, or weed competition, its size and quality significantly increases. Therefore when harvesting rhizomes and roots, Indian basket weavers selected sandy soil types that produced the best plant material. In these sites, the rhizomes grew easily in the loose soils and reached great lengths. Silt and clay beds usually were not suitable areas for vesting, since the soils were not easily penetrable, reducing the rhizome length and straightness. The cultivation of the proper kind of sedge or bracken rhizomes (long, straight, few bends or kinks) involved the cutting of rhizomes from the parent plant, and weeding around the plant. This caused rapid elongation of new, long and straight rhizomes to grow out of the spur of the parent plant with lengths of up to six feet recorded in the literature. In the case of conifer roots, sometimes sandy soil was hauled in and placed around the roots of certain trees to provide a soil medium that produced straighter and longer roots. The Indian vesting of conifer roots of lengths up to four feet have been recorded. Conifer roots with gnarls and knots make splitting the branches difficult. Sedge rhizomes, bracken fern rhizomes, gray pine roots and ponderosa pine roots are still highly valued by gatherers from various tribes (Miwok, Pomo, Maidu) for basketry starts, sewing strands and foundations of coiled baskets. Tools used today include a digging stick, metal fork or trowel. Little is known about the impacts of Indian soil and weed management or the pruning of roots and rhizomes on selected plant species. Indians today often assert that Indian tending of areas stimulates increased vegetative production, actually increasing the size of a managed tract.

Tillage and Burning

The major underground plant parts harvested by California Indians for foods were bulbs, tubers, and corms. Major genera commonly harvested included *Brodiaea, Calochortus, Allium, Perideridia,* and *Camassia.* California Indians generally dug bulbs and corms with a sharpened digging stick in the spring or summer after the plants had leafed out, flowered, or gone to seed. Underground storage organs are an important means of propagation among perennial plants. Many of the California native bulbs and corms important to Indians can reproduce by offsets, which occur in the sheath of the stem or around the base of the bulb. Tillage is defined as the loosening of the soil to vest underground perennial plant parts such as roots, corms, bulbs, and tubers. It also may involve replanting or subsequent dividing of underground parts and leaving of individual fragments or smaller clumps in the soil.

Digging with a digging stick has generally not been considered a management technique by resource managers or scientists, but it is possible that the digging of certain bulbs, corms and tubers, actually was a form of tilling and thinning which resulted in enhancement of certain plants, both in quality and numbers. Propagation of tuberous plants by hunting and gathering groups has taken various forms. The Cahuilla Indians selectively harvested the larger corms for food, leaving or replanting the cormlets to ensure a crop the following year. Harvesting of corms, bulbs, and tubers by Pomoans in the California Coast Range, aerated the soil and resulted in the severing of bulblets from the parent bulbs, increasing the size of the plant bed. In California, Indian-potatoes, the corms of Brodiaea and Calochortus species, grow in beds and were easily harvested. The Karuk Indians claimed that by digging these corms more grew up each year. Wild onions also were reported to multiply in numbers when intensively harvested by indigenous groups. Brodiaea species grew in plots and were irrigated by the Owens Valley Paiute to increase the natural yield of the corms. Some Indians today assert that the removal of bulbs and corms stimulate plants the following year. Several species of *Brodiaea, Allium* and *Sanicula* are still gathered by California Indian tribes. Digging implements include sticks, whittled broom handles, and crowbars.

Burning is defined as the deliberate setting and timing of fires in various plant communities. There are many historical accounts and several studies which describe the setting of fires by California Indians, suggesting that purposeful burning occurred in various plant communities. The reasons for burning were numerous. For example, certain flat forest areas were fired by Indians at intervals to destroy small trees and brush and leave open stands of the larger trees. This was to lessen the chance of surprise attacks by enemy tribes. Sometimes trees were felled with fire for different purposes such as providing a log as a bridge for crossing a stream. Fires were set by the Indians for game management. Burns kept the underbrush down and facilitated the search for game. Many tribes also set fire to chaparral as a means of forcing out rabbits and other small animals in order to capture them for their flesh and pelts. Other rodents were smoked out and woodrat nests burned to capture them. Annual burning also ensured ample forage for deer, antelope, and tule elk. One of the ways in which grasshoppers and caterpillars were caught was to burn a field and then gather up the singed insects. Another major purpose for the setting of fires was to modify the morphological growth of certain plant resources. Fires were set to increase berry production of certain plant species such as huckleberry (*Vaccinium* spp.). Fires were also set to manipulate the branch architecture and bark color of plants which could than be harvested the following year to make a particular cultural product. Many of the plants that provided basketry materials were repeatedly burned to provide straight shoots. Some Indian elders today recall that such species as maple, willows, redbud, sourberry and hazelnut were fired to stimulate the production long withes. Certain bunchgrasses such as deergrass were also burned to increase stolon production thereby increasing the size of the colonies as well as encourage the production of flowering stalks. Burning off the land increased the ease of harvest of certain plant parts. For example, fallen leaves and brush reduced the visibility of acorns and thus, increased the search time for these seeds. Therefore, burning under the oaks in certain areas enhanced the gathering of acorns. Indians utilized fire in order to change plant species composition. Burning cleared brushlands and grass lands so that brodiaeas and other bulbous-rooted species useful for food would grow more abundantly. Areas in Southern California were burned to improve the production of seed-bearing plants such as chia. Years after Indians were forced off their lands, they continued to collect wild foods on adjacent lands in selected areas burned by ranchers and farmers. Indian informants still recall that the abundance and quality of mushrooms, sanicles, brodiaeas, and other valued plants were enhanced after burning.

A Dwindling Resource

Both public and private large-scale land development projects often ignore the cultural and environmental needs of the surrounding local Indian populations by promoting vast monocultures of trees and agricultural crops with genetically uniform cultivars, or building planned urban developments which displace culturally important plant species. In fact, some of these plants such as willows (*Salix* spp.), sedge (*Carex* spp.), worm wood (*Artemisia* spp.) and *Ceanothus* spp. are often categorized as "weeds" or "pests" and are deliberately eliminated with herbicides, chaining, burning or other removal techniques. Many public lands managed for timber, livestock, recreation and other resource values contain plants still culturally important to Indian groups. Yet Native Americans often remark that these plant populations are sparse, discontinuous, and of an unsuitable quality for use in the manufacture of cultural items. The Indians say that plants such as deergrass (*Muhlenbergia rigens*) in the Sierra foothills, or sedge (*Carex barbarae*) along streams, or bear grass (*Xerophyllum tenax*) in the northern ponderosa pine forests are poor quality and need to be harvested, protected, and tended. Elders remember how much more abundant mariposa lilies (*Calchortus* spp.) and Indian potatoes used to be, covering whole hillsides and meadows. Gatherers

also notice how sparse berry and seed crops such as manzanita berries and acorns are today compared to half a century ago.

Moreover, Indians increasingly face "no trespass" signs, barbed-wire fences, and government permit procedures, in their search for suitable areas to harvest these preferred plant species. A Yokuts woman used to gather sedge for basketry on private property, but last year upon her return, the owner had bulldozed the site. Often the plant part of interest to Native Americans goes to waste on private property. Fruits such as elder berries and manzanita berries, salad greens such as sour dock (*Rumex* spp.) and Indian-potatoes such as sanicle are not a part of the modern Anglo diet, yet Indians still gather these edible plants.

Plant Gathering Policies

Many of our past California public land policies have favored land uses and management strategies that have deterred Indians from plant gathering on wildlands, even though these areas were once their traditional vesting grounds. For example, certain types of mushrooms, sourberry, big-leaf maple (*Acer macrophyllum*), deergrass, and hazelnut (*Corylus cornuta* var. *californica*) historically were preferentially harvested on burned sites. Fire exclusion policies of the U.S. Forest Service, the National Park Service, the Bureau of Land Management and other government agencies have limited the ability of Indians to burn vegetation in conjunction with gathering. As a result, plant resources collected only in burned areas are not readily available. In the past, plant gathering has occurred in many California public lands on a case-by-case approval basis and in some cases Indian people have been denied gathering access (for such purposes as collecting acorns), leaving them with few alternatives for plant procurement. Recently all California State Parks and some National Parks have developed Indian plant gathering policies. But these policies still require government "approval" for Indian plant gathering activities such as gathering basketry materials, edible plants, or construction materials through a permit procedure. In several cases Indian elders have been denied permits, for gathering such plant resources as five-finger fern. The rationale for these permit procedures is based on the possible negative environmental impact from plant gathering activities and on the compatibility of plant gathering with other park social and environmental objectives. Often the resource manager equates wild vegetation with vegetation that is left alone or not altered significantly through human use. The Indian harvesting of renewable, above-ground plant parts (berries, leaves, and seeds) is often seen as an acceptable, nondestructive gathering method, while the array of other management and har-

11

vesting techniques utilized by Native Americans such as coppicing, rhizome severing, corm-digging, and burning are often seen as being in conflict with conservation objectives and possibly harmful to the plants. If Indians' cultural needs are to be adequately addressed by these permit procedures, then resources managers must broaden the focus of public policy from merely the effects of Indian activities on other uses, and how to control these effects, to include the cultural and economic bases for Indian plant gathering and how these can be integrated within prevailing management systems. For example, today in most cases, little is known about the role and importance of plant gathering in Indian cultures: which plants are actively collected by Indian groups and what vegetation management and harvesting techniques are used. Studies that document specific collection and management practices and assess the impact of such practices on the plant species collected, surrounding vegetation and other cultural and natural resources of the area will provide park managers needed information for granting use-rights to Indian gatherers. In many public land agencies the old management goal of plant protection and preservation has been replaced with the philosophy of encouraging natural processes. For example, the National Park Service plans to restore each park as nearly as possible to a structure within which natural fires and other natural disturbances may be allowed to occur. To do this, resource managers will not only need to assess the role Indians played in the past management and maintenance of ecosystems where plant resources were gathered, but also they will need to study horticultural techniques and their impacts on vegetation. A recent study that I conducted of Southern Sierra Miwok, ethnobotanical knowledge and plant horticultural skills is a contribution in this direction. My study documented the effects of two horticultural practices on two plant species, deergrass and redbud. The deergrass is managed with controlled burning in the fall, to encourage the production of flower stalks which provide the foundation (warp) material for coiled baskets. The redbud is subjected to coppicing once a year in the fall to stimulate the production of usable branches for basketry material. On public lands in Yosemite National Park and Sierra National Forest I mimicked these Indian practices. I simulated dry-season burning to see whether it affected the development of new tillers and the production of flowering stems of deergrass and I evaluated the effects of fall coppicing on the regeneration of redbud. Regeneration was specified as shoot production, both ground stems and branches. Results from these field experiments indicated that both management practices increased the desired plant characteristics that Indians look for to meet their cultural needs. In the burn treatment all of the deergrass plants vigorously developed new

tillers. In fact, many of the deergrass plants that had hollow centers (because of accumulated dead material) after the burn produced many new tillers, filling in their interiors. There was a thirteen percent increase in deergrass flowering the year following burning. All redbud shrubs that were coppiced vigorously resprouted, producing many long, straight withes with red bark. These usable shoots increased significantly with coppicing. Moreover, coppicing also removed lanky red bud branches and dead or dying limbs, controlling the potential spread of diseases.

Linking Wildland and Cultural Conservation

Public lands containing plant populations important to Indians can be defined both as "cultural" and "natural" resources. The correct management and maintenance of these resources should emerge from the sharing and combination of Indian knowledge with the expertise of cultural and natural resource managers. The challenge however, will be to resolve differences in terminology, values, perceptions, and objectives among cultural scientists, resource managers, and Indian populations regarding plants and their uses and management .

As public land agencies begin to create new possibilities for Indian gathering on public lands, their role as a regulating body will continuously evolve. Thus, it is not clear whether the agency's role will be to passively permit Indians to gather plants through a permit process, or to act as advocates of maintaining, tending and encouraging growth of plants important to Indian people. Such questions can be better addressed if gathering policies are designed according to a knowledge of Indians' cultural needs, the differences in gathering strategies and resource management techniques utilized among Indian cultural groups and their ecological impacts on plants and the surrounding plant community. This new knowledge may offer biologists, ecologists and resource managers alternative, innovative ways of managing noncommercial plant species and plant communities in wildlands. Therefore, Indian techniques to manage the vegetation should be tested and, where appropriate, combined with modern management practices. Since this knowledge will benefit public land management, Indians should be compensated for the services provided by their cultural knowledge. Compensation could occur through such activities as facilitating Indian plant gathering as a legitimate land use; applying indigenous horticultural techniques to enhance cultural resources; and involving Indians in the design of plant studies. For example, Indian participation is required to con duct studies that locate and protect traditional collection sites which are now, or were formerly, used for plant gathering purposes. These sites could be registered with the National Register of Historic Places or perhaps receive a new designation such as "Native People's Plant Gathering Site." Public land managers and environmental organizations can also facilitate the purchase of private lands or access to use of these lands for gathering purposes. Land access is essential, for tribes interested in reviving and maintaining traditions, and developing their own incentives for returning to plant gathering activities within the current socio-economic structure. Resource policies which have been best for the general public have not generally included the wants and needs of the Indian minority. Given the current small scale level of Indian harvesting and horticulture, their view of humanity's relationship with nature, and their goals, it is quite feasible that gathering policies can be developed without compromising other public lands goals.

References

Aginsky, B. W. 1943. "Culture Element Distributions" XXIV *Central Sierra Anthropological Records* Vol. 8:4.

Anderson, M. K. 1989. Unpublished Western Mono, Chuckchansi Yokuts, Southern Sierra Miwok and Central Sierra Miwok field notes.

———. 1988. "Southern Sierra Miwok Plant Resource Use and Management of the Yosemite Region." Master's Thesis. Department of Forestry and Resource Management. U.C. Berkeley.

Bean, L. J., and K. S. Saubel. 1972. "Temalpakh: Challis Indian Knowledge and Usage of Plants." Morongo Indian Reservation. Malki Museum Press.

Driver, H. E. 1939. "Culture element distributions: X. North west California." *Anthropological Records* Vol. I:6.

Drucker, P. 1939. "Culture element distributions: V. Southern California." University of California Publications in *Anthropological Records* Vol. l: I .

Harrington, J. P. 1932. "Tobacco Among the Karuk Indians of California." *Smithsonian Institution Bureau of American Ethnology Bulletin 94*. United States Government Printing Office.

Heffner, K. 1984. "Following the Smoke: Contemporary Plant Procurement by the Indians of Northwest California." Unpublished manuscript. Six Rivers National Forest.

Hunter, J. E. 1988. " Prescribed burning for cultural resources." *Fire Management Notes* Vol. 49:2. U.S. Forest Service.

Levy, Richard. 1978. "Eastern Miwok." *Handbook of North American Indians*, Vol.: 8. Heizer (ed.) 1978: 398-413.

Lewis, H. T. 1973. "Patterns of Indian Burning in California: Ecology and Ethnohistory." Ballena Press Anthropological Paper No. 1.

Merrill, R. E. 1923. "Plants Used in Basketry by the California Indians." UCPAAe 20: 215-242. Berkeley.

Murphy, E. V. 1959. "Indian Uses of Native Plants." Mendocino County Historical Society. Fort Bragg, CA.

Nabhan, G. P. 1986. "Native American crop diversity, genetic resource conservation and the policy of neglect." *Agriculture and Human Values* 2: 14-17.

Peri, D. W. 1985. "Pomoan plant resource management." *Ridge Review*, Mendocino. 4:4.

Peri, D. W. and S. M. Patterson. 1976. "The basket is in the roots, that's where it begins." *Journal of California Anthropology* Vol. 3:2.

Powers, S. 1976. *Tribes of California*. University of California Press. Berkeley, CA.

Reynolds, R. D. 1959. "Effect of Natural Fires and Aboriginal Burning upon the Forests of the Central Sierra Nevada." M. A. Thesis. Univ. of Calif., Berkeley.

Schulz, P. E. 1954. "Indians of Lassen Volcanic National Park and Vicinity." Loomis Museum Association. Mineral, CA.

Shipek, F. C. 1977. "A Strategy for Change: The Luiseno of Southern California." Ph.D. Dissertation in Anthropology at the University of Hawaii.

Steward, J. H. 1930. "Irrigation without Agriculture." *Papers of the Michigan Academy of Sciences, Arts, and Letters* 12: 149-156.

Storer, T. 1. and R. Usinger. 1963. *Sierra Nevada Natural History*. University of California Press, Berkeley.

van Wagtendonk, J. 1972. "Refined Burning Prescriptions for Yosemite National Park." National Park Service Occasional Paper # 2.

Reprinted with permission from Fremontia, the Journal of the California Native Plant Society, *April 1990.*

11

11

12 International Resource Guide to Forestry

12

ANCIENT FORESTS FOREVER

© Ray Troll, 1990

Global Forests, Atmospheric Composition, and Climate Change

Michael Pilarski

Think of the Forest as a Reef

The world's forests are a major part of the terrestrial carbon cycle. The 38% of the earth's land surface that contains forest also stores 60% of the land's carbon. No forest on Earth stores more carbon per acre than the ancient forests of the Pacific Northwest. Some of those contain more than 700 tons per acre of carbon.

These high-carbon forests also store large amounts of water. Think of a sponge with a structure that absorbs water. Think of the huge trunks of trees, living and dead, as well as downed logs, snags, understory forest and shrubs, the ferns and mosses below. Think about the truly astronomical numbers of leaf and needle surfaces that all can hold a film of water.

It is almost exactly like a reef made of wood. The structure provides the habitat for salmon and owl alike and is an important interface connecting air, earth and water.

—Northcoast Environmental Center

Think of the Forest as a Lake

Bill Mollison has taught permaculture designers to look at the forest as a lake. All life forms are predominantly water and that includes living trees. Consider also all the rotting logs, forest litter, and soil humus like a big sponge. Then there are all the roots and soil life; again, mostly water. A healthy functioning forest is a tremendous amount of water. You take away the forest and the organic matter and the land can hold little water. Think of the forest as a lake.

FORESTS ARE CRITICALLY IMPORTANT in climate stabilization. Forest destruction has already set in motion climate changes which will manifest increasingly extreme weather over the next several decades or centuries. If humanity does not successfully undertake worldwide reforestation and soil regeneration within the next several decades, it is likely Earth's climate will increasingly deteriorate from the standpoint of human habitation.

Most climatologists agree we will have more, bigger storm events and higher wind speeds. This means we are going to have more blowdown in forests. Those tree species and soil types which do not give good wind fastness will suffer most. This means we must take care in planning logging cuts that do not open up the windward edges of forests. Trees which naturally grow on the edges of forests retain their branches low to the ground. They have sturdier trunks to withstand the stress of wind. Trees from the forest interior are leggy in comparison, and not as wind resistant. When the natural edge of a forest is removed the exposed interior trees often blow down. This is called "windthrow" in forestry terminology. Bill Mollison calls this "edgethrow." Clearcuts lead to edgethrow. Heavy thinning can lead to increased blowdown. Seed trees left in seed tree cuts often blow down. Anticipation of more severe wind should lead foresters to choose harvesting methods which minimize chance of blowdown.

Climate Change and Changing Forest Composition

Climatologists and foresters are discussing how fast forests can move in the face of changing climate. Can they migrate fast enough to keep ahead of climate change? Are the forests so fragmented that they can't travel as fast? It might sound strange to consider a forest moving. We tend to think of forests as static. The concept of climax forest gives the idea of long-term stability.

Yet, forests and plants can move quickly through the landscape. Here, in north-central Washington and adjacent British Columbia, is the northernmost populations of sagebrush (*Artemesia tridentata*), cactus (*Opuntia*), mariposa lily (*Calochortus*) and associated plants. These are plant communities from the southwest deserts of Arizona and New Mexico which migrated here after the last ice age, coming up through the Great Basin, eastern Oregon, the Columbia Basin in eastern Washington and up into Canada. They made this journey of several thousand miles in perhaps as short a time as 5,000 years.

Study of plant geography through the ages shows us that plants (with their attendant microorganisms, insects, and animals) migrate around the globe in response to changing climates. The only constant in nature is change. Life ebbs and flows across the landscape.

What does this have to do with restoration forestry? If the climate radically changes, our present-day plant distributions will be altered to reflect the changes. Where it gets drier, drought-tolerant species already present will prevail and new ones will move in, as more moisture demanding species die. Foresters speculate we may have to help plant species move around, seeding and planting more adapted species. In other words, forestry based on native species and on local seed stocks may become irrelevant if the climate changes radically enough.

Species being stressed by climate change and UV radiation are not going to be healthy. Examples of forest dieback are increasing around the world. Species selection for tree planting under present climate patterns may be for naught. A wide range of species adapted to different climates is a safer strategy then a narrowly-adapted range of stock.

What Are the Stakes of Restoration Forestry?

All oxygen-based life on earth may be at stake. Humans are changing earth's atmosphere with industrial pollutants, and by reducing the world's biomass. Destruction of forests, vegetation and soil structure/humus levels have changed the Earth's hydrologic cycles. The atmosphere is becoming increasingly desiccated. The forests are the humidifiers of the air through transpiration of groundwater, through crown interception of rain and snow and subsequent evaporation and sublimation back to the atmosphere.

John Jeavons stated in a May 1993 conversation that recent studies show that the world has lost 88% of its forests compared to prehistoric levels. I pointed out that most authorities estimated we'd lost only 30 to 50%. He countered that while there may be still 50% of the forested area left, almost all of it has been degraded, high-graded and cutover many times and there is only 12% of the forest biomass remaining compared to 10,000 years ago. He may be right. And where has all that carbon gone?

Earth's oxygen production has been declining since agriculture began with a specially precipitous decline since the industrial revolution. We are still wiping out oxygen-producers at an accelerating pace. We are on a course with disaster. Now is the time to put on the brakes and plant trees, tend the planet and give nature room to breathe. Plants exhale oxygen for us and fix carbon into biomass, soil banks and majestic forests.

Forests, Oceans and Ultraviolet Radiation

Forests are harmed by increased UV. As forests weaken they become more susceptible to disease, insects and drought. As more forests die there is less oxygen produced and this translates into less ozone (ozone is produced from oxygen) and more UV and less trees and less oxygen etc. A vicious cycle has been set up and unless we act soon to change it, we can expect civilization to crumble and perhaps the extinction of Homo sapiens, if not most oxygen-based life on Earth.

"New scientific developments require an immediate re-examination of the utility of clearcut logging, particularly of UV-B sensitive species on south-facing slopes.

At a U.S. Department of Energy conference in June of this year, Dr. Alan Teramura, a leading researcher on the bio-effects of UVR, reported that "UV-B produces a noticeable effect on plant growth through DNA damage, photosynthesis depression, on yield depression, altered membrane permeability, decreased leaves and branches, stunted height, and decreased biomass accumulation," (excerpt from the article "Forests, Clearcuts, and UV Radiation" by Bruce Torrie in *No Sweat News*, Fall 1993, p. 9).

What percentage of earth's oxygen is produced by land plants vs. ocean life is still debated, but evidence is that the bulk of oxygen comes from land-based photosynthesis. Ocean life is also being negatively impacted by pollution and by increased ultra-violet (UV) rays due to ozone thinning. Plankton are very susceptible to UV and if ozone continues to decrease and UV increase we might see the ocean's oxygen-producers knocked out of commission. Some of the ocean's most productive zones for plankton and other oxygen-producing sea organisms are near the poles, exactly where ozone depletion is worst.

Many parts of the world are already in oxygen deficit, such as cities and deserts. Their oxygen is carried in from oxygen-producing areas via global air circulation. The oxygen dispensers on Mexico City's streets may be commonplace elsewhere in the world within several decades.

"By mid-January, oxygen levels inside Biosphere II, the self-contained, experimental Earth-under-glass located near Oracle, Arizona, had dropped from 21 percent to only 15 percent. Carbon dioxide levels had risen alarmingly—to more than ten times normal. With the Biospherians inside the glass gasping for breath and administering doses of the drug acetazolamide to fight the debilitating effects of oxygen starvation, the backers of the $150 million project decided to start pumping oxygen into Biosphere II's sealed environment.

While the "oxygen deficit" in Biosphere II received wide media coverage, another story concerning the decline of oxygen in the atmosphere of Biosphere I—The Earth—went largely unnoticed. If some recent scientific reports are correct, acetazolamide may become the most sought-after-drug of the 21st century."

—From "More Trouble for the Earth's Atmosphere" by Gar Smith in the Spring 1993 *Earth Island Journal*

The article went on to relate that earth's oxygen, hydroxyl and stratospheric temperature levels are all falling. All bad news.

The New York Times in April 1993 reported that satellite measurements indicate an abundance of ozone-destroying chemicals remained in the atmosphere over the Northern Hemisphere much longer this winter than last and the hole in the protective ozone layer has grown significantly, researchers said. Ozone levels above parts of Canada, Scandinavia, Russia and Europe were down 10 percent on average from last winter! More than twice the usual year-to-year variation.

It is ironic that in 1992 the USA space shuttle made a special mission to monitor ozone depletion. Ironic because it has already been a few years since Russian scientists blew the whistle on the NASA space shuttle program for destroying a large chunk of the earth's ozone. Each shuttle launch includes many tons of chlorine in the fuel mix and as a result a giant dose of ozone-depleting chlorine is dumped into the stratosphere. Each launch consumes a significant chunk of earth's total ozone. A few more decades of chlorine-powered shuttles and we will all need space suits.

A Few Thoughts on Solutions to the Global Climate Change/Ozone Depletion Crises

Are there solutions? A combination of restoration forestry and a doubling of the world's forest cover can lead to reoxygenation of the troposphere, increase stratospheric ozone, draw down atmospheric carbon dioxide and stabilize the climate. It is feasible that in 100 years we could double the earth's present amount of forest biomass

Most solutions so far have centered on stopping the production of substances which harm the atmosphere. Few people are talking about pro-active solutions to help heal the atmosphere once we stop destroying it. Here's how. There are five main components of my proposed solution:

1. Massive soil enhancement and humus build-up

2. Massive tree-planting (See Friends of the Trees International Green Front Report) to double world forest cover

3. Ocean mineral enrichment

4. Diminish use of fossil fuels

5. Stop production of chemicals and biocides harmful to the atmosphere and to life. Most especially, stop all production of chlorine and chlorine products immediately.

6. Create a network of fresh-water ponds throughout all agricultural areas to grow algae for fertilizer. Algae are efficient oxygen and biomass producers. Daryl Kollman of Cell Tech, Inc. has stated that greening an area the size of the state of Colorado in algae ponds could compensate for the CO_2 imbalance in our atmosphere.

How to Regain Stratospheric Ozone

According to climatologist Adam Trombley, one way we can regain higher levels of stratospheric ozone is to produce huge amounts of oxygen at Earth's surface via trees and plants. The oxygen column gradually pushes up through the atmosphere until increased oxygen replenishment takes place at higher altitudes. In the stratosphere the oxygen molecules are changed by UV (ultraviolet rays) to ozone.

The Soil. This is where we may get the biggest bang for our buck, and the quickest return on investment(i.e. the most carbon/oxygen change). There are 1,473,059,000 hectares (3,682,647,000 acres) of cropland in the world. I propose a crash 10-year program to increase all cropland soil organic matter content by 1% average. That is 1% in the top acre-foot slice of soil. An acre-foot of soil weighs approximately 1,800 tons. 1% is 18 tons per acre. This would yield 66,276,000,000 tons of organic matter. Soil organic matter/humus is approximately 60% carbon (dry weight). This equals 39,748,000,000 tons of carbon sequestered from the atmosphere. This is 39.7 billion tons of carbon.

Note I am talking about a 1% increase of soil organic matter in the top acre-foot of soil. Most humus in soils is in the top 2 to 6 inches, so to average 1% in 12 inches we might actually have to increase organic matter content by as much as 2 or 3% in the top 4 to 6 inches of soil. This increase is a global average. It will be harder to raise and maintain organic matter levels in arid and semi-arid land soils and also harder to do it in tropical soils with annual crops. We need to greatly increase acreage in perennial food crops and decrease acreage in annual food crops.

How do we increase soil organic matter by 1%? From my 20 years of experience and research in organic agriculture I firmly believe that the world has the techniques which can accomplish this goal, if society puts enough resources and labor into it. An added benefit is that food production would substantially increase and soil erosion rates greatly decrease.

The percentage of organic matter in soils varies tremendously. Most agricultural soils would lie in the 1% to 5% range. A rich garden soil might run between 4% to 10%. Peat soils can be up to 50% organic matter. Tallgrass prairie soils of the U.S. Midwest had up to 10% organic matter prior to the plow. Industrial, mechanized chemical agriculture depletes soil organic matter, as do some traditional agriculture systems.

In other words, It is feasible to increase organic matter content of farm soils by anywhere from 1% to 5%, depending on how much the organic matter had been depleted, mineral content, rainfall, temperatures, etc. With the best soil-building practices on each site, soil organic matter levels on farms can be increased from up to 2% on drier sites to up to10% on moist, rich sites.

Soil-building techniques include: green manuring, cover crops, use of livestock manure and human waste stream, composting, mulching, soil inoculants (mycorrhizae, azotobacters, algaes), legume and N-fixing crops in rotation, strip cropping, terracing; keyline, soil aeration; utilization of all agricultural waste, meticulous recycling of organic matter from farm, market and household parts of the food chain, as well as many, many others. These soil-building techniques are familiar to organic farmers, gardeners and permaculturists.

Organizations and Periodicals Concerned with Climate Change

Atmosphere Alliance
P.O. Box 10346,
Olympia, Washington 98502
Tel: (206) 661-2817

Publishes *No Sweat News*, The Journal of Grassroots Action to Protect the Atmosphere. There are lots of organizations working to save the forests, save the whales, save indigenous peoples, etc. This is one of the first (and boldest) groups working to save the atmosphere.

Center for Climatic Research
University of Wisconsin
1225 West Dayton St.
Madison, Wisconsin 53706
Tel (608) 262-1234

Climate Alliance News
Service Center for Development Cooperation
Jaana Matikainen
Fredrikinskatu 63A8
SF-00100 Helsinki, FINLAND
Tel: 358-06944233/Fax: 358-06941786

A newspaper which provides background information on the Climate Alliance Action Days and some ideas about building an international campaign against climate disruption.

Climate-related Impacts Network Newsletter
Environmental and Societal Impacts Group
National Center for Atmospheric Research
P.O. Box 3000
Boulder, Colorado 80303
Tel: (303) 497-1619/Fax: (303) 497-1137

Quarterly. Free.

Climate Network Africa
P.O. Box 21136
Nairobi, KENYA
Tel: (254-2) 22-6028/Fax: (254-2) 56-8167
EcoNet: gn:econewsafric.

Their quarterly, English-language newsletter, Impact, presents articles on the relationships between forests, farming, energy and climate change. Subscriptions: US$50/year; free in Africa.

Ponderosa Pine
P.O. Box 1753
Davis, California 95617
Tel: (916) 757-1633

Ponderosa Pine is a man who organized a 1993 conference in Davis, California that brought together many experts in the field of ozone depletion and UV affects. They strategized possible ways to increase ozone in the stratosphere. Ponderosa Pine has also produced a mind-boggling video interview with Adam Trombley, one of the first climatologists to bring ozone depletion to public attention.

Remineralize the Earth
152 South St.
Northampton, Massachusetts 01060
Tel: (413) 586-4429. Joanna Campe, Editor.

This is the leading source of information on remineralization of soils for agriculture and forestry. Also a source of information on Hohn A. Hamacker and his climate-change theories proposing a coming ice age.

Books on Climate Change

Air Pollution's Toll on Forests and Crops
James J. MacKenzie and Mohamed T. El-Serry, eds. 1989. Yale U. Press. 376 pp.

Up to date information and technical evidence. Mainly on forests in Europe and U.S.

Deforestation Rates in Tropical Forests and Their Climatic Implications

Norman Myers. £12 postpaid from Friends of the Earth UK, 26-28 Underwood Street, London N1 7JQ, England.

The most up-to-date information on tropical deforestation currently available. Includes country-by-country reviews of Latin America, Africa, and Asia, analysis of such factors as future deforestation, the role of shifting cultivation and tree plantations, and recommendations for action.

Effects on Carbon Storage of Conversion of Old-Growth Forests to Young Forests

Mark E. Harmon, William K. Ferrell, Jerry F. Franklin In: *Science*, Vol. 24(4943), February 9,1990: 699-701.

This article lays to rest the theory that we can fix more carbon by cutting old-growth forests and replacing them with young, vigorous, fast growing plantations. Respected forest ecologists point out that it takes at least 200 years before new forests replace the lost biomass.

Fire in the Environment: The Ecological, Atmospheric, and Climatic Importance of Vegetation Fires

P. J. Crtuzen and J. G. Goldammer. 1993. 400 pp.

This volume represents the first organized synthesis of global fire ecology and defines the most urgent problems to be tackled scientifically.

Global Biomass Burning: Atmospheric, Climatic, and Biospheric Implications

Joel S. Levine, editor. 1991. $75. 569 pp.

The burning of biomass—forests, grasslands, and agricultural fields after the harvest—is much more widespread and extensive than previously believed; most biomass burning is thought to be initiated by humans and is on the increase. This comprehensive volume is the first to consider biomass burning as a global phenomenon and to assess its impact on the atmosphere, on climate, and on the biosphere itself. The 63 chapters by 158 scientists—including leading biomass burn researchers from third-world countries, such as Brazil, Nigeria, Zaire, India, and China, where biomass burning is so prevalent—point to biomass burning as a significant driver of global change on our planet.

Global Climate Change and Life on Earth

Richard L. Wyman, ed. 1991. Routledge, Chapman and Hall: NY. 279 pp.

The forestry chapter outlines the role of forests in the atmosphere's carbon composition.

The Hole In The Sky: Man's Threat to the Ozone Layer

John Gribbin. Updated. Bantam. $5.99.

Long-term Implications of Climate Change and Air Pollution on Forest Ecosystems

R. Schlaepfer, ed., 1993. In: Progress Report of the IUFRO Task Force, "Forest, Climate Change and Air Pollution." IUFRO World Series Vol. 4. 132 pp.

Ozone: How Deep Will the Burning Go?

Keith C. Heidorn. Article in *Watershed Sentinel*, Oct./ Nov. 1993. pp. 22-23.

Dr. Keith Heidorn is a meteorologist and consultant in atmospheric and marine issues. This article offers a look at the effect of ozone depletion and increased Ultraviolet radiation (UV) on plant and marine life. Following is one paragraph. A copy of the article, with an accompanying background paper and references is available from the *Watershed Sentinel* on request.

Unlike aquatic plants, terrestrial vegetation evolved under widely varying levels of UV radiation. As a result there is a wide range of tolerance and adaptation in terrestrial vegetation. Increased UV-B radiation may affect terrestrial plants through impacts on photosynthesis, plant growth, competitive balance in a mixed community, pollination and flowering, DNA and cellular functions, and susceptibility to disease, environmental stress and pollution. Approximately two thirds of plant species or varieties studied are susceptible to damage from increased UV-B radiation.

Soils and the Greenhouse Effect

A. F. Bouwman, ed., 1990. John Wiley & Sons. 575 pp. $135.

This book takes a look at the effect of soils and vegetation on the fluxes of greenhouse gases, the surface energy balance and the water balance, as well as the effects of deforestation and agriculture.

Forests Around the World: A Bibliography

In the last 5,000 years, global forests have been reduced from covering 50% of the planet to less than 20% with most of that decline coming in the last 100 years. Some areas show a staggering reduction of forests.

Africa has lost over 23% of its tree cover since 1950, and in Central America the loss is over 38%. The great Himalayan Ecosystem has lost over 40% of its forests in the last 30 years. The Tropics, where 50% of all animal and plant species live, lose an area the size of Louisiana every year to deforestation. Globally, the loss is estimated to be almost 70 acres of trees every minute.

—Richard W. Fox

World Forest Statistics

It is impossible to know just how much forest is left in the world. Governments claim one thing, environmentalists claim another. One thing we do know for sure. There have been many proven cases of government forestry officials overestimating forest coverage and amounts of timber. I do not know of any cases where there has been proven to be more forests than official figures. FAO's 1993 figures on forest deforestation state that things are much worse than they had been saying in the 1980s.

Here are a few forest statistics from *Global Forests* by Laarman and Sedjo. Published in 1992, it gives relatively up-to-date figures, but from official sources.

40% of the world's land surface is forested, 27% closed forest and 13% open forest and scrub forest. This is 1/2 to 2/3 pre-agriculture levels. 17 million hectares were cleared annually for cropland in the tropics between 1981 and 1990.

The countries with the largest forest acreage are the USSR with 21% of world forest cover, Brazil 14%, Canada 7%, USA 6%, Zaire 5%, China 4%, and Indonesia with 3%.

Some countries with a small percentage of forest cover are Ireland, which has only 5% forest cover; Australia with 6% forest cover, United Kingdom 8%, Netherlands 9%, China 12-13% and Europe and India both have less than 20% forest cover.

Thirty-two, developing countries have forest coverage under 10%, including: El Salvador 7%, Mongolia 6%, Kenya 5%, Uruguay 4%, Pakistan 3%, Afghanistan, Haiti and Iran only 2%, and Algeria, South Africa and Lesotho with a minuscule 1% forest cover.

The countries with the most forested hectares per person are: French Guiana with 114 hectares of forest per person, Surinam 42, Guyana 22, Papua New Guinea, Bolivia and Canada have 12, Belize 10, New Caledonia 5, Finland 4, and Sweden and Australia with 3 hectares of forest per person. (1 hectare = 2.5 acres).

Northwest Europe has about 65-75 million hectares of managed forests. The rest of the world combined has about the same area under management, about 65-75 million hectares.

Logging Bans

The idea of a moratorium on timber harvesting has been proposed in a number of countries. This radical idea has actually been made law in a few regions or even whole countries (notably Thailand, The Philippines and Bolivia, Laos, Kenya and Tanzania). Oftentimes, a cutting moratorium applies only to letting new contracts. Cutting rates may not drop for several years. Enforcement problems and outright corruption hinder implementation.

In Bolivia, the severity of the declines in mahogany forests stimulated the issuance of a Presidential Decree in January 1990 declaring an "Historic Ecologic Pause." One of the provisions of this "Pause" is a five-year freeze on approving new logging concessions with the goal of developing a more sustainable and rational use of forest resources than has so far been practiced. Unfortunately, much of the mahogany trade is still from illegal sources.

Thailand banned logging a few years back, but illegal logging on large and small scale continues. Thailand's military/business interests also moved much of their operations to neighboring Burma and Laos to escape the ban. In 1991, Laos put a two-year ban on logging to curb destructive, wasteful logging practices. Kenya has banned any cutting in natural forests. Wood comes from plantations established over the past three decades.

In 1993, Tanzania banned the export of hardwood in raw form, in a desperate move to save its forests. Forestry officials fear that hardwoods are in danger of extinction, particularly ebony. Tanzania consumed at least 40 million cubic meters of wood for firewood and timber, while up to 400,000 hectares of forests are being cleared every year.

Australia's State of New South Wales has banned cutting on all remaining virgin, tropical rainforests within New South Wales.

Until the world adopts restoration forestry and builds up its forests, there will be increasing calls for logging bans.

Books with World Overviews

Introduction to World Forestry

Jack Westoby. 1989. Basil Blackwell: Oxford, UK. 228 pp.

As head of the Forestry Department of the FAO, Westoby had intimate knowledge of forestry and foresters from around the world. Westoby's book is one of the best overviews of the world forestry situation and highly recommended for its penetrating analysis of the social and political aspects of our present-day forest crisis. He also gives a historical perspective of forest cover in parts of the world. The last sections of the book give guidelines towards a sustainable forestry.

Westoby argues that it is not demographic pressure as such that threatens the world's forests, but rather the rapidity of population changes. Particularly the increasing number of landless, the shifted rather than the shifting cultivators, Westoby calls them. "It is social relations, not simply the pressure of numbers which is destroying the tropical forests," he writes.

In most Third World countries, political power rests in the hands of people more interested in facilitating exploitation than controlling it.

...Nor are the developed countries without their share of the blame. Says Westoby, "It is the support of first world countries which keep in existence those third world regimes whose resource destructive policies are responsible for contemporary tropical deforestation."

...Foresters, says Westoby, have served their masters too conscientiously, and have "far too often tamely done as they have been told, and have remained gagged." To remedy the situation, he says, the voices of foresters and of environmentalists should sound in unison, "and their professional organizations should protect members with the courage to denounce anti-social resource policies.

Thus the domestic partners in the pillage of the tropical forest consist not only of those who facilitate, join in, or condone the ruthless and reckless exploitation of the forests for timber; they also include all those forces in society which, by denying access to land and water resources to the many, retaining it in the hands of the few, oblige the growing army of landless people to press further into the forest.

—Jack Westoby

Global Forest Resources

A. S. Mather. 1990. Bellhaven Press: London. 341 pp.

One of the most comprehensive books on the subject. Covers the extent and distribution of forests, how they are used, controlled and managed; socio-economic factors, and government policies. Environmental aspects and international developments are addressed throughout.

Global Forests

Jan G. Laarman and Roger A. Sedjo. 1992. McGraw-Hill.

A well researched, university-level textbook on the current forest situation, problems and possible solutions. A journey through the world's forests which is hard to put down once you start reading.

Let There Be Forest

Arnold and Connie Krochmal. 1986. PUDOC (The Centre for Agricultural Publishing and Documentation): Wageningen, The Netherlands. 96 pp. $12.50. Available from: Bernan-UNIPUB, 4611-F Assembly Drive, Lanham, Maryland 20706-4391.

In *Let There Be Forest*, the Krochmals have written one of the best summaries on how to accomplish reforesting the world. About half of the book is devoted to outlining the present, distressing state of affairs in the world's forests. The other half outlines strategies to accomplish the goal of world reforestation. The emphasis is on countries of the south. Highly recommended to all friends of the trees.

A World Geography of Forest Resources

S. Haden-Guest and John K. Wright, eds. 736 pp.

Regional and country descriptions of forests by several dozen authors. Forest regions, management, history, and industries are covered.

World's Forests for the Future: Their Use and Conservation

Kilaparti Ramakrishna and George M. Woodwell, eds. 1993. Yale Univ. Press.

An anthology of authors presenting an overview of the world forest situation and recommendations. The result of a meeting of a group of international forest scientists, economists and policy-makers who met at Woods Hole, Massachusetts in October of 1991.

Books on Forests and Forestry— International

Changing Landscapes: An Ecological Perspective

I. S. Zonneveld and R. T. Forman, eds. 1990. Springer-Verlag: New York.

Coastal Temperate Rain Forests: Definition and Global Distribution with Particular Emphasis on North America

J. F. Weigand and P. Alaback. 1990. Conservation International: Portland, Oregon.

Cyprus: A Chronicle of Its Forests, Land and People

J. V. Thirgood. 1987. University of British Columbia Press: Vancouver. 390 pp. $ 38.50.

A view of Cyprus's forests and their positive management by man.

The Death of Trees

Nigel Dudley. 1985. Pluto Press.

Useful reference book which goes over temperate as well as tropical trees.

Deforestation: Social Dynamics in Watersheds and Mountain Ecosystems

D. C. Pitt, ed. 1988. Routledge. 224 pp. £35. Available from Natural History Book Service.

Ecological Imperialism: The Biological Expansion of Europe, 900-1900

Alfred W. Crosby. 1986. Cambridge University Press. 368 pp.

Through the biological introduction and invasion of European people, diseases, domesticated plants, animals, pests, and weeds, Crosby shows how North America, Argentina, Australia, among other places have become "Neo-Europes."

A Forest Journey: The Role of Wood in the Development of Civilization

John Perlin. 1991. 445 pp. $14.95.
Available mail-order from: agAccess Agricultural Book Service, P.O. Box 2008, Davis, CA 95617.

Perlin explores how abundance or scarcity of wood has shaped culture, economy, politics and technology through the ages. Great illustrations and maps.

The Forester's Companion

N.D.G. James. 4th ed. Basil Blackwell, Ltd., 108 Cowley Rd., Oxford, OX4 1JF, United Kingdom.

An indispensable guide for foresters for the past 35 years. Crammed with facts, figures, charts. Affordable.

Forests and Forestry in China

S. D. Richardson. 1990. Island Press. 360 pp. $26.95 paper.

Professor S. D. Richardson is rated as the West's foremost expert on China's forests. Here is a chance for a look at the fascinating forests of China and how they are being managed.

Forests in India, Environmental and Production Frontiers

V. P. Agarwala. 1990, 2nd ed. Oxford & IBH Publishing Co: New Delhi. 338 pp.

A good review of the history and management of forests in India.

Forests in Trouble: A Review of the Status of Temperate Forests Worldwide

Nigel Dudley. 1992. Worldwide Fund for Nature. Gland, Switzerland.

Forests of France

J. L. Reed. Faber & Faber: London 296 pp.

Publishing year not given, looks to be about 1960. National forest history plus regional accounts.

Forests. The Shadow of Civilization

Robert Pogue Harrison. 1992. University of Chicago Press: Chicago. 288 pp. $24.95.

A comprehensive philosophical analysis from a historical perspective of the role forests have played in the evolution of humankind.

Global Deforestation and the Nineteenth Century World Economy

John F. Richards and Richard P. Tucker. 1988. Duke Univ. Press, 6697 College Stn., Durham NC 27708.

The impact of European expansionism on physical environments and societies in remote regions of the globe.

A Green History Of The World

Clive Ponting. 1992. St. Martin's Press. Hardcover, $24.95.

A historical look at how degradation of ecosystems through time has led to the collapse of advanced civilizations from Mesopotamia, Rome, and the Mayans.

Growing Exotic Forests

B. Zokel, G. Van Wyr and P. Stal. 1987. 508 pp. $65.95. Available from agAccess (See Book Sources).

12

Many of the authors in *Restoration Forestry* deplore the broad-scale use of non-native forest plantations. Still, I feel that there are places for non-native trees in production forestry. Preferably in mixed species plantings containing natives. Those who are interested in growing non-native trees will find this book useful. Bear in mind that each of the trees described are native to somewhere and the book is valid in those places even for the native purist. A comprehensive textbook which covers tropical and temperate zones. Extensive references.

Irrigated Forestry in Arid and Semi-Arid Lands: A Syntheses

F. B. Armitage. 1985. International Development Research Centre, Box 8500, Ottawa, Canada K1G 3H9. 160 pp.

Past experiences in forestry plantations are given for about 20 countries, mostly in Asia and Africa. The different types of irrigation are reviewed as well as tree establishment and tending, water management and use. Includes a special section of key sources plus hundreds of references.

Man of the Trees—Selected Writings of Richard St. Barbe Baker

Karen Gridley, ed. 1989. 115 pp. Available from Ecology Action of the MidPeninsula, 5798 Ridgewood Road, Willits, CA 95490.

Richard St. Barbe Baker is credited with being responsible for planting more trees then any other person in the world's history. Baker started the organization "Men of the Trees" in 1922 in Kenya, Africa. He was advisor to Franklin D. Roosevelt on the Great Plains shelterbelt, the CCC and the WPA. He initiated an international plan to plant a green wall of shelterbelts around the Sahara. St. Barbe Baker inspired many tree groups in dozens of countries to plant trees and was the inspiration for founding Friends of the Trees Society in 1978. He died in 1982 at the age of 92, still on the road for the trees. His work continues.

My Life, My Trees

Richard Saint-Barbe Baker.

Richard Saint-Barbe Baker's autobiography.

Patterns of Life: Biogeography of A Changing World

Howard Mielke. 1989. Unwin Hyman: Boston. 370 pp.

Biogeography is the study of the patterns of life on Earth—past and present. This is a fascinating and up-to-date look at the evolution of life on Earth and how life has interacted with and changed the world's climate and atmosphere. One interesting tidbit from the book was that if the combined weight of all life on earth over the ages was added up, it would equal the weight of the planet.

The Struggle for Land and the Fate of the Forests

Marcus Colchester and L. Lohmann, eds. 1993. World Rainforest Movement, Penang, Malaysia and Zed Books, London. 389 pp.

Deforestation, it argues, is an expression of structural inequalities within tropical countries and in the relations with the industrial North. Throwing aid money into the development pot will only accelerate forest loss if these structural issues are not simultaneously addressed.

Temperate Broad-Leaved Evergreen Forests

J. D. Ovington, ed. Ecosystems of the World Series #10.

The several dozen volumes in the Ecosystems of the World Series constitutes one of the most in-depth, standardized looks at world vegetation.

Towards a Global Temperate Forest Action Plan

Proceedings of the Native Forest Network First International Temperate Forest Conference. Nov. 16-17, 1992. Available from Sustainable Media , PO Box Meander, Tasmania, 7304, Australia. 102 pp.

Offers an up-to-date overview on temperate rainforests, especially in the southern hemisphere. There are notable articles on biodiversity, the role of invertebrates in forest ecology, world strategies for conservation and the wood trade around the Pacific Rim

Trees and Man—The Forest in the Middle Ages

Roland Bechman. 1984 in French, 1990 in English. Paragon House: NY. 326 pp.

Fascinating coverage of natural resources, agriculture, history, and politics.

Who Will Save the Forests? Knowledge, Power and Environmental Destruction

T. Banauri and F. Apffel Marglin, eds. 1993. Zed Books. 195 pp.

This book examines conflicts over the management of forest resources in various parts of the world, including North America, Europe, and the South. The authors show how Western scientific knowledge, in particular, has been used to marginalize the knowledge and practice of age-old rural communities despite the fact that it is these societies that have managed the environment in sustainable fashion down the centuries.

World Deforestation in the Twentieth Century

John F. Richards and Richard P. Tucker. 1988. Duke Univ. Press, 6697 College Station, Durham, NC 27708.

Does not cover the whole world situation, but gives a detailed look at certain parts. Part I: Deforestation in the Developing World; Part II: Linkages—The Global Timber Trade; Part III: Forests of the Developed World (i.e. USA, USSR, Tasmania, etc.).

International Forestry Organizations

THE WORLD HAS THOUSANDS of professional forestry organizations—local, regional, national and international in scope. In this section are listed some of the larger organizations with an international scope (mostly in Europe). The degree to which each of these organization's activities are consistent with restoration forestry varies. Inclusion of a group here does not imply that everything it is doing reflects restoration forestry. Most are certainly not.

The careful researcher and networker, however, can obtain useful information by participating in these international forestry networks. We are all part of the dialogue. Each voice that speaks out contributes to the evolution of new forestry practices.

[For further forestry organizations see also the sections on Latin America, Asia/Pacific, Africa, USA, Canada, etc.]

Center for International Forestry Research (CIFOR)

Jalan Gunung Batu 5
P.O. Box 162
Bogor, 16001, INDONESIA

The Center for International Forestry Research (CIFOR) was established in 1992 as the eighteenth of the international centers in the Consultative Group on International Agricultural Research (CGIAR). The creation of the center is one of a number of efforts to improve the quantity and quality of forestry research in the pan-tropics of the developing world. Jeffrey Sayer is the first Director General of CIFOR. Professional staff were being sought in 1993 in many fields of forestry.

The work coming out of the CGIARs is a mixed bag. Some of it is good, but mostly the CGIARs dance to the tune of the transnational financial/industrial syndicates. We will see if the work of CIFOR helps restore forests or helps harvest them quicker. Hopefully the former, as CIFOR will likely soon be one of the most influential, international sources for forestry information.

Conservation International

1015 18th St. NW
Washington, DC 20036 USA
Tel: (202) 429-5660

CI works closely with government agencies throughout the world to integrate people as part of the ecosystem. In Costa Rica, CI gives technical and financial support to the 500,000-hectare La Amistad International Biosphere Reserve, which encompasses 14% of Costa Rica's territory.

Conservation International has a Rainforest Teaching Kit designed for school children ages 5 through 12, which contains a 25-minute video and study guide.

Edinburgh Center for Tropical Forests

Forestry-Darwin Building
University of Edinburgh
Mayfield Road
Edinburgh, EH9 2LN Scotland, UNITED KINGDOM
Tel: (44-31) 662-0752

The Edinburgh Centre for Tropical Forests (ECTF0), founded in 1990, has established itself as a major international centre for tropical forest management, conservation, research and education.

Environment Liaison Center International (ELCI)

P.O. Box 72461
Nairobi, KENYA
Tel: (254-2) 562015, 562022/Fax: 562175

Established in 1974, ELCI promotes cooperation and communication among NGOs worldwide and serves as a link between them and the United Nations Environment Program. Supports environmentally sustainable development and agriculture, organizes workshops and conferences, and publishes the bimonthly *Ecoforum*.

European Forest Institute (EFI)

Torikatu 34
SF-80100 Joensuu, NORWAY
Tel: 358-73-12 43 95/Fax: 358-73-12 43 93

The EFI was launched in 1993. The purpose of EFI is to undertake research on forest policy, including its environmental aspects, on ecology, multiple use, resources, and health of European forests and on the supply of and demand for timber and other forest products and to prepare forecasts.

European Tropical Forest Research Network (ETFRN)
c/o ATSAF e.V.
Ellerstr. 50
D-53119 Bonn, GERMANY
Tel: (+49-2 28) 98 46-0

This is a new address as of 1st January, 1994. Their new Fax number is not available as *Restoration Forestry* goes to press.

ETFRN was initiated by the Commission of the European Communities in 1991. The 5/93 issue of ETFRN Newsletter has the names and addresses of 14 European organizations which act as National Nodes in the ETFRN. ETFRN offers a forum for scientists, decision-makers and others to discuss questions on tropical forests, to initiate workshops and Task Forces on tropical forestry, and to support concrete research projects. The *ETFRN Newsletter* carries useful information for international networkers and is also noteworthy for an extensive calendar of forestry conferences throughout the world.

A task force on "Sustainable Management" has been established.

Forests, Trees and People Programme
Community Forestry Unit
FAO Via del Terme di Caracalla, Rome, 00100, ITALY

Launched in 1987 to explore methods which will support people's efforts to grow, manage and utilize trees and forests, the FTPP publishes an excellent quarterly newsletter with up-to-date articles on community forestry and book reviews.

Available free from IRDC/Swedish U. of Ag. Sciences, 75007, Uppsala, Sweden. FAO also publishes many useful guides and manuals for community forestry development workers. All are available in English, many in French and Spanish, and are distributed free. Also available are filmstrips and videos. Send for FAO Publications Catalogue or Community Forestry Publications by FAO.

International directory to 5,000 Forest, Trees & People Programme members. *Forest, Trees and People Newsletter* No. 21, August 1993, is a special issue members register in four volumes.

Between these four directories over 5,000 members of the FTPP Programme are listed. The majority of members are professional foresters from universities, government land agencies, development organizations, and NGOs. This is one of the best directories to consult if you want to tap into the world's professional forester circles. The registers list each member's name, organization, address, phone, fax, E-mail numbers and main activities.

The members' registers can be ordered from the various centers where the data bases are presently being kept and are available free of charge.

English speaking members in Africa, Europe, Latin & North America. FTPP c/o IRDC. Swedish University of Agricultural Sciences, 75007, Uppsala, SWEDEN.

Latin America (plus other Spanish speaking members): FTPP c/o Sr. Carlos Herz, 12 de Octubre 1430 y Wilson, Apartado 17-12-833, Quito, Ecuador, Fax 593-2-506255.

Francophone Africa (plus other French speaking members: FTPP c/o SILVA, 21 rue Paul Bert, 94130 Nogent-sur-Mame, France. Fax: 33-1-48763193.

Asia and the Pacific Region (English): FTPP c/o The Director, RECOFTC, Att. Dr. Viriyasakultom, Kasetsart University, Bangkok 10900, Thailand.

Foundation BOS
P.O. Box 23, 6700 AA
Wageningen, THE NETHERLANDS
Tel: 08370-95353/Fax: 08370-24988

The activities of BOS include: Publishes a newsletter in which all types of information on tropical forestry are incorporated. (see *BOS NiEuWSLETTER* in periodicals listing). Publishes a series of BOS desk-studies, called BOS-Documents. Maintains a register of tropical foresters called BODIS. Maintains contacts with all kinds of organizations, national and international. Keeps up a question-answer service for people and organizations on tropical forests and tropical forestry.

Global Forest Foundation
Postbus 9, 6700 AA
Wageningen, THE NETHERLANDS

Institute for World Forestry
Federal Research Centre for Forestry and
Forest Products
Leuschnerstr. 91
D-21031 Hamburg 80, GERMANY
Tel: +49-40-739 62-404/Fax: +49-40-739 62-480

Institute of Tropical Forestry
Call Box 25000
Rio Piedras, PUERTO RICO 00928
Tel: (809) 766-5335/Fax (809) 250-6924

US Forest Service branch station. Publishes an *Annual Report*.

International Forestry Students Symposium
Haarweg 75,
6709 PR Wageningen, THE NETHERLANDS
Tel: 08370-11704

The 19th IFSS symposium (held Sept. 1991 in Wageningen/Ede, Netherlands), brought 130 forestry students from over 35 countries to participate. The conference was titled "Forests, a growing concern," and its themes were: Land Allocation: Who First? and, Forest Resource Utilization: How and For Whom to Use? The results of the symposium are published.

International Society of Tropical Foresters (ISTF)
5400 Grosvenor Lane
Bethesda, Maryland 20814 USA
Tel: (301) 897-8720/Fax: 897-3690

ISTF has been providing information on the management and protection of the global tropical forests since 1950. ISTF has 2200 members in 110 countries. To meet the need for greatly improved management of the remaining natural forests, rehabilitation of degraded forests, and planting of deforested and marginal agriculture lands, the Society coordinates an expanded exchange of technical information between field technicians, international researchers and policy makers worldwide. *ISTF News* contains information about recent developments, programs, conferences. $5/year student. $20/year individual. $30/year organization/library.

International Tropical Timber Organization (ITTO)
International Organizations Center, 5th Floor
Pacifico-Yokohama, 1-1, Minato-Miral, Nishi-Ku
Yokohama 200 JAPAN
Tel. 045-223-1110/Fax 045-223-1111

The ITTO has commissioned a study on "Guidelines for the establishment and sustainable management of planted tropical forests." The findings of this commission should make interesting reading, albeit that it will be heavily influenced by international timber industry giants.

International Union for the Conservation of Nature and Natural Resources
Avenue du Mont-Blanc
CH-1196 Goland, SWITZERLAND

International Union of Forestry Research Organizations (IUFRO)
Alfred-Moeller-Strasse
D-O-1300, Evewalde-Finow, GERMANY
or UNFAO, Via delle Terme di Caracalla
1-00100 Rome, ITALY

IUFRO member organizations represent eight to nine thousand forest scientists from around the world. Their newsletter, *IUFRO News*, contains an extensive calendar of forestry conferences around the world.

International Union of Societies of Foresters
22 Walker Street,
GB-Edinburgh, EH3 7HR, UNITED KINGDOM

NGO Liaison Service
Palais des Nations
CH-1211 Geneva 10, SWITZERLAND

Serves as a link between NGOs and UN agencies.

Organization for Tropical Studies, Inc. (OTS)
P.O. Box DM, Duke Station
Durham, North Carolina 27706 USA
Tel: (919) 684-5774/Fax: (919) 684-5661

OTS especially works with Central and South American nations. OTS publishes *Tropinet*, a 4-page newsletter which profiles research institutions, and new journals and lists short courses, conferences, and job vacancy announcements throughout the world. Quarterly. US $5/year; $9/2 years; $12/3 years.

Pro Silva
c/o D. Helliwell
Yokecliffe House, West End
Wirkworth, Derbyshire, DE4 4EG, UNITED KINGDOM

An holistic approach to natural methods of forest management.

Reforesting Scotland
51 Iorn Street
Edinburgh EH6 8QJ, SCOTLAND
Tel: +44 (0)31 555 4641/Fax: +44(0)31 554 1634

Reforesting Scotland is an organization dedicated to sustainable forestry and land-use in Scotland and worldwide. It is replanting native trees and studying the most natural forest stands left in Scotland.

Reforesting Scotland in concert with *The Ecologist* published "The Scottish Forest Charter" a 10-point plan for reforesting Scotland. The expansion of forestry plantations of fast growing, exotic conifers has, between 1950 and 1980 been responsible for the destruction of over 30% of the remaining native woodland areas in Scotland. These plantations have brought little benefit to local communities, many are owned by absentee owners, pension funds and foreign companies and many have damaged valuable wildlife habitats.

Rural Development Forestry Network
Overseas Development Institute
Regent's College, Regent's Park. Inner Circle,
London NW1 4NS UNITED KINGDOM
Tel: 44-71-487-7413/Fax: 44-71-487-7590

A leading organization in this field with an international network of 1700 members, 70% of whom are in developing countries. RDFN produces a biannual newsletter and papers written through experience gained in the field, in French, Spanish, as well as English. Formerly known as the Social Forestry Network. Membership is free.

SILVA-Network

Dept. of Forestry: Attn. P. Schmidt
Agricultural University Wageningen
P.O. Box 342
6700 AH Wageningen, THE NETHERLANDS

The SILVA-Network is a European university cooperative program aiming at international forestry education, which includes 21 academic forestry institutes from 14 countries.

Social Forestry Network

[See: Rural Development Forestry Network]

Societé International des Forestiers Tropicaux

45 Bis, Avenue de la Belle Garbrielle
F-94130 Nogent-Sur-Marne, FRANCE

Society "le Bois Natural"

3, rue Claude Odde
F-42007 St. Etienne Cedex, FRANCE

Treeroots Network

2995 Waterloo St.
Vancouver, British Columbia, V6R 3J4 CANADA
Tel: (604) 731-2545/Fax: 731-3391

The Treeroots Network promotes the sustainability of local ecosystems throughout the world, through appropriate community control of trees, forests, forest lands and wastelands. The Treeroots Network helps to develop linkages between Southern and Northern groups and NGO's.

Tropical Forest Foundation

1725 Duke Street, Suite 660
Alexandria, Virginia 22314 USA
Tel: (703) 518-8834/Fax: (703) 518-8974

A non-profit educational organization recently founded by a coalition of major NGOs (such as World Wildlife Fund) and by timber industry and wood product manufacturers (such as Georgia Pacific and Mitsubishi). There is also involvement by key officials in major timber exporting countries such as Malaysia, Indonesia and Brazil. A stated goal of TFF is to promote more sustainable forestry practice; however, judging from its founders, we would expect a heavy corporate bias.

Tropical Forest Management Trust

6124 SW 30th Ave.
Gainesville, Florida 32608 USA
Tel: (904) 331-2007

Formed in 1992 by a group of scientists and academics to explore and promote sustainable forestry. Efforts to date include projects in Latin America and Madagascar (In conjunction with CARE and VITA).

TFMT has produced an educational forestry Video "Promising Approaches to Tropical Forest Management in Latin America." This 35-minute video on natural forest management interviews experts and footage of community-based forest management projects in Mexico, Costa Rica and Ecuador. Available in English or Spanish for $18 each.

Tropical Forestry Action Plan (TFAP)

TFAP was founded in 1985 by the United Nations Food and Agriculture Organization (FAO) to stimulate forest planning in developing countries throughout the world. Unfortunately, most TFAP energies have gone into increasing timber harvests. TFAP and the ITTO (International Tropical Timber Organization) are part of the "evil empire"—tools of governments and transnational corporations for global forest mismanagement.

For a detailed and a differently-biased account of TFAP and its history, order BOS Document No. 11: Tropical Forestry Action Plan, recent developments and Netherlands involvement. Address under Foundation Bos this section. The report goes into some detail about the international criticism of TFAP.

United Kingdom Tropical Forest Forum

c/o Royal Botanic Gardens
Kew, Richmond, Surrey TW9 3AB, UNITED KINGDOM
Tel: +44-81-332 62 99. Fax: +44-81-332 62 94

University of Stellenbosch

Faculty of Forestry
Private Bag X5018
7599 Stellenbosch, SOUTH AFRICA
Fax: 27-22 31-77 36 03

Prof. B. Bredenkamp is the contact for a seminar on Minimum Data Requirements for Sustainable Forest Management to be held April 24-30, 1994.

World Conservation Monitoring Center

219 Huntingdon Road
UK-Cambridge, CB3 0DL UNITED KINGDOM
Tel: 44-223-277314/Fax: 44-223-277136

An independent, non-governmental, international organization, established in 1988, providing information on the status, protection and management of the earth's living natural resource. Together with IUCN, WCMC has produced two volumes (Asia and the Pacific, and Africa) of a three-volume *The Conservation Atlas of Tropical Forests*. These atlases outline important tropical forest issues and country forest maps for each tropical region. The third volume, *The Americas*, is in preparation and will be published in 1994.

Other WCMC projects include: Tropical Timbers Database and Tropical Managed Areas Assessment.

World Tree Foundation
Jan Mossel, Zuideinde 1, P.O. Box 103
2420 AC Nieuwkoop, THE NETHERLANDS
Tel: (01725) 72480/FAX (01725) 73260

Jan is building a standardized global database of the oldest, largest and most famous or sacred trees throughout the world. Networking internationally with tree loving citizens on six continents.

Tree Organizations in Ireland

Crann
Aughavas via Cavan,
Co. Leitrim IRELAND

The Tree People of Ireland. An organization devoted to planting trees in urban areas and farmland. They publish a newsletter.

Irish Forestry Board
Sidmonton Place
Bray Co, Wicklow, IRELAND
Tel: 01-2867751/Fax 01-2868126

Irish National Council for Forest Research and Development (COFORD)
Agriculture Building, UCD
Belfield, IRL-Dublin 4, IRELAND
Tel: 353-1-706 77 00/Fax: 353-1-706-11-80

COFORD was established in April 1993 and is part funded under the European Community (EC) STRIDE Forestry Sub-Programme. It aims to strengthen forestry research in Ireland and to liaise with forestry institutions around the world.

Irish Woodworkers for Africa
Tom Roche
113 Arden
Vale, Tullamore, Offaly, IRELAND

Tree Council of Ireland
Fourth Floor, St. Martin's House, Waterloo Road
Dublin 4, IRELAND

Organization devoted to planting trees.

12

International Forestry Journals

HERE ARE A NUMBER of major forestry journals in the world, most with an international scope, and mostly from overdeveloped countries. Their politics vary depending on their position on the continuum between the extremes of restoration forestry and conventional, industrial forestry. Many will send sample copies on request.

(See also various international sections: Latin America, Asia/Pacific, Africa, Australia, New Zealand, and others. Besides looking under periodical sections, look also under organizations since many publish journals or newsletters.)

Directories to Forestry Periodicals

Directory of Selected Tropical Forestry Journals and Newsletters

1993. 127 pp. A joint project of the Forestry Support Program, the International Society of Tropical Foresters (ISTF), and the International Working Group of the Society of American Foresters. Available from: Forestry Support Program, Attn: Journals and Newsletters Directory, USDA Forest Service/IF/FSP, P.O. Box 96090, Washington, DC 20090-6090 USA.

The most comprehensive directory on the subject. It describes close to 500 periodicals from many countries. Well-indexed, by country and subject, with useful annotations. It will be revised periodically. This directory will facilitate and enhance the work of anyone involved in tropical forestry and related fields. Its weakest point is a lack of coverage of the smaller, more radical, grass-roots forestry and environmental groups.

International Directory of Wildland Fire

Disc version, 1993. Printed version, 1990. International Association of Wildland Fire. 671 pp.
See review and address in the Directories section.

This directory lists 500 forestry journals and newsletters from around the world.

International Directory to Periodicals in Print

This large reference book covers virtually all sub-

jects. Researchers can find it at large public libraries or universities.

Forestry Abstracts

International Forestry Bureau
Farnham House, Farnham Royal
GB-Slough SL2 3BN, GREAT BRITAIN

This abstract journal is for the really serious forest researcher. Abstracts of thousands of articles, books and reports from all corners of the world every year. Available at large libraries and universities.

International Forestry Periodicals

Bois et Forets des Tropiques

Centre Technique Forestier Tropical
45 bis. Ave. de la Belle Gabrielle
F-94130 Nogent-sur-marne, FRANCE

Journal subscription is 120 F.

BOS NiEuWSLETTER

Foundation BOS, P.O. Box 23, 6700 AA
Wageningen, THE NETHERLANDS
Tel: (08370) 95353/Fax: 24988

A bulletin of the Foundation for Dutch Forestry Development Cooperation. This newsletter is one of the best ways to keep abreast of tropical forestry developments. Each issue has articles, book reviews, announcements of meetings, symposia and job openings. Sub: Dfl. 25 for students; Dfl.50 for others in Europe; Dfl. 60 outside Europe. Foundation BOS also maintains a register of tropical foresters, and runs a question-answer service for people and organizations on any aspect of tropical forestry. Many documents available.

Commonwealth Forestry Review

Commonwealth Forestry Association
c/o Oxford Forestry Institute
South Parks Road
Oxford, England OX1 3RB, UNITED KINGDOM
Tel: (44-865) 275-072/Fax: (44-865) 275-074

Each issue contains 200-300 pages of forestry information worldwide. Quarterly. Subscriptions: Individuals $21/year; institutions $40/year.

Commonwealth Forestry Handbook
Commonwealth Forestry Association. Address as above.

One issue every two years. 13th edition 1993. The 200-page handbook lists members of the Commonwealth Forestry Assoc., and publishes statistics on forest resources by country.

DANIDA Lecture Notes
Danish International Development Agency, DANIDA Forest Seed Centre
Krogerupvej 3 A
3050 Humleback, DENMARK
Tel: (45-4) 219-0500/Fax: (45-4) 916-0258
Occasional. English. Free of charge.

Information on seed procurement, tree improvement and gene-resource conservation. Also publishes DANIDA Technical Notes, which has a similar focus but is published more frequently.

DESFIL Newsletter
Development Strategies for Fragile Lands (DESFIL)
2000 M Street, NW, Suite 200
Washington, D.C. 20036, USA
Tel: (202) 331-1860/Fax: (202) 331-1871

Focuses on issues relating to steep slopes and tropical lowlands. Worldwide in scope. Quarterly. English and Spanish. Free of charge.

Environmental Conservation
The Foundation for Environmental Conservation
7 Chemin Taverney
1218 Grand-Saconnex, Geneva, SWITZERLAND
Tel: (41-22) 798-2383/Fax: (41-22) 798-2344

An environmental perspective on forestry. Recommended. SFrs 245/4 issues/yr., or US $181.00.

Forest Ecology and Management
Box 211
NL-1000 AE Amsterdam, THE NETHERLANDS
An international journal.

Forestry
Journal of the Institute of Chartered Foresters
Oxford Univ. Press, Journ. Sub. Dept.
Walton St.
Oxford, OX2 6DP, UNITED KINGDOM

Forestry and Development
IMWOO (Institute for Social Science Research in Developing Countries), P.O. Box 90734, 2509 LS
The Hague, The Netherlands
Tel: (O70) 3510574/Fax: 351513

A series through which the Dutch social research community presents current thoughts. It includes a guide to research institutions in The Netherlands. Price Dfl. 38,50 (US$20) plus postage.

Forest Harvesting Bulletin
Contact Mr. R. Heinrich, Chief, Forest Harvesting and Transport Branch
Forest Products Division, FAO
Via delle Terme di Caracalla
00100 Rome, ITALY

A new biannual bulletin to strengthen networking among forest harvest experts, training, education and research institutions and FAO. The aim is to develop and promote appropriate, sound forest harvesting systems. Two issues per year. English. Free of charge.

Gate
German Appropriate Technical Exchange
P.O. Box 5180 Dag-Hammarskjöld-Weg 1
D-6236 Eschborn 1, GERMANY

Gate is a free, quarterly magazine full of questions, answers, and information for international development workers. Its focuses are technology dissemination and environmental protection. I have been impressed with its quality and relevance.

International Journal of Ecoforestry
Ecoforestry Institute Society
PO Box 5783, Station B
Victoria, British Columbia, V8R 6S8, Canada
Tel:/Fax: (604) 598-2363

A new journal with the first issue published in Spring, 1994. The journal will be produced by the Ecoforestry Institute Society's staff working with Bob Nixon, the editor of Forest Planning Canada.

IRED-Forum
3 Rue de Varembé, Case 116
1211 Geneva 20, SWITZERLAND
Tel: (41-22) 734-1716/Fax: 740-0011

This quarterly journal is "the communication tool of an international network of 1000 peasant associations, artisans' and women's groups, organizations for development action in urban surroundings and of centers and institutes giving their support to grassroots groups." Articles focus on news from the member organizations and other networks, appropriate technology, tools and methods, tips and documents for action. Excellent networking.

Subscriptions: US$30/yr. for Europe/USA/Canada, US$12 for Third World from the address above or IRED's regional offices in Zimbabwe (P.O. Box 8242, Causeway, Harare). Nigeria (SEAG, B.P. 12675, Niamey). Zaire (B.P. 2375, Bukavu). Rwanda (B.P. 257, Cyangugu). Colombia (Calle 54 No. 10-81, Of. 501, Santa Fé de Bogotá). Sri Lanka

12

(No. 64, Horton Place, Colombo). and China (27, Bai Shi Qiao Rd., Beijing 100 081).

ITTO Tropical Forest Management Update

ANUTECH Pty Ltd.
GPO Box 4
Canberra, ACT 2601 AUSTRALIA
Tel: (61-62) 49-5861/Fax: (61-20) 49-5875

This is a publication of the world timber cartels, so any of this newsletters recommendations should be given especially close scrutiny. Six issues per year. English. Free of charge.

IUFRO News

International Union of Forestry Research Organizations (IUFRO)
Seckendorff-Gudent-Weg 8
A-1131 Vienna, AUSTRIA
Tel: (43-222) 820-151/Fax: (43-222) 829-355

Quarterly. English and Spanish. free of charge.

IUSF Newsletter

International Union of Societies of Foresters (IUSF)
G.P.O. Box 1697
Brisbane, 4001 Queensland AUSTRALIA
Tel: (61-7) 234-0304/Fax: (61-7) 234-0156, 234-0304

A 10-page newsletter for member societies. Two issues per year. English. Free of charge.

Journal of Tropical Ecology

Cambridge University Press
40 West 20th Street
New York, New York 10001-4211

Quarterly. Subscriptions: Individuals $61/year. Institutions $140. Developing countries $35.

Journal of Tropical Forestry

Society of Tropical Forestry Scientists
State Forest Research Institute Estate
Polipathar, Jabalpur 482 008, INDIA

Quarterly. English. Subscriptions: Individuals US$25/yea, institutions $100-200.

Journal of World Forest Resource Management

P.O. Box 42
Bicester, Oxon OX6 7NW
England, UNITED KINGDOM
Tel: (44-869) 320-949

This journal was established to provide a forum for the increasing number of in-depth studies of the management of the global forest resource, and reforestation. Also, to ensure the world has enough wood in the middle of the next century and beyond. Its subjects of interest are: resource inventories, global trends, forestry policy forest economics, forest ecology, and social aspects of forest management. Two issues per year. English. Subscriptions:

$49/year (US $89). Edited by Alan Grainger, (also Secretary of the International Tree Crops Institute).

New Forests

Kluwer Academic Publishers
Spuiboulevard 50, PO Box 17
3300 AA Dordrecht, THE NETHERLANDS
in the U.S.A. contact: New Forests, c/o 101 Philip Dr. Norwell, MA 02061.

An international journal on the biology, biotechnology and management of afforestation and reforestation. Its audience is forest scientists, foresters, nursery managers, conservationists, and students in temperate and tropical countries.

Quarterly Journal of Forestry

Forestry Society of England
P.O. Box 21
GB-Herts, SG6 4ET, UNITED KINGDOM

Tropical Timbers

2 Bug Hill
Waldingham, Surrey, CR3 7LB, UNITED KINGDOM

A monthly magazine on the world timber trade. Free sample copy.

UNASYLVA

Food and Agriculture Organization of the United Nations (FAO)
Via delle Terme di Caracalla
00100-Rome, ITALY
Tel: (39-6) 5797-4778/Fax: (39-6) 5797-5137

One of the best journals covering world forestry matters. Informative current articles, book reviews and international forestry news. Most of it is progressive. Recommended. English, French and Spanish. Quarterly. US$20/year.

Environmental Organizations

THE ENVIRONMENTAL MOVEMENT is worldwide. A movement so big, localized and decentralized that it is hard to gauge. Love for the land, nature and community abounds in human hearts everywhere. This love for the earth expresses itself through gardening, growing plants, interacting with the natural environment, and taking a stand for the environment. Oppressive economic and police state mechanisms cloud much of this expression at present.

It is the biggest, most famous environmental organizations who get most of the press. Small, local organizations are seldom noticed, but do most of the really effective work. There are countless thousands of un-named, unofficial, non-registered small groups of people working for the environment. Here are some of the larger organizations and networks.

(See also international environmental organizations based in the USA.)

African NGOs Environmental Network

P.O. Box 53844
Nairobi, KENYA
Tel: (254) 28138

One of the largest networks of environmental groups in Africa, promoting sustainable community-based development and conservation.

Asia-Pacific People's Environmental Network (APPEN)

Sahabat Alam Malaysia, 43 Salween Rd.
Penang 10050 MALAYSIA
Tel: 04-376930

An informal network of more than 350 NGOs in the Asia-Pacific. APPEN's main objectives are the collection and dissemination of information pertaining to development and environmental issues, contributing towards regional collaboration, investigating, reporting and campaigning on such issues as genetic resources and seeds, sustainable agriculture, pollution, forestry, wildlife, multinationals, nukes and toxics. Publications include their quarterly *The Asian-Pacific Environment* (subscriptions: US $15 outside of Asia) and a *Directory of Environmental NGOs in the Asia-Pacific Region*.

Sahabat Alam Malaysia is one of the most active environmental NGOs in southeast Asia.

Directory of Country Environmental Studies: 1993 Ed.

INTERAISE Directory Project, World Resources Inst., 1709 New York Ave. NW, Washington, DC 20006. $20 for printed version. $50 for diskette version.

An annotated bibliography of environmental and natural resource profiles and assessments. Updated and expanded from the 1990 edition. Covers 350 national studies from developing countries.

Directory of Environment/Development NGOs

Jose Da Costa—Project Coordinator
ENDA Third World, European Delegation
21023, rue de la Folie Regnault
75011 Paris, FRANCE
Tel: 33 (1) 43 72 09 09/Fax: 33 (1) 43 72 16 81

The list was compiled for the UN Conference on Environment and Development (UNCED) in Rio de Janeiro in June 1992.

The Ecologist

Agriculture House, Bath Road
Sturminster, Newton, Dorset DT10 1DU
UNITED KINGDOM
Tel: 44-258-473476/Fax: 44-258-473748

The Ecologist has been publishing for 20 years and has earned its reputation as one of the most relevant, influential and radical of the international, environmental journals. Each issue has about six in-depth feature articles on forestry, agriculture, energy, development, indigenous peoples, and other environmental topics, as well as book reviews and letters.

For USA subscriptions contact: MIT Press Journals, 55 Hayward St., Cambridge, Massachusetts 02142-9949. Subscription: Student/retired $25; Individual $30; Single issue $6.

ENVIRONESIA

WALHI-Friends of the Earth Indonesia
Jalan Penjernihan I
Kompleks Keuangan no. 15
Pejompongan, Jakarta 10210, INDONESIA
Tel: (62-21) 586-820/Fax: (62-21) 588-416

Environmental issues in Indonesia dealing with sustainable development. Quarterly. English. Free on exchange basis.

Friends of The Earth (UK)—Tropical Rainforest Campaign

26-28 Underwood Street
Islington, London N1 7JQ UNITED KINGDOM
Tel: (44-71) 490-1555/Fax: (44-71) 490-0881

One of the most active international campaigns for the rainforests. They publish a newsletter, *Rainforest Action Report.*

Environmental Conservation

The Foundation for Environmental Conservation
7 Chemin Taverney
1218 Grand-Saconnex, Geneva, SWITZERLAND
Tel: (41-22) 798-2383/Fax: (41-22) 798-2344

A professional magazine by an influential, large NGO. Recommended for its analysis and global view. SFrs 245/4 issues/yr., or US $181.00.

Green Magazine for Our Environment

The Northern and Shell Building
Freepost, Little Heath, Romford, Essex RM6 1BR
UNITED KINGDOM

Native Forest Network

Tim Cadman and Beth Gibbings
112 Emu Bay Road
Deloraine, Tasmania, 7304 AUSTRALIA
Tel: (003) 622-712/Fax: (003) 623-056
e-mail: peg:cadwood

NFN is a global, autonomous collective of forest activists, conservation biologists, and non-governmental organizations. Their goals are to protect Earth's remaining native forests, both temperate and tropical. And, to recognize the rights of indigenous peoples and forest dwellers and to ensure that cultural values of ecosystems are identified and protected. An NFN newsletter entitled the *Native Forest News* is produced out of Tasmania. The proceedings from their 1992 international conference in Australia and 1993 North America Temperate Forest Conference are recommended.

Rainforest Information Centre

P.O. Box 368
Lismore, New South Wales, 2480 AUSTRALIA
Tel: (066) 218-505/Fax: 222-339

RIC was one of the first tropical rainforest activist groups and is still probably the most effective. RIC's many projects include sustainable timber management with the Siona-Secoya, Amazonian tribes who have recently been granted title to their ancestral territory. Similar eco-forestry projects in Ecuador (see CIBT), Papua New Guinea and the Solomon Islands, all of which are coordinated with local government or NGOs. RIC publishes the *Eco-Forestry Trainer's Manual* and *Eco-Forestry Management Plan Trainer's and Operator's Field Guide.*

Their newsletter, *World Rainforest Report*, is one of the best ways to keep up with news on tropical rainforests. Highly recommended! A$15/yr. in Australia. Overseas subscription rate AS$25/yr. RIC's World Rainforest Report, is available in the USA from: WRR, Rainforest Information Center, Box 111, Shattuck Ave., Berkeley, CA 94707. $20 for four issues.

Sarawak Peoples' Campaign

P.O. Box 344, Station A
Vancouver British Columbia, CANADA V6C 2M7
Tel: (604) 669-5444/Fax: (604) 687-5575

Southeast Asia Rainforests: A Resource Guide and Directory

Martha Belcher and Angela Gennino, eds. 1993.
Rainforest Action Network, 450 Sansome, Suite 700, San Francisco, CA 94111, USA. $10 ppd. in USA. $13 ppd outside USA.

Profiles 250 groups working on the rainforest issue, plus a country-by-country overview of the major threats to southeast Asia's rainforests and the indigenous people who depend on them; along with statistics on forests and deforestation.

World Rainforest Movement

8 Chapel Row
Chadlington, OX73 NA UNITED KINGDOM
Tel: (4460) 876-691/Fax: (4460) 876-743

Marcus Colchester.

World Rainforest Movement

Attn: Martin Khor Kok, Third World Network
87 Cantonment Rd.
Penang, MALAYSIA

An international network of environmental groups.

World Wildlife Fund International (WWF)

CH-1196 Gland, SWITZERLAND
Tel: (022) 64-71-81

WWF is the world's largest private conservation organization with 23 national headquarters and over a million supporters. In 30 years it has funded thousands of projects in 130 countries, including habitat protection, conservation education, and sustainable forest management.

Forestry and Overseas Development: A Resource Guide

DEVELOPMENT IS A LOADED WORD with different meanings to different people. At worst, it is a tool for continued imperialism and exploitation. Development, to some, means bringing people into the international cash economy. Development can be the antithesis of healthy, locally-based, self-reliant communities. The dominant industrial paradigm of development (i.e. growth) is actually de-developing much of the southern nations, as well as many rural areas within the borders of the industrialized world.

Development/aid projects have, by and large, failed to improve people's lives. During the 1980's, however, some lessons have been drawn from these many failures. Participation is a word that is now on many people's lips in the development/aid field. Many of the better community development projects and grassroots movements have been identified and we have evaluations, critiques and articles about these success stories.

True sustainable development is participatory, locally-controlled and leads to greater self-reliance and ecological sustainability. In this section, I point out some resources for the latter brand of development.

Organizers in rural, forest-based communities in countries of the north would do well to study the progressive wing of the development/aid crowd. Part of what works in the South has validity in the North.

Strategies for success include:

- Local people are involved at all stages of projects, from formulation to planning to implementation and evaluation.

- Planning and implementation are not linear processes. They have many reiterative feedback loops.

- Communication/information is a two-way flow. Everyone learns from each other. Everyone has valuable information and viewpoints.

- Projects should be aimed at meeting the need of the poorest first.

Non-Governmental Organizations

There are many kinds of NGOs:

1. United Nation agencies such as FAO, UNEP, UNDP, and UNESCO, maintain offices and projects in most countries of the world.

2. Large multi-million dollar NGO's, such as Nature Conservancy, World Wildlife Fund and CARE have projects in many countries.

3. Medium-level NGOs have projects usually oriented to one or several countries and are relatively well funded

4. Small international NGOs network overseas, and have few overseas projects, small budgets, and few people involved.

5. Domestic NGOs operate only within their country.

6. Grassroots NGOs operate locally. May have some affiliation or representation on a regional or national level through coalitions or networks.

7. Underground grassroots NGOs and small, local, informal grassroots groups are not registered with any government. In countries with repressive governments, some self-help groups wish to remain unseen or as little noticed by the government as possible.

International Directories to NGOs

Dictionary of Environment and Development: People, Places, Ideas and Organizations
Andy Crump. 1993. MIT Press. $16.95

Directory of Environment/Development NGOs
Jose Da Costa, Project Coordinator
ENDA Third World European Delegation
21023, Rue de la Folie Regnault
75011 Paris, FRANCE
Tel: (33-1) 4372-0909/Fax: (33-1) 4372-1681

List released at UNCED ("The Earth Summit") in Rio de Janeiro, June 1992.

12

Directory of NGO's in OECD Member Countries

OECD. 1990. 708 pp. $90. Available from Agribookstore.

Provides concise descriptions of the aims, development education work and development activities of 2542 non-government organizations in Europe, USA, Canada, Australia, New Zealand and Japan. Cross indexed by activity, topic and country.

Natural History Book Service Catalog of Books on Philosophy and Theory of Sustainable Development

A special catalog of books contributing to the philosophical, ethical and theoretical framework within which the concept of sustainable development is evolving. For address see Natural History Book Service Ltd. entry in the Book Sources section.

Sourcebook on Sustainable Development

The International Institute of Sustainable Development

Heather Creech, Information Scientist, IISD, 161 Portage Avenue East, 6th floor, Winnipeg, Manitoba, R3B O4Y, CANADA

This first edition identifies many of the key sources of information on sustainable development, including organizations, publications, electronic networks and databases.

U.N. Development Education Directory

UNCTAD/NGLS/34. 1992, 7th edition. Published by UN Non-Government Liaison Service (see address in following section.)

Who is Who at the Earth Summit

1993. VisionLink Education Foundation, 181 Bio Dome Drive, Waynesville, NC 28786. 500 pp.

This is the most thorough list of who attended the Earth Summit held in Rio, Brazil in 1992. Over 30,000 entries indexed alphabetically by name, country and organization. Includes subcategories for organizations accredited to UNCED, advisors, non-government organizations, media, Global Forum, Wisdom Keepers, government, and spiritual leaders.

Women, Trees and Forests in Africa—A Resource Guide

Paula Williams. Environment Liaison Centre International (ELCI): P.O. Box 72461, Nairobi, KENYA.

Available in French and English, free of charge.

1992 Directory of Women in Environment

See address under WorldWIDE Network under Organizations, this section.

Includes women from 115 countries.

Development Organizations

Board on Science and Technology for International Development (BOSTID)

National Academy of Sciences, National Research Council
2101 Constitution Ave.
Washington, DC 20418, USA

BOSTID has produced several dozen well-researched, practical books on trees, crops, livestock, aquaculture, and technology. Some titles of special interest to restoration foresters include: *Sowing Forests from the Air, Firewood Crops: Shrub and Tree Species for Energy Production* (vols. 1 and 2), *Lost Crops of the Incas, Tropical Legumes: Resources for the Future, Underexploited Tropical Plants with Promising Economic Value, Calliandra: A Versatile Small Tree for the Humid Tropics, Casuarinas: Nitrogen-fixing Trees for Adverse Sites, Leucaena: Promising Forage and Tree Crop for the Tropics, Mangium and other Fast-Growing Acacias for the Humid Tropics.*

BOSTID publications may be available to you without charge if you write requesting further information.

Canada Africa International Forestry Association

2995 Waterloo St.
Vancouver, British Columbia, V6R 3J4, CANADA
Tel: (604) 731-2545/Fax: (604) 731-3391

A liaison group connecting forestry organizations in Africa and Canada. Also the office for the Tree Roots Network. Agroforestry is the chief emphasis. Their newsletter is a forum on tropical forestry, social forestry, agroforestry, farm forestry, conservation and NGO activities.

Canadian Crossroads International

31 Madison Ave.
Toronto, Ontario, M5R 2S2, CANADA

A private, non-profit organization that sends Canadian volunteers to assist with self-help development, agriculture, education and health projects in 30 developing countries, as well as bringing volunteers from the Third World to help in Canada. Their quarterly *Crossworld* (C$7/yr.) publishes good articles about development strategies.

Canadian International Development Agency (CIDA)

200 Promenade du Portage
Hull, Quebec, K1A 0G4, CANADA

Contributes million of dollars to projects in Africa, Asia, and Latin America including forestry and agriculture development. Publishes the quarterly *People-Centered Development Forum*, free in Canada.

CARE

660 First Ave.
New York, New York, 10016 USA
Tel: (212) 686-3110

CARE is the world's largest, private, non-sectarian NGO with development projects in many countries. Forestry and agriculture have long been important aspects of their programs, which are often cited as some of the most successful examples of aid projects.

CUSO

135 Rideau St.
Ottawa, Ontario, K1N 9K7, CANADA
Tel: (613) 563-1242

Each year CUSO places 120 people overseas for two- or three-year stints doing development work.

Environment Liaison Center International (ELCI)

P.O. Box 72461
Nairobi, KENYA
Tel: (254-2) 56-2015/Fax: (254-2) 56-2175

A major coalition of over 500 grassroots NGOs from the South. See Africa section for review.

Institute for Development Anthropologists

99 Collier St. #302, PO Box 2207
Binghamton, New York, 13902, USA

Organized 15 years ago to foster "the application of anthropology to humane and compassionate development among disadvantaged people," IDA has become another voice in the analysis of development within the "development agency paradigm." The promotion of local participation in all stages of development and the awareness of indigenous knowledge has been a hallmark of the program since its inception.

Institute for Food and Development Policy

398 60th St.,
Oakland, California 94618, USA
Tel: (510) 654-4400

Critical analysis and news on development and a watchdog for World Bank, IMF, restructuring, etc. They publish *Food First News & Views*. Membership/subscription is $30/yr. Free sample copy upon request.

International Foundation for Development Alternatives (IFDA)

Case Postale 1260
Nyon, SWITZERLAND

Publishes a bi-annual journal, the *IFDA Dossier*, with contributions on diverse topics and regions. Promotes dialogue on alternative approaches to development. Recommended.

MATCH International Centre

1102-200 Elgin St.
Ottawa, Ontario, K2P 1L5, CANADA

Links Canadian and Third World women to work together for change. Projects in Nicaragua, Peru, Zimbabwe, and other Third World countries.

Plant a Tree in Africa

120 York Rd.
Swindon, Wilts, SN1 2JP UNITED KINGDOM
Tel: 0793-32353

"Our aim is to collect information on grass-roots social forestry projects in Africa and to raise funds and seek co-financing of such projects."

Sustainable Development Network (SDN)

Chuck Lankester, Director SDN, UNDP,
Division of Global and Interregional Programmes,
One United Nations Plaza
New York, New York, 10017, USA
Tel: (212) 906-5000/Fax: (212) 906-6952

The United Nations Development Programme (UNDP) is making good progress in establishing a Sustainable Development Network (SDN). This activity is a follow-up to the 1992 UN Conference for Environment and Development, when UNDP was given the mandate to serve as the lead agency for capacity-building.

UN Non-Government Liaison Service

Palais des Nations
CH-1211 Geneva 10, SWITZERLAND
Tel: 41-22-734.60.11/Fax: 41-22-733-65.42

The USA address is UN Non-Government Liaison Service, Room DC2-1103, United Nations, New York, NY 10017. Tel: (212) 963-3125).

A United Nations support service for NGOs. Publishes a quarterly newsletter *Go-Between*, $5/yr. They publish various international directories to NGOs.

Volunteers in Technical Assistance (VITA)

1815 N. Lynn St., #200
Arlington, Virginia 22209, USA
Tel: (703) 276-1800

VITA has been providing technical information and assistance to developing countries for several decades. VITA will do research and find technical advisors for many aspects of restoration forestry and sustainable agriculture.

Women, Environment and Development Network (WEDNET)

Ms. Rosemary Jommo, WEDNET ELCI Coordinator,
Environment Liaison Centre
P.O. Box 72461, Nairobi, KENYA
or: Dr. Bonnie Kettel, Canadian Coordinator for
WEDNET, Faculty of Environmental Studies, York
University, North York, Ontario, CANADA M3J 1P3.

The Women, Environment and Development Network is an innovative research and information-sharing project launched by the Environment Liaison Center International (ELCI) in 1989.

ELCI publishes *WEDNEWS*, an English-language periodical for the Women, Environment, and Development Network (WEDNET) Project. Topics include the role of women in the management of water, livestock, agriculture, forests, etc.

Women, Ink.

International Women's Tribune Center (IWTC)
777 United Nations Plaza, Third Floor
New York, New York 10017, USA

The United Nations Development Fund for Women (UNIFEM) established Women, Ink. to market and distribute resource materials on women and development. It distributes materials published by UNIFEM and other organizations including books, journals, papers, technical guides, and training materials.

Women and Environmental Education and Development (WEED)

736 Bathurst St.
Toronto, Ontario, M5S 2R4, CANADA
Tel: (416) 516-2600

WEED provides a forum for communication and conducts research on and relating to women in the fields of health, ecology and environment, planning, community development, and urban and rural sociology.

World Neighbors

5116 N. Portland Ave.
Oklahoma City, Oklahoma 73112
Tel: (405) 946-3333

World Neighbors is an international organization working since 1951 to promote effective development and self-reliance. World Neighbors has one of the better reputations in development circles. Among many other projects and publications, they produce practical guides to dryland farming: *Planting Tree Crops, Contour Farming with Living Barriers*, and *Integrated Farm Management*. Write for a free catalogue of teaching materials. The Indonesian branch (P.O. Box 471, Denpasar, Bali 80001, Indonesia) runs the Agroforestry Seed Info. Clearinghouse, the SE Asia Sustainable Agriculture Network, and many community based Agroforestry programs in Philippines and Indonesia. World Neighbors Nepal (P.O. Box 916 Kathmandu, Nepal; Tel: 411-308) runs agroforestry and health programs in India & Nepal.

WorldWIDE Network
(Woman in Development and Environment)

1331 "H" St. NW, #903
Washington D.C. 20006, USA
Tel: (202) 347-1514/Fax: (202) 347-1524

A dynamic and innovative international network of women who are actively solving environmental problems. They hosted a Global Assembly of Women and the Environment on November 4-8, 1991 in Miami, Florida. They have published a *1992 Directory of Women in Environment*.

Development Periodicals

DevelopNet News

Volunteers In Technical Assistance (VITA)
1815 N. Lynn Street, Suite 200
Arlington, Virginia 22209
Tel: (703) 276-1800/Fax: (703) 243-1865
e-mail: (BITNET): VITA@GMUVAX
Internet: VITA@GMUVAX.GMU.EDU

Monthly through e-mail on Bitnet and Fidonet. English. Subscriptions: $15/yr.; free to those unable to pay; free via e-mail. Hard copy version is 8-pages issued quarterly.

Development Education Exchange Papers (DEEP)

FAO Freedom from Hunger Campaign/ Action for Development
Via Terme di Caracalla
Rome, 1-00100 ITALY

DEEP reviews 10 to 15 newsletters or publications in each issue which are seldom covered in even the alternative media in America and Europe. Each review gets deep into the concepts presented and stimulates thought. Six issues per year. English, French, and Spanish. Free of charge.

Development in Practice

Oxfam Publications
274 Banbury Road
Oxford, OX2 7DZ, UNITED KINGDOM

A new journal started by Oxfam in 1991. It aims to stimulate debate about overseas development from the perspective of non-governmental organizations. It will also act as a forum for the exchange of information about new resources. Social Forestry will be one of its topics. Three times a year. 1991 subscription is $37.50 in the USA; £30 in Europe; and £40.50 for the Far East.

Development Forum

DC-1 Bldg.
1 United Nations Plaza, Room 559
New York, New York, 10017, USA
$25/yr. (6 issues).

Fenix

P.O. Box 10.133

NL-2130 CC Hoofddorp, THE NETHERLANDS

One of my favorite international magazines covering development and agricultural issues was *Ideas and Actions*, published by a branch of FAO. Several years ago its funding was pulled, even though it was one of the world's best magazines promoting local self reliance and independence. Besides insightful articles it always reported on success stories.

There was such a hue and cry after it was shut down that part of its staff have regrouped and are publishing under the new name *Fenix* (Phoenix, rising from the ashes). If *Fenix* is anywhere as good as its predecessor then it is useful reading for anyone concerned with local development strategies and world views which challenge the EuroAmerican hegemony.

Moving Pictures Bulletin: The Quarterly Guide to Films on Development and the Environment

Television Trust for the Environment
46 Charlotte St.
London, W1P 1LX, UNITED KINGDOM

Designed to inform subscribers how to obtain films on development and environment issues.

Third World Resurgence

87 Cantonment Road
102140 Penang, MALAYSIA

Published by the highly-regarded Third World Network to give voice to Third World cultures.

Transnational Network for Appropriate/Alternative Technologies (TRANET)

P.O. Box 567
Rangeley, Maine, 04970, USA

TRANET is a nonprofit, transnational network of social activists from around the world. For over a decade, I have considered TRANET as one of the premier international networks of groups and individuals working for positive change. Each of TRANET's quarterly newsletters reviews an extensive list of resources for many sectors of human endeavor including forestry and agriculture.

Books on Sustainable Development

Agriculture and Natural Resources Strategy

July 1989. CARE. No. 1 of Agriculture and Natural Resources Technical Report Series.

A useful document on CARE's brand of development. The six CARE programming principles for their projects include: Working with the poor, participation, sustainability, adaptability, significant scope, fundamental change.

Bridging the Global Gap: A Handbook to Linking Citizens of the First and Third Worlds

Medea Benjamin & Andrea Freedman. 1989. Global Exchange: 2940 16th St. #307, San Francisco, California, 94103. 337 pp. $11.95 + $1.80 shipping.

One of the best books on the growing citizens' diplomacy movement, environmental tourism, human rights, fair trade, aid, consumer and corporate accountability, government by the people, overseas voluntary service and other U.S.-Third World cooperative efforts. Includes a resource guide with hundreds of organizations around the world listed with addresses and short annotations.

Deforestation or Development in the Third World?

M. Palo and G. Mery (eds.). Vol. III, 1990 . Bulletin No. 349, Finnish Forest Research Inst.: P.O. Box 37, SF-OO381, Helsinki.

A comprehensive account of tropical rain forest management.

Deforestation: Social Dynamics in Watersheds and Mountain Ecosystems

J. Ives and D.C. Pitt (eds.). 1988. Routledge.

Ecological Aspects of Development in the Humid Tropics

1982. National Academy Press: Washington DC.

Ecological Development in the Humid Tropics: Guidelines for Planners

A. E. Lugo et al. 1987. Winrock. 362 pp. $19.50.

Forest Resources of Africa; an Approach to International Forest Resource Appraisals

R. Persson, Skogshgskolan, 1975-1977, Stockholm, SWEDEN. (Institutionen for skogstaxering, Rapporter och Uppstatser, 18, 22). Two volumes containing 294 and 224 pages respectively.

"Forestry and Development"

The Netherlands Review of Development Studies.
Volume 2, 1988/89. IMWOO, (Institute for Social Science Research in Developing Countries): P.O. Box 90734, 2509 LS The Hague, The Netherlands.
Tel: (0)70-3510574/Fax: (0)70-351513
Price Dfl. 38,50 (US$20), plus postage and additional costs.

The second volume of a series through which the Dutch social research community presents current thoughts. Ten articles. It includes a guide to research institutions in The Netherlands.

Fragile Lands of Latin America—Strategies for Sustainable Development

John O. Browder, ed. 1989. Westview Press.

12

Guidelines for Training in Rapid Appraisal for Agroforestry Research and Extension

Commonwealth Science Council. 1989. London and Forestry Commission, Harare: Zimbabwe.

The guidelines for training, research, and extension personnel in rapid appraisal methods for development of agroforestry in peasant land use systems are based on four key principles: interactive research, learning by doing, interdisciplinarity and understanding of constraints, and conflicts over access to resources. Though developed and used in Zimbabwe, the quality and comprehensiveness of these guidelines make it useful for community forestry extension workers in other countries.

The Himalayan Dilemma: Reconciling Development and Conservation

Jack D. Ives and Bruno Messerli. 1989. The United Nations University: Rutledge, London. 295 pp.

While this book gives little detail on how the Nepalese manage their land, it clearly states that peasant farmers are quite skilled at land management, much more so than is credited them by development authorities and foreign aid personnel.

Innocents Abroad in the Forests of Nepal: An Account of Australian Aid to Nepalese Forestry

D. M. Griffin. 1988. Anutech Pty. Ltd.: GPO Box 4, Canberra, ACT 2601, AUSTRALIA. 188 pp. A $28.50.

Elucidates the history of over 2 decades of Australian aid to Nepalese forestry, focusing on the Nepal Australian Forestry Project (NAPP), for which the author has been director since 1975. Griffin discusses the conditions under which community forestry efforts are most likely to succeed. His review & analysis of literature on forestry development generally, and on Himalayan forestry in particular, are most useful.

Linking Self-help Groups and Banks in Developing Countries

E. Kropp, et al. 1989. GTZ/APRACA (Asian and Pacific Regional Agricultural Credit Association). Maliwan Mansions, Phra Atit Road, Bangkok 10200, THAILAND or GTZ, postfach 5180, D-6367 Karben 1, GERMANY. 186 pp.

Local Organizations. Intermediaries in Rural Development

Milton J. Esman and Norman T. Uphoff. 1984. Cornell University Press.

Good book on grass-roots development.

No Life Without Roots: Culture and Authentic Development

Thierry Verhelst. Originally published in French in 1987. Published in English, 1990. ZED Books See address in Book Sources section.

No Life Without Roots stresses the cultural dimensions of any meaningful effort towards self-reliance. The major argument of the book is that the starting point for a genuinely alternative development path must be local knowledge and values. Verhelst looks unflinchingly at the economic exploitation and political oppression exercised by the countries of the North as the basic cause of the Third World problems.

Persistent Poverty—Underdevelopment in Plantation Economies of the Third World

George L. Beckford. 1972. Oxford Univ. Press: U.S. Distributor, Biblio Distribution Center, 81 Adams Drive, Totowa, New Jersey 07512. 246 pp.

Power From the People: Innovation, User Participation and Forest Energy Development

Matthew S. Gamser. 1988. 224 pp. $21.25.

Through the analysis of forest energy technology development the author illustrates the importance of user participation in developing new technologies and discusses the management of technological change. This means tapping the knowledge of everyone involved—from the research and development scientists to the local farmers and housewives.

Rural Appraisal: Rapid, Relaxed and Participatory

Robert Chambers. 1992. Institute of Dev't Studies Discussion Paper 311, IDS Pubs: Univ. of Sussex, Brighton BN1 9RE, United Kingdom.

The term "Participatory Rural Appraisal" describes a growing family of approaches and methods to enable local people to share, enhance and analyse their knowledge of life and conditions, to plan and to act." This book presents a useful summary of what has happened in the field, along with a wealth of resources indexed by country.

Social Forestry: Communal and Private Management Strategies Compared

Case Studies presented at a conference February 14, 1991. The Paul H. Nitze School of Advanced International Studies (SAIS): 1740 Massachusetts Ave. NW, Washington DC 20036-229. Tel: (202) 663-5691. 44 pp.

This is an important addition to the dialogue on incorporating communal vs. private ownership of trees in social forestry projects. The aim of the publication is to give insight into how changes can take place at the grassroots level with the ideas and involvement of local people.

One case study was by Gerald F. Murray who outlined the development of the Agroforestry Outreach Project (AOP), a tree-planting project in rural Haiti. By 1990, AOP had involved 150,000 peasant families in planting more than 40 million trees.

Staying Alive: Women, Ecology and Development
Vandana Shiva. Zed Books: London 1988.

Vandana Shiva's books are well worth reading. One of the most penetrating insights into the causes of world misery and what to do about it.

Third World Guide '89/90: The World Seen by the Third World; Facts, Figures, Opinions
Roberto Remo Bissio (General Ed.). 625 pp. £15
Available from: Third World Pubs: 151 Stratford Road, Birmingham, B11 1RD, United Kingdom.

A country-by-country guide to the history, politics and economics of the Third World, with commentaries on various subjects concerning the Third World and its relations with the North, such as debt, transnationals, trade and population. A radical analysis of international inequalities, claimed to be "the first reference book about the Third World, made in the Third World, to reach the Third World."

Towards Green Villages. A Strategy for Environmentally-sound and Participatory Rural Development
Anil Agarwal and Sunita Narain. Available from: Center for Science & Environment, 807 Vishal Bhawan, 95 Nehru Place, New Delhi, 110019 INDIA.

Towards Green Villages is a strategy for greening India. Deals with tenure, legal and political issues. Existing examples are cited. This study shows how environmental planning can be done from the bottom up. Starting with local people planning and then extending to the social, legal and political structures.

To the Hands of the Poor: Water and Trees
Robert Chambers, N. C. Saxena and T. Shah. 1989. New Delhi and Oxford. IBH Publishing Co.

The authors suggest that while the development efforts of NGO's offer some promise of helping the poor, tens of millions of the poor could gain at once and on a vast scale by abolishing restrictions, changing regulations, and clarifying rights, supporting these reforms with multiple channel communication to inform the poor of their entitlements. Although this book is written about India, its new ways of viewing regulations and access to water and tree resources will be of value in other regions.

"Women and Forestry"
Paula Williams. 1993. *WedNews*, Special Issue, No. 5. pp. 17-18. *WedNews, Newsletter of Women*, Environment and Development, P.O. Box 72561, Nairobi, KENYA. Tel: (254-2) 562015, 562022, 562172. Fax: 562175

This article discusses women's involvement in forestry and related natural resource management activities in Africa. Several forestry projects and related programs have been done, and studies of them are documented from the many African countries in which they took place. The projects are sponsored and supported by NGO's and the Environment Liaison Center International (ELCI).

WATKAEN DEVELOPMENT?

From: LINK

Ecotourism: A Resource Guide

Some of the Different Types of Responsible Travel

Adventure travel; ecotourism, environmental or ecological travel; scientific expeditions and research; citizen diplomacy; political solidarity/brigades; cross cultural exchange; educational and language study; reality tours; retreats, centers, communities, and volunteering/work camps.

"It is wonderful to see a section on Eco-Tourism included within a book of this kind. The listed resources are but a few of the hundreds of organizations that are forming to put good use to people's current aspirations to go below the tourist fluff and do something which will make a positive difference in the world. If each traveler would make a new heart connection with just one person from some other culture, creed or tradition, do one day of restoration work for the planet and spent one hour in deep communion with another species each year, we would soon have no need for wars— and perhaps no hunger or poverty as well!"

—Dianne G. Brause, Director of One World Family Travel, Co-Founder of Lost Valley Educational Center and Vice-President of the Board of Seven Generations Land Trust.

Earth Restoration Movement

The idea of an Earth restoration movement is catching on. There are millions people of all ages, concerned about the environment, who want to plant trees, do erosion control, stream restoration, and earth healing work. Many of them want to travel to some far away, exotic place. With proper direction and some training, this energy can do much good. By tending to their own backyards, neighborhoods, towns, cities, and forests, people can learn practical skills for when they travel abroad. Learning the language immeasurably increases effectiveness in other cultures.

Love, respect, caring, humor, attentiveness, and friendship are what people respond to. It also helps if one is a willing, hard worker and can offer useful expertise in tree planting, agroforestry, water systems, natural health care, permaculture and hundreds of other practical skills. But this raises some serious questions. When is a person trained enough to be of help? What technologies are appropriate to introduce into a culture? Respect for cultural integrity?

"Eco-tourism Re-examined"

(Excerpt from the article: "Eco-tourism Re-examined" by M. Passoff in *Earth Island Journal*. Vol. 6(2): 1991. pp. 28-29.)

Passoff objects to the commonly held beliefs that eco-tourism has little adverse impact on the environment or that it benefits local economies. He cites examples where eco-tourism contributes little financial benefit outside of large cities, contributes to local inflation, and encourages additional environmental degradation such as logging. He has developed a list of suggestions for proper ecotourism:

1. limit the number of tourists in an area to avoid over-exploitation of resources

2. hire local people at good salaries

3. provide advanced training for local staff

4. provide financial assistance such as scholarships to local communities

5. encourage tourists to write letters in support of quality eco-tourism

6. provide information to tourists about the host country's environmental concerns and politics

7. lobby host countries to be environmentally responsible. Passoff also provides a list of questions a potential tourist can ask tour companies in order to determine how green an eco-tour is.

How to Make Money on Ancient Forests Without Cutting Them Down

Michael Pilarski

I remember standing in Bill Mollison's backyard looking up at a very steep, densely forested rim of a volcanic caldera on the New South Wales/Queensland border in Australia. Bill was telling me someone had just donated the land to the Permaculture Institute and it was someday going to be worth a lot of money for research purposes. At the time it didn't make sense to me. But now, throughout the world, researchers and eco-tourists are paying money to visit wild ecosystems. There are few pristine, native ecosystems and forests remaining. Their value for research, recreation and spiritual fulfillment is higher than for timber or agricultural use.

Individuals (or companies) with relatively untouched forests may well consider putting in lodging facilities and charging visitors as a source of income rather than cutting down the forest. Such facilities would spin off further jobs on the local level. Too many visitors in too small an area can ruin what people came to see, so care must be exercised in planning and operating such facilities.

Directories and Resources on Ecotourism

Alternatives to the Peace Corps

Becky Buell, Victoria Clarke, and Susan Leone, eds. 1992. Food First—Institute for Food and Development Policy, 398 60th St., Oakland, California 94618. Tel: (800) 888-3314. 72 pp.

A book for volunteers that believe U.S. foreign policy has had a destructive, rather than sustainable and constructive, effect on the Third World. Gives opportunities to find appropriate work which is "supportive of indigenous, community based development."

Directory of Low Cost Vacations With a Difference

J. Crawford. 1989. Pilot Industries, Inc.: New York. 68 pp.

Going Green: The Ecotourism Resource for Travel Agents

A supplement to *Tour & Travel News*. October 25, 1993. 78 pp. Free copies of *Going Green* are available by calling (516) 562-5829 and asking for Jamie; or write: Diane Merlino, c/o Tour & Travel News, 600 Community Dr., Manhasset, New York 11030.

This supplement includes a great resource guide by Dianne G. Brause which lists a calendar of events, organizations, recommended reading, books, periodicals, guidebooks and directories. The many articles offer a variety of viewpoints on the foundations of ecotourism, and on some of the complex initiatives shaping the field.

Hostelling North America—A Guide to Hostels in Canada and the United States

American Youth Hostels and Canadian Hostelling Association. Published annually. 1992/93 edition. 360 pp. $1 to AYH or CHA members, $5 to non-members. Available from AYH, 733 15th St., Suite 840, Washington DC 20005. or CHA, 1600 James Naismith Dr., Suite 608, Gloucester, Ontario K1B 5N4, Canada.

A directory to all hostels in the U.S. and Canada which gives all information needed to utilize hostels for inexpensive travel and networking. Hostels are often located in ecologically interesting areas such as near national parks.

Travel Programs in Central America

Central America Information Center
Available from: IFTF, PO Box 3834, La Mesa, California 92044. Published three times a year.

Encouraging U.S. citizens to travel to Central America to see, first hand, the results of U.S. foreign policy on society and the environment.

Volunteer Vacations: Short-term Adventures That Will Benefit You & Others

Bill McMillon. 1993. Chicago Review Press, 814 N. Franklin St., Chicago, IL 60610. 458 pp. $11.95.

This directory of 240 organizations includes personal stories and pictures of volunteers involved in a whole variety of adventures that also give personal growth as well as service to their global neighbors—both human and not.

Wilderness U: Opportunities for Outdoor Education in the U.S. & Abroad

Bill McMillon. 1993. Chicago Review Press, 814 N. Franklin St., Chicago, IL 60610. 458 pp. $11.95.

This is the first directory of national and international outdoor education programs offering hundreds of healthy, ambitious alternatives to standard study.

World Congress on Adventure Travel and Ecotourism: 1992 Conference Proceedings

The Adventure Travel Society. Tel: (303)649-9016/ Fax: (303) 649-9017. $40. The 1993 World Congress was held in Manaus, Brazil, Sept. 20–23.

Organizations Concerned With Ecotourism

Andaluz Ecological Tourist Center

Casilla 1715 0066C, Quito, ECUADOR
Tel: 450-992

Proposes to demonstrate ecological strategies for viable businesses which use tourism to support themselves and other educational activities within local communi-

12

ties. Projects involve organic agriculture, community education, and appropriate technology.

Annapurna Conservation Area Project
Ghandruk Village
Kaski District, NEPAL

The Annapurna Conservation Area covers 2,600 sq. km. in central Nepal. It is an example of how too many Western tourists (trekkers) upset the delicate ecological balance between land and life in the Himalayas. The project was set up to conserve the ecology of the Annapurna region. It is one of the more innovative approaches to development/conservation, involving local people in the whole process. ACAP also educates trekkers to minimize their negative impact on the ecology and people.

ANTENNA (Asian Tourism Action Network)
15 Soi Soonvijai 8, New Petchburi Rd.
Bangkok, 10310 THAILAND

A network in Asia and the Pacific promoting locally-controlled tourism designed in harmony with nature. Publishes bimonthly *ANTENNA Headlines* and a series of Asian Tourism Dossiers with country reports and case studies. ANTENNA can also be contacted through its office in India at the Equasions address.

Asociación Talamanqueña para el Ecoturismo y la Conservación
Puerto Viejo de Talamanca, COSTA RICA

ATEC supports and promotes small, local enterprises in the forests and beaches of Talamanaca. They can set you up with places to stay or eat or tour guides in the Indigenous, Afro-Caribbean, and Latino communities. They also give guidelines for how to be a positive presence and information on regional environmental issues.

Ayacara Project
Pablo Sandor, Avenida Suecia 567
Providencia, Santiago, CHILE

The Sandor family owns 16,000 hectares on the Huequi Peninsula in southern Chile, much of it ancient forest. They are creating a center for environmental work and conferences, ecotourism, recreation and meditation.

Center for Responsible Tourism
2 Kensington Rd.
San Anselmo, California 94960

Community Baboon Sanctuary
Bermuda Landing, BELIZE

The residents of the area have agreed to manage their forests in order to encourage the survival of the black howler monkey. There is an arrangement for sharing the income from the tourist trade among the villages. Guides are available from the sanctuary museum and there are plans for a community-owned guest house.

Earth Travel Round Table
James Stark
P.O. Box 1051
Point Reyes, California 94956
Tel: (415) 663-8807

Stark is working with Dianne Brause to create an international responsible travel database which will help connect tourism activists around the world as well as eco-travelers.

Eco Institute of Costa Rica
Apdo. 8080/1000
San Jose, COSTA RICA
Tel: 33-2200/Fax: 21-2801

Director/Editor, Deirdre Evans-Pritchard. Publishes *Sustainable Tourism Newsletter*, which is small, but carries news from around Central America. 3 issues/yr.

Ecotourism Association of Australia
P.O. Box 3839
Alice Springs, Northern Territory, 0871, AUSTRALIA
Tel: 61-89-528-308/Fax: 61-89-531-308

Ecumenical Coalition on Third World Tourism
P.O. Box 24, Chorakhebua
Bangkok 10230, THAILAND
Tel/Fax: 662-510-7287

ECTWT organizes training programs in Asia, Africa and Latin America to provide skills and knowledge needed to organize people's groups on local and national level to resist the onslaught of tourism. They have a book available: *Tourism: An Ecumenical Concern* by Koson Srisan ($12) which covers the history of the responsible tourism movement in Asia and the coalitions' response and efforts to "tell the truth about the negative impacts of tourism, to effect its transformation as well as to seek alternatives to it."

Equitable Tourism Option (Equasions)
K. T. Suresh
168 8th Main Road, Near Indira Nagar Club
1, Bangalore 560 008 INDIA
Tel: (812) 582313/Fax (812) 582627

Foundation for Tropical Research and Exploration
Casilla 10077
La Paz, BOLIVIA
Tel: (591-2) 795364/Fax: 797511

Consultants in ecological research who also promote local ecotourism.

Green Evaluation Program

Ecotourism Society
P.O. Box 755
N. Bennington, Vermont 05257

The Green Evaluation Program is a set of guidelines for responsible ecotourism businesses. The first Guidelines were published in September, 1993 after a period of consultations with a wide range of travel industry and conservation organizations around the world. They are, in effect, the budding certification procedures for ecotourism.

The International Institute for Peace Through Tourism

3680 Rue de la Montange
Montreal, Quebec, H3G 2A8, CANADA
Tel: (514) 281-1822/Fax: (514) 848-1099

Dedicated to fostering and facilitating tourism initiatives that contribute to international understanding and cooperation and an improved quality of environment. The Institute is compiling a Code of Ethics and Guidelines for Sustainable Tourism. Also has available a booklet summarizing the numerous studies presented at the First Global Conference: "Tourism, A Vital Force for Peace," held in Vancouver in 1988.

One World Family Travel

81868 Lost Valley Lane
Dexter, Oregon 97431
Tel: (503) 937-3351/Fax: (503) 937-3646

Dianne G. Brause created One World Family Travel as a resource to help individuals learn about the ethics of sustainable travel and to connect them with organizations and resources who do so responsibly. She and James Stark are currently devising an on-line database which is designed to support primarily the small family-owned, community-based, environmentally supportive and culturally sensitive travel options. Write or call for information on declaring yourself a "Sustainable Traveler."

Toledo Ecotourism Association

P.O. Box 75
Punta Gorda, BELIZE

TEA is a model for locally-controlled ecotourism, especially in regards to equitable sharing of the wealth. Six Mayan villages and 1 Garifuna village have formed ecotourism groups and 5 guest houses are under construction. The November, 1991 TEA Report contains useful information.

Tourism Concern

Froebel College
Roehampton Lane
London, England SW15 5PU UNITED KINGDOM
Tel: 071-272-1749

Travelers' Earth Repair Network (TERN)

Friends of the Trees Society
P.O. Box 1064
Tonasket, Washington 98855
Tel/Fax: (509) 485-2705

TERN is a networking service for travelers who want to make a positive contribution to the environment in the course of their travels. TERN links travelers with contacts and hosts involved in reforestation, forest preservation, sustainable agriculture, forestry, permaculture and other work related to trees and earth repair. TERN can produce specialized, computer generated lists based on the interest of the traveler and the destinations they are visiting. TERN also functions as an organic farm apprenticeship program in the U.S.A. If you are interested in becoming a TERN traveler or a TERN host, write Friends of the Trees for an application form.

Tropical Rainforest Ecotourism

Apdo 47343, Los Chaguaramos
Caracas, VENEZUELA

Travel Magazines

International Travel News (itn)

2120 28th St.
Sacramento, California 95818
Tel: (916) 457-3643

Certainly the best bargain, price per page, for travelers' magazines and one of the better in its field. Each issue contains a number of articles and lots and lots of advertising, especially for trips/treks/tours, and airline deals. 6 issues a year. $16.00/year. Outside U.S. $26.00/year.

South American Explorer

P.O. Box 18327
Denver, Colorado 80218
Tel: (303)320-0388

Highly recommended if you are traveling to South America. Always has interesting articles, plus the editor, Don Montague, has a great sense of humor which he exercises a lot. Chuckles from one end to the other. Besides the humor and articles it does have a good amount of useful advertising, classified ads, and travel tips. Quarterly. *South American Explorer* also has an extensive catalogue of travel guides, books, music tapes, videos, etc.

Has clubhouses in both Lima, Peru and Quito, Ecuador. Their South American Address is:

Casilla 3714, Lima 100, PERU.

Transitions Abroad

Box 344
Amherst, Massachusetts, 01004
Tel: (413) 256-0373

12

"The Guide to International Study, Work and Travel since 1977." This is my favorite travel magazine. For one thing it is the most politically correct (in my opinion). Each issue has short, interesting articles, but it's main value lies in the large amount of information on travel opportunities, tips, and advertising. Each issue focuses on a different region of the world. One issue a year is devoted to an annual "Educational Travel Directory" which reviews hundreds of useful books for the educational and budget traveler. Highly recommended. Bimonthly. $18/year.

"*Transitions Abroad* has helped independent world travelers plan their own adventures, be a Third World service volunteer, join a research expedition, find short-term jobs and internships abroad, stay with a host family and learn a language... information and ideas for cultural immersion travel."

Books on Ecotourism

Backpacking and Camping in the Developing World
Scott Graham. 1988. Wilderness Press, 2440 Bancroft Way, Berkeley, California 94704. 144 pp. $11.95.

A how-to adventure guide for traveling on your own or with a group. Practical, concise advice on currency exchanges, camping items, health care, airline tickets, protecting valuables, etc.

Belize: A Natural Destination
Richard Mahler and Steele Wotkyns. 1991, Juhn Muir Pubs. PO Box 613, Santa Fe, NM 87504. 288 pp. $16.95.

This tour guide offers you the opportunity to participate in the conservation ethic which is being used in Belize to both promote tourism and preserve the region's magnificent flora and fauna.

Beyond Safaris: A Guide to Building People-to-People Ties with Africa
Kevin Danaher. Africa World Press, Trenton, NJ. Available from Global Exchange, 2041 Mission St., #303, San Francisco, CA 94110. Tel: (415) 255-7296. $12.95.

Promotes cross-cultural and political support with many resources, including a directory of travel agents, tour operators and organizations developing tourism in Africa.

Bikas-Binas Development—The Change in Life and Environment of the Himalaya
Ludmilla Tuting and Kunda Dixit, eds. Jauhari Printers: Varanasi. 400 pp. Available from Ratna Pustak Bhandar, Bhotahity, Kathmandu, Nepal.

This book aims to discuss the links between ecology, development, and tourism. Most of the contributors are from India. They don't paint a pretty picture of tourists. If you really want to hear what Third World people think, read this book.

The Challenge of Tourism. Learning Resources for Study and Action
Alison O'Grady, ed. 1990. Ecumenical Coalition on Third World Tourism: Bangkok. 82 pp. U.S. $12.

"Aimed at schools and general readership. An excellent presentation of the impact of tourism on the 'third world.' A lively publication."—Survival International.

Costa Rica: a Natural Destination
Ree Strange Sheck. 1992. Juhn Muir Pubs. PO Box 613, Santa Fe, NM 87504. 307 pp. $16.95.

The author of this book works with Monteverde Conservation League of Costa Rica which is one of the most famous ecotourism sites on the planet. This guide covers tropical forests, rushing rivers, exotic animals, uncrowded beaches, high mountains and awesome volcanoes as well as city life, history and culture.

Earth Trips: A Guide to Nature Travel on A Fragile Planet
Dwight Holing. 1991. Living Planet Press. $12.95.

A guide to ecotourism by Conservation International and Living Planet Press. Where to go, what to see, how much it will cost, and how to get involved in conservation efforts.

Ecotourism and Resource Conservation
J. A. Kusler, ed. 1991. Ecotourism and Resource Conservation Project.

Many analyses of successful projects.

Ecotourism: The Potentials and Pitfalls
Elizabeth Boo. 1990. World Wildlife Fund, PO Box 4866, Hampden Post Office, Baltimore, Maryland 21211. Tel (301) 338-6951. 72 pp.

This book is the result of a study done by WWF to determine the links between tourism and protected natural areas as well as the impacts of nature tourism in order to create development strategy for this type of tourism. The countries studied were Belize, Costa Rica, Dominica, Ecuador & Mexico.

Environmental Vacations: Volunteer Projects to Save the Planet
Stephanie Ocko. Second Edition, 1992. John Muir Publications: Santa Fe, New Mexico. 248 pp. U.S. $16.95.

Although the book lists several dozen organizations, it is not a resource guide but rather a general introduction to the world of environmental vacations—how to get involved, what sort of experiences to expect, and how to prepare.

Nature Tourism: Managing for the Environment
Tensie Whelan, ed. 1991. Island Press. 220 pp. U.S. $19.95.

Nature tourism includes trekking, bird watching, photography, safaris, mountain climbing and river rafting. This book features various authors discussing the nature tourism industry mainly from the point of view of governments and corporations, rather than that of local people who are most impacted by tourism development. I think you would find different viewpoints on the desirability of nature tourism if all sides were consulted.

The Peace Corps and More: 114 Ways to Work, Study and Travel in the Third World.
Medea Benjamin. 1991. Global Exchange, 2141 Missions St. #202, San Francisco, CA 94110. 92 pp. $6.95.

Rainforests: A Guide to Research and Tourist Facilities of Selected Tropical Forest Sites in Central and South America
James L. Castner. 1990. Feline Press, PO Box 7219, Gainesville, Florida 32605. 380 pp.

A worthwhile book. We could use similar guides to all parts of the world. Castner's book deals with the countries of Peru, Ecuador, French Guiana, Venezuela, Trinidad, Costa Rica, and Panama. This book will be valuable to the natural history scientist and others who are interested in helping the rainforests survive. The author describes and evaluates select locations in each country and discusses how to best get there. For each country there are appendices which list noteworthy books, sources of maps, tourist information services, and conservation and scientific organizations/institutions. One of its best features is a partially annotated bibliography of books, journals, and magazines dealing with rainforests.

See the Third World While It Lasts: The Social and Environmental Impacts of Tourism
Evelyn Hong. $15.95. Consumers Assoc. of Penang, 87 Cantonment Rd., Penang, Malaysia.

A good book on tourism's impacts. Hotels are net drains on foreign exchange. Makes a case for ecological tourist resorts.

The Silent Jungle: Ecotourism Among the Kuna Indians of Panama
M. Chapin. 1990. Cultural Survival Quarterly. Vol. 14 (1): pp. 42-45.

The Tourists Arrive and Bam! We Are Dead
Survival International. In: *Survival*, Issue 28.

An overview of tourism which suggests that every visitor examine their conscience and take responsibility for their actions.

Training Rural Residents as Naturalist Guides: Evaluation of a Pilot Project in Costa Rica
David B. Clark and Hector Gonzalez. December, 1991. *Conservation Biology*. Vol. 5 (4): pp. 542-546.

Work, Study, Travel Abroad—The Whole World Handbook
Del Franz, ed. 1990. Council on International Educational Exchange. St. Martin's Press: New York. 474 pp.

A sourcebook for traveling the world with information on jobs, internships, and educational opportunities. Descriptions of nations and extremely brief cultural notes included. A good place to start.

Work Your Way Around the World
Susan Griffith. 1991. Vacation Work: Oxford. 432 pp.

A how-to book with numerous useful and insider tips for successfully finding work around the world. Besides generating income for travel, work is essential to ecotourism; travelers must give something environmentally or socially beneficial back to the Earth for the resources they consume while traveling.

12

13 Forestry Practices in Boreal Forests

Gus diZerega

13

Boreal Forest Directory

The artificial life-cycle

THE BOREAL FORESTS stretch around the northern tip of the globe and account for 29 percent of the world's total forest area. The boreal forest ecosystem, a worldwide belt of about 1000 kilometer width, is an important consumer of carbon dioxide, fixing an amount of carbon in the environment just slightly less than the endangered tropical rainforests.

The boreal forest is the largest terrestrial forest ecosystem in the world. It is vital to maintaining the hydrology of northern land masses, integral in moderating the north's climate, and crucial in mitigating the effects of global warming and the melting of the polar ice caps. This forest is under attack around the planet from the taiga of the former Soviet Union to its southern fringes in Alberta.

Research into boreal forest ecosystems has been minimal, and boreal forests have been largely neglected because until a few years ago, they had very little monetary value. With the advent of new pulp mill technology, it became possible to utilize hardwood species like poplar and aspen to make high quality pulp. Many temperate and tropical rainforests have already been depleted by logging so the focus is now towards the northern forests. The effects of large-scale logging on the boreal ecosystems include soil destruction, erosion, and species extinction. The global repercussions must be studied as they are poorly understood.

—Excerpt from "Boreal Forests: A Global Concern and a Canadian Responsibility" by Gray Jones. Fall 1992. Western Canada Wilderness Committee, *Alberta Branch Educational Report*, Vol. 11 (7).

Organizations Concerned with Boreal Forests

Alaska Boreal Forest Network
c/o Arctic Audubon Society
Box 82098
Fairbanks, Alaska 99708

Canada's Future Forest Alliance
Box 93
New Denver, British Columbia, V0G ISO, CANADA
Tel: (604) 358-2660/Fax: (604) 358-7950

Swedish Society for Nature Conservation
(See address in Sweden section.)

Taiga Rescue Network
Storgatan 42, S-666 00
Bengtsfors, SWEDEN
Tel: +46-53111710/e-mail: PNS:ROGOLS
(ROGOLS@PNS.APC.ORG)

Western Canada Wilderness Committee, Alberta Branch
9526 Jasper Ave. #6
Edmonton, Alberta, T5H 3V3, CANADA
Tel: (403) 487-7616

Conferences on Boreal Forests

Boreal Forests of the World II: 2nd International NGO and Indigenous Peoples and Nations Conference on Boreal Forests
Athabasca, Alberta, Canada. May 19-25, 1994.

The theme of the conference is "The Future of Northern forests—Cultural and Biological Effects of the Consumption of Boreal Forest Products." For more information on the conference contact: Friends of the Athabasca, Mary Richardson, Box 30089, Athabasca, Alberta, T0G 0B0 Canada. Tel: (403) 675-6207/Fax: (403) 675-6186.

International Scientific and NGO Boreal Forest Conference
Held in Jokkmokk, northern Sweden, Sept. 30-Oct. 4,

1992. A historic conference which spawned an international network of environmental groups, The Taiga Resource Network.

Its Canadian contacts are: Canada's Future Forests Alliance (address below), and The Canadian Forests Caucus, Lucie Lavoie, 121 Banning St., Thunder Bay, Ontario, T7B 3J1 Canada. Tel: (807) 344-2356. See pages 46–47 of March 1993 *Forest Planning Canada* for an article on the conference and a list, with contact addresses, of 28 countries around the world working on boreal forest issues.

The 20th IUFRO World Congress

To be held August 6-12, 1995 in Tampere, Finland.

Contact Prof. Risto Seppala, Finnish Forest Research Institute, Unioninkatu 40 A, 00170 Helsinki, FINLAND. Tel: 3 58-0-85 70 51/Fax: 3 58-0-62 53 08.

Inventory and Management of the Boreal Forests

Conference to be held in Anchorage, Alaska, September, 1994. For more information contact: Mr. Vernon J. LaBau, USDA Forest Service, Forestry Sciences Lab., 201 E. 9th Ave., Suite 303, Anchorage, Alaska. Tel: (907) 271-2585.

5th World Wilderness Congress: A Project of the WILD Foundation

The theme is Wild Nature and Sustainable Living in Circumpolar Regions. Conference held September 24-October 1, 1993 in Tromso, NORWAY.

Periodical

Taiga News

International Working Group on Boreal Forests
c/o Karin Lindahl
AJTTE, PO Box 116
S-962 23, Jokkmokk, SWEDEN
Tel: +46-971-17037/Fax +46-971-12057

Taiga News is a newsletter produced by the Swedish Society for Nature Conservation to draw attention to northern boreal forests around the world. International coverage.

Books and Articles on Boreal Forests

The Boreal Ecosystem

J. A. Larsen. 1980. Academic Press: New York.

"Boreal Forests"

A special issue of *Unasylva* 170, Vol. 43. 1992. (address in International Forestry Journals section).

This issue contains articles and resources on boreal forests.

A Systems Analysis of the Global Boreal Forest

Herman H. Shugart, Rik Leemans and Gordon B. Bonan, eds. 1992. 565 pp.

A synthesis of patterns and processes that occur in boreal forests. Reviews the principal mechanisms that control the forests' pattern in competition, wildfires, and climatic change on boreal forests. They end up talking about using the information in the first global scale computer model of the dynamic change of a biome.

Fire and Vegetation Dynamics: Studies from the North American Boreal Forest

Edward A. Johnson. 1992. 125 pp.

This book assembles the relevant studies of fire intensity, rate of spread, fuel consumption, fire frequency and fire weather in the North American boreal forest.

"Save Boreal Forests"

Western Canada Wilderness Committee, Alberta Branch (see address in Organizations). *WCWC News*. Vol. 11, No. 7, Fall 1992.

This special edition contains much information on Canada's boreal forests. Wide-scale clearcutting is occurring at an alarming rate to feed some of the world's largest pulp mills. As timber practices crush fragile soils, threaten wildlife habitat, and mills spew pollution, Canada's northern forests suffer damage that will last hundreds of years.

Forestry in Sweden

Sweden has 10% of global forest product exports on less than 1% of the world forests.

—Statistic from Global Forests, Laarman and Sedjo, 1992

MOST PEOPLE CONSIDER the gradual reduction of our forest land and timber harvest inevitable. Forests in most of the world are shrinking every year. While it is hard to find countries we can use as models of restoration forestry, there are some countries which have had notable successes in increasing forest cover. Increasing forest area and better management can provide a great number of jobs, initially, and employ a much greater number in the long run as increased, stable yields develop. Consider the following account of Swedish forestry in this century. Sweden deliberately under-harvested for several decades to increase the value of timber holdings. Longer rotations produced higher quality wood and higher returns also.

In earlier decades of the present century, Sweden faced timber supply shortages because it had grossly overcut its timber stock without adequate renewal.

Five decades of forest management, intensively undertaken and consistently applied, have restored the Swedish long-run sustained yield to a new peak of 90,000,000 cubic meters a year. This is a level which effectively maximizes the potential yield from the Swedish forest land base. Partly for reasons of value enhancement of the maturing timber stock, however, the actual cut has been held to only 67,000,000 cubic meters although this level will rise over the course of the present decade. From this base, which had been seriously eroded 50 years ago, forestry and forest products now form the largest industry in the country. The Swedish forest sector is the major contributor of exports and the largest sectoral source of direct and indirect employment in a nation with one of the highest per capita GNP's in the world.

[Excerpt from: "The Truck Loggers Association's Brief to the Forest Resources Commission of British Columbia, 1990." In: *Forest Planning Canada*, March 1991.]

The Swedish model of forest management is not without problems. It is industrial forest plantation management. Trees are harvested at a young age; forests lack biodiversity and stand structure, and there is little protected wild land in Sweden. Sweden has a law that you must clearcut but Switzerland has a law banning clearcutting. So, while Sweden has experience to contribute to restoration forestry, it also has much to learn about

Sweden

restoration forestry practices as outlined in *Restoration Forestry*.

A Ravaged Edge of the Taiga

(The following is from an article by Swedish Society for Nature.)

Sweden is seen as a progressive leader when it comes to the overall care of the forests, But this is only the case if we consider the timber-producing tree species. The forests of

13

the modern, intense forestry cannot accommodate all the original plant and animal species. The implementation of clearcutting, planting, clearing, thinning and then cutting again imposes an artificial life-cycle in which the trees don't have a chance to grow old.

In Sweden there is less than 5 percent of virgin forest left. In these few scattered remnants of virgin forest, logging still continues. So far only 2.6 percent of the forest in Sweden has been protected from logging. Outside the mountain region, only 0.4 per cent is protected. A total of 15 per cent of the Swedish forests may need protection in reserves if biological diversity is to be sustained. There are more than 1,000 forest species on the official endangered species lists. Many common species in the forest have declined dramatically in numbers.

Still, there is hope of a change for the better since the Swedish forestry industry has begun to review its methods. However the need for new and more considerate forestry methods is pressing. This would seem to apply not only in a model country like Sweden but also in many other places around the world.

Swedish Society for Nature
Box 245
S-401 24 Goteborg, SWEDEN
Tel: 46-31 803835/Fax 46-31 153305

The major, popular organization for nature conservation and environmental protection in Sweden. with over 200,000 individual members in 260 local groups. This group points out that Sweden's timber industry is far from ecological.

The Swedish Society for Nature calls for the international community to put pressure on Sweden to:

+ Stop clearcutting.

+ Stop devastating forestry methods. Fertilizing, draining and the planting of non-native species of trees are methods incompatible with genuine concern for the environment.

+ Forest species need a protection net. Reserves should cover between 5 and 15% of the forest and be distributed to make migration and spread of species possible.

+ The remaining virgin forests must be protected.

Forestry Resources in Sweden

Forests of Opportunity
Prof. Jan Remrod.

It tells the story of Sweden's Forests and Forest industry. Recommended by David Bellamy.

"Sweden's factory forests"
L. Gamlin. 1988. *New Scientist.* Jan. 28, 1988.

Scandinavian Journal of Forest Research
Scandinavian University Press
PO Box 2959 Tøyen
N-0608 Oslo, NORWAY
Tel: 47-22 57 54 00/Fax 47-22 57 53 53

Quarterly. Annual subscription rate is NOK 870 (Approx. US$125).

Swedish Forestry Association
Bragevaegen 30, Box 273
S-18252 Djurshom, SWEDEN

"Swedish Forestry Techniques with Possible Applications in the Third World"

A project sponsored by Swedish International Development Agency, SIDA, Gunilla Sundquist (editor), The Forest Operations Institute, Box 1184, S-163 13 Spanga, Sweden.

Conventional Forestry Resources in Norway

Norwegian Forest Research Institute
Hogskoleveien 12
14332 AS, NORWAY
Tel: 47-9-948972/Fax 47-9-942980

Norwegian Forestry Society
Det Norski Sgogselskap
Wergelandsvn. 23B
N-Oslo 1, NORWAY

13

Boreal Forest Resolution

Taiga Rescue Network

Ban on Primary (Old-Growth) Forest Cutting Proposed in Scandinavia and Conterminous United States

International Non-Government Organizations Conference, October, 1992,
The Boreal Forests of the World, Jokkmokk, Sweden

To: Governments of the Countries in the Boreal Region
From: The participants of the International NGO conference

Resolution

WE CALL FOR A BAN on cutting in temperate and boreal primary (old growth) and ancient forests of Scandinavia and conterminous United States. We also call for the adoption of comprehensive conservation plans that will ensure biodiversity protection and sustainable ecosystems before commercial logging is permitted in undeveloped areas of Russia, Alaska, and Canada.

Any further development of primary boreal forest in Canada, Alaska, and Russia should be community-based projects which do not interrupt the original function of the boreal. We seek an immediate reduction of the allowable cut to sustainable levels of harvest.

In the temperate forests of British Columbia, we also call for a reduction of 50 percent of the annual allowable cut by industry and an immediate moratorium in all core wilderness areas proposed for protection.

This resolution was adopted by consensus by the 110 participants of the conference, representing environmental organizations and groups in 20 countries.

Out of this conference, an international network of environmental groups was formed. In Canada: Canada's Future Forests Alliance, Colleen McCrory (604) 358 2333 and the Canadian Forests Caucus, Lucie Lavoie, 121 Banning St., Thunder Bay, Ontario, T7B 3Jl. (807) 344-2356. The following is the platform and purpose statement for the Taiga Rescue Network.

The Taiga Rescue Network Platform

Boreal Forests in Danger

The threats against the boreal forests of the world are increasingly severe. Forestry practices are destructive in large parts of the boreal forest region, without adequate care for soil conservation or biodiversity. In other areas native forests have been and continue to be wiped out due to intensive forestry practices. Large scale exploitation has seriously reduced biodiversity in large parts of the boreal forests. Currently logging is rapidly expanding into the remaining undisturbed and unfragmented areas within the boreal region.

Our Future Depends on Healthy Forests

Our global future, including a healthy climate, clean air and water, our spiritual well-being and sustainable economies depend on healthy forests. The use of forest resources must only take place on an ecologically sustainable basis.

Humanity must acknowledge the right for all species on Earth to survive in viable populations within their natural distribution and take appropriate measures to safe guard those rights. Important biological processes, including cycles of nutrients, must be safeguarded. To ensure these goals, a substantial part of the remaining old growth boreal forests must be protected from industrial exploitation. In addition, the biodiversity of second-growth, deforested and degraded boreal forest must be restored. Methods and techniques for sustainable forestry in the boreal zone must be implemented.

Clearcutting that compromises biological values must be replaced with methods that ensure sustainable use. Industrial pollutants must be reduced below critical loads. It is a priority to stop the use of all fertilizers and pesticides. The use of genetically engineered organisms and exotic species must be halted and native genotypes restored.

The rights of forest dwelling local and indigenous peoples and nations within the boreal region must be recognized and the ecological basis for their culture, society and economy must be guaranteed. Their traditional models for sustainable management of the boreal forest area, past and present, must be respected.

Current boreal forest biomass represents a carbon sink equal to or larger than the tropical forests. Any sustainable use of the boreal forests must leave this carbon sink functionally intact. The consumption of paper and timber in the affluent countries must be reduced to lessen pressure on forests as sources of raw materials. This reduction is also necessary to allow an increasing con-

13

sumption of wood and other forest products in the developing countries under environmentally sound conditions. The waste of fibres must be minimized through recycling and waste auditing.

Aims and Methods of the Network

The purpose of Taiga Rescue Network is to strengthen and support the cooperation between individuals, NGOs and indigenous peoples and nations concerned with protection, restoration and sustainable use of the boreal forests.

Vital Tasks for the Network Are To:

- organize the exchange of information between participants

- facilitate the exchange of information on transnational corporations, aid schemes and international financing

- facilitate the mapping of the international forest trade, at the company level, and markets, thereby connecting products with their places of origin

- draw international attention to the importance of maintaining natural and healthy forests in the boreal region, as well as to present threats to the boreal forests

- strengthen the cooperation between participants on boreal forest issues including the sharing of strategies and methodologies

- facilitate and strengthen the cooperation and exchange of information between concerned scientists, environmental organizations and indigenous people and nations

- facilitate international campaigns to protect, restore, and maintain the boreal forests

- promote and support discussions and actions on the subject of international agreements on forest issues

- monitor and lobby multinational development organizations

- support and facilitate non-violent direct actions in defense of the boreal forests and their people

Excerpt from the Tiaga Rescue Network Platform Resoulution to Ban proposed Old Growth cutting.

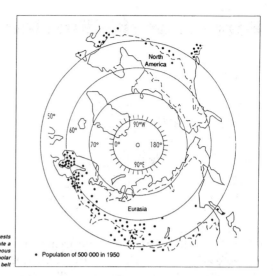

The boreal forests constitute a homogeneous circumpolar vegetation belt

● Population of 500 000 in 1950

Forests of the Russian Far East

The Soviet Union, with more than a quarter of the earth's nine billion forested acres, leads the world in timber resources. Its 36 trillion board-feet of timber stock, concentrated mainly in Siberia and the Far East, is twice that of the United States and Canada combined. But the Soviets use only 30 percent of their wood resources and want to increase production dramatically.

(From the article "Forest Glasnost," by Teresa Carp in American Forests, Sept./Oct., 1990.)

THERE IS LOTS OF WORK for restoration foresters in the former Soviet Socialist Republics (FSSR). It appears restoration forestry models are as hard to find in the FSSR as in North America. The most accessible areas have been overcut, particularly in the European republics.

The forests of Siberia are the world's largest. Totaling 600 million hectares and covering 2.3 million square miles, these forests cover an area the size of the continental United States. They represent 54 percent of the world's coniferous forests, 37 percent of the world's temperate forests and 21 percent of the world's total forested area. In comparison, the Amazon rainforests of Brazil are almost 50 percent smaller.

Much of the taiga is very slow growing and the timber of relatively low market value. The difficult climate and distance from markets have kept these extensive forests from being exploited. Reforestation is difficult and natural regeneration exceedingly slow. Much of this forest is suited to preservation or careful use for subsistence activities. As in much of the Alaska and Canadian interior, the fragile but climatically durable ecosystem is best left alone.

The forests of the Russian Far East are under pressure for dramatic increases in logging by timber companies from the U.S., Japan, and Korea. Noteworthy are Weyerhauser of Washington, and South Korea's Hyundai. Inefficiency and poor infrastructure have kept exploitation at a relatively low level in the Russian Far East. Western forest industry is promising new and bigger trucks and logging equipment,

better roads, and more automation to remove Russian forests more efficiently and faster. Weyerhaeuser has clinched a long-term (20-30 years) logging agreement with the organization that has jurisdiction over the forests of the Botcha River Basin. Policy makers in Siberia are currently debating whether to permanently protect the Botcha River Basin as a nature preserve or national park. If the Basin is left unprotected, Weyerhauser will begin building logging roads into this wild, pristine area—home to the endangered Siberian tiger.

Weyerhauser offers to Russian Far East forest managers and the Russian economy not only hard currency exchange and infrastructure development, but the promise of modern high-yield American-style silviculture. However the taiga is very different from the Pacific Northwest or the U.S. Southeast, and their silvicultural methods are not practical or likely profitable. It's really all about removing Russia's Far East old-growth forests.

Hyundai has doubled its logging rate in the nearby Primorsky region in the past year. Recently, it illegally began to cut on the western slopes of the Sikhotealin Mountains, endangering the equally pristine Bikin River Watershed.

Similar to the situation in North America, indigenous people have received more autonomy, respect, and government support for economic development in the last decade. This has both enhanced, and in some ways threatened, their self-reliance through increased "benefits" of civilization. The economic crisis in the former Soviet Union has even struck these remote, native (and native-hybrid) people. The changes in management goals and power shifts have often put people responsible for game, fish and wildlife management suddenly in the position of forest and timber managers. Ineptness, power struggles and corruption abound.

There is need for communication between FSSR foresters and restoration foresters in other parts of the world. This process is just beginning to happen via visiting delegations of foresters, environmentalists and private individuals. The Siberian Forest Protection Project sponsored a 1993 delegation of sustainable foresters from

North America, including Herb Hammond of Silva Forest Foundation, and Tracy Katelman of the Institute for Sustainable Forestry.

Restoration forestry would aim for improved management of forests near population centers, restoration of degraded forests, and preservation of existing wild areas.

Slave Labor Logging

Living under slave-like conditions, 15,000-20,000 North Korean workers are logging Siberian forests for two big Russian-North Korean timber companies. "Tyndales" is operating in six or seven areas in the Amur region. "Urgalles" is logging along the Urgal-Izvestkovyy railroad, Khabarovsk region, where productive forests have been clearcut within ten kilometres of the railroad. Officially, the North Korean workers are volunteers, but they live and work under conditions similar to those of Russian prisoner camps. The logging camps are under strong North Korean police control. Workers trying to escape are caught by the police and sent home to North Korea, where they simply disappear.

—Excerpt from "Forced Labour Logging Russia's Forests," by Alexei Grigoriev in *Taiga News* No.6, June 1993

Much of the area around the southern Lake Baikal region was logged by German and Japanese prisoners of war kept in labor camps a decade after the end of World War II.

Organizations and Periodicals Concerned with Russian Forests

Association of the Small Peoples of the Soviet North

This Association was set up in 1989 by the many indigenous peoples who inhabit the vast tundra, taiga, and forest regions from the Finnish border to the Pacific. They live from fishing, hunting and reindeer herding. The area is comprised of 2 autonomous republics and 26 autonomous "ethnic regions." The indigenous people are now outnumbered in their areas by Russian immigrants brought in for logging, mining, power stations, oil and gas production, and hydro-electric stations. Collectively these native peoples inhabit the largest remaining block of forest left on the planet.

Biodiversity Conservation Center

G-270, a/ya. 602
119270, Moscow, RUSSIA
Tel: (095) 111-41-80
Contact: Eugene Simonov
email: biodivers@glas. apc. org.

The BCC was recently created to guide conservation action among numerous Russian conservation non-governmental organizations. Their membership includes managers of many forest preserves. Their experts are ready to exchange data on the systems of Russian forest management with interested international partners. (See article on p. 14 of the *Inner Voice*, March/April, 1994.)

Mir Corporation Homestays

85 South Washington St., #210
Seattle, Washington 98104
Tel: (206) 624-7289 or (800) 424-7289
Fax: (206) 624-7360

Offers individual traveler services and homestays in selected cities in Russia, the other Commonwealth States and the Baltics.

Russian Forest Sciences (Lesovedenie)

Allerton Press, Inc.
150 Fifth Ave.
New York, New York 10011, USA

Starting in 1993, Allerton Press is publishing the Russian forestry magazine, *Lesovedenie* (Russian Forest Sciences). It is a cover-to-cover translation from Russian into English. The first issue included nine articles plus reviews.

Scientific Collective of Alternative Forestry Management

Murma River Basin, Bolshemurtinsky Leskhoz, Krasnoyarsk Region

A group of local scientists within the Institute of Forestry have formed an organization to develop a pilot project involving sustainable forestry and ecosystem management within the 60,000-hectare Murma River basin. (Mentioned in *Pacific Environment Resources Center's Trip Report* from their June 13–July 4, 1993 Sustainable Forestry Trip.)

Siberian Forests Protection Project

Pacific Environment and
Resources Center (PERC)
Fort Cronkhite, Bldg. 1055
Sausalito, California 94965 USA
Tel: (415) 332-8200/Fax: (415) 331-2722

A nonprofit policy research and public education center focusing on international environmental improvement. The Siberian Forests Protection Project works with Russian and Siberian environmentalists and government officials. The project sends them information about destructive logging currently taking place, policies that promote forest protection, and sustainable forestry practices. PERC sends equipment such as photocopiers and computers to Siberian forest activists, helping them become internationally linked through electronic mail. The project also works to publicize the issue of Siberian forests and develop long-term plans that will both protect forests and lead to sustainable forestry practices in the Siberian Taiga. For example, PERC is assisting Russian environmentalists in forming a new Siberian network, Friends of the Siberian Forests. In 1993, PERC sponsored a tour of restoration foresters from North America to the Russian Far East.

PERC has a new 30-minute documentary film, entitled "Logging Siberia" available for $29.95. The film is a good introduction to forestry issues and the environmental movement in Siberia, focusing on the forests around Lake Baikal.

PERC is producing a booklet of practical recommendations and guidelines for sustainable forestry practices in Siberia's boreal forests.

Who Is Who in Service to the Earth

1993. 2nd edition. (Address and review in the Directories Section).

Thousands of entries from around the world on many subjects. The first edition had addresses of over 50 organizations concerned with Soviet-American relations, including student exchanges, people-to-people programs, sister-cities, pairing projects, parallel studies and so forth. If you are seeking contacts in the FSSR or wish to travel there, this directory is a good resource.

Books on Russian Forests

The Disappearing Russian Forest: A Dilemma in Soviet Resource Management

Benton Farr and Kathleen Braden. 1988. Rowman and Littlefield. 272 pp. £36.60.

With Soviet environmental affairs becoming more prominent in western eyes, this book focuses on the crisis facing the Soviet forest industry caused by resource depletion and regional imbalance in the supply and demand for commercial timber. It assesses the problems and considers the alternatives open to the industry and its leaders. Technical but full of information. Covers the whole country. The author's conclusions are: intensify management of western forests where growing conditions are better and where transport costs are lower, and improve wood utilization and reduce waste.

The Forests of the U.S.S.R.

V. P. Tseplyaev. 1961. Moscow. 521 pp.

Translated from Russian by the Israel Program for Scientific Translation, Jerusalem, 1965.

A detailed look at the forests of the former USSR. A region by region look at the species composition, ecology, plant associations and extent of natural forests. Many photos.

Russian-English Forestry and Wood Dictionary

W. Linnared. 1966. Commonwealth Agricultural Bureaux, Commonwealth Forestry Bureau Tech. Commun. 6, Farnham Royal, England. 109 pp.

Former Soviet Socialist Republics Conventional Forest Institutes

The following addresses are from the 1990 International Directory of Wildland Fire.

All Union Research Institute of Silviculture and Mechanization of Forestry (VNILM)
Ul. Institutskaya 15
SU-141200 Pushkino, Moscow Region, RUSSIA

Estonian Agricultural Academy
Faculty of Forestry
Ul. Riya 12
Tartu, ESTONIA

Georgian Agricultural Institute
Faculty of Forestry
Voenno-Gruzinskoy Dorogi
Tbilisi, GEORGIA

Institute of Forestry Technics
Faculty of Forestry
Institutskij per. 5
St. Petersburg, K-15, RUSSIA

Institute of Technology
Faculty of Forestry
ul. Sverdlova 13
Minsk, RUSSIA

Kazakh State Agricultural Institute
Faculty of Forestry
Prespekt Abaya 5
Alma-Ata, KAZAKHSTAN

Latvian Agricultural Academy
Faculty of Forestry
Ul. Lenina 2
Elgava, LATVIA

Lithuanian Agricultural Academy
Faculty of Forestry
Noreikishkes, Kaunas, LITHUANIA

Primorye Agricultural Institute
Faculty of Forestry
Prospekt Blyokhera 44
Ussuriysk

St. Petersburg Academy of Forestry
194018 St. Petersburg
Institutski per., 5 LTA
St. Petersburg, C.I.S., RUSSIA

Tashkent Agricultural Institute
Faculty of Forestry
Ob. P.O. Institutskoe
Tashkent, UZBEKISTAN

Ukranian Agricultural Academy
Faculty of Forestry
Goleseyevo, Kiev, UKRAINE

14 Forestry Practices in Tropical Forests

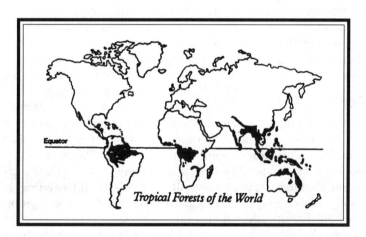

Tropical Forests of the World

Equator

14

Special Considerations for the Management of Tropical Rainforests

Michael G. Smith and Michael Pilarski

IN RESEARCHING THE LITERATURE on forestry in the tropics, we found very few examples of forest management projects where timber was extracted in a manner that could reasonably be called sustainable. Similarly, when the Green Cross Certification Co. and other sustainable timber certification programs set about the quest for sources of sustainably-harvested tropical timber, it took them years to find even a single project that qualified. In the last few years this situation seems to have improved, particularly in Latin America where small grass-roots cooperatives, frequently made up of indigenous Americans, have begun to develop and practice sustainable management in their rain forests and other tropical forests. Still, the number of such projects worldwide, and particularly the area of forest they manage, remain astonishingly small. What are the reasons for this scarcity?

Species Diversity

There are a number of considerations facing the tropical forester, and particularly complicating the prospect of sustainable forest management in tropical rainforests, which are not as problematic in temperate ecosystems. Foremost among these is the immense species diversity of tropical rain forests. For example, the Costa Rican National Institute of Biodiversity (INBIO) has catalogued over 500 species of commercially marketable timber trees in Costa Rica, of which 150 can be found in a few hectares of lowland rain forest. Compare this to the several dozen species found in the temperate forests of the Pacific Northwest.

Although this diversity is what makes tropical rain forests so unique, valuable and beautiful, it presents a number of problems to sustainable management attempts. First of all, little is known about the biology, ecology or silviculture of the great majority of these species. This profound lack of knowledge often amazes temperate foresters and biologists, but we must understand that the forests of Europe and North America have been studied

scientifically for centuries (and we are still years away from truly sustainable management) while the rain forests of Central and South America, Southeast Asia, etc. have been studied by only a limited number of individuals in the last few decades. By far the largest and most thorough understanding of the ecology of rain forests is to be found with the indigenous people who have inhabited them for millennia. Unfortunately, this knowledge is usually overlooked by foresters and resource managers.

The other side of the diversity coin is that trees of any particular species are relatively rare in the rain forest. Although stands of only a few species are occasionally found, particularly in extremely swampy or otherwise severe conditions, it is much more typical to find only one or a few mature individuals of any given timber species per hectare of primary rain forest. One of the consequences is that tropical rain forests are less susceptible to large-scale disease and insect damage than less diverse forests. The low density of each tree species makes it more difficult for a species-particular disease or pest to spread, and even if the populations of one or a few species are reduced or eliminated, there are many others to fill the gap.

Selectively harvesting only a few timber species results very rapidly in the depletion of those species from the rain forest and the loss of ecological integrity. This means that for rain forest management to be sustainable it must maintain the ecological balance among a very large number of species. Considering the scarcity of information about many of these species, this is a truly formidable task. Another difficulty is that the existing markets for tropical woods, both local and international, are not prepared to consume small quantities of diverse and little-known species, but would prefer a steady supply of a few well-known and valued timbers such as teak, mahogany, etc. The tropical rain forest manager therefore has the additional responsibility of creating a market for the timber he supplies.

Terrain and Climate

Another major impediment to forestry in tropical rain forests is the difficult and fragile nature of the terrain. Rain forests are typically wet and poorly drained. Clay subsoils are common, with virtually no topsoil to speak of. Roads are therefore expensive to build and to maintain, and cause a great deal of ecological damage; they disrupt drainage, increase erosion, and interrupt habitat, particularly for arboreal mammals such as monkeys, sloths, and the like. Furthermore, roads are likely to be damaged or destroyed by the torrential downpours of the monsoon or rainy season, which can also make work of any kind impossible during several months of the year.

The best solution to this dilemma is to use draft animals instead of heavy machinery for the extraction of timber. Oxen, horses, elephants, and water buffalo have all been used with good result in the tropics. Water buffalo are especially suited to work in swampy areas. Their large, spreading hooves and enormous strength enable them to pull a load quite effectively in terrain where a tractor would quickly become bogged down. Furthermore, since one water buffalo pulls the load of a team of oxen, the trail need only be wide enough for a single animal to pass. Whole logs can be loaded onto carts, sleds, or even flat boats, or the efficiency of the operation can be increased with a small portable sawmill, processing the logs on site and extracting only the usable timber. This last method also has the advantage of returning unwanted biomass such as bark and branches to the ecosystem. Another low-environmental impact extraction technology is the use of cables attached to poles or to standing trees. Although the installation of such a system requires a considerable initial investment, in many instances it would cost less than the construction of suitable roads.

Unlike in dry forests, the role of fire is usually of minor ecological importance in rain forests under natural conditions. The exception to this rule occurs when excessive forest clearing results in reduced local precipitation, for example, in Indonesia. We are accustomed to hearing about the role of tropical rainforests in mediating the global climate, particularly through carbon storage and emission of oxygen and water vapor, but the effect of tropical forests on the local climate must be given due consideration as well.

Other Ecological Factors

There are many other ecological differences between a temperate forest and a tropical rain forest. One of these that effects timber management practices is the high density of long, thick, and very strong vines and other epiphytes. These vines, or lianas, frequently grow up one tree and pass from it to other trees in the canopy layer, binding them strongly together. In order for the first tree to be selectively harvested without bringing down or damaging its neighbors or becoming entangled and unable to fall, it is necessary to cut the vines some time before the planned harvest. Several months may be necessary for the vine to dry out and lose its binding strength. Unfortunately, it is not generally possible to be certain from the ground which vines pass through any particular tree, so extreme caution must be exercised.

One advantage that rain forest trees have in terms of extraction, processing, and marketing is their typical shape. Many tropical rain forest species grow straight to great heights, putting out branches only in the high canopy because of the extreme competition for sunlight. This results in long, very straight, and entirely clear timber with good structural and esthetic qualities. Trees grow quickly and reach enormous sizes. In some areas, a DBH of 2 meters, even above the often-extensive buttress roots which require special felling techniques, are not uncommon. Many times even the branches are of considerable size, although the prevalence of tension wood may make processing difficult.

Due to the continual heat and humidity and the thriving populations of bacteria and fungi, tropical rain forests probably have the highest rate of organic matter decay of any ecosystem in the world. The result is that, unlike temperate forests, they store the large majority of their organic matter in the living tissues of trees and other plants. While a temperate forest eventually builds up a deep humus-rich topsoil (which is also the home to most of its species and numerical biodiversity), a tropical rain forest typically maintains a thin covering of decomposing leaves and other litter over extremely poor (clay or rock) subsoil. Rain forest plants tend to have wide but superficial root systems, since all the water and organic matter they need are to be found within a few centimeters of the surface. This makes them remarkable susceptible to toppling by wind or erosion when the forest is opened up nearby them.

Because of the virtual absence of topsoil and the fact that most of its life forms are found on top of the soil or in the canopy, a cleared rain forest becomes degraded much more rapidly than other types of forests, and is correspondingly harder to restore. The small amount of remaining organic matter is quickly carried away by heavy rains, leaving the naked clay to bake under the tropical sun into a cracked and brick-like terrain as inhospitable to plant life as a city street. For all of these reasons it is highly recommendable to selectively harvest either individual trees or small, narrow areas modeled on natural treefall clearings, leaving an abundance of mature trees nearby to reseed and recolonize the area as rapidly as possible.

14

Restoration and Regeneration

There is still considerable argument as to whether, or to what extent, an area can be restored to tropical rain forest once it has become degraded. It is probable that the original diverse combination of climax species can never be replaced, but certainly some degree of restoration is possible, depending on the extent of ecosystem, soil and climate degradation and the proximity of a healthy forest for species restocking. A good way to start is by first planting resistant nitrogen-fixing trees (there are a multitude of suitable tropical leguminous tree species) and fast-growing herbaceous plants such as bananas, and later establishing native tree species in the shade of these pioneers. The enrichment of partially-logged or cleared secondary forests is unquestionably possible and highly successful, and should be recommended to restore to health rain forests which have been poorly managed in the past.

The major obstacle to such efforts is the lack of information about nursery techniques for many of the species involved. Many tropical tree species are difficult to propagate. Some common problems are the need for high humidity to germinate, low tolerance of sunlight, dryness, or waterlogging; unusually long germination periods and rapid (3-4 days, in some cases) loss of seed viability. Combined with the difficulty of acquiring native tree seeds, these factors can unduly complicate nursery practices.

On the other hand, many tropical rain forest trees produce large quantities of unusually robust and resistant seeds. The rate of successful germination is often high since these species are adapted to the intense competition for light on the forest floor. Similarly, some seedlings can be maintained in the nursery for long periods of time, since under natural conditions they can wait years for a nearby treefall to let in enough light for them to begin a spurt of rapid growth. Seedlings of many species survive well when transplanted bare root, in pseudo-stake, or even as unrooted branch cuttings, but some are more fragile and should be transplanted with the root ball intact.

Cultural Considerations

Foresters accustomed to conditions in the temperate forests of over-developed countries may encounter a number of unexpected setbacks in the tropics. Many things that we take for granted may be unavailable there, from the cooperation of government agencies, to access to electricity, machinery, replacement parts, trained personnel, and roads. Many foresters working in the tropics are either from the developed world or trained there. Although well-intentioned, they may do more harm than good by attempting to apply techniques more suited to Europe and North America, or by failing to consider local ecological or cultural conditions.

Cultural and political conditions vary widely throughout the tropics, and are ignored by the would-be forest manager only at great risk to the project. For example, in many areas of Central and South America, small landholders don't have legal ownership of their property and are encouraged to clear the forest in order to maintain their property rights. Local agricultural methods must be taken into consideration, including shifting cultivation and the utilization of secondary forest products for food, medicines, and fibers. For forest management to be truly sustainable it must consider the full range of human and ecological activities which take place in the forest.

Finally, the political and economic well-being of the local people must be given primary importance. If local people feel that the project threatens them by limiting their options, or that the profit of harvesting operations is not helping them and their community, they will oppose it and the project will ultimately fail. The best, most environmentally and socially sustainable forest management projects are naturally those which are initiated by the local people themselves to meet their own present and future needs. Forest dwellers generally understand and appreciate the local ecology better than any outsider and are more likely to implement conservationist strategies since their own lifestyle and future survival is at stake. The role of the professional forester in these situations is, ideally, to provide ideas and technical assistance, but not to design or control the development of the project.

Perhaps even more than in other parts of the world, forestry in the tropics must always be considered and planned as an integrated part of other human activities.

Because of the high human populations and the scarcity of suitable agricultural lands and other resources, tropical forests are under enormous pressure to be converted to cropland, pastures, fuelwood, and building materials. There is no hope for sustainable forest management without a plan for sustainable food and fuel production as well. One strategy that has been recommended for tropical rain forest preservation is to surround core refuges with areas of sustainable timber harvest, and these in turn with buffer zones made up of agroforestry plantations (integrated tree systems for human food, livestock fodder and forage, and possibly other uses such as building and crafts materials) and extractive reserves for other secondary products.

Conclusions

Although the complexities of tropical forest management may seem insurmountable, surely they are not. They must not be, if tropical rain forests are to have any hope of surviving through the next century. Protectionist strategies such as parks and reserves have limited applicability, and will eventually fail if human population growth and resource scarcity continue to increase the pressure against the remaining forests. What are needed are many small-scale, locally-controlled management initiatives which respect and capitalize on the local knowledge and culture. In this section you will read about two such initiatives, one in the lowland rain forest of Costa Rica and the other in the Philippines. There are a few other good examples in various parts of the tropics.

Another extremely important effort, and one in which Northern foresters, biologists, ecologists and silviculturists can potentially have the largest and most immediately beneficial contribution, is a massive research campaign on tropical trees to increase the understanding necessary for their effective management. High priority areas for research include seed and nursery management, reproductive ecology and phenology, natural forest regeneration, and harvest sustainability levels. We need to experiment with new efficient and low-impact harvesting, processing and extraction techniques and with more integrated forestry/agroforestry/agricultural schemes. The sustainable management of tropical forests is currently constrained as much by the lack of this knowledge and of reliable technical procedures as by any economic or political pressures.

14

Sustaining Tropical Forests Through Environmentally-sound Harvesting Practices

D. P. Dykstra and R. Heinrich

Sustaining Tropical Forests

ALTHOUGH ALMOST EVERYONE AGREES that the sustainability of tropical forests is a necessary objective, there is much confusion over the precise meaning of "sustainability." We prefer to think of sustainability in the context of human use and the aspirations of people in developing countries to thrust off the yoke of poverty. In this context, FAO defines sustainable development as "the management and conservation of the natural resource base and the orientation of technological and institutional change so as to enable the attainment and continued satisfaction of human needs for present and future generations" (FAO, 1991). Similarly, the Brundtland Commission (WCED, 1987) says that "sustainable development is development that meets the needs of the present without compromising the ability of future generations to meet their own needs."

To contribute to sustainable development, then, a critical aspect of the utilization of tropical forests is that the activities associated with this utilization must not irreversibly compromise the potential of the forest to regenerate and continue to provide the industrial wood and non-wood forest products, environmental services, social benefits and global values (such as the maintenance of biodiversity) that are essential for the well-being of both current and future generations. In fact, the goal should be to maximize the aggregate potential of the forest to provide these goods and services over the long term. This implies that where industrial wood is to be removed from tropical forests, harvesting operations must be carried out in such a way as to leave the forest in a condition that favors a rapid recovery to its pre-harvest state or to some other state that is silviculturally, ecologically and sociologically desirable.

Since the 1950s, a series of research papers have quantified the nature and extent of damage associated with logging operations in tropical forests. Perhaps the most influential of these have resulted from studies in Africa by Dawkins (1958) and Redhead (1960), and from a series of studies in Southeast Asia by Nicholson (1958 and 1979), Wyatt-Smith and Foenander (1962), Fox (1968), Marn and Jonkers (1982).

More recently, similar studies have been published for the Latin America and Caribbean region by Jonkers (1987), Hendrison (1989), Schmitt (1989) and Costa Filho (1991). From these studies, it seems clear that the extent of damage commonly associated with logging operations in tropical forests is inconsistent with the preservation of many non-timber forest values. Thus, although current logging practices may permit the sustained yield of wood, they are likely to interfere with the sustainability of other services and functions provided by tropical forests.

Furthermore, there is evidence that the degree of damage is increasing as logging operations extend over more rugged terrain and become increasingly mechanized, relying to a greater extent on horsepower rather than on technical competence (Fox, 1968; Nicholson, 1979; Marn and Jonkers. 1982). This is an alarming trend because it suggests that the sustainability of both timber production and non-timber services is increasingly at risk in tropical forests.

Harvesting Technologies To Sustain Tropical Forests

This paper makes a distinction between harvesting and logging. As used here, logging refers simply to the process of felling and extracting wood from forests whereas harvesting includes pre-harvest planning, technical supervision and post harvest assessments that reflect concern about non-timber resource values and the future state of the forest. "Harvesting technology" is a collective term that refers to the use of scientific and engineering principles in combination with education and training to improve the application of labor, equipment and operating methods in the harvesting of industrial timber.

We believe that sufficient information now exists to permit sustainable harvesting operations in virtually any area of tropical forest worldwide. Furthermore, the motivation for doing so is not just to promote sustainability; at least three recent studies (Marn and Jonkers, 1982; Hendrison, 1989; and Schmitt, 1989) have demonstrated clearly that harvesting operations designed to satisfy requirements for sustainability can simultaneously reduce harvesting costs by a substantial margin through improved planning and technical control.

The key to promoting sustainability of tropical forests during wood harvesting operations is to utilize the best knowledge available regarding five critical elements: harvest planning, forest roads, felling, skidding and yarding, and post-harvest assessments. The following sections address these elements individually.

Harvest Planning

Comprehensive planning of harvesting operations is essential in order to set the stage for sustainable harvesting practices and also to reconcile greater technical control during harvesting with the need to reduce costs. However, there is considerable evidence that harvesting operations in tropical forests are rarely preceded by thorough planning of the kind that is commonplace in temperate forests (Schmidt, 1987; Hendrison, 1989; FAO, 1989b). Furthermore, observations made by Nicholson (1958, 1979) over more than two decades suggest that, if anything, harvest planning for tropical forests is less common now than it was during the colonial era.

As in temperate forests, harvest planning in tropical forests should include the collection of detailed timber inventories and topographical data, plus other information essential for laying out a transportation system. A transportation plan should ensure that the logging crews have efficient access to the trees to be harvested; it should therefore circumvent problem areas, avoid streams and minimize the total area disturbed by roads, landings, skidtrails and cableways. Suggested procedures for collecting the necessary data to permit this kind of planning are provided by Marn and Jonkers (1982) and Hendrison (1989).

A harvesting plan should also specify the equipment to be used and the timing of operations, and should include contingency plans for severe storms and other extreme events. It should consider the possibility of complementary harvesting of non-timber forest products (for example, the cutting of rattan or tapping of resins prior to the timber harvest, or fuelwood gathering after the harvest). Local communities should be consulted about potential scheduling problems or opportunities (for instance, to take advantage of labor availability during slack agricultural periods). The normal onset of the rainy season should be considered, as should the time of seedfall in areas where seed is not produced year-round; in deciduous or semi-evergreen forests, for example. In

some cases, harvesting operations may need to be scheduled to avoid conflicts with the reproductive cycles of animals or plants of value to local people.

Although harvest planning implies an increase in initial expenditure, it can help avoid many problems and can substantially decrease overall costs by reducing wastage and improving efficiency of operations. A study by Marn and Jonkers (1982) found that operations preceded by comprehensive planning were characterized by better organization and supervision, fewer accidents, fewer merchantable trees left unfelled and fewer logs lost after felling. In addition, operations utilizing comprehensive harvest planning were found to cost 20 to 45 percent less overall than comparable operations carried out under virtually identical conditions but for which only minimal harvest planning was done (Marn and Jonkers, 1982; Hendrison, 1989). Perhaps more importantly, total soil disturbance and damage to residual trees was significantly less in the case of pre-planned operations than in operations undertaken with a minimum of planning.

Roads

Roads are unquestionably the most problematic feature of timber harvesting operations. An estimated 90 percent or more of the soil erosion resulting from timber harvesting in the tropics is directly attributable to roads (FAO, 1977). Nevertheless, except in cases where large waterways can be used, roads are essential for industrial timber extraction and providing access for management and control purposes. Building roads involves removing vegetation and rearranging the soil to permit an easier passage for vehicles. Such actions are almost always accompanied by increased rates of erosion. To minimize erosion and reduce its destructive effects, road locations must be planned in advance and according to proper layout and construction procedures.

Competent technical supervision of road layout and construction is essential. By restricting the area cleared for haul roads to the minimum width possible while still allowing for efficiency and safety, soil erosion can be reduced and the area retained in forest increased. For example, guidelines developed for rain forests in northern Australia specify that the maximum clearing width should be less than 7.5 m for major haul roads and less than 5 m for secondary haul roads (Ward and Kanowski, 1985). This contrasts sharply with the average road clearing width of 18.4 m, reported in a recent study in Papua New Guinea (FAO, 1989a).

Felling Operations

By itself, selective felling practically mimics natural tree falls and is generally considered to be relatively benign from an environmental perspective (Hamilton, 1988).

Indeed, the forest gaps created by trees felled properly under any of the selective harvesting systems common to the tropics are often indistinguishable from gaps caused by natural tree falls (Jonkers, 1987). Nevertheless, improper felling can cause considerable damage to advanced regeneration and can also reduce efficiency in skidding operations.

Of particular importance is the common situation of tree crowns interconnected by woody climbers. Under such conditions the tree being felled can pull neighboring trees with it, thereby breaking or uprooting them. In fact, shifting cultivators reportedly take advantage of this, pulling down large blocks of forest by felling a single, climber-infested tree. Pre-harvest cutting of climbers is essential in such areas, and can substantially reduce damage to residual trees. For instance, one study (Fox, 1968) found that the cutting of climbers several months in advance of felling reduced the number of trees knocked over or broken by as much as 50 percent. Because many of the residual trees damaged or destroyed during felling are in the pole-sized classes that will form the commercial timber crop for a subsequent harvesting entry, sustainability of timber production depends upon saving as many of these trees as possible. In addition, much of the floral biodiversity in tropical forests resides in trees that do not attain large sizes and are not currently utilized for timber (K. D. Singh, FAO Forestry Department, personal communication, 1991). Therefore, ensuring minimum damage to young trees and regrowth is also important from the point of view of biodiversity conservation.

Improper felling techniques are another common problem in tropical forests. According to DeBonis (1986), felling crews are often untrained and, in some cases, do not understand the need to make an undercut to direct the fall of a tree. Once the trees have been felled, proper cross-cutting is essential in order to maximize the value of the tree and to reduce wastage. A recent global assessment of the tropics suggests that the percentage of felled timber left unutilized in the forest is more than twice as high in the tropics as in the temperate regions (Dykstra, 1991). Utilization of these residues through improved felling and cross-cutting techniques could substantially reduce the area of tropical forest that has to be logged each year to provide the current volume of tropical industrial roundwood.

Skidding and Yarding Operations

Most logging in tropical forests is done with ground skidding equipment. Cable yarding has the potential of substantially reducing road requirements and soil disturbance in steep or swampy areas (Aulerich, Aulerich and Piedrahita, 1990) but its proper application requires a highly skilled crew and even so it will probably be more costly and may result in more extensive damage to residual trees (Nicholson, 1979).

Conventional ground skidding systems cause two forms of damage in tropical forest operations. The skidders tend to wander through the forest searching for felled trees, thus causing a proliferation of skid trails and resulting in excessive damage to residual trees and advance regeneration. The skidders also cause soil disturbance and soil compaction, thus increasing the potential for erosion and retarding both regeneration and the growth of residual trees. Both of these problems can be substantially reduced by comprehensive pre-harvest planning as discussed earlier. Comparative studies have shown that skidding costs can be reduced by one-third or more through comprehensive planning coupled with competent technical supervision (Marn and Jonkers, 1982; Hendrison, 1989). In addition, when pre-planning of skid trail locations is combined with directional felling of trees toward the skid trails, the number of merchantable logs left in the forest can be reduced substantially (Marn and Jonkers, 1982).

Where appropriate, low-pressure ground skidders can be used to reduce soil disturbance and soil composition, particularly on steeper slopes or permanently damp soils. (Buenaflor and Heinrich, 1980). Animal skidding is also a feasible alternative in many areas and the use of draught animals, such as elephants or oxen, has been shown to significantly reduce soil disturbance, soil compaction and damage to residual trees (Sundquist, 1985; Cordero, 1988).

Post-harvest Assessments

As stressed at the beginning of this article, harvesting is one part of overall forest management. Therefore, regular feedback regarding the success or failure of harvesting operations with respect to long-term sustainability of the forest is essential. Part of this feedback can be provided through post-harvest assessments. Such an assessment should report on operation costs and revenues, an evaluation of the degree to which both silvicultural and non-timber objectives are met, the extent of damage to residual trees, the area disturbed by roads and trails, the quality and quantity of regeneration, etc. Requirements for post harvest operations such as the revegetation of skid trails and landings should be noted. Finally, it is essential that the results of the post-harvest assessment be communicated to the harvesting crew. Financial incentives for good work and penalties for substandard work will reinforce a company's commitment to sustainable harvesting practices.

Reprinted with permission from Unasylva *169, Vol. 43, 1992.*

14

Mangrove Forests

Alfredo Quarto

MANGROVES ARE THE RAINFORESTS OF THE SEA. Mangroves play many vital roles. They act as breeding and nursery grounds for much of the world's commercial fisheries. Literally millions of coastal fisherfolk depend on a healthy mangrove ecosystem for their livelihood. Mangroves act as buffers against wind and storm damage. In both the Philippines and Bangladesh, many lives have been lost to the ravages of hurricanes which wreak more severe havoc upon mangrove-cleared coastlines. In fact, it is believed that thousands of people have died recently as the direct result of loss of the protective mangrove buffer zone. This serious situation continues to accelerate worldwide due to the aquaculture industry. Mangroves offer shoreline stability, thereby protecting the sea grass and coral from damaging siltation. The mangroves also offer sustainable small-scale forest industries, including charcoal production, firewood and building materials.

Though mangroves play such an important part in maintaining a balanced coastal ecology, these forests are quickly being cleared to make room for prawn farms. Prawn aquaculture has spread along the coasts of Asia, Africa and Latin America. As prawn ponds are enplaced, huge tracts of mangroves are destroyed, resulting in major ecological problems world wide.

Certain groups are implementing reforestation programs in attempts to re-establish healthy mangrove ecosystems. Yad fon (Rain Drop) Association based in Trang, Thailand, has initiated several village-level programs to help the local fishers and farmers learn self-management skills to protect and sustain their local resource base, including the mangrove forest. Efforts to replant the mangroves in denuded areas and protect the remaining forests and coastal waters are now being implemented. These kinds of grassroots efforts within the villages of Trang Province have already brought promising results. Very important in this effort is the direct involvement of the local people who in turn are now meeting with neighboring villagers to teach others about sustainable coastal resource management.

The Mangrove Action Project will network with such groups and offer assistance when and where possible.

Three primary objectives for the MAP coalition are:

1. To protect and restore the mangrove forests worldwide.

2. To protect and promote the rights of local coastal peoples, including fisherfolk and farmers, especially in relation to local people retaining their rights to sustainably manage their own coastal resources.

3. To promote a worldwide awareness of both the importance of mangrove forests and the rights of coastal peoples to manage their local resources. As well, to expose the direct threats posed by such industrial developments as prawn farming, tourism, charcoal production, mining and other expanding industries...as they affect both the mangrove forests and the indigenous coastal peoples. MAP hopes to put pressure on the World Bank and other international monetary lending institutions to curtail further loans that support prawn farms or other aquacultural developments.

MAP will help sponsor an international conference or seminar to be held early next year (1994) in Trang. MAP is planning to publish an up-to-date booklet on remaining mangrove forests and those threats posed by the expansion of the prawn industry to both mangrove ecology and the local coastal peoples.

This is excerpted from literature published by the Mangrove Action Project. Reprinted with permission.

The Mangrove Action Project (MAP)
Alfredo Quarto (co-director)
P.O. Box 1854
Port Angeles, Washington 98362-0279, USA

14

Other Resources on Mangroves

Accion Ecologica/Campaign for Defense of the Mangroves
Gina Chavez
Casilla 17-15-246
CQE, Quito, Ecuador
Tel: 593-2-547-516/Fax 593-2-547-516

Asia-Pacific Symposium on Mangrove Ecosystems
Hong Kong, September 1-3, 1993.
Ms. Linda Yam, Conference Secretariat
Research Center, The HK University of
Science and Technology
Clearwater Bay, Kowloon, HONG KONG
Tel: 8 52-3 58 69 10/Fax 8 52-3 58 13 34

International Society for Mangrove Ecosystems
c/o College of Agriculture
University of the Ryukyus
Nishihara, Okinawa, 903-01, JAPAN

The ISME was established in 1990 to promote research and surveys and to cooperate with other organizations in promoting the conservation, rational management, and sustainable use of mangroves and to create and manage an international data bank on mangrove ecosystems. ISME now has 259 members from 46 countries. Quarterly newsletter *Mangroves*. Preparing a manual for mangrove vegetation planting.

Pusat Pengembangan Masyarakat Agrkarya
(Center for Agro-Action Community Development
Ir. Akhmad Jaeroni
Jalan Kalibata Timur 31 A. Pasar Minggu
Jakarta 12510, INDONESIA
Tel: 7992651-7996783

Yad fon (Rain Drop) Association
Pisit Chansnoh, President
105-107 Ton-Poh Rd.
Tambol Tubtiang
Amphur Muang, Trang-9200, THAILAND
Tel: 075-219737

14

Tropical Forests: Publications on Management

IF YOU THINK finding information on restoration forestry in the temperate zone is difficult, try finding restoration forestry practices in the tropics! It is even harder. Even Duncan Poore, with massive financing and personnel from ITTO (International Tropical Timber Organization) could only find less than 1 percent of tropical logging which could, at any stretch of the imagination, be called sustainable.

Notwithstanding, information on restoration forestry practices in the tropics is growing at a fast pace. Here is a selection of books on tropical forest management followed by books on tropical forest ecology.

(See also book reviews in Asia/Pacific and South/Central America sections.)

Alternatives to Deforestation: Steps Toward Sustainable Use of the Amazon Rain Forest
Anthony B. Anderson, ed. 1990. Columbia Univ. Press. 281 pp. $65.

A valuable contribution toward sustainable forestry in the tropics. These 17 papers presented at an international conference in Belem, Brazil (1988) report on ways to derive economic sustenance from rainforests without destroying them. It includes sections on Natural Forest Management, Landscape Recovery and Agroforestry.

Characteristics, Properties and Uses of Timbers: Southeast Asia, Northern Australia and the Pacific–Vol. 1
W. G. Keating and Eleanor Bolza. 1982. Inkata Press: Australia. 400 pp.

Describes 362 species, all with multiple uses. He lists 32 uses for trees, descriptions, characteristics, properties of density, strength, durability, etc. Very easy-to-understand layout.

Common Forest Resource Management: Annotated Bibliography of Asia, Africa and Latin America
1993. FAO CFN 11. Available from Forests, Trees, and People Programme. FAO. See International Organizations section for address.

The authors describe and analyse the local systems of Common Forest Resource Management and the role of externally sponsored assistance. Key issues are highlighted such as systems of tree and land tenure, the erosion of traditional rights, the reactions of right holders to change and measures take to assert old rights or establish new ones.

The Conservation of Genetic Resources in Managed Tropical Forests
R. H. Kemp. 1992. *Unasylva* #169: pp. 34-40.

Discusses pros and cons of selective logging.

Deforestation of Tropical Rain Forests: Economic Causes and Impact on Development
Torsten and Markus Diehl Amelung. 1992. J. C. B. Mohr: Tubingen.

A systematic, statistical attempt to determine the impact on tropical forests of different economic sectors such as agriculture, forestry, mining and hydro-power. "Even a large reduction of international trade in tropical hardwood is not likely to directly reduce logging substantially, since the bulk of tropical hardwood is consumed in tropical countries."

Deforestation or Development in the Third World? Vol. III
M. Palo and G. Mery, eds. 1990. Bulletin 349, Finnish Forest Research Inst., P.O. Box 37, SF-OO381, Helsinki, FINLAND.

A thorough account of tropical rain forest management.

Deforestation Rates in Tropical Forests and Their Climatic Implications
Norman Myers. 1993. Available from Friends of the Earth, United Kingdom. £12 ppd.

This new report from Norman Myers, author of the classic, rainforest text *The Primary Source*, contains the most up-to-date information on tropical deforestation currently available. The report includes country-by-country reviews of Latin America, Africa, and Asia, analysis of

14

such factors as future deforestation, the role of shifting cultivators, grand-scale tree planting, and recommendations for action.

Myers found that the tropical deforestation rate has increased by 90 percent during the 1980s, and without new safeguards this rate will increase further in the 1990s. Due to forest burning there was a 41 percent increase in carbon release from tropical forests from 1979-1989. When the enhanced emissions of methane and nitrous oxide are added to this total, tropical deforestation is estimated to be contributing between 18 and 19 percent of the build-up of greenhouse gases.

Deforestation: Social Dynamics in Watersheds and Mountain Ecosystems
D.C. Pitt, ed. 1988. Routledge. 224 pp. £35. Available from Natural History Book Service.

Developing Rain Forest Products
1992. Island Press.

Representatives of more than 30 institutions in 12 countries and three indigenous nations gathered in Panama City in June, 1991 to exchange views on the sustainable harvesting and marketing of plant products from tropical rainforests, with the objective of developing rain forest products that contribute to local economies. For further information, contact Conservation International, 1015 18th St. NW Suite 1000, Washington DC, 20036. Tel: (202) 429-5660

Ecology and Land Management in Amazonia
Michael J. Eden. 1990.

Environmentally Sound Small-Scale Forestry Projects: Guidelines for Planning
F. Folliot and J. L. Thames. 1983. VITA, 1815 N. Lynn St., #200, Arlington, Virginia 22209. Tel: (703) 276-1800.

This small book is designed for field staff. Concise text, and lots of easy-to-understand illustrations. Step by step planning for small-scale forestry projects in developing countries. VITA also has similar titles for agriculture and irrigation/water supply.

FAO's 1990 Reassessment of Tropical Forest Cover
In: *Nature & Resources*. Vol. 27. (1). pp. 21-26.

Forest and Watershed Development and Conservation in Asia and the Pacific Lawrence S. Hamilton, ed. 1983. Westview Press. 559 pp.
Eight case studies from various nations.

French-Language Tropical Forestry Bibliography

The French National Node of the European Tropical Forest Research Network (address in International Forestry Organizations) has recently published its first bibliography containing 224 abstracts of publications, which have been elaborated in the field of tropical forestry in the French-speaking world since 1991. The bibliography contains an index on persons, subjects, and countries.

A Guide to Species Selection for Tropical and Sub-Tropical Plantations
D. B. Webb, Smith, Wood & Henman. 1984. Tropical Forestry Paper No. 15. £19.50. Available from Natural History Book Service.

Growing Exotic Forests
B. Zokel, G. Van Wyr and P. Stal. 1987. 508 pp. $65.95. Available from agAccess (See Book Sources).

This book gives lots of information for tropical and temperate climates. Extensive references.

Intensive Multiple-Use Forest Management in Kerala, India
FAO Forestry paper No. 53. 1984.

The International Tropical Timber Organization: Kill or Cure for the Rainforests?
Marcus Colchester. 1990. The Ecologist #20. pp. 166-173.

Lessons of the Rainforest
Suzanne Head and Robert Heinzman, eds. 1990. Sierra Club Books: San Francisco. 275 pp. $14.95.

This book has 18 well selected articles by notable authors on rainforest topics.

Logging Technology for Tropical Forests— For or Against?
T. Johnson and P. Lindgren. 1990. Prepared for ITTO by Forest Operations Institute, Sweden.

The Management of Tropical Moist Forest Lands: Ecological Guidelines
Duncan Poore and Jeffrey Sayer. 2nd ed. 1987. IUCN. 69 pp.

123 recommendations for sustainable management, including mistakes to avoid. Particularly valuable for novices.

Management of the Forests of Tropical America: Prospects and Technologies
J. C. Figueroa, F. H. Wadsworth, and S. Branham. 1978. Institute of Tropical Forestry: Rio Piedras, Puerto Rico.

Natural Forest Management in Latin America
H. F. Maitre, et al. 1992. FAO.

Natural Forest Management in Africa
FAO Forestry Paper No. 88.

Natural Forest Management in Asia
FAO Forestry Paper No. 89.

Each of these FAO Papers is filled with statistics and some case studies, based on national reports prepared

14

specifically for the book. Being official reports, we can be certain that problems have been glossed over, figures padded, etc. Still they should provide useful general overviews for the countries covered.

Natural Management of Tropical Moist Forests
F. Mergen and J. R Vincent, eds. 1987. Yale University Press: New Haven, Connecticut.

Neotropical Wildlife Use and Conservation
J. G. Robinson and K. H. Redford, Eds. 1991. Univ. of Chicago Press. 490 pp. $28.

Mainly covers large mammals. 28 multi-authored chapters: four on subsistence hunting, four on wildlife farming, plus a chapter on ecotourism and habitat protection from Madre Dios region of SE Peru. Lots of documentation.

Networking in Action: Forestry Extension Materials in Review
E. Shanks. 1992. ODI/RDFN Network Paper No. 14a. ODI: London. 112 pp.

A synthesis of over 170 items of forestry extension literature sent to the Rural Development Forestry Network by its members from over 35 countries. Includes essay descriptions and an annotated bibliography.

No Timber Without Trees
Duncan Poore. 1989. Earthscan Pub: London. 252 pp.

Duncan Poore, the principal author of the book and leader of the study team has been Professor of Botany in Malaya, Director General of the International Union for the Conservation of Nature, and Director of the Commonwealth Forestry Institute at Oxford.

The conclusion of the report, which was presented to the ITTO in June 1989, has already made conservation history. After a detailed analysis of the majority of the main producers of tropical timber worldwide, it concluded: "The extent of tropical moist forest which is being deliberately managed at an operational scale for the sustainable production of timber is, on a world-scale, negligible." The study found that less than one-eighth of one percent of tropical forests where timber extraction is occurring, were being logged sustainably.

Much of this one-eighth of one percent, is hotly contested by Australian rainforest activists since Poore rates the Queensland tropical logging industry as practicing sustainable forestry. They have a horrible reputation in Australia.

Not by Timber Alone: Economics and Ecology for Sustaining Tropical Forests
Theodore Panayotou and Peter S. Ashton. 1992. Island Press.

Obstacles to Tree Planting in Arid and Semi-Arid Lands
J. Burley. 1982. UNU. 52 pp. £5. Available from Natural History Book Service (address in Book Sources section).

Comparative case studies from India and Kenya. Burley is great at unraveling social dynamics.

Plantation Forestry in the Tropics
Julian Evans. 1992, 2nd ed. Oxford University Press. 400 pp. £30.

Establishment and management of tree plantations. Up-to-date silvicultural practices: planning, seeds, nurseries, establishment, maintenance, thinning, pruning, rotations, ecology, integration with other land uses, agroforestry, protection forestry, social and community forestry. A useful book with hundreds of references.

Proceedings: Workshop on Impact of Man's Activities on Tropical Upland Forest Ecosystems
Faculty of Forestry. 1986. U. Pertanian Malaysia, 43400: Serdang, Selangar, Malaysia. 694 pp.

Many papers on impact, and on management.

Race to Save the Tropics. Ecology and Economics for a Sustainable Future
Robert Goodland ed. 1990. Island Press. 225 pp. $24.95.

Discussions of the origins of rainforest depletion and suggestions of economic and technological solutions, including agroecology and sustainable forestry.

Rainforest Buffer Zones: Guidelines for Protected Area Managers
Jeffrey Sayer. 1991. IUCN. 94 pp.

An illustrated guide for planners and managers of nature reserves, with 34 case studies related to legal and institutional constraints, rural development, non-wood products, research, education and tourism in forest buffer zones.

The Rainforest Harvest: Sustainable Strategies for Saving the Tropical Forest?
S. Counsell and T. Rice, eds. 1992. Friends of the Earth.

Proceedings of an international conference in May of 1990 on new directions for rain forest conservation, official strategies and marketing of rainforest products.

Rainforest Regeneration and Management
A. Gomez-Pompa, T. C. Whitmore, and M. Hadley, eds. 1991. MAB Book Series, Vol. 6. Parthenon Pub.: Lancaster. 457 pp. $90.

Part of the "Man and the Biosphere" series from UNESCO, this volume explores the implications for management of present scientific knowledge on rain forest regeneration, and identifies gaps in information and understanding.

14

Saving the Tropical Forests

Judith Gradwahl and Russell Greenberg. 1988. Earthscan. 207 pp. $12.95.

This worthwhile book focuses on alternative management. Case studies of forest reserves point to innovative projects in sustainable agriculture, natural forest management, and forest restoration. About 10 real life case studies for each of these categories.

Shrubs in Tropical Forest Ecosystems

A. K. Banerjee. 1989. World Bank. 132 pp. $9.95. Considers the potential of shrubs for solving fuelwood and fodder shortages. Covers characteristics, growth features, propagation, and management.

Silviculture in the Tropics

Hans Lamprecht. GTZ. (see address under GATE in International Development Periodicals.)

Slash and Burn Farming in the Third World Forest

William J. Peters and Leon f. Neuenschwander. 1988. Univ. of Idaho Press, Moscow, ID. 113 pp.

A brief look at a big subject, but a good place to start to learn about slash and burn forest agriculture, also called swidden agriculture. The authors stress the ecological soundness of traditional methods of cultivation and the cultures of their practitioners.

Small-scale Forest-based Processing Enterprises

FAO Forestry Paper 79. Food and Agriculture Organization of the United Nations (FAO): Distribution and Sales Section, FAO, Via delle Terme di Caracalla, 00100 Rome, ITALY.

The State of Forest Resources in the Developing Countries—An Interim Report

FAO. 1988.

Sustainable Forestry in Tropics— An International Workshop

Workshop held January 3-7, 1991 in New Delhi. Theme was Sustainable Forestry for People. Organized by Indian Environmental Society. For more information contact: Dr. Desh Bandhu, U-112A (3rd Floor), Vidhata House, Vikas marg, Shakarpur Delhi-110092, INDIA. Tel: (New Delhi) 722-2279

Surviving the Cut: Natural Forest Management In the Humid Tropics

Nels Johnson and Bruce Cabarle. 1993. World Resources Institute: Washington, DC.

Past forest management failures are analyzed, as well as more productive, more sustainable, and more equitable practices.

Sustainable Harvest and Marketing of Rainforest Products

Mark Plotkin and Lisa Famolare, eds. 1992. Island Press: Covelo, California. U.S. $20.

Focusing on non-timber forest products that can be extracted with little or no damage to forest ecosystems. This book presents alternatives to deforestation that are technically and economically feasible, and compatible with conservation, cultural survival, and community development.

Technologies to Sustain Tropical Forest Resources

U.S. Congress Office of Technology Assessment. 1984. 343 pp. $10.

Resource guide with chapters on organizations dealing with tropical forests and a host of forest technologies.

Trees As Cash Crops: Commercial Value of Trees and Forests in Babati District, Tanzania

Ulla Larsson. 1990. Working Paper 136, Swedish University of Agricultural Sciences, International Rural Development Center: Box 7005, S-750 07 UPPSALA, SWEDEN.

Tropical Forest Education Guide for English-Speaking Teachers

Lydia Anderson. World Wildlife Fund.

Tropical Forestry Database

Edinburgh Center for Tropical Forests, Darwin Building, Mayfield Road, Edinburgh, EH9 3JU, UK.

The Center is compiling a database of individuals with expertise in all fields related to tropical forest management.

Tropical Rainforest

Arnold Newman. Available from: Facts on File, 460 Park Ave. S., New York, New York, 10016. Tel: (212) 683-2244. 256 pp. $40.00.

Well-illustrated with color photographs. Unfortunately, the text does not match up to the illustrations. His seven-step blueprint for tropical rainforest's survival is heavily oriented to large-scale, corporate scenarios. In spite of the text, which I had many disagreements with, the book has some redeeming features, notably: a classification of traditional indigenous agricultural systems, as well as contemporary agroforestry and sustainable agriculture systems; a large compilation of useful statistics; useful appendices which include student and teacher aids, rainforest films, tropical timbers to avoid and North American alternative timbers; a lengthy bibliography, usefully subdivided into categories.

Tropical Rain Forest: Ecology and Management

T. C. Whitmore, A. C. Chawick, and S. L. Sutton, eds. 1983. Blackwell: London, UNITED KINGDOM.

Tropical Silviculture

L. R. Holdridge. 1957. FAO Forestry and Forest Products Studies No. 13, Vol. 2.

Tropical Timbers of the World

M. Chudnoff. 1984. USDA Forest Service Ag. Handbook No. 607.

Wise Management of Tropical Forests

F. R. Miller and K. L. Adam, eds. 1992. Oxford Forestry Institute. 288 pp.

Proceedings of the 1992 Oxford Conference on Tropical Forests, including 23 papers as well as conclusions and recommendations. Authors recognize that any solution to tropical forest loss will depend on major political and social, economic and agricultural changes.

14

Tropical Forests: Publications on Ecology

Amazonian Rain Forests Ecosystem Disturbance and Recovery
C.F. Jordan. 1987. Springer-Verlag: New York.

Amazon Watershed
George Monbiat. 1990. Michael Joseph. Pub.

An exciting adventure story by an investigative reporter who risks his life investigating the timber trade in the Amazon. The trail of timber exploitation, bribery and nasty deeds leads to the Brazilian military, U.S. and Brazilian governments, and large corporations.

Costa Rica Country Environmental Profile: A Field Study
Gary L. Hartshorn, et al. 1982. Tropical Science Center: San Jose.

Costa Rican Natural History
D. H. Janzen, ed. 1983. University of Chicago Press.

Dynamics of Soil Organic Matter in Tropical Ecosystems
David C. Coleman, J. Malcom Oades, and Goro Uehara. 1989. NIFTAL (address in Agroforestry Organizations).

Dynamic Properties of Forest Ecosystems
D. E. Reochle, ed. 1981. Cambridge University Press.

Ecological Effects of Fire in South African Ecosystems
Peter de V. Booysen and Neil M. Tainton, eds. 1984. 426 pp.

The Ecology of Neotropical Savannas
Guellermo Sarmiento. 1984. 235 pp.

Guellermo Sarmiento is an unquestionable authority on the grasslands of the New World. His book is the first modern, integrated view of the genesis and function of this important natural system—a synthesis of savanna architecture, seasonal rhythms, productive processes, and water and nutrient economy.

The Ecology of a Tropical Forest: Seasonal Rhythms and Long-term Changes
E.G. Leigh, et al. eds. 1982. Smithsonian Institute: Washington, DC.

Research on an island in the Panama canal which has been studied intensively for 60 years by the Smithsonian Institute. It is one of the most studied rainforests in the world.

Fire in the Tropical Biota: Ecosystem Processes and Global Challenge
J. G. Goldammer, ed. 1990. 497 pp.

The impact and role of fire in tropical ecosystems. It also studies the impact of tropical wildland fires and biomass burning on global ecosystem processes.

Forest Succession: Concepts and Applications
Darrell C. West, et al. 1980. Springer-Verlag.

Hydrology of Moist Tropical Forests and Effects of Conversion: A State of Knowledge Review
UNESCO. 1990. Available from: UNESCO, Div. of Water Sci., Int. Hydrological Prog., Science Sector: 7, place de Fontenoy, 75700 Paris, FRANCE. 224 pp.

An Introduction to Tropical Rain Forests
T. C. Whitmore. 1990. Clarendon Press: Oxford. 226 pp.

This readable book is packed with photographs. A worldwide overview by one of the most respected rainforest experts.

The Last Rain Forests—A World Conservation Atlas
Mark Collins, ed. 1990. Oxford Univ. Press: New York. 200 pp. large format $29.95.

Another gorgeous, coffee-table rainforest book. The text is fairly good, covering ecology and sociology of the rainforest. The outstanding feature of this book is the detailed atlas showing where the remaining rainforests are. These maps show lowland rainforests, mountain rainforests and mangrove forests.

A Neotropical Companion
John C. Kricher. 1989. Princeton University Press. 436 pp.

Neotropical Montane Forests: Biodiversity and Conservation
H. Balslev, ed. 1993. 114 pp.

Abstracts from a symposium held on June 21-26, 1993 in New York. Helps to document biological and ecological diversity in neotropical wet and moist montane forests and place it in contrast to other neotropical areas.

Nutrient Cycling in Tropical Forest Ecosystems
Carl. F. Jordan. 1985. John Wiley & Sons.

Reproductive Ecology of Tropical Forest Plants
K. S. Bawa and M. Hadley, eds. 1990. Parthenon Pub. MAB Book Series: Lancaster, United Kingdom. 421 pp. Vol. 7.

Examines how reproductive ecology, defined in a broad sense to include seedling establishment and regeneration, can be helpful in the management of tropical forest resources. Many references and a detailed index make it valuable to both researchers and practitioners.

Timber, the Environment and Wildlife in Malaysian Rain Forests: Final Report
A. D. Johns. 1989. Institute S.E. Asian Biology, University of Aberdeen, Scotland.

Tropical Forest Ecosystems. A State of Knowledge Report
UNESCO/UNEP/FAO. 1978.

Tropical Forests: Botanical Dynamics, Speciation and Diversity
L. B. Holm-Nielsen, I. Nelson, and H. Balsev, eds. 1989. Academic Press. 380 pp.

Tropical Forests in Transition
J. G. Goldammer. 1992. 280 pp.

A look at the paleoecology of tropical forests, changing environmental conditions and human impacts to model the future of the tropical forest in a changing environment. The aim of the book is to strengthen multidisciplinary thinking in disturbance ecology.

Tropical Nature: Life and Death in the Rain Forests of Central and South America
Adrian Forsyth and Ken Miyata. 1984. Scribner's. 248 pp. $11.00.

A modern classic which describes, from a deep ecological perspective, the incredible diversity and beauty of the tropical rainforest.

Tropical Rain Forest Ecosystems. Biogeographical and Ecological Studies
H. Leith and M. J. A. Werger, eds. 1989. Ecosystems of the World Volume 14B, Elsevier Science Pub. 713 pp. $250.

One of the most authoritative books to date with forty-five authors. It concentrates on biogeographical aspects such as species composition, diversity and geographical variation. A region by region account of all the world's main tropical forest regions is given.

Tropical Rain Forests of the Far East
T. C. Whitmore. 2nd ed. 1984. Clarendon Press: Oxford. 349 pp.

Considered one of the definitive treatises on tropical rainforest ecology, vegetation, and man's impact. Good overview. Scientific but readable.

Tropical Trees and Forests: An Architectural Analysis
F. Halle, et al. 1978. Springer-Verlag.

Tropical Trees as Living Systems
P. B. Tomlinson and M. H. Zimmermann, eds. Cambridge University Press.

14

14

15 Forestry in Africa

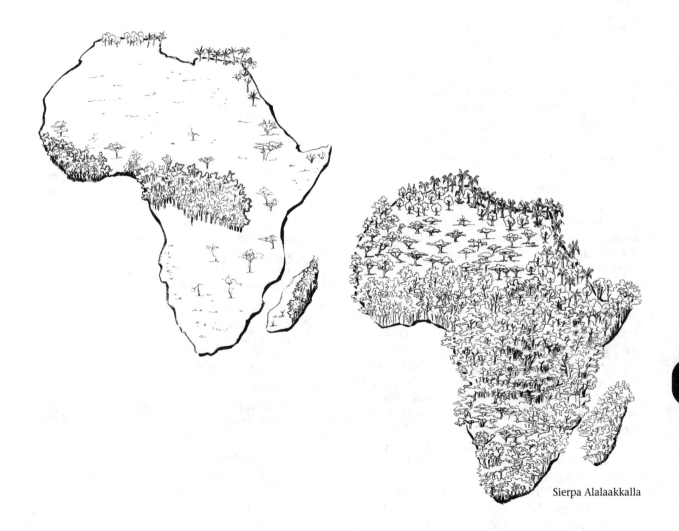

Sierpa Alalaakkalla

Forestry Organizations in Africa

Introduction

AFRICA IS A VAST CONTINENT and naturally endowed with a wide array of forests and many amazing trees. Unfortunately, most of Africa's forests have been taking a beating from logging, grazing, conversion to export and subsistence agriculture, wood-cutting, erosion, and war.

Africa is a grass-roots sort of place. It has to be. People have to be self-reliant. Governments aren't likely to help the poor. In fact, governments are usually set up to keep people poor. Africa is still strongly agricultural, although the people's self-reliance has been eroded by the past several centuries of exploitation and war. Africa is also a place of laughter, hope and strength. Africa is full of surprises.

There are undoubtedly as many examples of restoration forestry in Africa as anywhere in the world. There is a tremendous amount of information on agroforestry being generated in Africa and there are many examples of sustainable, traditional cultures.

There is a lack of information on sustainable forestry coming out of Africa. Perhaps there is more in French and other languages. Perhaps it is part of the general (and deliberate) neglect of Africa in the world media. We invite people to send information on forestry in Africa to Friends of the Trees Society's address for future publications.

Some of the following are local tree organizations from Africa who have corresponded with Friends of the Trees Society. They are concerned with small-scale agroforestry, sustainable agriculture, environmental protection and feeding their people. Africa has tens of thousands of such local groups, a reflection of the village, tribe and kinship bonds that have supported African cultures through millennia.

This is a cursory look at the world of NGO's in Africa. I have concentrated on NGO's focused on trees. I have attempted to categorize African organizations into two sections: 1) NGOs, mostly small and 2) Conventional forestry organizations, e.g. government and university.

To make it easier to find listings for particular countries, the lists are organized alphabetically by country. Thus the reader can look up Ethiopia in two places instead of having to go through all the listings.

African NGOs (Non-Governmental Organizations)

The Forestry Association of Botswana (FAB)
P.O. Box 2088
Gaborone, **BOTSWANA**
Tel: (267) 35-1660/Fax: (267) 30-0316

FAB is an NGO started in 1983 by people concerned with fuel wood and pole shortages in Botswana and the consequences of overcutting. Its aims are to act as a focal point for NGO forestry activities, to lobby, advise and cooperate with government agencies, and to promote forestry research and education. FAB sells and sometimes gives away tree seedlings, has an active extension program which places volunteers in reforestation programs, and produces publications on tree planting. Publishes *Journal of the Forestry Association of Botswana*. One issue per year. Subscriptions: P 5/issue (US $4)

Department of Community Development
Ministry of Agriculture
Christopher Dig Ghamogha
P.O. Box 2729
Yaounde, **CAMEROON**
Tel: 22 4834

Reforestation, permaculture, tropical rainforests, agroforestry, environmental conservation. Tree planting with Lun Women's Group. Promotion of self help.

PRISERI, Private Sector Research Institute
Professor C. N. Ngwasiri
P.O. Box 170
Buea, **CAMEROON**
Tel: 32 26 85

A project to counter the degradation of Cameroon's natural resources by encouraging rural farmers to plant certain trees and plants as a part of their agricultural practices, and creating nurseries for these plants.

Santo Antao Rural Development Project
MDRP-DR Vila Ribeira Grande
Santo Antao, **REPUBLICA DE CABO VERDE**
(Cape Verde Islands)

The Cape Verde Islands are off the west tip of Africa. The islands are surrounded by water, but they are a dry place indeed. It didn't always used to be that way. After European colonization, the forests were felled and the islands largely dried up. Its 300,000+ inhabitants live on a land area of 1,557 square miles of islands scattered across the ocean.

Friends of the Trees received an impressive pile of information on large-scale reforestation projects and sustainable agriculture underway in Cape Verde to feed the people and build the soil. Their experience is a valuable addition to knowledge on tree establishment in tough, dryland situations. The dry, rocky, steep mountainsides would give the most optimistic tree-planter pause.

Some SARDEP publications include: *Erosion and Conservation on Santo Antao, Proceedings of 1st and 2nd National Soil and Water Conservation Seminars of Cape Verde, The Regional Development Plan for Santa Antao with chapters on Forestry, A manual on introduced forestry species for arid and semi-arid zones in Portuguese*, the first such publication in that language.

German Technical Co-operation, MOA
P.O. Box 60054
Addis Ababa, **ETHIOPIA**
Tel: 251-1-155490

Designate, demarcate and prepare management plans for both national and private forests. Deribe Gurmu, Team Leader.

Gambian-German Forestry Project
P.O. Box 504
Banjul, **GAMBIA**
Tel: 220 96075/Fax: 220 95144

Pilot community forestry project to involve the rural population in the management of natural forests.

Worldview International Foundation
P.M.B. 94
Banjul, **GAMBIA**

Facilitate the building of grassroots institutions; organize & train voluntary village-based development workers to identify problems and solutions with the people; and mobilize communities for action to address desertification and acute forest depletion.

ECASARD (Ecumenical Association for Sustainable Agriculture and Rural Development)
Bernard Y. Guri
P.O. Box 9712 Airport
Accra, **GHANA**

Network for sustainable agriculture and agroforestry. A good place to find out about organic farmers in Ghana. Church agencies and Private Voluntary Organizations engaged in agricultural and rural development.

Friends of the Trees Society—Ghana
P.O. Box A227
La, Accra, **GHANA**

Autonomous group inspired by Friends of the Trees Society (USA). Reforestation, agriculture, seeds, women's projects, livestock, tree planting, seed collection. Contact for other projects in area. Chphas Nii Kotey Kotei, Director.

The Future is in our Hands
P.O. Box 154, Trade Fair Site
Accra, **GHANA**

Projects in reforestation, agriculture, tree planting, tree nursery, gardening, and poultry/livestock. Seeking travelers with knowledge and experience. Ebenezer Nortey-Mensah, Director.

Ghana Student Conservation Assoc. of Africa
Collins Boakye-Agyemang
P.O. Box 1331,
Mamprobi, Accra, **GHANA**

HELP-SOCIETY c/o N.M.P
Wollor E. Topor
Box 46
Accra, **GHANA**

A refugee organization. Socio-economic self-help for reconstruction of neighboring war-torn country. Reforestation.

Young Farmers Research & Development Society
Mr. Emmanuel Ansah
P.O. Box 419
Madina, Accra, **GHANA**

Organizing rural communities to do group farming, demonstration farms and tree nurseries. Teaching farmers the benefits of tree planting & agroforestry.

African NGO's Environmental Network (ANEN)
Simon Muchiru
P.O. Box 53844
Nairobi, **KENYA**
Tel: 011 254 28138

Sustainable, community based development. One of the largest networks of environmental groups in Africa.

Environment Liaison Center International (ELCI)
P.O. Box 72461
Nairobi, **KENYA**
Tel: (254-2) 562015, 562022, 562172

An international coalition of over 500 NGOs from The South. ELCI does much useful work with women, envi-

15

ronment and development. ELCI provides funding for NGO's in The South, ranging from $100—$10,000 for practical field projects with environmental dimensions. ELCI's newsletter *Ecoforum*, is a useful international networking tool.

Green Belt Movement

P.O. Box 14832
Nairobi, **KENYA**
Tel: 254-24634

The Green Belt Movement's founder, Professor Wangari Maathai, is well-known in Kenya and internationally as a vigorous campaigner and implementor of programs to combine community development with environmental protection. The Green Belt Movement has enhanced the self-reliance and self-confidence of tens of thousands of people living in poverty, showing them that planting trees does make a difference to the quality of life for themselves and as a safeguard for the future.

The movement has planted 10 million trees, established 1,500 nurseries, and provided employment for 50,000 women planting, distributing and caring for seedlings and trees. The Green Belt Movement has shown to be an effective method for rural development and has spread to twelve other African countries.

International Center for Agroforestry (ICRAF)

P.O. Box 30677
Nairobi, **KENYA**
Tel: 254-2-521-450/Fax: 254-2-521-001
See entry in Agroforestry section.

Kenya Energy Non-Governmental Organizations (KENGO)

Karuna Road, P.O. Box 48197
Nairobi, **KENYA**

A large coalition of NGOs.

Kenya Indigenous Forest Conservation Project—KIFCON

P.O. Box 71943
Nairobi, **KENYA**
Tel: 252-2-767700/Fax: 252-2-767947

Kenya Volunteer Development Services

P.O. Box 310
Bungoma, **KENYA**

A regional organization promoting, and offering training courses in, organic farming, income generation, tree nurseries, water source protection, soil erosion, poultry farming and fish farming. Silvanus A.B. Malaho.

Kenyan Woodfuel Agroforestry Project

P.O. Box 56212
Nairobi, **KENYA**

Manor House Agricultural Centre

Private Bag
Kitale, **KENYA**
Tel: 20488

Teaches agriculture, forestry, horticulture, organic farming, appropriate technology, etc. MHAC accepts 25 to 30 trainees per year and has volunteers from other countries as teaching assistants. Moses M. Mukolwe, Director

Nguruka Women Group

P.O. Box 1170
Embu, **KENYA**
Tel: 0161-20618

Reforestation, agriculture, forest preservation, agroforestry, tree nursery and gardening. Mrs. Helen Murangiri.

Technical Study Tours Ltd.

P.O. Box 50982
Nairobi, **KENYA**
Tel: 254 2 791227. Fax 254 2 780461

Organizes and conducts international technical study tours in agriculture, forestry, agroforestry, livestock and environment. Training in agroforestry extension in Kenya.

Tom Mboya Agroforestry Center

Rusinga Island, P.O. Box 135
Mbita, **KENYA**

Ugunja Appropriate Skills Training Centre

P.O. Box 330
Ugunja, **KENYA**

UNEP (United Nations Environment Program)

P.O. Box 30552
Nairobi, **KENYA**

UNEP is a major United Nations international organization. One of it's periodicals of special note is Desertification Control Magazine.

Plenty Lesotho

c/o USC, Private Bag A 139
Maseru 100, **LESOTHO**
Tel: 266 315502

Sustainable development project by grass-roots organic farmers from the USA. Projects include woodlot establishment.

Centre National de Recherche sur L'Environnement

Daniel Razafimamonjy
B.P. 1739
Antananarivo, 101, **MADAGASCAR**
Tel: 261-2-23962

Working with local residents to improve the management of regenerating rain forests as part of an integrated conservation and sustainable development project.

COMODE Magazine
B.P. 8357
101 Avtananarivo, **MADAGASCAR**
Tel: (261-2) 341-93

The focus is on Madagascar's wildlife and environmental issues. Quarterly. French and Malagasy. Subscriptions: US$15 per year.

Africa Tree Center
R.T. Mazibuko
P.O. Box 90
Plessislaer, 4500, Natal
REPUBLIC OF SOUTH AFRICA

Friends of the Trees Society would especially like to honor R. T. Mazibuko, who has dedicated his life to the trees and his people for over half a century. Through drought, flood, starvation, and oppression, Mazibuko has steadfastly planted trees around his area. He has educated and trained many young Africans and inspired thousands more to plant trees. A legendary tree figure, the caliber of Richard St. Barbe Baker and Wendy Campbell-Purdy. He has been granted many awards, but deserves more. If you want to help people and trees in South Africa, send a donation to the Africa Tree Center to further its valuable work.

Forestek CSIR
Jeremy Evans
P.O. Box 395
Pretoria, 0001, **REPUBLIC OF SOUTH AFRICA**
Tel: 27 012 8412620/Fax: 27 012 84 12689

Conducting Rapid Rural Appraisals for biosphere reserves and a national biomass initiative. Permaculture projects, woodlot projects, and in-depth participatory research for the above and community forestry projects.

South African Perpetual Forests
North Terrace House, 19 North Tee
Hackney, **REPUBLIC OF SOUTH AFRICA**

Transvaal Nature Conservation
Private Bag X209
Pretoria, 0001, **REPUBLIC OF SOUTH AFRICA**

Trees for Africa
P.O. Box 2035
Gallo Manor, 2052, **REPUBLIC OF SOUTH AFRICA**

This non-profit NGO promotes agroforestry, small-farm forestry, woodlots and permaculture. Works with schools and community groups, leads public awareness campaigns, sponsors contests, provides seedlings. Good networking among community forestry groups in South Africa.

Africa Cooperative Action Trust—ACAT
P.O. Box 283
Mbabane, **SWAZILAND**
Tel: 42446

Trains grassroots workers on use and conservation of their limited natural resources and promotion of tree planting for soil conservation.

Skillshare Africa
P.O. Box A129
Mbabane, **SWAZILAND**
Tel: 43476

Establishment of tree nurseries for sale to local people and for community woodlots and orchards.

Uganda Youth in Production Association
P.O. Box 8762
Kampala, **UGANDA**
Fax: c/o 256-41-245597

A local organization and grass roots youth group with training in rural development, forestry, agriculture, reforestation, livestock, seeds, agroforestry, recycling, health care, and renewable energy. Emmanuel A. Katombozi, Executive Coordinator

Women's Tree Planting Movement
Ruth Mubiru
P.O. Box 10352
Kampala, **UGANDA**

A national organization which runs a forestry research station, gives seminars and administers women's projects in forestry and tree-planting, resource management, agriculture, and agroforestry.

Association of Women's Clubs
Farai Samhungu
Box 4A 339
Harare, **ZIMBABWE**

Development Support Service of IRED
Rudo Chitiga- Machingauta
P.O. Box 8242
Causeway, Harare, **ZIMBABWE**

Facilitates the sharing of skills and resources among sustainable development NGOs in southern and East Africa.

Natural Farming Action Group
Chikikwa, Private Bag 2014
Chimanimani, **ZIMBABWE**

Promotion, support and practical implementation of natural farming methods and environmental conservation with a special focus on women and communal lands.

National Association of Non-Governmental Organizations (NANGO)
P.O. Box 8465
Causeway, Harare, **ZIMBABWE**
Tel: 263-4-791251/Fax 263-4-794973

Tree Society of Zimbabwe
P.O. Box 2128
Harare, **ZIMBABWE**

15

Zimbabwe Institute of Permaculture
P.O. Box 8515
Causeway, Harare, **ZIMBABWE**
Tel: 397037/726911

Bridget O'Conner and John Wilson. A 150-acre demonstration farm for permaculture production and training in reforestation, permaculture, herbs, agroforestry, livestock, fruit, rainwater harvest, market garden, education, organic gardening, development of appropriate structures for energy efficiency, textiles, and brick production. A newsletter is published.

This is also the address for the Natural Farming Network which facilitated exchange visits between organic farmers of Zimbabwe and Kenya in 1990 and 1991. The farmers were enthusiastic.

Conventional Forestry Organizations in Africa

The following institutes are among the major forestry institutes in their country, mostly government and universities. They are indexed alphabetically by country.

Institut de Technologie Forestiere
Route de Tazoult
Batna, **ALGERIA**

Algeria has northern Africa's most impressive tree planting and shelterbelt projects.

Centre Technique Forestier Tropical
BP 303
Ouagadougou, **BURKINA FASO**

Ecole Nationale Forestiere de Dinderesso
BP 1105
Bobo-Dioulasso, **BURKINA FASO**

National Center for Forest Tree Seeds (IUFRO)
01 P.B. 2682
Ouagadougou, **BURKINA FASO**
Tel: (226) 301232

Centre de Recherches Forestieres de Nkolbisson
BP 2102
Yaounde, **CAMEROON**
Tel: 23-26-44

Centre Universitaire de Dschang
Department de Foresteria
BP 138
Yaounde, **CAMEROON**

Ecole Nationale des Eaux et Forets
BP 69
Mbalmayo, **CAMEROON**

Centre Technique Forestier Tropical du Congo
BP 764
Pointe Noire, **CONGO**

Directin des Eaux et Forests et des Resources Naturelles
BP 98
Brazzaville, **CONGO**
Tel: 812459

Faculte d'Agronomic
Department de Sylviculture
BP 30
Yangambi, Sous Region de la Thsopo, **CONGO**

Department of Forestry & Wood Technology
El Shatby
Alexandria, **EGYPT**

Hosted March 21-24, 1994 conference on Silviculture of Protection Forestry in Arid Regions and the Agroforestry Potential. Contact S.A.E. Kandeel.

Alemaya University of Agriculture
Forestry Department—Prof. Andrew Barnes
Box 138
Dire Dawa, **ETHIOPIA**
Fax: 251-5111525

Awassa College of Agriculture
Forestry Department
P.O. Box 5
Awassa, Sidamo, **ETHIOPIA**
Tel: 06-200221

Forestry and Wildlife Resources Institute
Wondo Genet
P.O. Box 128
Shashemene, **ETHIOPIA**

Forestry Research Centre
Kasetsart University
Box 1034
Addis Ababa, **ETHIOPIA**

International Livestock Center for Africa
Dept. of Environmental Sciences and Plant Production
P.O. Box 5689
Addis Ababa, **ETHIOPIA**

National Herbarium
Addis Ababa University
P.O. Box 3434
Addis Ababa, **ETHIOPIA**

Soil Conservation Research Project
P.O. Box 2597
Addis Ababa, **ETHIOPIA**

Ecole Nationale des Eaux et Forets
BP 396
Libreville, **GABON**

Forestry Research Institute
   University Post Office Box 63
   U.S.T. Kumasi, **GHANA**

School of Forestry
   P.O. Box 214
   Sunyani, **GHANA**

Centre Forestier de Seredou
   BP 31
   Seredou, **GUINEA**

Ecole Forestiere
   Mamou, **GUINEA**

Centre Technique Forestier Tropical de Cote D'Ivoire
   BP 33
   Abidjan 08, **IVORY COAST**

Centre de Perfectionnement des Metiers din Bois
   Koumassi, **IVORY COAST**

Ecole Forestiere du Banco
   032 BP 233
   Abidjan 03, **IVORY COAST**

Ecole Forestiere
   BP 1490
   Bouafle, **IVORY COAST**

Kenya Forestry College
   P.O. Box 8
   Londiani, **KENYA**

Kenya Forestry Research Institute
   Attn: C. K. Kiriinya, P.O. Box 2041
   Nairobi, **KENYA**

Lesotho Agricultural College
   Forestry Department
   Maseru, **LESOTHO**

Centre pour le Exploitation et la Regeneration
Forestieres et la Technologie din Binis
   Morovia, **LIBERIA**

Forest and Range Management Institute
   P.O. Box 16369
   Zawia, **LIBYA**

Center for Training of Professionals in Forestry
(Centre de Formation Professionnelle Forestiere)
   PB 117
   Morondava, **MADAGASCAR**

   Started in 1978. Training, publications and reforestation. Rolf Lehmann, project chief.

Forestry Research Institute of Malawi
   P.O. Box 270
   Zomba, **MALAWI**
   Tel: 265-522866/Fax 265-522782

Malawi College of Forestry
   Private Bag 6
   Dedza, **MALAWI**
   Tel: 265-220-275

Centre de Formation Pratique Forestiers de Tabakoro
   BP 1719
   Bamako, **MALI**

La Station des Recherches Forestieres
   Ministere de L'Agriculture
   Rabat, **MOROCCO**

Instituto Medio Agrario de Chimolo
   Chimolo, Manica, **MOZAMBIQUE**

Ministerio Da Agricultura—DNFFB
   Anna Sequeira, Forestry Extension Manager
   P.O. Box 1406
   Maputo, **MOZAMBIQUE**
   Tel: 258-21-460096

Vida Silvestre (Mozambique)
   Direccao Nacional de Florestas e Fauna :Bravia
   (DNFFB)
   Ministerio da Agricultura
   Praca dos Herois Mocambicanos
   Maputo, **MOZAMBIQUE**
   Tel: (258-1) 460-036. Constantino Mendes, Editor

   Portuguese-language quarterly. Natural resource news in Mozambique. US $20/year.

Federal Department of Forestry
   P.M.B. 1223
   Benin City, Bendel State, **NIGERIA**

Federal University of Technology
   Dept. of Forestry and Wood Technology
   P.M.B. 204
   Akure, Ondo State, **NIGERIA**
   Tel: 234 34 200090/Fax: 234 34 230450

Forestry Research Institute of Nigeria
   PMB 5054
   Ibadan, **NIGERIA**

Journal of Tropical Resources
   Department of Forest Resources Management
   University of Ibadan
   Ibadan, **NIGERIA**

   English-language Quarterly. Subscriptions: US $125 per year.

Nigerian Federal School of Forestry
   Department of Forest Research
   PMB 19
   Jos, **NIGERIA**

15

Savanna Forestry Research Station
PMB 1039
Samaru—Zaria, Kaduna State, **NIGERIA**
Tel: 069-32591

Agronomiques du Rwanda, Department de Foresterie
BP 617
Butare, **RWANDA**

South African Forestry Research Station
Private Bag X1
Winterton, 3340, **REPUBLIC OF SOUTH AFRICA**

University of Stellenbosch
Faculty of Forestry
Private Bag X5018
7599 Stellenbosch, **REPUBLIC OF SOUTH AFRICA**
Fax: 27-22 31-77 36 03

Hosted a conference on Minimum Data Requirements for Sustainable Forest Management, April 24-30, 1994. Contact Prof. B. Bredenkamp.

Association of Foresters in the Sahel
c/o El-hadji Sene, Parc de Hann
BP 1831
Dakar, **SENEGAL**

Conservator of Forests
Department of Agriculture and Forestry, Forestry Division
Youyi Building
Brookfields, Freetown, **SIERRA LEONE**
Tel: 223445

Direction des Eaux et Forets
Parc de Hann
BP 1831
Dakar, **SENEGAL**
Tel: 210628

Centre National de Recherches Forestiers
BP 2312
Dakar, **SENEGAL**
Tel: 213219

Ecole Nationale des Agents Techniques des Eaux et Forets
BP 5
Ziguinchor, **SENEGAL**

Forestry Training School
Bambawo, Keneman District, **SIERRA LEONE**

Arab Institute of Forestry and Range Management
P.O. Box 142
Lattakia, **SYRIA**

Arid Zone Afforestation Research Project
Box 1570
Dodoma, **TANZANIA**

College of African Wildlife Management, Mweka
P.O. Box 3031
Moshi, **TANZANIA**

Forest Industries Training Institute
P.O. Box 1925
Moshi, **TANZANIA**

Forestry Development Project
P.O. Box 3526
Zanzibar, **TANZANIA**

Olmotonyi Forestry Training Institute
P.O. Box 943
Arusha, **TANZANIA**

Serenegeti Research Institute
PO Seronera, Via Arusha, **TANZANIA**

Sokoine University of Agriculture
Faculty of Agriculture and Forestry
P.O. Box 3009, Sub-Post Office Chuo Kikuu
Morogoro, **TANZANIA**

Tanzanian Forestry Research Institute
P.O. Box 30072
Kibaha, **TANZANIA**

Centre de Formation Professionelle Agricole de Tove–CFPA
Section Forestiere
BP 401
Kpalime, **TOGO**

Ecole d'Exploitation Forestiere de Remel
Menzel Jemil, **TUNISIA**

Institut Sylvo-Pastoral
8110 Tabarka, **TUNISIA**

Makerere University
Faculty of Agriculture and Forestry
P.O. Box 7062
Kampala, **UGANDA**
Tel: 56931

Myabyeya Forestry College
PO Private Bag
Masindi, **UGANDA**

Nakawa Forest Research Station
P.O. Box 1752
Kampala, **UGANDA**

Uganda Forest Department
P.O. Box 31
Entebbe, **UGANDA**

Ecole Technique Forestiere
Bengamisa, **ZAIRE**

Division of Forest Research
P.O. Box 22099
Kitwe, **ZAMBIA**

15

Tree Improvement Research Center
> National Council for Scientific Research
> P.O. Box 21210
> Kitwe, **ZAMBIA**

Zambia Forest College
> Private Bag, Mwekera,
> Kitwe, **ZAMBIA**

Forest Research Center
> P.O. Box HG 595
> Highlands, Harare, **ZIMBABWE**
> Tel: 267-14-47070/Fax: 267-14-47066

> Publishes English-language Quarterly, *FORMAT: Forestry Research Matters*. Free on exchange basis.

Zimbabwe College of Forestry
> P.O. Box 660
> Mutare, **ZIMBABWE**
> Tel: 263-20-60158/Fax: 263-20-61566

Frequency of African Countries Appearing in English-Language Networks for Sustainability

In the process of international networking for Friends of the Trees Society and during preparation of this Africa section, I have read many journals and international directories containing thousands of addresses of African people and groups involved in tree planting, sustainable agriculture, agroforestry, and development projects. These address lists reflect the amount of English-language information about sustainable systems going between countries. For some countries I can find hundreds of addresses, for others I can find none. There are a number of reasons for this relative abundance or scarcity of connections, such as language barriers, areas with war or civil strife, relative presence of Aid/Development agencies from the North, and rejection of information/control from the North.

Many addresses
> Ghana
> Kenya
> Nigeria
> Tanzania

Common addresses
> Botswana
> Burkina Faso
> Ethiopia
> Ivory Coast
> Malawi
> Mali
> Senegal
> Sierra Leone

> Sudan
> Uganda
> Zimbabwe

Some addresses
> Algeria
> Benin
> Congo
> Gambia
> Lesotho
> Morocco
> South Africa
> Togo
> Tunisia
> Zambia

Few addresses
> Guinea
> Libya
> Madagascar
> Mauritania
> Mauritius
> Mozambique
> Namibia
> Rwanda
> Somalia
> Swaziland
> Zaire

Very few addresses
> Angola
> Burundi
> Cape Verde Islands
> Central African Republic
> Chad
> Egypt
> Equatorial Guinea
> Gabon
> Guinea-Bissau
> Liberia
> Libya
> Niger
> Seychelles
> Western Sahara

15

15

16 Forestry in South & Central America

South and Central America Directory

FULLY-FUNCTIONING, TROPICAL RAINFORESTS are not quiet places, especially at dawn when the jungle's incredible diversity and exuberance of life celebrates the new day. The jungles of South and Central America have long been considered mysterious, dangerous, endless lands. But they are becoming more finite and smaller all the time.

Restoration forestry has a lot to teach and a lot to learn in Latin America. The world as a whole has a lot to learn from the indigenous forest peoples who have lived for millennia in close touch with their ecosystems. These descendants of many generations of forest dwellers have forest knowledge which modern people can hardly imagine. Latin America hasn't always been Latin. Even today it is much more than Latin. There are still millions of Native Americans. They are still persecuted heavily in most countries. There are also many descendants of African blood, especially on the Atlantic side of the continents, who have little political or economic power outside of the Caribbean.

The report from South and Central American forests is similar to most of the world. Forests are dropping at a fast rate, soil erosion is a problem in many places. Governments are repressive and exploitative in most countries, and the USA covert action team stalks the countryside with a big stick.

In spite of the problems, people are developing restoration forestry to meet the needs of the human community and the needs of the land. Good ideas abound; good models are still hard to come by.

South & Central America Forestry Organizations

Arbofilia

Apdo 512 Tibas
1100, COSTA RICA
Tel: (506) 35-54-70

Association for the Protection of Trees. This volunteer organization helps farmers in the ravaged Central Pacific region around the Carara Biological Reserve manage their land in an environmentally-sound fashion, concentrating on protecting watersheds and aiding propagation of native species of plants and animals. They offer tours of their operations.

The address of their US affiliate is: Arbofilia, Audubon Society of Portland, 5151 NW Cornell Road, Portland, Oregon, 97210, USA.

Asociacion Comunitaria de Pobladores para el Desarrollo y la Ecologia (ASOGOPODE)

Calle 64, No. 13-46, Of. 303
Santa Fe de Bogota, COLOMBIA
Tel: 212 51 79

Reforestation.

Belize Center for Environmental Studies

P.O. Box 666
C.A. Belize City, BELIZE
Tel: 501-2-45545/Fax 31197

The foremost environmental center in Belize. Established in 1988 to build local environmental awareness and to work with government to establish increased environmental protections. The Center has available a *Belize Environmental Directory*. Ms Lou Nicolait, Director.

Brazilian Agroforestry Network (REBRAF)

CX Postal 70060
Rio de Janeiro 22422, BRAZIL

NGO promoting agroforestry among low income and forest communities, training courses and documentation. Identifies projects and prepares proposals for funding. Suely Anderson, Executive Director.

Centro Agronómico Tropical para la Investigación y Enseñanza (CATIE)

CATIE 7170
Turrialba, COSTA RICA
Tel: (506) 56-0858/Fax: (506) 56-6282 or 56-1533

The largest Central American research organization working in forestry, agroforestry, and agriculture. Cooperates with many local, governmental, and international organizations. Their many projects include:

- OLAFO, a combined project of CATIE and many local groups throughout Central America working on the research and development of management schemes for valuable forest understory plants including ornamentals, medicinals, natural insecticides, and fibers for crafts.

- F/FRED in the Western Hemisphere. The Central American Tree Crop Production Project is part of F/FRED, a project for the coordination of database management activities of multipurpose tree species (MPTs).

- INFORAT was established through a cooperative agreement of CATIE and the Swiss Development Cooperation (ÇOSUDE) to collect, process, and distribute forestry information produced in Latin America. During its eight years of activity, INFORAT has developed a databank that includes 1,600 documents on agroforestry and 1,700 on fuelwood and alternative energy sources. It has produced specialized bibliographies on renewable natural resources (5,236 references) and agroforestry (680 references), which are available in English.

- CATIE publishes various journals and newsletters and has many publications available (mostly in Spanish).

Central American & Mexico Coniferous Resources Cooperative
North Carolina State University
Box 8007
Raleigh, North Carolina, 27695-8007 USA
Tel: (919) 737-2738/Fax: 821-0611

CAMCORE was founded in 1980 by forestry professionals concerned by the genetic degradation of Central American pine species. They collect seeds from superior trees of pines and endangered hardwoods and plant them on the forest lands of members in nine countries.

Central InterComunal del Oriente Lomerio
Casilla 4213,
Santa Cruz, BOLIVIA
Tel/Fax: (591-33) 46714

A large forestry project involving 18 Chiquitano Indian communities in Bolivia. The plan involves selective harvesting of marketable species, natural regeneration enhancement, reforestation of degenerated agriculture and pasture lands, and timber processing in a central mill.

Centre Technique Forestier Tropical
BP 116
97310 Koureu, FRENCH GUYANA

Cofyal Yanesha Forestry Co-op
C.N. Shiringamazú, Km 40, Carretera
Central, Palcazú, Oxapampa, Pasco PERU
Tel: (51-14) 422-796, 408-846/Fax: 406-706

This Indigenous cooperative formed with the objectives of creating a source of employment for its members; directing forest management, harvesting, and the integrated use of Yanesha communal forests to promote the industrialization and marketing of wood products; and supporting the development of native communities. They utilize an innovative system of strip-clearcutting with over half the forest in permanent shelterwood preserves. The system was developed by the Tropical Science Center in collaboration with the local people to mimic both natural treefall and the Yanesha's traditional system of shifting cultivation. See article in *Restoration Forestry*.

Desarrollo Forestal Participativo en Los Andes
FAO, Apartado 21-190
Quito, ECUADOR

Friends of Lomas Barbudal
691 Colusa Ave.
Berkeley, California 94707 USA
Tel: (415) 526-4115

Formed to protect the Lomas Barbudal Biological Reserve in Guanacaste, Costa Rica constantly threatened by wildfire. The Friends have recently begun projects to establish living firebreaks.

Fundacion Neotropica
Apdo. 236—1002
San Jose,' COSTA RICA
Tel: 33-00-03

Fundacion Neotropica manages the Centrol BOSCOSA, a center for forestry conservation and development on the Osa Peninsula in Costa Rica.

The BOSCOSA Project is an integrated conservation and development initiative being carried out on the Osa Peninsula in southwest Costa Rica within the 70,000 hectares of the Golfo Dulce Forest Reserve. The objective of the project, initiated in 1988, is to stabilize land use within the forest reserve and conserve the remaining forest cover as a buffer zone for the neighboring Corcovado National Park. The project is implemented by the Fundacion Neotropica. The project includes eight grassroots associations on forest management, small-scale forest industry, agroforestry, project administration, and environmental education. Two of the groups have purchased wood processing equipment and are putting 700 hectares (ha) under forest management. Local orga-

16

nizations have also reforested 100 ha and planted peren-nial crops on another 100 ha during the past three years. (Excerpt from article "Pilot natural forest management initiatives in Latin America: Lessons and Opportunities." M. Kiernan, et al., in Unasylva 169, Vol. 43, 1992. pp. 16-23.)

Fundacion Peruana para la Conservacion de la Naturaleza (FPCN)
Chinchon 858/A, San Isidro, Aptdo. 18-1393,
Lima, PERU
Tel: 422 796

Guaraquecaba Program in Brazil: Conservation of the Atlantic Forest
Clovis R. S. Borges, President of the Society of Wildlife Research and Environmental Education (SPVS)
Rua Gutemberg, 345 Batel
80.420-030-Curitiba, Paraná, BRAZIL
Fax: +55-41-242-02 80

An international program to conserve Brazil's Atlantic tropical forest, an important area for biodiversity. In-cludes an conservation plan to protect the forest ecosys-tem and allow sustainable human use of the area.

Huichol Forestry Project
c/o ADEMSO, Apdo 5-270,
Guadalajara, Jalapa, C.P. 45042, MEXICO
Tel: (52-3) 622-1719/Fax: 622-3978

Two indigenous Huichol communities have been managing their threatened forests, making furniture in local cooperatives, and educating neighboring communi-ties about alternatives.

INIFAP—Mexico Forestry Research
Patricia Negreros Castillo, Director
Calle 62, No. 462-205
Merida, Yucatan, MEXICO
Tel: 99 24-77-64/Fax: 99 23-93-03

Research focusing on environmentally friendly alter-natives to industrial forestry.

IXETO
Juárez Independencia esq. con Centenario
Villa de Etla, Oaxaca, MEXICO
Tel: (52-951) 61397 or 60598 ext. 233

IXETO is an organization of Zapotec Indian communi-ties in mixed pine-oak forests of Oaxaca and Sierra Juarez, each of which manages its own forest and sawmill.

Karawala Sumu Community
CIDCA-Bluefields, Contigua Hotel
Hollywood, Bluefields, NICARAGUA
Tel: (505) 82-735

This Misquito Indian group operates a communal portable sawmill for boat construction and timber sale.

Monkey Bay Wildlife Sanctuary
P.O. Box 187
Belmopan, BELIZE

Monkey Bay Wildlife Sanctuary is a non-government membership organization that serves as a model for private land stewardship. The sanctuary protects 1,070 acres of tropical forest and savanna, bordered by the Sibum River. Projects include a field research station, outdoor education center, tree nursery, organic garden, overnight accommodations and camping facilities. It's goal is to preserve wildlife and demonstrate that a natural unmanaged forest can be a local economic asset.

Organización de Ejidos Productores Forestales (OEPF)
Av. Lazaro Cardenas s/n Edificio, Prode May
Felipe Carillo Puerto, Quintana Roo 77200 MEXICO
Tel: (52-983) 40307/Fax: 40191

OEPF is a union of 19 Maya communities in northern Quintana Roo which attempt to manage their mahogany forests sustainably for the production of lumber, railroad ties and other wood products. They concentrate on com-munity empowerment and forestry training, and intend to plant 10 trees for every 1 they cut.

Organization for Tropical Studies
Universidad de Costa Rica
San Pedro de Montes de Oca
COSTA RICA

A prestigious research institute associated with univer-sities in the USA.

Plan Piloto Forestal
Infiernillo 157, Esq. Efrain Aguilar
Chetumal, Quintana Roo MEXICO
Tel/Fax: (52-983) 24424

Since 1983, 42 communities in Quintana Roo have organized to manage their forests, process and market timber and tap chicle resin. One of the first community forestry projects to be certified by Green Cross and SmartWood.

Proyecto Desarrollo del Bosque Latifoliado
P.O. Box 427
La Ceiba, HONDURAS
Tel/Fax: (504) 43-1032

Listed by the Rainforest Alliance's Smart Wood Certi-fication Program as a source of sustainably produced sawn-wood. Included in the project are ten Integrated Management Areas on the North coast of Honduras.

16

San Juan Parangaricutiro
Indigenous Forestry Enterprise
Cupatitzio No. 25-206, Uruapan
Michoacan C.P. 6000, MEXICO
Tel: (52-451) 321-65, 414-49/Fax: 414-92

An exemplary, large-scale, vertically-integrated forestry enterprise involving communal forest management, lumber and charcoal production and export, and a furniture, parquet and molding industry, all in an indigenous community.

Silvolab Guiana
Olivier Laroussinie
BP 316
97379 Kourou, FRENCH GUIANA
Fax: +594-32-43-02

A multinational project is planned for the Amazonian Region where 12,000 ha of natural tropical rainforest will be managed in a sustainable way for timber production through the application of forest research to test various silvicultural systems on a large scale

Third World Institute—NGONET
c/o Patrick McCully
Casilla Correo 1539
Montevideo 1539, URUGUAY

This project aims to distribute information on environment and development which reflects the priorities of groups in the South, especially grassroots, indigenous, and women's groups.

Tropical Forestry Program
World Wildlife Fund—U.S.
1250 24th St. NW
Washington, DC 20037 USA
Tel: (202) 778-9712
Michael Kiernan, Coordinator

WWF is the world's largest private conservation organization. WWF has many projects in Latin America, mainly centered on preservation.

WWF has set up a Natural Forest Management Network of forestry projects in Latin America to whom WWF provides technical and financial assistance, and enables communication between the different projects.

Tropical Science Center
Apartado 8-3870
San Jose 1000, COSTA RICA

Unidad Comunal Forestal de Ixtlán de Juárez
Domicilio Conocido, Ixtlán de Juárez
Oaxaca, MEXICO
Tel: (52-951) 45105

A large communal enterprise which manages pine-oak, cloud and tropical rain forests, a large sawmill, a small factory for tool handles, a box factory, and a tree nursery.

Union de Comunidades y Ejidos Forestales Zapotecas y Chinantecas (UCEFO)
Domicilio Conocido
Capulalpan de Méndez
Ixtlán, Oaxaca MEXICO
Tel: (52-951) 69233

An association of ten Zapotec community forestry enterprises in the pine-oak and cloud forests of Oaxaca who have wrested control of their forests from the exploitative industry and are now striving to manage them sustainably for the benefit of their communities.

University for Peace
Universidad para la Paz
Aptdo 199
1250 Escazu, COSTA RICA
Fax: (506) 49 19 29/53 542 27

The University for Peace is the home base of Gerardo Budowski, one of the most well-known and respected tree personages in Central America. Universidad para la Paz conducts periodic courses on forestry, including non-timber products.

South & Central American Forestry Periodicals

All periodicals are in Spanish unless otherwise noted.

Acción Ecologica
C/O Gina Chavez
Casilla 17-15-246
CQE, Quito, ECUADOR
Tel/Fax: (593) 547-516

Argentina Forestal
Camara Arg de Aserradores de Maderas
Alsina 440
1087 Buenos Aires, ARGENTINA
Journal.

BIOTICA
Instituto Nacional de Investigacion sobre Recursos Bioticos
Apdo Postal 63
Xalapa, Veracruz, MEXICO

A quarterly on topics such as agro-ecosystems, tropical forest ecology, botany, the economic uses of plants, and species lists of plants and trees in particular forests.

Boletin Informativo Rifalc
Centro de Informacion Bioagropecuaria y Forestal
Direccion de Bibliotecas-U.N.N.E.
Las Heras 727
Resistencia Chacó, ARGENTINA 3500
Tel: (54-722) 7764

16

eight-page newsletter covers a diverse range of issues concerning forestry. Free to NGOs.

Bosques y Desarrollo

Editor, ACIF
Carrera 8 No. 19-34, Oficina 602
Bogota, Cundinamarca, COLOMBIA

Each issue focuses on Andean forestry issues such as agroforestry, community forestry, forest research and environmental education.

Bosques y FUTURO

Editor, ACIF
Calle 19 No. 3-50, Oficina 701
Bogota, COLOMBIA

A quarterly focusing on environmental concerns in forests in Argentina, Bolivia, Colombia and Peru.

Desarrollo Forestal Campesino

FAO/Holanda
Proyecto Desarrollo Forestal Participativo en Los Andes
Casilla 17-21-0190 (Eloy Alfaro)
Quito, ECUADOR
Tel: (593-2) 45-0696/Fax: (593-2) 44-2249
Internet: PAULA@FAO.EC.

Forestry extension, agroforestry, community forestry and the sustainable development of Andean communities.

Documentos Recien Ingresados a BASFOR

Red Nacional be Informacion Forestal (REDINFOR)
Apartado 14-0297
Lima, PERU
Tel/Fax: (51-14) 37-7912

Reviews publications on forest management, forest industry, conservation, ecology and agroforestry.

Quarterly. Subscriptions: US $20/yr., free on exchange basis.

Informandonos: Newsletter of the APECO Research Network

Peruvian Association for Conservation of Nature (APECO)
Parque Jose de Acosta 187
Magdalena, Lima-17, PERU
Tel: (51-14) 616-316/Fax: (51-14) 633-048

Six issues per year.

Red Latinoamericana de Bosques Tropicales

Fundacion Natura
Av. America 5653 y Voz Andes
Casilla 17-01-253
Quito, ECUADOR
Tel: (593-2) 44-7341/Fax: 43-4449

A quarterly distributed to NGOs in the Latin American Tropical Forestry Network. It covers environmental management of tropical forests, indigenous populations, Amazon treaty activities, land management alternatives, and related news.

Revista Forestal Centroamericana (RFC)

Turrialba, COSTA RICA (see CATIE address in Organizations)

A triennial magazine that focuses on natural resource issues in Central America, with an emphasis on forestry. Articles written in Spanish, contain English summaries, as well as key words and literature citations. US$20 for those in Central America; US$25 for the Caribbean, South America, Africa, and Asia; US$35 for other countries.

Revista Forestal Latinoamericana

Instituto Forestal Latinoamericano
Avenida los Chorros De Milla (Apartado 36)
Merida 5101, VENEZUELA
Tel: (58-74) 440-535/Fax: (58-74) 448-906

This 100 to 150 page journal focuses on Latin American forestry issues. Spanish, with English and French summaries. Quarterly. US $50 per year.

Instituto Forestal Latinoamericano also publishes *Bibliografia Forestal Latinoamericano*, which provides a coded and indexed compilation of bibliographical summaries and digests of the literature on tropical forests, forest products, and industries. 3 issues per year in Spanish, containing 150-200 pages.

Forestry Conferences in Central America

First Central American Forestry Congress

Held in Flores Peten, Guatemala from August 29 to September 4, 1993. For further information contact: Dr. J. Bockor, Proyecto Dessarollo Forestal Communal DIGEBOS/GTZ, 71. ave 6—80, Zona 30, GUATEMALA. Tel:/Fax: 502-2-735214

The event was attended by 210 delegates from Central America, Belize, Mexico, Panama and other participants from the USA, Germany, Finland, Spain, England, Netherlands, Chile and Peru. The theme for this congress was "The Humid Tropical Forest: a Development Alternative in Central America." The congress was held in concert with the third Guatemalan Forestry Congress.

A report about the Congress mentioned a meeting of representatives of farmers and indigenous people which took place in Quetzaltenango, Guatemala from August 24-26, 1993, based on the theme "The Perspectives of Rural Communities Participating in the Sustainable Management of Humid Tropical Forests."

Fifth Symposium of the Silviculture in Latin America: "Silviculture and Sustainable Development in Tropical America"

Cali, Colombia, 20-24 September 1993.
Contact: Gonzalo de la Salas, Coordinator S1-07-09

16

Working Group; Apartado Aereo 091676.
Fax: (571) 213 92 19

International Symposium/Workshop on the Management and Rehabilitation of Degraded Lands and Secondary Forests in Amazonia
Para, Brazil, 18-22 April.
Contact: Dr. John Parrotta, International Institute of Tropical Forestry, USDA Forest Service, Call Box 25,000, Rio Pedras, Puerto Rico, 00928, USA.
Fax: (809) 766-6302

Latin American Forest and Conservation History Conference
February 18-22, 1991. San Jose, Costa Rica.
Contact: Harold K. Steen, Forest History Society, 701 Vickers Avenue, Durham, N.C. 27701.
Tel: (919) 682-9319

Books and Articles on Forestry in South & Central America

Amazonia: Voices from the Rainforest: A Resource and Action Guide
Angela Gennino, ed. 1990. Rainforest Action Network, 301 Broadway, Rm. A, San Francisco, California, 94133 USA. 92 pp. $8.50.

A tool to help those who want to support the efforts of grassroots organizations in the Amazon basin to defend their forests. This guide lists and describes 250 organizations from 26 countries, each with objectives, programs, needs and resources; plus a country-by-country overview of the major threats to Amazonia's rainforests and the indigenous people who depend on them; along with statistics on forests and deforestation.

Damage-Controlled Logging in Managed Tropical Rain Forest in Surinam
J. Hendrison. 1991. Ecology and Management of Tropical Rain Forests in Surinam: 4. Available at PUDOC, P.O. Box 4, 6700 AA Wageningen, THE NETHERLANDS.

Conventional logging operations and controlled logging experiments were compared in a forest area of 640 hectares during the period 1982-1984. Controlled felling was shown to reduce felling damage significantly and to be more efficient than conventional logging.

The Forests of continental Latin America (Including European Possessions): A bibliography of selected literature, 1920-1950
F. J. Flick. Government Printing Office. 1952. Washington, D.C. (USDA Bibliographical Bulletin 18). 193 pp.

Forest Preservation in the Western Highlands of Guatemala
T. T. Veblen. 1978. Geogr. Rev. 68:417-434.

This example of grassroots forest preservation is mentioned by Gary S. Hartshorn in "Tropical and Subtropical Vegetation of Meso-America," Chapter 12 of *North American Terrestrial Vegetation*, pp. 366-390.

In describing the coniferous humid forests of northern Meso-America, Hartshorn mentions the widespread forest destruction in this forest type and cites the following positive example:

"An interesting exception in the Guatemalan highlands is the Totonicapan furniture industry based on Pinus ayacahuite dating to the sixteenth century (Veblen, 1978). The remaining white pine forests are held communally and vigorously protected by the communities of woodcutters and carpenters dependent on the forests for their livelihood."

"Natural Forest Management by the Yanesha Forestry Cooperative in Peruvian Amazonia"
Gary S. Hartshorn. In *Alternatives to Deforestation: Steps Toward Sustainable Use of the Amazon Rain Forest*, pp. 128-137.

Long, narrow (30-40 m. wide) strips are clear-cut to maximize utilization of timber and to facilitate natural regeneration of trees. The strips are rotated through a production forest so that uncut primary forest or advanced secondary forest borders a harvested strip.

"The Struggle for the Forest: Conservation and Development in the Sierra Juárez"
David B. Bray. 1991; in *Grassroots Development 15/3*, pp. 13-25.

Detailed history of a people's movement in Mexico to remove the control of local forests from big business and implement ecological management practices.

Sylvicultural Guides: Central American Multipurpose Trees
CATIE
see address in organizations.

Fourteen separate guides by various authors on incorporating multipurpose trees into small farms and rural communities.

Toward a Green Central America: Integrating Conservation and Development
Valerie Barzetti and Yanina Rovinski, eds. 1992. Kumarian Press, 630 Oakwood Ave., Suite 119, West Hartford, Connecticut 06110-1529, USA. 110 pp. US$14.95.

Six national case studies which were almost entirely designed and managed by local organizations

16

who are taking charge of their problems. One study is on the Kuna island communities, made up of people whose ethics and philosophy reflect a deep respect for nature and are relatively successful in combining ancient knowledge with modern techniques.

Views From the Forest: Natural Forest Management Initiatives in Latin America

Matthew A. Perl, Michael J. Kiernan, D. McCaffrey, R. J. Buschbacher, and G. J. Batmanian. WWF. 1991. Available free upon request from Tropical Forestry Program, World Wildlife Fund, 1250 24th St. NW, Washington DC 20037. Tel: (202) 778-9712.

The report from a workshop held in Costa Rica in 1991. Project profiles are given of the 14 Latin American forestry projects which were represented at the workshop. Report discusses technical, social, and economic limitations to widescale adoption of sustainable forestry practices.

Caribbean Forestry Resources

Caribbean Forestry News

USDA Forest Service
Caribbean National Forest
Call Box 25000
Rio Piedras, PUERTO RICO 00928-2500
Tel: (809) 766-5335

Two issues a year. Spanish and English. Free of charge at this time.

Caribbean Technical Cooperation Network on Forestry and Related Environmental Matters

Mr. Narine Lackhan
Deputy Director of Forestry, Forestry Division
Long, Circular Road
Port-of-Spain, TRINIDAD AND TOBAGO
Tel: 809-628 40 07
or: Mr. Claus-Martin Eckelmann
Associate Forestry Officer, c/o FAO Representation
P.O. Box 822
134-138 Frederik Street
Port-of-Spain, TRINIDAD AND TOBAGO
Tel: 809-625 09 95

This network strarted in 1983. After several name changes the Network was formalized in 1991 at the 17th session of the Latin American and Caribbean Forestry Commission held in Venezuela. The main activities of the Network are to facilitate the exchange of information and to organize training courses and workshops. To date, there are focal points in Antigua and Barbuda, Dominica, Haiti, Barbados, Grenada, Jamaica, Belize, Guyana, Montserraat, Saint Kitts and Nevis, Saint Vincent and the Grenadines, Trinidad and Tobago, and Saint Lucia.

Department of Forestry and Soil Conservation

173 Constant Spring Road
Kingston 8, JAMAICA
Tel: 809-9242125/Fax: 809-9242626

Greening the Earth/Ecosystems Tropical Forestry

General Delivery, Luquillo 00673, PUERTO RICO

A local organization with a demonstration farm used for reforestation education.

NGO News for the Eastern Caribbean

Island Resources Foundation
Red Hook Center, Box 33
St. Thomas 00802 Virgin Islands
Tel: (809) 775-6225/Fax: (809) 770-2022

English-language quarterly. Free to environmental NGO's in the eastern Caribbean and to others on an as-available basis.

Grassroots Forest Management Initiatives in Central America: The Role of Local People's Organizations

Merilio Morell

"Let those who know do the talking."

—Peasant Participation Workshop
April 1991, Costa Rica

THE WORKSHOP on "Peasant Participation in the Decision-Making Process and the Management of Forest Resources" was planned as a means of consultation with farmer-group representatives. Its objective was to learn what the groups felt was needed to support their development processes and to promote their active involvement in sustainable forest use. The workshop offered the participants a forum to discuss their experiences and ideas freely, without external pressures.

Held in Costa Rica from 18–26 April 1991, the workshop was attended by 31 representatives from 13 forest organizations in Mexico, Guatemala, El Salvador, Honduras, Nicaragua and Costa Rica. The common characteristic of the organizations invited was experience in forest management for rural community benefit and conservation.

The proceedings were drafted by the participants and are included in the document published by JUNAFORCA and entitled *Seminario de Participacion Campesina en el Proceso de Toma de Docisiones y Manejo de los Recursos Forestales: Síntesis, Conclusiones y Recomendaciones*. Copies may be obtained from the Forests, Trees and People Programme, FAO, Viale delle Terme di Caracalla, Rome.

People's Organizations

Nohbec Ejido
Chetumal, Quintana Roo State, Mexico

This ejido (communal village holding), created in 1936, represents the interests of 200 members. The land registered under its communal ownership covers 23,000 ha, of which 20,000 ha are forest land. From 1936 to 1954 the main activity was the extraction of gum, after which the forest land was logged under concession by a government enterprise until 1982. In 1983 the ejido classified its land as permanent forest and initiated a pilot forest management plan, which gave it a direct interest in the economic returns and prioritized sustainable forest use.

Indigenous Community of San Juan Nuevo
Michoacán State, Mexico

The Comunidad Indígena de San Juan Nuevo was made a collective producer organization in 1981. It comprises 950 members whose land, under semi-collective title, covers 18,300 ha, of which 11,300 ha are natural softwood forest. The community dates back to 1715 when the original title deeds were issued under colonial rule. From 1940 to 1950 its members engaged in resin tapping; from 1950 to 1973 there was a ban on forest activities throughout the State of Michoacán; from 1974 to 1978 forest activities focused exclusively on forest protection; finally, in 1983, commercial logging was limited. Current activities are based on management plans that pursue sustainable forest use. The organization has logging equipment, a sawmill, a furniture factory, a chipper and a resin-processing plant.

Ejido Forest Producers' Association of Southern Quintana Roo
Mexico

The Sociedad de Productores Forestales Ejidales represents the interests of ten ejidos, including Nohbec and San Juan Nuevo. The association began its activities in 1983 to facilitate the formulation of forest management plans and acquired official status in 1986. It provides administrative, marketing, forest management, policy development and legal services. The ejidos represented cover a total area of 330,000 ha, of which 130,000 ha are tropical rain forest.

Resin and Wood Group of Chagüite Grande
Comayagua, Honduras

The organizational initiatives of the Grupo de Resina y Madera de Chagüite Grande began in 1974 with the creation of an agroforestry precooperative. Its management board was subsequently set up and granted legal

16

status in 1988 with the help of the government and international organizations. About 40 members operate over an area of 1630 ha, of which 1,500 ha are softwood forest. The installation of a sawmill and power generator as well as changes in marketing processes have considerably enhanced the social and economic conditions of the community and have given its members a clear understanding of the benefits of sustainable forest use.

Regional Agroforestry Cooperative of Colón-Atlántida Honduras

This organization, also referred to as COATLAHL, was established in 1976 and groups 14 farmer associations that use public land for forestry activities. Its objective is to obtain credit for its members, enhance the marketing of wood and wood products, and ensure that operations are conducive to sustainable forest use. COATLAHL has experienced a number of crises since its inception because of insufficient administrative experience and weak leadership. Since 1988 the organization has been instrumental in increasing the incomes of its members and constitutes an important factor in forest management.

Paquí Community
Totonicapán, Guatemala

With a population of 3,000, the Asociación Paquí has used the local forests, which they consider their own, for more than 100 years. Their main products have been fuelwood and timber for housing and craft work. The community currently has 470 ha of forest land. It acquired legal status in 1962 when it began to operate as an organization with the aim of defending ownership rights to the forest and maintaining the collective status and sustainable use of the resource.

Soil Conservation and Reforestation Group of Cambricán Quetzaltenango, Guatemala

The 12,000 inhabitants of the municipality of Cambricán depend directly on agriculture and handicrafts for their livelihood. Their land comprises 3,800 ha of farmland and 1,300 ha of woodland. The Grupo de Conservación de Suelos Comites de Reforestación de Cambricán arose partly because of the need to conserve the forest as a means of preventing the degradation of agricultural land and, in part, as a means of using forest land as collateral. Soil conservation activities began in 1960 while the conservation groups were established in 1977 and the reforestation groups in 1985. Considerable progress has been made in creating terraces, infiltration ditches, non-vegetative contour works and gully stabilization. The organization has enabled the community members to play an active role in forest extension work through a radio station and in formal education. Although this community does not depend primarily on the forest, the development of its organizational activities has been forest-based. The use of forest land as credit collateral has played an important role in developing industrial and transport activities.

Cantonal Agricultural Center of Hojancha
Guanacaste, Costa Rica

The Hojancha community has a population of approximately 6,000 and a total of 20,000 ha of land, divided among 500 farms. The Centro Agrícola Cantonal del Hojancha is basically a government-sponsored rural extension organization with community representatives on its governing board. It began to promote reforestation as an economic alternative in the 1970s in response to low livestock prices. The strategies employed have made forestry one of the main economic activities of Hojancha.

JUNAFORCA, Community Forestry National Board
San José, Costa Rica

JUNAFORCA is a coalition of grassroots NGOs. Its creation was proposed during the First Community Forestry Meeting, held in San José in November 1989, when grassroots NGOs decided that they needed a mechanism to defend their interests at the highest government levels. JUNAFORCA's objectives are to promote forest policies that correspond to peasant community and resource realities; suggest changes in national development plans; demonstrate that forestry is a natural concomitant of the peasant farmer's activities, provided there are adequate incentives; and in general, act as a means of communication between the government and the community of NGOs composed of Costa Rican peasant farmers. Nationally, JUNAFORCA speaks for 50 NGOs which are represented on a regional basis on its governing board.

Indigenous Community of Leymus
Rio Coco, North Atlantic Autonomous Region, Nicaragua

The Comunidad d Indígena de Leymus, 568 kilometres from Managua, is made up of some 700 ethnic Nicaraguans (Miskitos), grouped in 142 families. The community has a total forest and farmland area of 6900 ha. Its conifer forests have been logged by outside companies since 1922, at no economic gain to the community itself. The leaders and elders set up a Community Forestry Commission in 1989 to safeguard forest ownership and to learn forest use and conservation techniques. This commission is divided into working groups on, for example, resin tapping and women's integration. It also serves as a forum to examine and discuss communications problems, education and national development policies.

Amigos del Cantón RojasConservation Club
Municipio de Sensuntepeque, Cabanas, El Salvador

The Amigos del Cantón Rojas club was set up by farmers to facilitate access to a United Nations Development Programme/FAO-sponsored agroforestry project. The club is representative of organizations in 24 other cantons in the project area. These organizations are made up of both landowners and landless men and women from the canton. Although essentially established to facilitate access to project credit, the clubs have also served to channel education and public service needs to the authorities, negotiate land-leasing terms as well as produce income-earning, capital-generating activities for agricultural investment. The main lesson learned by the farmers has been that unity helps to solve problems.

El Balsamar Agrarian Reform Cooperative
Sonsonate, Canton Cuisnahuat, El Salvador

According to its members, the Asociación Cooperativa de la Reforma Agraria El Balsamar was set up in March 1980, mainly to respond to hunger and unemployment. By forming a cooperative, they gained access to some 600 ha of government land. The original 65 members formed an administrative council and committees on coffee, livestock, cereals and balsam trees, developed along sustainable lines. Their main obstacles are a lack of organizational, administrative expertise, technical skills and financial support. The cooperative has enabled them to secure government help and to spread resources and responsibilities equitably among members.

Agricultural Cooperative of Cruz Urrutia Centeno
Jalapa, Nueva Segovia, Nicaragua

This cooperative acquired legal status in March 1990, but originally dates from a community organization established in 1984, which enabled 56 members including 14 women, to acquire user rights to some 350 ha. The organization was formed to cope with the political and economic difficulties which armed conflict in Nicaragua had brought to the rural areas. Although the situation has now changed, the cooperative helps with problems linked to insufficient credit, high input costs and agricultural development policies. The cooperative is also active in forestry, focusing on reducing the cost of firewood for its sugar plant and establishing live fences. It is also attentive to conservation of the community's water and fauna resources.

The preceding organizational profiles are from an article by Merilio Morell: "Grassroots Forest Management Initiatives in Central America: The Role of Local People's Organizations" in Unasylva *171, Vol 43, 1992. Morell summarizes the experiences of 13 NGOs in Mexico and Central America as described by their leaders. These NGOs were selected to attend a Peasant Participation Workshop in Costa Rica.*

16

The Forests of Chile

PHOTO CREDIT: HAROLD

Fog at Cani

WHEN MOST PEOPLE THINK of temperate rainforests they envision the great rainforests of Oregon, Washington and British Columbia or perhaps Tasmania and New Zealand. Very few know of the Chilean temperate rainforests. Southern Chile is similar to British Columbia and New Zealand with its steep fjord country and dense forests.

Chile is 10% forested, of which 31% is wilderness. However, like the rest of the world, Chile's forests are undergoing decimation by national and multinational corporate interests. Many native forests are being clearcut and replaced with monoculture plantations, mainly Monterey pine (*Pinus radiata*). Monterey pine grows faster in Chile than anywhere else in the world. Plantations have under 20-year rotations. A number of people and organizations in Chile and abroad are endeavoring to slow the assault on Chile's forests and protect remaining roadless areas.

Over 1.5 million hectares of Chile's native temperate forest and rainforest have been cleared since 1975 and replaced by exotic plantations. Development policy instituted under Augusto Pinochet exacerbated this process, but new legislation may help slow the conversion. Ninety percent of the Chilean export of woodchips goes to Japan.

Restoration forestry in Chile focuses on native species and endemic ecosystems. It aims to reform legislation so landowners can benefit from managing their existing native forest or replanting native species instead of exotics (current policy rewards only conversion to exotic tree farms). CODEFF is sponsoring its first three-day workshop in January 1994 for small landowners, introducing sustainable/restoration forestry concepts and promoting alternatives to wholesale conversion to monoculture. This process of educating landowners and policymakers is just starting but appears promising.

Ancient Forest International's (AFI) 1990 Chile Expeditions

The Bosque Valdiviano is a little known and seldom-traveled wilderness, where steep mountains drop to a clear, cold sea and the forests are healthy, old and magnificent. Dominated by valuable hardwood species and countless ferns and mosses, the forest also harbors the last great stands of alerce (pronounced ah-lair-say) (*Fitzroya cupressoidies*). This giant cedar is the largest tree in South America, exceeding four meters in diameter, and one of the three most long-lived species on Earth. Estimated to reach 3300-4000 years of age, it edges out the giant sequoia but not the bristlecone pine, which lives up to 4800 years.

In Puerto Montt, the expedition's jumping-off point, we watched immense piles of hardwood chips being loaded onto cavernous Japanese ships. Multi-national timber interests have a voracious appetite for high-quality wood chips, which provide fiber for fax paper, rayon fabric and other everyday items for which most consumers seldom consider the true cost.

The araucaria (*Araucaria araucana*), also known in English as the monkey puzzle tree or Chilean pine, is an odd-looking conifer that was among the earliest tree types to evolve on Earth. Fossil remains date back 200 million years. The araucaria can live up to 1800 years and reach 2.3 meters in diameter. It is valued as a commercial species and has been largely depleted, particularly under the administration of Pinochet, who allowed relaxation of protective laws and the subsequent cutting of previously untouched forests. In March 1990, Chile's newly elected democratic president Patricio Aylwin reinstated the araucaria's status as a national monument, but pressure from the timber industry continues to threaten preserves.

Araucaria araucana is unique within the genus for its tolerance to cool temperate climates. In autumn the araucaria yields large nuts, which are a vital food source and sacred symbol for local human populations. This near-extinct relict of evolution is protected by the Chilean government but enforcement is insufficient. The araucaria's wood is prized for furniture, but the slow-growing tree takes up to 500 years to be of commercial value.

Ancient Forest International has coordinated purchase of

a 480-hectare (1200-acre) largely untouched araucaria forest in Chile's Region IX known as the Cañi Forest Sanctuary. It is the first international biosphere reserve in the Chilean forest. Write AFI for a Fact Sheet on this preserve.

New Forest Management Guidelines Expected in Chile

Important forest legislation was introduced in Chile in 1991. The long-awaited bill is partly due to an international protest coordinated by CODEFF (Comite pro Defensa de Fauna y Flora) in 1990 against large-scale conversion of native forests into exotic species tree farms. The strong opposition to a Chilean-Japanese effort to clearcut and convert 70,000 hectares of forest near Valdivia (known as the Terranova Project) catalyzed the government's formation of a select committee to study and suggest changes to national forest policy. We're still waiting for a finalized bill.

Organizations Concerned with Chilean Forests

Ancient Forest International

P.O. Box 1850
Redway, California, 95560
Tel: (707) 923-3015

Ancient Forest International (AFI) is working on the Chile forest issue and other temperate forest projects. Contact AFI for further information on Chile's forests and a documentary film.

Ayacara Project

Pablo Sandor
Avenida Suecia 567
Providencia, Santiago, CHILE

The Huequi Peninsula is found in southern Chile, a boat ride from the terminus of the Pan-America highway. The Sandor family owns 16,000 hectares on the Huequi Peninsula, much of it ancient forest. They are creating a center for environmental work and conferences, ecotourism and recreation, as well as meditation and other studies.

A portion of their land (3000 hectares) is slated to be the site of a sustainable forestry pilot project. This will be part of Vision 2020, a program designed as a network of Pacific Basin sustainable forestry projects in temperate zones. See Vision 2020 in Pacific Northwest Proposals section.

Cañi Outdoor Education Project

c/o Rod Walker
Casilla 51
Santiago, 12, CHILE

The newly established Cañi Forest Sanctuary encompasses 480 hectares (1200 acres) of old-growth araucaria (*Araucaria araucana*). An ongoing program for training teachers in ecology issues takes place in the Cañi Forest

Sanctuary. Most of the participants are Chilean educators, teachers-in-training, selected students and scientists.

Comite Nacional pro Defensa de Fauna y Flora (CODEFF)

Sazié 1885
Casilla 3675
Santiago, CHILE
Tel/Fax: 56-2-696-8562
John Moriarty

CODEFF, Santiago-based, formed in 1969, and is Chile's oldest and strongest environmental organization.

Fundacion Lahuen

Orrego Luco 054
Providencia, Santiago, CHILE
Tel: +56-2-234-2617

AFI's southern affiliate, the Santiago-based Fundacion Lahuen is the only Chilean non-government organization focused exclusively on preserving the native forest and its biodiversity. Inquiries may be in English or Spanish. Their basic brochure is available from AFI.

Books and Articles on Chile's Forests

"Case Study: Chile"

A. Lara. 1992. in *Forests in Trouble: A Review of the Status of Temperate forests Worldwide*. Nigel Dudley, ed. 1992. Worldwide Fund for Nature: Gland, Switzerland.

Chile's Native Forest: A Conservation Overview

Ken Wilcox. Ancient Forest International.

Available for $10 from AFI.

"Chile's Ancient Forest"

Earthwatch, Feb./March 1991.

"Alerce Dreams"

Sierra magazine, Jan./Feb. 1992.

"Disturbing the Ancients"

Buzzworm, Jan./Feb. 1992.

Copies of the above 3 articles are available from AFI.

Videos on Chile's Forests

"Expedition Alerce: Lost Forest of the Andes"

A film by Scott Holmquist and Matt Dibble. 1991.

A documentary film made for television. Get a view of some of the grandest forests in the Andes! This film documents AFI's journeys into the southern forests of Chile. It is available for $50 from Matt Dibble, 5628 North Fifth St., Arlington, VA 22205. (703) 525-1689.

Available from Ancient Forest International. AFI has a 12-minute video with basic information on Chile and AFI's work there. A documentary produced in Chile in Spanish may also be copied for those interested.

An Example of Grass-Roots Management in the Lowland Rainforest of Costa Rica

Michael G. Smith

The Context

COSTA RICA HAS A GLOBAL REPUTATION for natural resource conservation and forest protection built primarily upon its system of national parks and nature reserves. Ironically, along side this constellation of public and private preserves which dazzle visiting scientists and tourists with their natural splendor, the country also lays claim to the highest rate of deforestation (124,000 hectares/year) on the Central American isthmus and the highest rate of overall forest loss in the world in terms of percentage of national area (6.9% per year throughout the decade of the 80's, according to the World Resources Institute).

The pressures which have brought this situation about are commonplace throughout the tropics. The government is eager to lessen its large international debt by exporting local commodities as rapidly as possible for foreign exchange. Costa Rica's major industries are, therefore, bananas, coffee, beef, timber—all primarily for export, and tourism, each of which, when practiced on a large scale, can be extremely detrimental to the forests and other local ecosystems. Additionally, although the general economic status is higher than in many developing nations and the population density lower (0.57 people/hectare in 1989), there is still a great deal of rural poverty which leads to the felling of forests for timber sales and to expand agricultural lands. In the areas where unprotected forest still remain, subsistence farmers generally lack legal entitlement to their lands and are encouraged to fell forests in order to demonstrate "land improvement" and thereby protect their property rights.

All of these tendencies are at their worst in the Cantón of Talamanca, Limón Province, at the Southeasterly extreme of Costa Rica's Caribbean coast. This area of the country has been historically ignored by the national government and by international development agencies alike because it was considered a malarial expanse of swamps and jungles unfit for human habitation. It became home to the largest remaining groups of Indigenous

Costa Ricans and to the entire population of English-speaking Caribbean blacks, who were segregated to Limón Province until the 1960's. At that time, the large-scale application of DDT and other pesticides nearly eliminated the malaria-carrying mosquitoes, making the area safe for people of European descent for the first time. The rapid population-influx of the last few decades has been made up primarily of poor political and economic refugees from other Central American countries, particularly Nicaragua, Panamá and El Salvador, and from the Province of Guanacaste in Northwestern Costa Rica which has become so degraded by deforestation and overgrazing that agriculture there is increasingly difficult. The official neglect of the Cantón of Talamanca is obvious even today from the lack of educational and health facilities and the terrible maintenance of roads and other infrastructure.

Since Talamanca's agricultural economy based on cocoa production failed in the mid-1970's due to introduced diseases, the only alternatives to marginal subsistence farming have been: 1) working for the multinational fruit companies which continue to clear the jungle to expand their thousands of hectares of monoculture banana plantations, widely recognized as a prime contributor to erosion, habitat and wildlife loss, human health complications due to massive application of biocides, and social deterioration; 2) in the coastal areas, working for large-scale tourist resorts, sometimes called "ecotourism enterprises" and nearly always financed by foreign capital and giving few benefits to the local people; or 3) selling logging rights to the regional timber cartel which is known to remunerate landowners with as little as 1% of the resale value of the unprocessed logs.

The Association

In the face of this avalanching environmental devastation, a remarkable grass-roots initiative came into being in the tiny community of San Miguel, about 15 kilometers from the Panamanian border and 10 from the Caribbean coast. San Miguel is a scattered group of about 30 homesteads among primary and secondary rainforest with a mean annual rainfall of 240-270 centimeters. The only public buildings are a primary school and a small Catholic church. The nearest basic food store, tavern and bus stop are in the banana company town of Celia, five to ten kilometers from San Miguel's households. Most of that distance is passable in dry weather with a four-wheel-drive vehicle along the rudimentary timber-extraction and banana trail. The inhabitants are mostly Latino and mestizo immigrants, many of whom came from Guanacaste around 1970. The level of formal education among adults is typically to the 2nd or 4th grade. Nearly all make a subsistence living from corn, beans, tubers, fruits, and some livestock—supplemented by casual work for the banana company.

In the early 1980's, a number of San Miguel residents organized a community nursery in order to collaborate with a regional non-governmental development agency called Asociación ANAI, which at that time was distributing tree seeds to community groups throughout Talamanca and educating them in nursery, agroforestry, and silvicultural practices. ANAI's objective was to introduce native and exotic fruit crops which might replace the lost cocoa crop in the local economy. ANAI also complied with the local demand for more resistant cocoa varieties, and introduced a few high-value exotic timber species for experimentation.

When the goals had been achieved and San Miguel's nursery group was ready to disband, a number of the participants saw the need for the community to continue working together. They were particularly concerned about the rapid deforestation they saw in neighboring communities following the arrival of roads and loggers, and with the resulting loss of animal and plant species. They approached ANAI for a loan to buy themselves a parcel of land, and formally associated themselves under the name Asociación Sanmigueleña de Conservación y Desarrollo (San Miguel Conservation and Development Association) or ASACODE.

In the last few years this tiny conglomerate of poor farmers has developed a program of research, conservation and development projects which is truly staggering. They have devised a strategy for the integrated and sustainable management of local natural resources which includes timber harvesting, processing and marketing, native tree seed collection and sale, reforestation, wildlife protection and rehabilitation, tourism, sophisticated ecological and silvicultural research, community education, and local employment options. For technical, financial, and logistic support they have benefited greatly from the cooperation of ANAI and other organizations, but the design and implementation of each project has always rested firmly within the control of the community.

At first all necessary labor was done on a volunteer basis by members of the association. When minor financing became available first one and then more members were given salaries. Now ASACODE employs more than a dozen men and women of San Miguel and contracts part-time technical assistance from outside the community. After years of training and investment, the projects have begun to turn a profit and ASACODE is at the point of financial independence.

Research with Native Tree Species

When ASACODE first considered planting small parcels of native trees on their communal property, their main objective was to ensure the survival of threatened species from the tide of deforestation they saw approaching. As the project evolved, however, it became a sophisticated research effort which promises to generate an enormous amount of information necessary for the successful management of lowland rain forests of the region.

The final project design included mini-plantations of 40 native commercial timber species, each of which was established under three different light regimes: full sun, in what had been abandoned pasture when ASACODE bought the property; half-sun, in a young secondary forest, and full shade, under the intact rain forest canopy. 50 hectares of primary rain forest were set aside as a perpetual wildlife and germplasm reserve and the parcels and nursery area were laid out in part of the remaining 20 hectares, most of which had been degraded to various degrees by the previous owner. Each parcel contains 64 trees on a square grid with a spacing of three meters. The parcels in full sun are cleared every few months to keep weeds from overgrowing the seedlings; the half-sun parcels are cleared in alleys with the intermediate rows of natural regeneration managed only to eliminate excessive shade; the full-shade treatment is maintained only minimally.

The purpose of the experimental parcels is to generate silvicultural information about these 40 species, most of which have never been cultivated or studied in a scientific manner. The ignorance about tropical timber species is so profound that in many cases not even the most basic information is available, which strongly discourages management and reforestation attempts. By comparing growth and mortality rates among the three light treatments, each species will be assigned to its ecological category of sun-loving or shade-loving species. Their rate of growth and resistance to insects and weed competition will be compared so that certain species can be identified as particularly suitable for reforestation efforts. These measurements are taken on an annual basis, discarding the outer rows of each parcel to allow the for the "border effect." In additional rows between the main parcels, the

16

success and cost effectiveness of several transplanting techniques (bare-root, pseudo-stake, and root ball) are compared.

Planting began in December of 1989, and by the end of 1992, 36 of the 40 species had been established. The main cause of delay was the unavailability of seeds. Although nearly all the species are present in the surrounding forests of San Miguel, there was a lack of information about when and how to collect seeds. The reproductive cycles of tropical rain forest trees vary widely. Some produce fruit on a yearly basis, but because of the absence of defined seasons in Talamanca many others fruit continuously or sporadically throughout the year, or on a four- or six-month cycle, or even every four or seven years. For this reason it was deemed necessary to initiate a phenology study to supplement the experimental parcels.

Starting in January of 1991, ASACODE began its phenological study of the same 40 timber tree species in the forests of San Miguel. Six healthy and mature individuals of each species were located, measured, described, and mapped. If the tree was on private land assurance was obtained from the owner that it would not be cut for at least five years, the projected duration of the study. For species which are known to be dioecious, an attempt was made to include more individuals. With a few particularly rare species it was necessary to search in surrounding communities or in the nearby Gandoca-Manzanillo Wildlife Refuge. Some of the more distant trees require a half-day's hike through swamps and up steep ridges to visit, but they are nonetheless observed at least twice each month.

A strict observation schedule was implemented, although it is necessarily altered when inclement weather makes observation impossible. Each of the 240 trees in the study is visited every second week. From the time when flowering begins to the end of dissemination it is observed weekly. The phenology team, made up of two to three San Miguel residents and a part-time biologist advisor, notes the reproductive and vegetative state of each tree and compares these developments with local meteorological data obtained from their own pluviometer and a nearby solar illumination meter. They chart this information and prepare annual reports on the progress of their understanding of the phenological cycles of their trees. They have recently begun to publish pamphlets summarizing everything they have learned to date from both parts of the Native Species Project about some particularly important species. Much of this information is new to science.

The phenology team has also been trained in tree-climbing and seed-gathering techniques. Some of the species in the study have very light seeds adapted to wind distribution, which can only be harvested by climbing into the canopy just as the seeds reach maturity but before the tree lets them fall. The phenology study has for the first time enabled the precise timing necessary for such a delicate operation. ASACODE's phenology team is considered so expert in these operations that they have begun hiring themselves out to other groups and institutions, including the Costa Rican Forest Service.

After the seeds are harvested they are either sold or taken to ASACODE's nursery for germination. The germination rates of each species are measured under controlled experiments in specially-prepared beds. In cases where the results are unsatisfactory, various pre-germination treatments are tried. The team has also begun to experiment with seed viability and storage techniques. In this way ASACODE is slowly gaining expertise for the small local seed bank it hopes to establish in order to supply native tree seeds to regional reforestation initiatives.

Timber Harvest and Processing

Another of ASACODE's most important efforts has been the development of a sustainable timber harvesting and processing project. The research, training, and preparatory work for this initiative began several years ago, but the actual harvesting has only just begun in early 1993, so the long-term effects of the project remain to be seen. At present the association has access only to the private farms of its own members, a very small area for a sustainable management scheme, but this could be a blessing since the administrative difficulty will be much less, and they are able to begin processing and marketing on a small scale. If and when the project proves successful, other residents of San Miguel and neighboring communities will be eager to join in order to escape the tyranny of the regional logging cartel. It has always been an objective of ASACODE's to assist its neighbors and to provide them with a role model of locally-controlled sustainable development.

Each participating associate decides how much forest he would like to include in ASACODE's management project. The management parcels range from 5 to 20 hectares of primary or secondary rainforest and also vary widely in timber species and volume. ASACODE's management team conducts several surveys of the area. The first is a diagnostic survey of sample plots which counts all the trees, from saplings, to mature adults, to fallen logs. From this the health of the forest, and rate of natural regeneration are extrapolated, and the rate of sustainable harvest calculated. Typically this might be only a few trees per hectare per year, but with large trees and value-added processing, this still constitutes a reasonable income for the landowner. Next, a foot-by-foot inventory of all harvestable trees (over 30 cm DBH) yields the total timber volume for each species in the management area. These procedures were developed specifically for ASACODE's project by several consulting foresters because no existing inventory system was found to adequately predict

16

sustainable yield levels.

The next steps include marking the trees to be harvested and applying for cutting permits, a very long and complicated bureaucratic process frequently ignored or abused by large logging operations which can afford to pay bribes or fines. A liberation treatment, given four to six months before harvesting, frees selected trees from entangling vines which might damage or topple their neighbors or prevent them from falling freely. At this stage naturally fallen logs can also be harvested, for which no permit is required.

To extract the timber from the forest, ASACODE has chosen to rely on water buffalo, a relatively recent introduction into Central America, but one which shows enormous promise. Water buffalo are the only animals which can work effectively in the swampy conditions prevalent in San Miguel and other lowland tropical rain forests, and can pull a load where a tractor would barely pass. One water buffalo pulls roughly the same load as a team of oxen, and they are worked individually rather than in pairs, so the trail for timber extraction need only be about 120 centimeters wide.

Water buffalo are also intelligent and docile, and can be trained to obey simple verbal commands such as "go," "stop," "left," "right," "back up," and "turn around." The buffalo trainer ASACODE contracted to educate its forest management team had his own animals working without human oversight. Once familiar with the route they were to follow, the buffalo would simply be loaded up and sent off, and an assistant would be waiting at the other end of the trail to unload them and send them back. ASACODE's water buffalo are equipped with short triangular sleds made of reinforced sheet metal and attached to a harness around the animals' necks. The front end of the load—either whole logs or roughly-shaped blocks—is placed on this sled and the back end is allowed to drag in the mud.

Until recently, ASACODE has had to rely on inefficient and difficult-to-manage chain saw mills to process any lumber it wished to produce for its own use or for sale. In early 1993, however, the associates began operation of a small stationary mill they had constructed in nearby Celia. Now the raw timber is hauled by the buffalo to storage depots at the roadhead nearest to the logging operation, and from there carried by four-wheel-drive vehicle to the mill. ASACODE intends to construct a small furniture workshop, a charcoal oven, and other value-adding industries at the site to increase both the efficiency and the profit of their operations.

The earnings, which the associates will receive from participation in this project, are difficult to predict. The market value of many of the lesser-known timber species is not well known, but is sure to increase as many of these excellent woods attain greater acceptability. ASACODE expects the local demand for processed lumber to be greater than it can fill, since the nearest mill is an hour away over horrendous roads and there is a great deal of construction taking place in the vicinity of Celia. Already ASACODE has demonstrated that it can pay its associates several times the price they would receive from conventional loggers, and the intention is to return most of the profits from the mill to the members as well, retaining only enough for the maintenance and improvement of facilities and equipment, administration, salaries, and the repaying of debts.

Other Projects and Perspectives

In a sense, it is artificial to divide ASACODE's activities into separate projects, since they all have the same primary objective: the sustainable management of natural resources in a manner that is ecologically sustainable and maximizes local benefits. Nonetheless it is convenient for administrative purposes to differentiate individual projects, two of which we have examined in some depth above.

Among ASACODE's many other projects are a 50-hectare community reforestation effort in cooperation with governmental agencies; a green iguana restocking project in partnership with ANAI; a peccary breeding and rehabilitation project; a valuable forest understory plant management project (medicinals, ornamentals, natural insecticides and fibers) in collaboration with ANAI and CATIE; organic vegetable and medicinal plant gardens; many kinds of educational and training activities organized both independently and with cooperating institutions; and perhaps most ambitiously, a guest lodge with nature trails and trained guides.

Nearly all of these are unique and innovative projects, and the association has had to step carefully and slowly with no clear road to follow. Some of ASACODE's activities may fail technically or financially; most have already proved their viability. To the extent that they represent steps in the sustainable development of a community and the conservation of natural resources, and demonstrate that these two goals can be integrated harmoniously, all of ASACODE's projects must be declared highly successful. Only such locally-controlled initiatives as this—and there are remarkably few—offer any sustainable resolution of the confluence of environmental, economic and political pressures which are destroying Talamanca and so many other areas like it around the world.

To request more information about the activities described here, or to schedule a visit to ASACODE's facilities and projects, contact:

ASACODE

c/o Asociación ANAI
Apdo. 170 (2070)
Sabanilla, COSTA RICA

16

Restoring Mexico's Forests: The Work of *Cultura Forestal* on the Green Front in Tlaxcala

Jefferson Mecham

THE STATE OF TLAXCALA in central highland Mexico is located in a spectacular region of towering volcanic peaks skirted by forests of pine, oak, cedar and fir, and interspersed by ancient villages, some predating the Spanish invasion. Yet this rich land is in chronic socio-ecologic crisis most starkly evidenced by a poor majority and an appalling soil erosion problem. Deforestation of wooded slopes for fuelwood, agriculture and grazing has rapidly accelerated in this century, leading to severe land degradation and spreading desertification. So far, this has had the most profound effect on the region's growing population of rural poor.

But due to the efforts of one remarkable friend of the trees and his family and associates, hope lives for the region's forests. On their own land, Carlos Caballero Zamora and his family have been restoring a healthy forest ecosystem on what was an eroded wasteland. Over the last generation they have waged a tireless campaign against the advance of the desert. Today, their reforested land is a dramatic contrast to the barren gully-scarred landscape that surrounds them. For the Caballeros the green front begins at home, and over thirty years of thoughtful, caring labor—composting, planting, cultivating—has resurrected a forest that grows richer and more beautiful with time.

Not content merely to restore their own forest oasis as the land around them is destroyed, they have organized to educate and empower other people to manage and restore their own forests. This has been and continues to be a formidable task since it challenges deep-seated attitudes and traditions, and the institutionalized privileges of powerful special interests.

In 1964, Mr. Caballero formed the Escuela de Artesenía Forestal (School of Forest Arts) for his children and the people of his community. The importance of forests and how to care for them was taught along with a wide variety of wood artisan skills. The marriage of the ethical and the practical was to instill a thorough understanding and appreciation for the essential ecologic and economic roles

forests serve in supporting our lives.

In the early 70's, Mr. Caballero and a handful of other forestland owners formed ASILVITLAX—Asociación de Silvicultores del Municipio de Tlaxco, Tlaxcala, A.C. (the Tlaxco Association of Siviculturists). The organization's chief objective was to achieve the transformation of forest land-owners into genuine silviculturists: forest land-stewards capable of restoring and managing their own land in an ecologically and economically sustainable manner. The greatest obstacle to achieving this objective are the laws instituted to promote sound forestry.

Under the Mexican Ley Forestal (Forest Law) only government approved foresters are allowed to conduct forestry services (inventory, marking, etc.) and grant permission for harvesting. The law is intended to serve the common interest by placing forest management under the control of certified professionals. While such a monopoly may serve the short-term interests of the timber industry, it does not promote forest conservation. Instead, the regulations not only eliminate incentives and place obstacles impeding productivity, they actually hasten forest destruction. Mexican forestry authorities can (and often do) grant harvest concessions to timber companies regardless of the landowner's wishes. The timber companies have no incentive to practice good forestry on land they don't own. Neither do landowners when denied the responsibility for, and benefits from, the forests on their land.

In 1974, after years of frustration at the collusion between government foresters and the timber industry that was stripping forest from people's land while leaving them in poverty, ASILVITLAX sought permission from the government to manage their own forests. They clearly understood that if the people and communities who live in the forest are not allowed to care for, utilize, and benefit from them, the deforestation crisis in Mexico will never be resolved. After a decade of arduous political struggle against powerful vested interests, ASILVITLAX finally won management authority over their forests.

On 17 November 1984, Leon Jorge Castaños, the Mexican Secretary of Forestry, signed an agreement approving a pilot project granting ASILVITLAX the right to manage their own forests and perform their own forestry services—the first such concession ever granted in Mexico. This pioneering initiative allowed for the direct participation of forest owners in forest management. It is the first embodiment in Mexico of the idea that the organization, education, and empowerment of forest owners and communities for their own benefit is the best hope for providing a healthy forest for future generations.

The next year, in July of 1985, the Ninth World Forestry Congress was held in Mexico City. Among the "General Conclusions of the Congress" were the following:

...we recognize that the world's forests are being destroyed faster than they are being replaced and that isolated government efforts have not been able to stop or reverse this tendency. Therefore, we accept as fundamental to the confrontation of this situation, the most wide and genuine popular participation. This requires that the conditions be created to make possible the liberation of the extraordinary potential of the rural population for planning and executing integrated forest development strategies...

...it is essential that the owners of the forests become true forest stewards....

In 1986, in response to the Mexican government's call for greater participation of the people in solving the country's serious national problems, Mr. Caballero and his family formed Cultura Forestal, A.C., as a private, non-profit organization. It was created to extend their efforts at forest conservation and restoration to people throughout the region and the nation. The principal objectives of *Cultura Forestal*:

- promote and provide support to the movement for greater popular participation in forestry matters
- study, investigate and diffuse the ancestral values and traditions of forest peoples in the distinct forest regions of Mexico so as to induce greater respect and wiser use of the country's forests by all peoples
- promote the exchange of information between forestry institutions at international, national and regional levels with local producer organizations for the mutual benefit of all
- establish experimental models of alternative forest management
- investigate and demonstrate forest technologies, especially basic and intermediate technologies

- improve forest management by assisting forestland owners to manage their own forests and by helping enable them to become competent forest stewards
- contribute to the formation of local forestry cooperatives to promote the decentralization of forest management in Mexico

Cultura Forestal has been actively involved in research, teaching and demonstrating alternative forestry, particularly among the members of ASILVITLAX. They have developed an innovative silvicultural system for their region that is both ecologically sustainable and accessible to everyone, including those with very limited formal education. The Metodo Tlaxco de Renovacion Silvicola (Tlaxco Method of Forest Regeneration) uses simple guidelines that are easily understandable and biologically conservative to enable people to manage their own forests.

The Tlaxco Method has undergone years of experimentation and development by the members of ASILVITLAX. It has been well documented by Juan Caballero in his forestry thesis at the University of Durango. The method has been lauded by visiting forestry experts such as Dr. Wolfgang Moll (Justin Liebig University, F.R.G.), who called it "...the best silvicultural system available for this type of forest...." Although it has proven very effective for those actually using it, the system has been criticized in some Mexican academic circles as "simplistic. " The institutional conservatism that resists reform is reinforced by personal fears over livelihood if people are liberated from the technical monopoly of professional experts.

Such fears obscure the fact that there is more than enough work for everyone if the deforestation crisis is to be resolved. But, land will be restored and communities revitalized only on a foundation of enduring values and appropriate incentives. And only when all are allowed meaningful participation in the decisions which effect them. The work of Cultura Forestal is to instill a genuine sense of forest culture and stewardship and to empower people to manage their forest. And in so doing to restore the land, their communities, and their own lives.

If you would like to learn more about the work of Cultura Forestal , the following publications are available in Spanish at the address listed below. Please include a donation with your request.

Publications

Metas Forestales Deberan Ser Metas Nacionales
(Forest Objectives Should Be National Objectives)

Realismo Forestal: Crisis, Bosques y Cambios
(Forest Realism: Crisis, Forests and Change)

La Participacion de los Productores Forestales en la Aplicacion de los Servicios Tecnicos Forestales: el caso de ASILVITLAX,A.C.
(The Participation of Forest Producers in the Application of Technical Forestry Services: the case of ASILVITLAX,A.C.)

El Metodo "Tlaxco" de Renovacion Silvicola
(The "Tlaxco" Method of Forest Regeneration)

El Metodo Tlaxco de Renovacion Silvicola y la "Ciencia" Forestal
(The Tlaxco Method of Forest Regeneration and Forest "Science")

CULTURA FORESTAL, A.C.
Apartado Postal #4
Tlaxco, Tlaxcala 90250
MEXICO

16

Natural Forest Management with Strip Clear-cutting

J. Ocaña-Vidal

THIS ARTICLE BRIEFLY DESCRIBES an experimental silvicultural system called strip clear-cutting which is being tested in the Palcazu Valley of eastern Peru. The experience described in this article is of importance both for the promising results obtained and because the technique—developed by a multidisciplinary team with the coordination and active participation of institutions local communities and scientific experts—is being implemented by an indigenous Amazon people the Yanesha.

Central Forest/Palcazu Valley Project

The 469,500 ha of the Palcazu River basin, known as the Palcazu Valley, are located in the Central Forest area of Peru in the province of Oxapampa, in the department of Pasco. This area lies in the foothills of the Andes, upstream from the great Amazon basin (Selva Alta). For millennia, the Palcazu Valley was inhabited exclusively by the Yanesha. In more recent times, the Yanesha have been joined by settlers—primarily ranchers of European descent—and, to a much lesser extent, commercial loggers.

In 1980, studies were initiated for the Central Forest/ Palcazu Valley Resource Management Project, aimed at developing the area's resources with methods that guarantee long-term, sustainable productivity, and with appropriate technology which may be applied in other similar forest areas. The studies, supported by the United States Agency for International Development (USAID), revealed that, rather than being appropriate for sustained agriculture or ranching, the soils were mainly suited to forestry (JRB Associates, 1981; ONERN, 1970 and 1982; Brack Egg, 1981; Tosi, 1981) and that production activities should therefore be concentrated in this area.

The overall project was aimed at integrated and sustainable resource use; the management of natural forest, agroforestry and silvipastoral systems; and the management of water and hydrobiological resources, including the creation of protected areas for the conservation of watersheds and biodiversity (ecosystems, species and germplasm). It envisaged the local people, particularly the Yanesha, as protagonists, offering their customs, traditional technology and active participation in development planning and implementation.

Strip Clear-cutting

In the area of natural forest management, the government decided to experiment with a new silvicultural system developed by the Tropical Science Centre of Costa Rica: strip clear-cutting. This system is based on ecological observations of the gap-phase dynamics of natural tropical forests. The forest is harvested in long, narrow clearcuts designed to mimic the natural forest disturbance caused by the fall of a single large tree, followed by the subsequent natural regeneration over a period of 40 to 50 years. The economic basis of the system is complete utilization of all logs of more than 5 cm in diameter taken from the strips. Logs of more than 30 cm in diameter are cut for sawnwood while smaller logs are used for telephone poles, construction posts, etc. Critical aspects of the strip clear-cutting system include proper site selection, size and orientation of the strips, careful design of access roads to minimize erosion, use of animal power to remove logs from the strip, and no felling of trees adjacent to the strips for at least 15 years after harvest.

Within the overall management plan, the area in which strip clear-cutting is to be undertaken must be designated as permanent forest land. The specific areas to be cut are determined on the basis of a ground-level forest inventory. The dimension of the strips to be clear-felled must allow enough light to reach the ground level and stimulate the growth of natural regeneration, yet be narrow enough to ensure that seed from neighboring trees reaches the clear-cut area, either through the action of water and wind or with the assistance of animal vectors.

In the Palcazu Project, the width of the strips is determined by the height of the tallest natural trees (30 to 50 m), while the length is determined by the predominant ecological conditions of the surrounding terrain; for example, strips on flat ground where, the risk of erosion

16

is low, can be longer than strips on steeply sloping land. However, the total area of a strip rarely exceeds 0.5 ha.

In theory, the strips are best oriented on a 45° angle to the north-south axis (i.e. northeast-southwest, or north-west southeast). This angle permits the uniform distribution of light entering the strip, thereby fostering an even regeneration. In practice, topographical conditions, particularly the slope of the land and its contours—which need to be followed in order to minimize erosion—often require flexibility in the positioning of the strips.

Design and Construction of Access Roads

A full discussion of the implications of the strip clear-cutting system in terms of access roads is beyond the scope of this article. However, it is important to recognize that, since this forest management system is based on the harvesting of a series of non-contiguous areas, the access road system tends to be a complex network of small feeder roads. Particular attention must therefore be dedicated to ensuring that these roads are constructed and maintained in a manner that minimizes erosion.

Animal Power for Removing logs From the Strips

A fundamental element of the strip clear cutting management system being tested in the Palcazu Valley is the use of animal traction (primarily oxen) for the extraction of logs from the harvested area. The use of animal traction has multiple advantages, including minimal disturbance of the natural environmen, high flexibility and adaptability, low investment costs, and intensive labor requirements, thereby permitting the involvement of a large number of local people. These positive factors outweigh negative considerations such as the need to care for the oxen even during the period when they are not being utilized; the loss of efficiency when harvesting particularly large logs (more than 70 cm DBH); and the relatively slow pace of the oxen compared with mechanized equipment.

Harvesting Procedures

The first stage in the harvesting process is the removal of understory growth of less than 3 cm in diameter. Particularly important is the removal of climbing vines that might interfere with felling operations. Once clearing has been completed, harvesting begins with the smaller trees (i.e. those with a diameter of less than 30 cm). This timber, destined for use as telephone poles and construction posts after pressure treatment, must be removed from the strip as quickly as possible in order to avoid loss of moisture (moisture required for the pressure treatment).

The larger trees, those more than 30 cm in diameter, are felled last and require special care to ensure that they are felled in a manner that does not cause damage to the surrounding area. This is particularly important because the sustainability of the strip clear-cutting system is dependent on the natural regeneration of undisturbed trees in the surrounding area.

Social Considerations

A recurring pattern in the failure of many natural forest management systems is the inability of external forest managers to control land use over the long term. Involving local communities in the design and implementation of forest management systems can promote land-use stability by providing the residents of a region with a strong economic incentive to conserve the forest.

Socially, the Palcazu Valley project is based on the collective management of lands owned communally by the indigenous people. The project is based in an area designated by the Peruvian Government as a Yanesha Communal Reserve, covering an area of some 35 000 ha. Within the overall administrative structure of the Communal Reserve, ten communities joined together in 1987 to form the Yanesha Forest Cooperative Ltd. The main objectives of the cooperative, as determined by the members, are to provide work for its members under an overall forest management plan, to direct and implement the integrated exploitation of its forests, to promote the wood industry and market, and to support the community's development while maintaining its indigenous identity.

Results

The initial results of the Palcazu Valley experiment with strip clear-cutting are encouraging. Studies of two strips cut in 1985 indicate that harvesting and extraction of wood can be accomplished under local conditions without serious environmental damage, and that initial forest regeneration is rapid, abundant and diverse. Hartschorn (1988) focused on an initial grouping of ten species (90 percent of which were pioneer species), with Bismia basifera being the most important in Strip I and Cecropia sciadophylla in Strip 11. Similar results were obtained by Pariona and Bazan (1990).

A subsequent study by Pariona compared regenerating species from two strips cut in the forest of the Shiringamazu community with those within a 15 km radius in the surrounding primary forest. The study found that 48 of the 50 most common species were present in one strip and 40 in the other.

Regarding the potential profitability of the strip clear-cutting system, inventories carried out on the production strips revealed an average output of 125 different species and an average of 971 trees per hectare. In terms of output by type of product, on a per hectare basis the strips yielded 1 112 fence and vineyard poles (5 to 15 cm), 138 electricity poles (16 to 30 cm), 168.8 m3 Of sawlogs of more than 30 cm in diameter, 90.7 m3 of branches, stumps and twigs for charcoal, and an additional 16.86 m3 Of chips and cuttings. The system also leaves options open for the production of non-wood products such as resins, latex, ornamental plants, medicines, bark and wildlife from the surrounding forest.

On the social level, as part of an integrated approach to land-use planning, the strip clear-cutting system has helped to stabilize land tenure and safeguard the protected areas. It has also led to a greater understanding between the local population, the settlers and the loggers, and land disputes have virtually ceased. Similarly, there are no longer invasions of migrants and squatters.

The main achievement, regarding the local communities, is that they have begun to manage the forest and organize its exploitation themselves. The Yanesha Forestry Cooperative provides services, management support and training; motivates people to seek a better future; and represents an example of the success and pride of the Yanesha Nation.

Areas for Additional Work

The long-term success of the strip clear cutting system and the overall forest management plan will depend to a large extent on the capability of the Yanesha forest communities to manage the logging, processing and marketing operations. Extraction activities must be managed carefully to avoid environmental damage during periods of high rainfall. Processing facilities, particularly sawmill and the pressure treatment equipment, must be maintained in good running order, notwithstanding the challenging environment and the difficulty of access to spare parts. Considerable management skill will also be necessary to ensure that transport is available at the proper time and, if necessary, to alter the product mix in response to market conditions. Finally, an equitable distribution of the ultimate benefits among community members will be essential. The Yanesha must perceive direct and continuous benefits from the forest resource, or they will burn and farm the areas that have been clear-cut.

Extension and Expansion of the System

Efforts are being made to replicate the strip clear-cutting system in various parts of Peru, particularly in the Selva Alta. Both the government and the Yanesha Forestry Cooperative have demonstrated the system to indigenous and settler communities. Outside Peru, the system is being applied by two Ecuadorian indigenous communities who have been trained by Yanesha leaders.

Reprinted from Unasylva *169, Vol. 43, 1992.*

Bibliography

APODESA. 1989. *Experiencias Silviculturales y de Manejo de Bosques en America Latina.* Technical Document No. 20. Lima, Peru. Instituto Nacional de Desarrollo (INADE).

Brack Egg, A. 1981. "Ecological Evaluation of the Palcazu River Valley and Guidelines for an Environmental Conservation Program." *Em. JRB,* 2:D1-D39.

Buschbacher, R. J. 1990. "Natural Forest Management in the Humid Tropics: Ecological, Social and Economic Considerations." *Ambio,* 19(5): 253-258.

Chumpitaz, M. 1988. *Creacion e Implementación de la Administración Tecnica del Distrito Forestal de Iscozacin en la Cuenca del Rio Palcazu (Prov. Oxapampa-Dpto. Pasco)* (Ph.D. thesis). Lima, Peru, Universidad Nacional Agncola La Molina.

FAO/INFOR. 1985. *Curso de Extensión para Forestales en la Sierra Peruana.* Lima, Peru, Instituto Nacional Forestal y de la Fauna, Ministerio de Agricultura.

Hartschorn, G. 1988. Natural regeneration of trees on the Palcazu demonstration strips. Lima, JRB Associates.

JRB Associates, eds. 1981. *Central Selva Resources Management.* Lima, Peru, USAID.

More, T. 1987. *La Cooperativa Forestal Yanesha: Una Alternativa Autogestionaria de Desarrollo Indigena.* Amazonia Indígena, 7(13):18-27.

Ocaña-Vidal, J., ed. 1990. *Manejo de Bosques Naturales de la Selva Alta del Peru: Estudio de Caso del Valle del Palcazú.* Technical Document. Lima, Peru, INADE-APODESA.

ONERN. 1970. *Inventario, Evaluación e Integración de los Recursos Naturales de la Zona Villa Rica—Puerto Pachitea.* Lima, Oficina nacional de evaluación de recursos naturales.

ONERN. 1982. *Inventario y Evaluación Semidetallada de los Recursos Naturales de la Zona del Rio Palcazú.* Lima, Oficina nacional de evaluaci6n de recursos naturales.

Pariona, W. & Bazan, F. 1990. *Manejo Forestal por el Sistema de Fajas de Aprovechamiento Integral y Sostenido con Especial Referencia a la Regeneracion Natural en el Valle del Palcazú.* Ponencia del Taller "B" de la Reunion Internacional sobre Experiencias para el Desarrollo Sostenido de la Amazonia. Lima, Peru, APODESA-RONCO.

Stocks, A. 1985. *Subsistencia en las Comunidades Nativas del Valle del Palcazú.* Lima. Peru, PEPP/USAID.

16

Protecting Ecuador's Tropical Forests

Abundant Life Seed Foundation

THE TROPICAL FORESTS OF ECUADOR, comprising the Choco (Pacific coast) and upper Amazon watershed, are among the most diverse on Earth. The Ecuadorian Amazon is a large part of the world's largest neotropical refugia: while all around was frozen or arid during the Pleistocene Ice Ages, the humid climate permitted evolution to proceed uninterruptedly, producing the extraordinary biodiversity that exists today.

In the last 30 years over half of Ecuador's forests have been destroyed. The national policy of massive petroleum and resource extraction has financed the construction of a road network, encouraging poor, displaced, land-hungry settlers to colonize primary rainforest. The situation is worse on the Pacific side of the Andes where only 8% of the primary forest remains; recently, the destruction has moved into the Amazon basin.

Sustainable Timber in the Nor-Occidente

The sustainable forest management program began as an interventionary strategy in the Occidente (Pacific watershed) community of El Pan, which had sold their 1600-ha forest to a logging company for $2000, or $3-4 per tree. In association with the Ecological Trading Company, England, CIBT was able to offer the community $700-1000 per tree provided they adhered to a management program (sustainable harvesting, no heavy machinery) and milled their own timber on-site. The previous contract was able to be broken and the first harvest began in April 1990, the community receiving as much for the first twelve trees as they would have for their entire forest. It is intended to extend this model project, perhaps the first example of truly sustainable rainforest logging in the world, to other communities in the Occidente region. With 45% of the inhabitants reliant on the timber industry for their income, the remaining 8% of forest in the Occidente (including the Ecological Reserves) will soon be destroyed unless sustainable economic alternatives are speedily adopted. Each project will include the following activities:

1. Promotion of the project, giving communities an option other than selling their forests to timber companies.

2. Forest inventory: status of commercial and non-commercial species .

3. Management plan, providing the basis for sustainable operations.

4. Community instruction in each stage of the process.

5. Forest harvest.

6. Establishment and maintenance of nurseries.

The project calls for US$500,000 over 3 years.

Medicinal Plant Garden in the Jatun Sacha Biological Research Center

Medicines derived from indigenous botanical knowledge are worth U.S. $43 billion per year worldwide. The destruction of forests and forest cultures means the loss of a vast store of information and a potential economic base for these cultures. This is a model project for indigenous medicinal plant conservation and cultivation. At present over 80 species have been collected and successfully established.

Centro de Investigación de los Bosques Tropicales (CIBT)

Casilla 17-3-344-A, Quito, ECUADOR
Tel: 235-568/Fax: Fax 568-684

CIBT is involved with a variety of projects including the Permaculture Cayambe Rainforest Information Center, permaculture training, small-scale forestry projects, a mountain forest preserve and the demarcation of indigenous tribal territories.

CIBT is the Ecuadorian-incorporated, non-profit organization established by the Rainforest Information Center (RIC), which is based in Lismore, Australia. RIC has been active in Ecuador since 1985 when it was invited by the Awa Federation to assist in the Awa Project, a Colombian/Ecuador binational effort to protect the rainforest habitat of the Awa people by establishing a manga ("sleeve" or line of demarcation) around their territory to form the nation's first Ethnic Forest Reserve. CIBT is also helping mark the boundaries of the two million-acre Huoarani tribeland, and has demarcation projects underway or planned for other areas including the territory of the Zaparo, one of the least contacted groups in South America.

A sustainable timber management program is currently being planned with the Siona-Secoya, Amazonian tribes who have recently been granted land title to their ancestral territory. The management plan will also feature the establishment of mixed tropical fruit tree nurseries and orchards.

Permaculture Cayambe Rainforest Information Center

A project of Centro de Informacion de Bosques Tropicales Permaculture Cayambe is an integrated model of sustainable agriculture in Cayambe, Ecuador. RIC is purchasing, designing and developing permaculture farms to serve as long-term models and extension centers for sustainable agriculture in the Cayambe region. Permaculture Cayambe is working at ground level with the regional indigenous federation representing over 5,000 people in the 30 communities involved in this project.

At this point what people need to see first are not more modernization programs, agricultural courses, or technical advice, but successfully functioning examples that are accessible and immediately relevant to the betterment of their own lives and that of their family and community. Very few poor Ecuadorians have ever seen a sustainable agricultural model, let alone one appropriate to their means and circumstances. If they exist at all there are far too few of them.

If the immense human energies directed at destructive colonization could be channeled to restorative inhabitation, we could create an abundance in rural communities which would would obviate the need for emigration. Permaculture offers a means for doing just that, but models are urgently needed....

CIBT is the leading center for permaculture education in South America. CIBT hosted the largest permaculture design course held in the world thus far (to my knowledge. 97 people attended their 1992 permaculture design course held in Esmeraldas, Ecuador, including seven indigenous groups. Four permaculture courses are scheduled for 1994, including the first permaculture teacher training course in South America.

CIBT's USA affiliate is the Rainforest Information Center in Santa Fe, New Mexico (see listing under "International Environmental Organizations Based in the US").

This report is drawn from The World Rainforest Report, *newsletter of the Rainforest Information Centre, Lismore, Australia.*

16

16

17 Forestry in East Asia and the Pacific

Children of the Green Earth

East Asia and the Pacific Directory

See also the sections: Books on Tropical Forestry Management and Tropical Forestry Ecology

THE FORESTS OF SOUTHEAST ASIA AND THE PACIFIC are being logged, degraded, converted and destroyed at a fast pace. Indonesia and Malaysia are supplying most of the world's tropical timber today. Thailand and the Philippines have pretty much run out of forest and now Thailand is consuming Burma's forests and has its eye on Laos.

Papua New Guinea, New Caledonia, the Solomon Islands and other Melanesian islands have substantial amounts of wild forest yet, but the logging industry is working on them. Hopefully the Melanesian peoples are still wild enough to keep the multinational logging machine from logging all their forests.

The Indian subcontinent has been largely stripped of forest cover and much of the remainder is lopped for livestock forage. The village cultures of India and Nepal and surrounding peoples have shown an amazing resilience and stability in the face of massive problems (notably colonialism and neo-colonialism).

As well as the bad news, there is an incredible amount of experimentation going on with trees and forestry throughout Asia and the Pacific. As we start to realize the value of traditional agroforestry and agriculture systems, there will be lots to learn from these peoples. Asia is seething with the old and the new. Expect to see innovative solutions to our forest crises come out of Asia and the Pacific.

Philippines

"In 1934, more than 57 per cent of the Philippines were carpeted by 17 million hectares of forests. Of this stock, virgin, unlogged forests spread over 11 million hectares.

Today, only scattered patches of 984,000 hectares of virgin forests remain, mostly in remote areas. These never-logged stands by themselves are equivalent to merely five years of wood supply." Juan Mercado, Nov./Dec. 1990 *CERES*.

Commercial Logging Ban in Philippines

After two years of battle in the Philippine Senate, Bill No. 1404, titled "Total Commercial Logging Ban" was passed. This bill calls for a ban on all commercial logging for thirty years to allow denuded forests time to regenerate. It would also promote sustainable forestry and aid local development by making provisions for a community forestry management program.

This sounds good on paper, but how will it fare on the ground? Nevertheless, it is a sign that the politicians in one country realize that it makes good political sense to ban logging after the forests are gone.

Thailand Resumes Logging in Burma

The government of Thailand has approved the reopening of 14 checkpoints along the Burmese border, allowing Thai logging companies to bring in timber from Burma. The border checkpoints approved to be reopened an April 27, 1993, were closed last year due to international criticism of the economic support that Thailand's logging industry provided for Burma's repressive military regime, the State Law and Order Restoration Council (SLORC). The resumption of Thai logging in Burma will accelerate the destruction of Burma's already ravaged tropical forests while providing the SLORC with lucrative funding for their repressive government.

According to a 1990 report by Friends of the Earth, Burma is losing 800,000 hectares of forest annually. It is believed that if logging continues at the present rate, Burma's teak forests will be completely logged out in less than three years.

Thailand has been the primary market for Burmese timber. In 1989 Thailand effected a logging ban within its borders because its own extensive logging had caused catastrophic soil erosion and floods. Unable to log at home, Thailand has looked to Burma for the 8 million cubic meters of wood it uses and exports annually. (Rainforest Action Network, Action Alert #84 June 1993.)

Directories on Forestry in Asia and the Pacific

Directory of Environmental NGOs in the Asia-Pacific Region

1990. Sahabat Alam Malaysia: 37 Lorong Brich, Penang, Malaysia.

A comprehensive, multi-sector listing of 100's of NGOs. Includes address, telephone, contact person, membership, activities, publications, achievements, problems and proposals. Recommended for anyone interested in environmental networking in the Asian-Pacific.

Forestry Researchers: A Directory of Forestry Researchers in the Asia Pacific Region

J. Roetzer and P. Saengduangdee, FORSPA Secretariat. Address in following section.

FORSPA has compiled a directory of forestry researchers in Asia and the Pacific, which lists more than 900 scientists working throughout the region. Entries include publications, professional experience, and brief biographies.

Forestry Organizations in Asia and the Pacific

Bhutan Forest School
Taba, nr. Thimphu, BHUTAN

Centre Technique Forestier
BP 411
Noumea, NEW CALEDONIA

An institute for tropical forestry.

Chinese Academy of Forestry
Wan Shou Shan
Beijing, 100091, CHINA

Fijian Ministry of Forests
Forest Department
P.O. Box 2218
Suva, FIJI

Forestry Research Support Programme for Asia and the Pacific (FORSPA)
FAO Regional Office for Asia and the Pacific
Phra Atit Road
Bangkok 10200, THAILAND
Tel: (66-2) 281-7844/Fax: (66-2) 280-0445

Publishes quarterly newsletter, *INFO FORSPA*, to inform readers of FORSPA's activities and disseminate research results. See also *FORSPA Directory* above.

Forest Research Center
Bai Bang-Vinh Phu, VIETNAM

Publishes quarterly newsletter *Forest Research* in both English and Vietnamese.

Kerala Forest Research Institute

Peechi, 680 653, Trichur, Kerala, INDIA

Liklik Buk Information Center
P. N. G. University of Technology
Private Mail Bag
Lae, PAPUA NEW GUINEA
Tel: 434781. Joy Sahumlal, Manager

Publishes information on alternative technologies with a special emphasis on agriculture and rural development.

Melanesian Environmental Foundation
P.O. Box 4830
Boroko, NCD, PAPUA NEW GUINEA
Tel: 675-25-8063

Their emphasis is on forestry education, including producing educational videos on forestry.

Melanesian Solidarity
PO Box 71
University of PNG, NCD, PAPUA NEW GUINEA
Tel: 675-25-6880/Fax: 675-25-4309

Working with forestry issues.

Nepal Forestry Teachers' Assoc.
Institute of Forestry
P.O.B. 43
Pokhara, Kaski District, Gandaki Zone, NEPAL

An NGO established to link natural resource and conservation groups within Nepal, educate people about forest and watershed degradation, disseminate forestry technologies in Nepal, and network with organizations worldwide.

Northeast Forestry University
Dept. of Forest Operations
8 Hexing Road,
150040 Harbin, P.R. of CHINA
Fax: 86-451-240146

Hosting a July 24-27, 1994 International IUFRO/NEFU/FAO Seminar on Forest Operations under Mountainous Conditions.

Pacific Island Association of NGOs (PIANGO)
c/o Development Services Exchange
P.O. Box 556
Honiara, SOLOMON ISLANDS

A network of environmental NGOs in 23 countries which runs training workshops and publishes a newsletter

Papua New Guinea Forestry College
P.O. Box 92
Bulolo, Morobe Province, PAPUA NEW GUINEA

Papua New Guinea Office of Forests
P.O. Box 5055
Boroko, Port Moresby, PAPUA NEW GUINEA

17

Papua New Guinea Office of Forests
P.O. Box 314
Lae, Morobe Province, PAPUA NEW GUINEA

Regional Community Forestry Training Center (RCOFTC)
c/o Faculty of Forestry, Kasetsart U.
Bangkhen, Bangkok 10900, THAILAND
Tel: 579-0108

Established in 1987 with the objectives of training technical and professional people from the Asia Pacific region in community forestry, organizing seminars and workshops and serving as a center for information exchange, technical assistance, and networking.

Regional Wood Energy Development Program in Asia
FAO-RAPA
Phra Atit Road
Bangkok, 10200, THAILAND
Tel/Fax: (66-2) 280-0760

RWEDP publishes a wide range of useful documents, some of which are listed below. Publications are free of charge to NGOs of The South.

- *Wood Energy Policies and Strategies: Some Issues.* 1987; 52 pages
- *Stove Programmes in Asia: A Status Report*
- *The Use of Woodfuels in Rural Industries in Asia and Pacific Region*
- *Catalogue of Wood Energy Institutions*
- *Wood Based Energy Systems in Rural Industries and Village Applications, Nepal.*
- *Development of Degraded Village Lands in India: Experiences and Prospects*
- *Case Studies of Farm Forestry and Wasteland Development in Gujarat, India.*
- *The Community's Toolbox: the Idea, Methods and Tools for Participatory Assessment, Monitoring and Evaluation in Community Forestry*

South Pacific Forestry Development Programme
FAO Private Bag 010
Port Vila, VANUATU
Fax: (678) 23619

Its purpose is to promote closer and more effective communication among forestry personnel and agencies in the South Pacific. *S. Pacific Forestry Newsletter* is a new quarterly on forestry, agroforestry, non-timber forest products, traditional plant uses.

South Pacific People's Foundation
620 View St., Suite 415
Victoria, BC, V8W 1J6 CANADA
Tel: (604) 381-4131/Fax: (604) 721-0409
or (604) 388-5258

Links organizations in Canada and the South Pacific. Forestry is one of their areas of work.

Ulatawa Estates Pty. Ltd.
Max Henderson
P.O. Box 1342
Rabaul, PAPUA NEW GUINEA
Tel: 92-01294/Fax: 92-1197

Native groups in PNG are selectively harvesting timber on their traditional lands using chainsaws, Alaskan mills and a portable Wokabout sawmill. They can supply woodturners with tropical hardwoods and highly figured pieces sliced from tree crotches and butts.

University Forest
The University of Tokyo
1-1-1 Jayri, Bankyo-ku
Tokyo 113, JAPAN

Hosting a Conference on Sustainable Forest Management on October 17-21, 1994. Contact Dr. Hidejiro Nagumo.

Forestry Periodicals in Asia and the Pacific

Asia Pacific Forest Watershed Newsletter
East-West Center
1777 East-West Road
Honolulu, Hawaii 96848 USA
Tel: (808) 944-7266/Fax: (808) 944-7970

The newsletter focuses on forest hydrology and soil and water conservation.

Annals of Forestry
374 Mohit Nagar, Lane 13, P.O.F.R.I.
Dehra Dun 248006, INDIA

A new scientific journal which intends to cover all aspects of forestry and agroforestry including basic science, silviculture, planning and management, economics and utilization.

Banko Janakari
Forest Research Div., Dept of Forestry
P.O. Box 3339
Kathmandu, NEPAL

This 50-100 page journal comes out eight times a year. Topics cover forestry in general and community forestry in Nepal.

CANOPY International
Ecosystems Research and Development Bureau

DENR College
Laguna 4031 PHILIPPINES
Tel: (63-94) 3481/Fax: 3628

Six issues a year in English. Available free. Environmental problems, protection, sustainability and management. The goal of the journal is to promote effective management of the various ecosystems in the Philippines.

Forest Research Newsletter

P.O. Box 314
Lac, PAPUA NEW GUINEA
Tel: (675) 424-188/Fax: (675) 424-357
Telex: PNGFRI

Two issues per year. English. Free.

Indian Environment

Indian Improvement Society
U-112, 3rd Floor, Vidhata House, Vikas Marg
Delhi 110 052 INDIA
Tel: (91-11) 22-3311

Three issues per year. English. Subscription: US $20 per year.

Indian Journal of Forestry

Bishen Singh Mahendra Pal Singh
23-A Connaught Place
Dehra Dun 248001, Uttar Pradesh, INDIA

Journal of Forestry of the Nepal Forester's Association

Nepal Foresters Association (NFA)
P.O. Box 2761
Babar Mahal, Kathmandu, NEPAL
Tel: (977) 22-1231

Two issues per year. English. Subscriptions: US $10 per year.

Journal of Tropical Forest Science

Forest Research Institute Malaysia
P.O. Box 201
Kepong, 52109, Kuala Lumpur, MALAYSIA

Tropical forestry from the Malaysian point of view. September 1988 was the first issue.

Forest Research Institute Malaysia has a new bi-annual publication, *Buletin FRIM*, which aims to disseminate research results for timber-related entrepreneurs, forestry researchers, environmentalists, forestry policymakers, industries, and the general public.

Pacific Islands Forestry News

Institute of Pacific Islands Forestry
1151 Punchbowl St., Room 323
Honolulu, Hawaii 96813
Tel: (808) 541-2628

An occasional newsletter focusing on agroforestry, and tropical forest research.

Wood Energy News

Regional Wood Energy Development Program in Asia, FAO-RAPA. Address in Organizations.

English-language quarterly. Free to developing countries in Asia and on an exchange basis for others.

Books on Forests and Forestry in Asia and the Pacific

Communal Management of Forests in South and Southeast Asia

P. W. Mol and K. R. Wiersum. 1990. Dept. of Forestry, Wageningen Agricultural University: The Netherlands.

The Conservation Atlas of Tropical Forests: Asia & the Pacific

N. M. Collins, J. A. Sayer, and T. C. Whitmore, eds. 1991. IUCN.

The first in a series of 3 vols. intended to inform the international community involved in the debate over the future of the world's forests. The maps have been compiled from satellite and radar imagery, aerial photos, and information from a range of sources. The text interprets them from a conservationist standpoint and describes the impact of deforestation in each region.

Conservation of Forests of India: An Ecologist's Tour

Bruce G. Marcot. 1993. Misc. Publ. US. Department of Agriculture, Forest Service, Pacific Northwest Research Stn., Portland, Oregon, USA (address in U.S. Government Forest Agencies section).

A well-written description of forest and wildlife conservation efforts in India.

Deforestation in the Postwar Philippines

David M. Kummar. 1991. University of Chicago Press, George Perkins Marsh Institute at Clark University.

The author spent four years in S. E. Asia researching this book. The book contains a literature review of tropical deforestation. It also includes a global overview, as well as a more detailed look at forest history in the Philippines, its trends and implications.

The Economic Value of Non-timber Forest Products in Southern Asia

Jene H. de Beer and Melanie J. McDermott. 1989. Netherlands Committee for IUCN: Amsterdam. 175 pp.

The emphasis is on Indonesia, Malaysia and Thailand. It includes plant and animal material sources and the use of their edible, non-edible, and medicinal products.

Forest Ecology

G. S. Puri, R. K. Gupta, M. M. Meher-Homji, and S.

17

Puri. 1989, 2nd ed. Oxford and IBH Publishing Co: New Delhi. 2 volumes.

Scientific treatments of many forest tree species and plant associations found in the Indian subcontinent.

Hugging The Trees—The Story of the Chipko Movement

Thomas Weber. 1988. Penguin Books. Ananda Offset Private Ltd.: Calcutta. 175 pp. $7.95.

Keepers of the Forest: Land Management Alternatives in Southeast Asia

Mark Poffenberger, ed. 1990, 304 pp. Kumarian Press: 630 Oakwood Ave. Suite 119, West Hartford, Connecticut, 06110-1529 USA.

Describes forestry management practices developed in SE Asia by NGOs and individuals as alternatives to unsuccessful official strategies. The book gives a careful documentation of forest management since the mid-seventeenth century, covers tools and techniques for participatory forest management, and examples of forestry activities in Java, Thailand and the Philippines.

Local Organizations in Community Forestry Extension in Asia

1993. GCP/RAS/131/NET Field Document 34. Available from Forest Trees, and People Programme, FAO. Address in International Forestry Organizations section.

The summary of the presentations and discussions in this book demonstrate that a wide variety of local institutions for natural resource management exist. They may offer the most efficient ways of achieving sustainable management of forest and tree resources. Successful strategies and inspiring examples are sited.

Natural Forests and Indigenous Tree Species: Management Principles and Silvicultural Options

The proceedings of a seminar held in Bangkok in 1990 with the following objectives: To sum up the knowledge on the management of natural forests and indigenous trees in Thailand; to select the best species and management options; to discuss the methods for rehabilitation of degraded lands.

The results of the seminar are being used in preparing the Thailand Forestry Sector Master Plan which is being drawn up by the Thai Royal Forest Department with UNDP and FINNIDA (Finland's government aid agency). FINNIDA is also involved in helping Nepal and other countries draw up National Forestry Plans.

"Potential for Sustainable Forest Management in Malaysia"

S. T. Mok, 1992. In *Unasylva* 169, Vol. 43, pp. 26-33.

Reviews traditional forest management in Malaysia and the prospects for sustainable forest management.

Research Policy for Community Forestry, Asia Pacific Region

Proceedings of a seminar Jan 8-11, 1990, 255 pp. RECOFTC Report No. 5. (See RECOFTC under Organizations).

40 papers on research policies for community forestry based on people's involvement, values, needs and sustainable development.

Rich Forests, Poor People: Resource Control and Resistance in Java

Nancy Lee Peluso. 1992. University of California Press: Berkeley.

An historical account of political conflict over Java's forest resources. The solution could be a kind of social forestry that transfers resources to the poor.

The Silviculture of Indian Trees

R. S. Troup. 1975. Controller of Publications: Delhi. 3 volumes.

The definitive source for information on biology of Indian trees and their forestry.

Studies on Social Forestry in India

Prakash M. Shingi, ed. 1990. Indian Institute of Management, Ahmendabad, and FAO/RAPA (see address under Regional Wood Energy Development Program in Asia, in organizations section).

Highlights lessons from India's diverse experiences in social forestry. Covers nursery management, species selection, community and farm forestry, afforestation, training, women's participation, and fuel.

Sustaining the Forests: The Community Approach in South and South-East Asia

Marcus Colchester. 1992. UNRISD Discussion Paper 35. UNRISD, Palais des Nations, CH-1211, Geneva 10, Switzerland.

Reviews the experience of community based forest protection initiatives.

The Unquiet Woods: Ecological Change and Peasant Resistance in the Himalaya

Ramachandre Guha. 1990. University of California Press: Berkeley.

A history of peasant resistance to commercial forestry, including the Chipko movement. The conflict is over differing concepts of property and alternative uses of forest resources.

The Wokabout Portable Sawmill

Rainforest Information Center

A team from Australia's Rainforest Information Center (RIC) recently finished a three-month ecological audit of a small portable sawmill, the Wokabout, in the Solomon Islands and Papua New Guinea. The team concluded that the mill can be an important step toward truly sustainable forestry in the tropics, but only if model harvesting programs and guidelines are developed. RIC's John Seed reports:

WHEN THE INTERNATIONAL TROPICAL TIMBER Organization studied sustainability in tropical forestry, it concluded that less than one-eighth of 1 percent of such forestry could be so defined. But even the small amount it did identify was based on definitions developed in Queensland, Australia, whose old foresters were notorious for cooking the books to back up their claims. The ITTO's conclusions have been vigorously attacked by Dr. Aila Keto and Professor Len Webb, among others, and we conclude with them that there is not a single example anywhere in the world of sustainable logging of a tropical forest.

Which makes all the more compelling the findings of a three-person RIC team that earlier this year visited Papua New Guinea and the Solomon Islands to conduct a three-month ecological audit of a small portable sawmill, the Wokabout. Because four men can carry the mill to a log and then carry the planks out, the Wokabouts theoretically require no roads or heavy machinery, which is usually the most damaging part of logging in the tropics. The mills are relatively inexpensive, so they can be locally owned by the people who live in the forest. With the right training and a sound management plan, the mill can be a viable alternative to large-scale industrial logging.

As part of our audit we searched out places where we might create models of sustainable forestry, or ecoforestry. Although there are already more than three hundred Wokabouts in PNG, the absence of suitable guidelines for their use means that a lot of needless destruction is taking place.

Also, because customary land ownership in the Pacific means that local indigenous communities often control the fate of the forests, people anxious for money and development get sucked into selling off their timber rights to logging companies. But in many cases the one thing that will stop a community from signing over those rights is if the timber can be seen to have some other value. Though the immediate financial returns from Wokabout milling are not as great as what the logging companies offer, many communities will spurn the companies if they can just get some return from their forests.

We have developed guidelines for sustainable forestry using the Wokabout in three sites on the Solomons and in PNG. These sites are described below, as are our funding needs to initiate them. The United Kingdom's Ecological Trading Company has agreed to buy all the timber produced under our guidelines for about 25 percent above what could be obtained by selling it anywhere else, and they've budgeted funds for monitoring our timber to be sure it actually does come from sustainable sources.

If we can launch our program, and it works, it will be a true alternative economic scenario, and the communities that receive the Wokabouts can become training grounds for sustainable forestry programs elsewhere.

Papua New Guinea

To save 54,000 hectares of the last intact coastal rainforest in Morobe Province from certain destruction by the PNG Forest Products Company (which has already worked through the rest of the coast), we hope to provide the Zia tribe with three Wokabout mills and a management plan for the villages of Salwarra, Popoi, and Sapo. Each mill will cut mainly timber that needs cleaning up after clearing gardens and plantations. We believe sustainable logging is possible here on a fifty-year rotation, requiring just 150 hectares (three per year) per mill.

The Wokabouts will be owned by the Village Development Trust and in possession of the villages as long as they adhere to the ecoforestry management plan.

Solomon Islands

A Korean logging company, Eagon Forestry, has recently obtained logging concessions on the south side of the island of Choiseul. Choiseul is covered with lush tropical forest, most of it pristine, and supports small villages dependent on the sea and the forest for survival.

So far only one village has signed over rights to Eagon, but Eagon devastated the village, relocating it to a smaller island offshore. Serious outbreaks of malaria followed the heavy machinery, water supplies were polluted, the company desecrated sacred sites, and disputes over land boundaries erupted. Eagon is aggressively negotiating to expand its operations.

The RIC team held meetings in eight villages. None have signed with Eagon, but all felt a need to develop, and were considering offers. All agreed that a Wokabout mill would secure their forests from Eagon and enable them to manage their own resources.

RIC believes that three mills strategically placed in this region of the Solomons would not only protect the forests and villages, but would probably result in a moratorium on all new logging contracts as communities realized there was an alternative. We need $45,000 for these three mills; all donations are U.S. tax deductible.

A 24-page report covering our evaluation of the Wokabouts and our overall Ecological Management Plan (each village will have its own) is available from the RIC Pacific Ecoforestry Project, Box 368, Lismore, Australia 2480 (Phone: 61-66-218-505; FAX: 61-66-222-339).

Briefly, these are our proposed sites. The Papua New Guinea project is funded already, but we are still seeking funds for the Solomon Islands.

Reprinted from World Rainforest Report, *January-March 1991.*

Doubling New Zealand's Forest Cover

Michael Pilarski

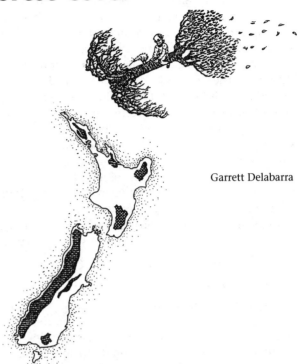

Garrett Delabarra

A Tree's-eye View of New Zealand

The illustration shows editor Michael Pilarski flying over New Zealand on a Kauri tree. The Kauri is one of New Zealand's totem trees. The shaded portions of the map are the areas of New Zealand with extensive natural forests remaining.

NEW ZEALAND IS A COUNTRY OF FRIENDLY PEOPLE and beautiful trees. Although New Zealand has its problems, it could become a model for the rest of the world in social equality and sustainable land use. It certainly won't be easy given the present economic climate, but often it is our difficult times that force us out of old habits.

New Zealand is about the same size as the United Kingdom and just a little smaller than Japan, but the population is only 3.5 million. New Zealand extends 1600 kilometers (1,000 miles) from 33° to 53° degrees South latitude. 50% of the land is steep, 20% hilly and 30% flat. The lowest average precipitation is 330 mm/yr. (13 inches) and the highest is 7,600 mm/yr. (300 inches). These extremes only lie 80 km (50 miles) apart from one another on the South Island!

Major native timber trees of New Zealand:

Kauri (*Agathis australis*)

Kahikatea (*Dacrycarpus dacrydioides*)

Totara (*Podocarpus totara*)

Matai (*Podocarpus spicatus*)

Miro (*Podocarpus ferrugineus*)

Rimu (*Dacrydium cupressinum*)

Northern Rata (*Metrosideros robusta*)

Red Beech (*Nothofagus fusca*)

Silver Beech (*Nothofagus menziesii*)

Tawa (*Beilschmiedia tawa*)

History of New Zealand Forests

New Zealand's forests are of an ancient lineage, having separated from Gondwanaland hundreds of millions of years ago, evolving in isolation from the rest of the world's flora. The main tree species are of ancient lineage, such as podocarps and conifers. Flowering plants (angiosperms) are mainly relegated to undergrowth and small trees.

There is some debate as to when Maoris (Polynesians) first arrived in New Zealand, but major colonization is generally put at around 1350 AD. When the Maoris arrived they found a predominantly forested land. Estimates range from 75% to 86% forested. Through the widespread use of fire, the Maoris reduced forest cover to about 56% of the land surface by the time the first European colonists arrived 150 years ago.

The European colonists set out with vim and vigor to reduce the forest via fire and logging, until today between 14% to 26% of the land is forested. Data on forest cover is a matter of debate in almost every country in the world. New Zealand is no exception. The lower figure is put forward by some conservationists. The higher figure is that set by the government Forestry Institute. The main discrepancy would probably be where to draw the line between low, native scrub and forest.

The Kauri (*Agathis australis*) is the largest tree in New Zealand, although some podocarps are taller. The older trees live to be over 1,000 years and are massive, up to 21 feet in diameter. Of the original 3 million acres of magnificent Kauri podocarp forest in Northland and Coromandel only a few isolated stands remain.

Most of the forest clearing was for grazing land (primarily sheep). Somewhere around 56% of New Zealand's land surface is presently used for grazing. Much of the land is steep or hilly and should have been left under forest since the erosion rates are high without the trees. As a result of deforestation and overstocking on grazing land, New Zealand has one of the highest erosion rates in the world. The New Zealand Land Resource Inventory (NZLRI) has shown that 13.8 million hectares, or 52 percent of New Zealand is affected by surface erosion (sheet, wind and scree) and 9.6 million hectares, or 36 percent, by mass movement erosion (soil slip, earth slip, debris avalanche, earth flow and slump). A nation's long-term productivity is tied to its soil resources and New Zealand, which relies on agriculture and forestry products for most of its exports, is especially vulnerable. The obvious answer to the erosion problem has been pointed out by many writers and experts over the years: Plant trees and more trees.

Forest Plantations

By the first decade of the 1900's it was obvious the native forests were mostly logged and future wood shortages were inevitable without new plantings. In 1919, a Forest Service was set up by the government and one of its priorities was planting trees. Between 1919 and 1935 over 125,000 hectares were planted by the Forest Service, mainly on the pumice plateau of the central North Island. A similar-sized area of private land was also planted in various parts of the country. Planting greatly slowed down between 1935 and 1960. By 1973 new plantings were going in at the rate of 40,000 hectares a year and by 1983 there were over one million hectares of planted forest in New Zealand, which is about 3.7% of its land surface.

These new forests have been a mixed blessing, however. For one thing, some of the new forests have been created at the expense of native forests. Native forests have been bulldozed and exotic conifer plantations put in their place (mainly *Pinus radiata*, commonly called Monterey pine or radiata pine). A dubious gain. *Pinus radiata* has some good points and bad points. Its chief attribute is its fast growth in New Zealand, being cut on a 25 to 35 year rotation. Its bad points: monoculture stands are vulnerable to disease or pest damage; and it is not a good species for soil building, erosion control or wildlife habitat. Short rotation forestry depletes the soil and leads to soil exhaustion and accelerated soil erosion after several rotations. Mixed species plantings which include both hardwoods and softwoods are much better.

Native trees should be used much more extensively for reforestation. So far, virtually none of the new forest plantings have been native trees. The reason given being that they are slow growing. While it is true that native trees may not be as fast as many of the exotic conifers, there is also no doubt that native timber fetches higher prices. Plus native trees have a pest/predator balance with their environment, do more to hold and build the soil, as well as provide habitat for native life forms. A native forest is a more complex ecosystem than an exotic monoculture plantation.

Friends of the Trees Society recommends a greater emphasis on planting native trees:

1. On some sites plant to approximate natural forests insofar as possible.

2. On some sites a mixture of native and exotic trees are appropriate.

3. On other sites a mixture of exotic trees is appropriate. In some cases successive plantings can be used with exotic trees providing site amelioration so that native trees can be established under the shelter of the exotics with the exotics eventually being taken out.

Windbreaks in New Zealand

New Zealand is a windy country as it is closely surrounded on all sides by the ocean. As a result, farmers adopted windbreaks and hedgerows after they cut down the native trees. Today, windbreaks and hedgerows are common sights in many parts of New Zealand. The Farm Forestry Association in particular over the past several decades has done much to increase the amount of windbreaks in the country. Kiwifruit orchards and other horticultural crops are almost always surrounded by windbreaks. The range of tree species used for windbreaks is very large, most of them non-native species from Europe or North America. Monterey cypress, Monterey pine, poplars, willows and casuarinas are the most widely used, but one can also find sequoias, western red cedar, Leyland cypress, oaks, feijoas, bamboos, pines, and many other species. Alders are increasingly favored over poplars and willows for horticultural windbreaks since alder roots are not as wide-ranging or as prone to suckering. Alders are nitrogen-fixing and their leaf litter contributes fertility to neighboring crops.

Windbreaks are usually single or double rows. By using timber trees, windbreaks can provide wind protection, plus eventually be harvested for timber. Trial plantings of windbreaks have yielded as high as $30,000 of timber per kilometer at 35 years.

Besides tree windbreaks, many pastures also have hedgerows of native shrubs, or exotics such as hawthorn, tree lucerne and pampas grass.

Conservation in New Zealand

17

19% of New Zealand's land area is in a comprehensive network of parks and reserves that includes more than 1500 individual areas. This is one of the largest percentages of land area in reserves of any country in the world. This sounds impressive and indeed it is. But New Zealand's conservation record is far from exemplary.

As in most of the world, conservationists have had to put up stiff fights for just about every protected area in the country. The pressures on the remaining undisturbed habitats continues in many areas. For instance the government still allows mining in National Parks. While I was in New Zealand the conservationists won a significant victory when the government declared much of the South Westland forests as protected reserve rather then giving the forest to the pulp chippers for Japan. Cutting in old-growth native forests is reduced, but is still ongoing. Conservationists are fighting to save these last remnants of the mighty forests which once clothed New Zealand.

Doubling New Zealand's Forest Cover

New Zealand's contribution to stabilizing the world's climate would be to double New Zealand's forest cover. This would have many positive side effects. For one thing it would solve a lot of New Zealand's soil erosion and flooding problems. For another, it would provide a tremendous resource for present and future generations. It would also provide meaningful employment for many New Zealanders both in the present and in the future. New Zealand has much to gain from doubling its forest cover and very little to lose.

Reforestation may be made out to be a drain on New Zealand's limited resources in a time of economic downswing. On the contrary, I believe it can be shown to be one of the best things New Zealand could do for its economy.

At this time, New Zealand unemployment is running at about 5%. Many of these people are on social welfare. It would not be much additional cost to pay some of these people an increased wage for tree planting and other ecosystem restoration work. The labor is no problem, although it will take some time to set up infrastructure and train people. There are ways of training large amounts of people quickly which are not widely utilized. Such as pyramid training schemes whereby the best experts in the field train small groups of people. These people in turn each train small groups and they in turn train small groups. In such a way, large numbers of people can be trained in a few years' time.

When afforestation projects are planned for multiple yields, rather then single yields of sawlogs, economic returns can be had in a much shorter time. For instance, honey plants can be incorporated into plantings, so beekeepers can gain income off land within a few years of planting. This calls for planting a succession of different plants so that there are herb and leguminous plants which start flowering a year or two after planting, followed by shrubs and finally by tree species which provide bee forage. Several people in New Zealand have conducted research which indicates that bee keeping can outyield sheep grazing in hill country as well as eventually yielding timber and other valuable products.

An additional benefit to doubling New Zealand's forest cover and stopping accelerated soil erosion is the country will look better. New Zealand has a reputation as a clean/green country. This is the basis of its tourist industry which is one of New Zealand's biggest earners of overseas money. Travel is the world's fastest growing industry and New Zealand can cash in on this in an even bigger way if it fixes up its environment. On the other hand, if its environment continues to degrade, it will also erode its tourist appeal.

What Will it Take to Double New Zealand's Forest Cover?

A plan to double New Zealand's forest cover is a tall order any way you look at it. The total land surface of New Zealand is 26.6 million hectares (discounting lakes and rivers). Official government estimates are that 23.1% is indigenous forest and 3.7% exotic forest for a total of 26.8% forested. This is very likely an inflated figure for several reasons: 1. Forest clearing and logging are ongoing and we can expect that this will continue into the future both for timber production and for land clearance. Thus we need to figure into our plan that part of these areas will need to be replanted. 2. Much of what is classified as "indigenous forest" is degraded scrub which could well use tree planting (with native species). Thus we might be closer to the truth to estimate that 20% (plus or minus several %) of New Zealand is forested to the extent that it would not need additional planting. 20% is 5.3 million hectares. 25% is 6.6 million hectares. For the sake of this exercise let us pick 6 million hectares of additional forest planting as our goal. This equals 15 million acres.

If we choose a 15 year period as our target plan that would average 1 million acres a year. This is by no means an unachievable goal. During the height of the planting in the 1970's, 120,000 acres were being planted a year. Thus our goal would only be eight times what had already been achieved a decade ago.

How much would it cost? Let us take an average planting density of 300 trees/acre. This is a high density which leaves room for mortality and thinning to end up with a good stand of high quality trees. At $1.00 a tree for growing, planting out and aftercare this would cost $300/acre or $300 million a year. Or a total of $4.5 billion for the 15 year program. This might sound like a lot to the average

17

taxpayer, but look at it in the light of present expenditures in New Zealand. The four navy frigates the government is considering buying for $2 billion would pay for 6 and a half years of the program. The military budget is running around $600 million a year, which would pay for two years of such a reforestation program. Cyclone Bola's erosion/flooding damage was rated at $150 million in a 5-day period.

Consider the returns for this investment. Not only do you save on erosion and flood damage losses, but much of the forests could eventually be harvested. At current rates, an acre of good timber can fetch $10,000 an acre (or even more) as stumpage, not to mention value added products.

How Many People Would it Take?

How many trees an average tree planter can plant per day varies depending on the terrain, soil type, the size of planting stock, and techniques such as scalping, shading, and mulching. For New Zealand we could safely estimate 500 trees a day per planter. If we take a 60 day planting season (the period of favorable weather for planting) each planter would plant 30,000 trees each season. At 300 trees to the acre that would give 100 acres per planter. Thus it would take 10,000 tree planters employed for a 2 month period each year to plant our million acres a year.

There already exists an infrastructure of forest nurseries which could be expanded. With pyramid training programs it would not be too difficult to train the needed number of tree planters and nursery workers.

When we look at the large ranks of unemployed in New Zealand we see labor is not a problem. However, it takes more labor to pull off such a program than tree planters alone. It would also take nursery workers to grow the trees, planners, administrators, foresters, site survey-ors, workers to provide aftercare, i.e. fencing, shading, reducing competition, and later on thinning and pruning on some sites.

If we had 10,000 tree planters only employed for 2 months of the year they could carry on much of the other work during the other parts of the year. Trained foresters are needed to do site analysis and draw up plans. Surveyers are needed to draw up boundaries. How much additional personnel it would take to carry out these other activities adjunct to the actual tree planting would take a much more detailed study. Perhaps on the order of an extra 2,000 people.

Thus our proposed scheme to double New Zealand's forest cover would create employment for an additional 12,000 people. The present New Zealand forest industry employs 45,000 people.

Planning is best done by multi-disiplinary teams drawing on a wide range of expertise: Foresters, soil conserva-tors, farmers, permaculturists, wildlife managers, bee-keepers, etc. The wider the range of expertise and knowl-edge brought to bear on planning the more likely there will be satisfactory results.

Where Will the Land Come From ?

The bulk of the land would come from eroding, marginal grazing lands. Steep hill lands with low productivity and low stocking rates. Some of this is currently owned by the State and leased to graziers. A fair way of dealing with privately owned land will have to be addressed. This could take a number of forms and could vary from case to case. Paying graziers for losses in income on such marginal land would not be high since net income from such lands is low. In addition to, or in lieu of, lost income payments the landowner could get a share in the future income gener-ated from logging or other income generation. In most cases, such reforestation would affect only part of any one grazier's land holding. In fact their overall production might be improved by curtailing erosion on marginal slopes which are contributing to deterioration of more productive lands downslope. Farmers also could have the right to thinnings for poles, posts, firewood, etc. The terms would have to be favorable to farmers or there would be heavy opposition.

Also bear in mind that forest cover (planting trees) does not necessarily have to translate into dense forests. Agro-forestry is already highly advanced in New Zealand. One aspect of agroforestry is planting trees at a low density in grazing land to provide pruned up timber and allow grazing at the same time. Trials in many parts of New Zealand show that graziers can improve income through agroforestry. In some cases, pasture with trees yields more graze than pasture without trees. Helping farmers and graziers put in agroforestry schemes as well as additional windbreaks and woodlots can add greatly to tree cover in New Zealand without reducing grazing land significantly.

The Farm Forestry Association would be a great ally in promoting these ideas. The FFA provides a bank of expe-rienced workers in this field. They already know how to establish trees on farmlands and make it pay.

Some of the area presently classified as indigenous forest has no or poor forest cover. Planting native trees in these areas can increase forest cover without cutting into arable land.

New Zealand also has 18.1% of its area classified as other, non-forested land—over 12 million acres. Most of this is above timberline or is otherwise incapable of supporting a tree cover. But undoubtedly some of it is capable of supporting tree cover and could benefit from reforestation. Most of this would end up being classed as conservation planting for soil and water conservation, and wildlife habitat, with no logging permitted.

17

Urban and Suburban Areas

Cities, suburbs, towns, villages and farmsteads all offer tree planting opportunities. There are many good reasons for increasing tree cover in these settled areas of New Zealand. Besides shade and beauty, trees buffer noise, pollution, dust, and unpleasant sights. Trees provide fruit, nuts, and many other useful products. They provide homes for birds and wildlife and places for children to play. Some cities in the United States manage their street trees on a rotation basis and the timber pays the parks department's budget. The total affect of making our living areas greener and more habitable can add the equivalent of many acres of forest planting. Many people are willing to plant trees if they are given the chance. Let us look at our waste areas and community areas with an eye to planting trees, shrubs and vines. Groups such as the Auckland Tree Council and Friends of the Urban Trees are already doing good work which can be used for models.

Conclusion

It would take a coalition of many groups, from many sectors of society, to bring about massive tree-planting in New Zealand. It would take quite a bit of public pressure to induce politicians to back such a scheme. The benefits so outweigh the costs that there may be a chance for such a public coalition to evolve and dramatically increase New Zealand's forest cover. The trees would like that.

The preceding was excerpted from a larger Friends of the Trees Society report on forestry, agriculture and horticulture in New Zealand.

Kauri Tree

(*Agathis australis*)

Forests in New Zealand: A Resource Guide

Tree Organizations and Periodicals in New Zealand

Forest Research Institute
Private Bag
Rotorua, NEW ZEALAND
Tel: 82-179

The Rotorua Forest Research Institute is the main government forest research institute. They publish the *New Zealand Journal of Forestry Science* and a newsletter, *What's New in Forest Research.*

Landsendt Subtropical Nursery
108 Parker Road
Oratia, Auckland, NEW ZEALAND
Tel: 818-6914

Landsendt Nursery has a wide selection of subtropical fruits, palms and other unusual plants. Their orchard and grounds contains one of the most diverse plantings of tree species to be found in New Zealand.

Native Forest Restoration Trust
P.O. Box 80-007
Green Bay, Auckland 7, NEW ZEALAND
Tel: (04) 724-250

A hands-on group restoring forests.

New Zealand Farm Forestry Association
P.O. Box 715
Wellington, NEW ZEALAND
or: FFA Secretary: John Larsen
Box 888
Gisborne, NEW ZEALAND
Tel: (079) 86-497

One of the most influential and forward-looking tree organizations in New Zealand. Responsible for planting millions of trees on New Zealand farms for windbreaks, agroforestry and woodlots. The FFA has over 2,000 members and many branch chapters. The FFA publishes a quality quarterly, *The New Zealand Tree Grower*. One of the best journals on agroforestry available in the world.

New Zealand Forestry
New Zealand Institute of Foresters
Box 12-314
North Wellington, NEW ZEALAND
Tel: (04) 727-421

This quarterly journal is the best way to keep up with New Zealand forestry. Many of the views expressed are progressive. Well-written articles on the past, present and possible future of forestry in New Zealand.

New Zealand Tree Crops Association
Tom Dinning (Sec)
P.O. Box 14-053
Hamilton, NEW ZEALAND
Tel: (071) 66-768

An outstanding organization promoting tree crops, especially fruit and nut crops. Over 2,400 members with local chapters and special interest groups (like chestnuts, walnuts, pears, etc.). The TCA is the New Zealand version of the North American Fruit Explorers and the Northern Nut Growers Association all rolled into one. They publish a quarterly journal, *Growing Today*.

Water & Soil Science Center (Aokautere)
Private Bag
Palmerston North, NEW ZEALAND
Tel: 67-154

The main soil conservation research center in New Zealand. Their windbreak trials containing hundreds of trees and shrub species is well worth a visit. The plantings include many types of basket willows. They publish a range of material.

Conservation Organizations and Periodicals in New Zealand

An Environmental Directory: A Revised Listing of Groups & Organizations
Environmental Council. 1988. 73 pp. Available from the Ministry for the Environment.

The most extensive listing of environmental groups in New Zealand. Over 400 groups listed with address and phone numbers.

Canterbury Environment Center

P.O. Box 2547
Christchurch, NEW ZEALAND

Conservation Corps

Labour Dept.
P.O. Box 3705
Wellington, NEW ZEALAND

The Department of Conservation funded $3 million for the Conservation Corps in 1988. This pays young people, ages 16-23, to carry on tree planting, erosion control, wild animal surveys, and similar useful work.

Department of Conservation

P.O. Box 10-420
Wellington, NEW ZEALAND
Tel: (04) 710-726

A government department created in 1985 to take over some of the responsibilities of the dismantled NZ Forest Service and the Dept. of Lands and Survey. DoC has charge of the native forest lands owned by the State, plus National Parks and many other functions.

"ECO" Environmental & Conservation Organizations of NZ (INC)

P.O. Box 11-057
Wellington, NEW ZEALAND
Tel: (04) 846-971

A coalition of 96 environmental and conservation groups. Publishes a newsletter eleven times a year with news from many environmental groups.

Friends of the Earth (NZ)

P.O. Box 39-065
Auckland West, NEW ZEALAND
Tel: (03) 68-379

Connected with Friends of the Earth organizations in 33 countries. Part of a worldwide Tropical Rain Forest Campaign.

Greenpeace New Zealand

Private Bag
Wellesley Street
Auckland, NEW ZEALAND
Tel: (09) 776-128

Greenpeace has an active NZ group, predominantly coordinating actions in Antarctica.

Joint Campaign on Native Forests

3 New St.
Nelson, NEW ZEALAND

An environmental center which keeps in touch with many different conservation groups in the Nelson area. They maintain a public shop where publications and information can be obtained.

Maruia Society

P.O. Box 756
Nelson, NEW ZEALAND

One of the major conservation groups working for the forests, environment and native animals of New Zealand. An outspoken staff doing excellent work. Their quarterly magazine, *Maruia,* contains some of the most outspoken and penetrating critiques of government policy. In 1992 they also had programs in the Solomon Islands, Papua New Guinea and Fiji.

Ministry for the Environment Information Center

P.O. Box 10-362
Wellington, 1, NEW ZEALAND
Tel: (04) 734-090

The library has an extensive collection of papers and books from the world which is open to the public.

New Zealand Association of Soil and Water Conservators

P.O. Box 145
Blenheim, NEW ZEALAND

The New Zealand Association of Soil Conservators is a professional organization of people involved in soil and water conservation work.

New Zealand Environment

36 Coyle Street
Sandringham, Auckland 3, NEW ZEALAND

One of New Zealand's best environmental journals.

Pacific Institute of Resource Management

P.O. Box 10-123
the Terrace, Wellington

PIRM was founded in 1984. Its four main areas of operation are disarmament, global environmental issues, resource management in New Zealand, and biotechnology. It publishes *Pacific World*, a quarterly journal with articles on environmental and peace issues throughout the Pacific.

Queen Elizabeth II National Trust

P.O. Box 3341
Wellington, NEW ZEALAND
Tel: 726-626

An independent organization established in 1977 to protect, provide and enhance open space in New Zealand. The National Trust helps private landowners put all or portions of their land into trust so that its natural heritage is protected for future generations. By August 1988, 295 covenants had been registered and a further 375 were approved and proceeding towards registration.

The Trust has developed native plant revegetation guides geared to specific regions of New Zealand.

Royal Forest & Bird Protection Society of New Zealand

P.O. Box 631
Wellington, NEW ZEALAND

The largest and most active conservation organization in New Zealand. Formed in 1923, the Society now has over 53,000 members in 53 branches around the country. Their quarterly publication *Forest & Bird magazine* is a quality, colorful journal on the natural history of New Zealand and the protection of its flora and fauna.

Tree Council: Auckland

Tel: 79-4420 ext. 8334 or Jim Holdaway 418-3242

Promoting tree planting around Auckland and helping to coordinate the efforts of other Auckland tree groups. Working to set up similar tree councils in other parts of New Zealand.

Tree Society of New Zealand

P.O. Box 9158
Newmarket, Auckland, NEW ZEALAND
Tel: (09) 773-649

Founded 35 years ago. Their main fields of work have been in preservation of historical trees, supporting Arbor Day, school children planting trees, encouraging local bodies to plant trees. One of their mottos is "The right tree in the right place."

Books on Forests and Forestry in New Zealand

1986 Forestry Handbook

Hamish Levack, ed. 1987. New Zealand Institute of Foresters: Wellington. 140 pp.

An overview of the forestry situation in New Zealand. It includes information and figures on ecology, people, silviculture, agroforestry, mensuration, harvesting, economics, utilization and sale of forest products, etc. Well referenced.

Biogeography and Ecology in New Zealand

Editor G. Kuschel. 1975. Dr. W. Junk Pub.

The ecology and distribution of New Zealand life forms including plants, birds, fishes, insects and introduced mammals.

Economic Plants of New Zealand

S. E. Brooke, R. C. Canbe, R. C. Cooper. 1988. Botany Div. DSIR Christchurch. 130 pp. $16.50.

A Field Guide to the Native Edible Plants of New Zealand

Andrew Crowe. William Collins Pub.: Auckland. $21.95

This book represents an enormous amount of work, and contains over 200 references. 300 edible wild plants are covered.

Great Trees of New Zealand

S. W. Burstall and E. V. Sale. 288 pp.

A beautiful coffee-table book with photos and detailed descriptions of 100 of New Zealand's biggest, most beautiful, and historic trees (native and non-native). Hundreds of other notable trees are listed.

The Harrowing of Tane Mahuta

Denys Trussel. 1988. An article in two parts. Issues Number 57 and 58 of New Zealand Environment , 36 Coyle St., Sandringham, Auckland.

An eloquent, penetrating analysis of what has happened to New Zealand's forests and ecosystems since the coming of the Pakeha (Europeans). Trussel gives valuable insight into the cultural mores, values and attitudes that allows and promotes the destruction of the living world around us. Recommended.

Indigenous Forests of New Zealand

A. Kirkland and I. G. Trotman. NZ Forest Service. Wellington.

The Invasion of New Zealand by People, Plants and Animals

Andrew Hill Clark. 1949. Rutgers University Press.

The Land Our Future: Essays on Land Use and Conservation in New Zealand

A. Grant Anderson, ed. 1980. Longman Paul Pub.: 182-190 Wairau Rd. Auckland 10. 324 pp.

Many well-written articles. The best overview on the subject I saw in New Zealand.

Land of Tane: The Threat of Erosion

Richard St. Barbe Baker. 1956. Lutterworth Press: London. 142 pp.

Tane is the Maori God of Nature. Richard St. Barbe Baker, world-renowned "Man of the Trees," first arrived in New Zealand in 1954. He discovered a reckless exploitation of the soil and a lack of tree sense which he declared was creating deserts in New Zealand. Richard married New Zealander Catriona Burnett and lived much of his last years at Mount Count Station in New Zealand (he died in 1982 at the age of 92).

It was St. Barbe Baker who inspired the author of this report to found Friends of the Trees Society. Upon my travels to New Zealand in 1989, I found St. Barbe Baker's warnings were not heeded and much of New Zealand still in the process of being turned into desert.

Landforms of New Zealand

J. M. Soons and M. J. Selby, eds. 1982. 392 pp.

The many photographs show what New Zealand's landscapes look like. A readable text on physiography and geology.

17

Lands in Collision: Discovering New Zealand's Past Geography
Graeme Stevens. 1985. 129 pp. $23.40.

Traces the evolution of New Zealand since it parted from Gondwanaland. Plate tectonics applied to New Zealand. It also the traces the development of New Zealand's fauna and flora.

The Living Mantle: Soils in the New Zealand Landscape
Les Molloy. 1988. Mollinon Rendel Pub. 239 pp. $75.

An excellent textbook on soils with hundreds of color photographs and readable text. A fine model for soil textbooks in other countries.

"Management of Shelterbelts for Wood Products: A literature review"
C.G.R. Chavasse. 1982. *NZ Jour. of Forestry* 27 (2): 189-206.

The Native Trees of New Zealand
J. T. Salmon. 1980. Reed Ltd. 384 pp.

With thousands of color photographs, this is perhaps the most lavish book on the subject. Also describes forests and botanical exploration.

The Natural History of New Zealand: An Ecological Survey
Gordon R. Williams, ed. 1973. A. H. & A. W. Reed: Wellington. 434 pp.

The New Zealand Beeches: Ecology, Utilization and Management
John Wardle. 1984. N.Z. Forest Serv. 447 pp.

A very thorough, state-of-the-art, well-referenced book on the southern beeches (Nothofagus species).

New Zealand's Forests
Harriet Fleet. 1984. Heinemann Pub., Cnr. College Road & Kilham Ave., Auckland. 175 pp.

A good account by a conservationist who traces the history of New Zealand forests from pre-European to present.

Plant Materials Handbook for Soil Conservation In Three Volumes
Published by Water & Soil Science Center. Address under New Zealand Organizations.

Volume 1: Principles and Practices
D.W.S. Van Krayenoord and R. L. Hathaway. $46.00.

Propagation of many non-native species of trees and shrubs. A useful book for the nurseryperson.

Volume 2: Introduced Plants
D.W.S. Van Krayenoord and R. L. Hathaway. $49.50

Describes and illustrates 200 trees, shrubs and herbaceous species.

Volume 3: Native Plants
K. M. Pollock. $22.00.

Soil conservation and erosion control values of 70 species of native plants, sources of plant materials and propagation.

Tutira: The Story of a New Zealand Sheep Station
H. Guthrie-Smith. 1969. 4th edition. Reed Pub.: Wellington.

This is a classic book on the changes that happened to New Zealand's native plants, ecosystems and soils in response to European settlement and forest clearing. Mr. Guthrie-Smith was a farmer and a meticulous observer of the land. It deserves careful study by all New Zealanders and would make good reading for ecologists and conservationists in other countries.

The Vegetative Cover of New Zealand
P. F. J. Newsome. 1987. National Water and Soil Conservation Authority, 153 pages. $38.50.

An illustrated account of the composition, appearance, distribution and ecology of New Zealand's plant cover. The enclosed map is colorful and educational.

To Save a Forest: Whirinaki

A beautiful book on one of the last low-elevation, old-growth, podocarp forests. The book is full of beautiful photography and details the efforts of conservationists to save this forest.

Sources of Books from New Zealand

Touchwood Books
Peter Arthur
P.O. Box 610
Hastings, NEW ZEALAND

A wide variety of new and used books in the fields of horticulture, gardening, botany, forestry, natural history, etc.

Forests in Australia: A Resource Guide

AUSTRALIA, THE LAND DOWN UNDER—full of magic places and many wonderful trees and forests. Australia is like nowhere else. Most of the population and forests are found along the continent's eastern fringe, where Australia's highest mountains and ridges catch ocean moisture. Most people think of red dust and eucalyptus forests when they think of Australia, but there are also lush subtropical forests found along the northern New South Wales and Queensland coasts. These remnant forests are the direct descendants of the 140 million-year-old Gondwanaland forests.

The Present Situation

Australia comprises 761 million hectares (ha) of land. (1 hectare = 2.5 acres). Of this, 41 million hectares (5.5%) is closed canopy forest and 65 million hectares (8.3%) is open forest (dispersed trees). A survey carried out in 1984 shows 87 million hectares (217 million acres) or 36 percent, of Australian forests and woodlands have been cleared since European settlement. This is a large proportion of the overall vegetation cover to have been lost in less than 200 years. But the most disturbing aspect of the survey is that large regions have lost 80-100 percent of their tree cover. The entire agricultural region of South Australia has had 87 percent of its trees cleared. Australia lost 9.6% of its forest area just between 1975 and 1990.

The negative effects of the loss of tree cover and consequent erosion and salt affected farmland has come under increasing scrutiny and concern over the past several decades, and increasing numbers of Australians have responded by protecting the environment and planting trees. Australia has many public tree planting projects (national to local) which can serve as models for other parts of the world.

How to get farmers to plant trees on marginal cropland

The Western Australia Dept of Conservation and Land Management has set up a pilot scheme, involving more than 100 farmers and 30,000 acres of farm land being planted to pine and eucalyptus plantations. The farmers get paid an annual return on their plantations from a trust fund, based on estimates of the trees final yield and suitable "rental" rates for the use of the farmer's land. The annual payments have met with enough favor by farmers that the department has developed an ambitious plan to put more than 100,000 ha of farmland under eucalypt plantations in the next 11 years. This would be quite commendable if they planted mixed plant communities to restore native plant cover that would perform ecological functions, as well as provide economic return.

200 Million Trees Campaign Reaches Target!

In 1985, Claire Ekas had an idea to plant 200 million trees around Australia. She initiated a 3-year program in September, 1985. By the time it ended in 1988, Australians had actually planted 202 million trees.

To achieve this vision Claire "concentrated on the positive" benefits of tree planting to inspire thousands of people into action through civic groups, schools, government, tree planting groups, grassroots, etc.

She not only counted trees her program had planted but all trees planted by government, industry, etc. Still, it was quite an accomplishment and her push put many more millions of trees in the ground. One person can make a difference!

Claire & Robert Ekas, Roberts Road, M.S. 342, Roadvale, 4310 Queensland, AUSTRALIA.

Landcare Movement in Australia

Australian land management policy has undergone a major shift in recent years towards actively supporting sustainable land use practices. A national Landcare movement has emerged with over 20% of Australia's 145,000 farmers currently (1993) participating in local landcare groups.

The reforms have been motivated by the extent and severity of land degradation with its attendant economic, social and environmental consequences, widespread community support for change, and the international debate on Ecologically Sustainable Development.

Some of the principles of landcare include:

* Extensive use of trees, shrubs and perennial plants
* A 'land ethic'
* The goal of sustainable production and ecologically-based natural resource management
* Intelligent design of landuse systems
* A systems approach to environmentally sensitive production
* Integration of environmental and production goals
* Ecosystem knowledge, ecological literacy and land literacy
* Community empowerment and focus

Extracted from issue #47 of Permaculture International Journal, *"Permaculture and Landcare" by Jason Alexander.*

LandcareNet

Janet Hoare, LandcareNet facilitator
School of Agriculture and Forestry
The University of Melbourne
Parkville, Victoria 3052 AUSTRALIA
Tel: int + 61+ (0)3 344 7172/Fax: int + 61 + (0)3 344 5570

Computer networking through LandcareNet now enables anyone with an interest in landcare to exchange information with others around Australia. LandcareNet enables landcare groups around Australia to link in with each other to share resources and experience, knowledge etc.

National Landcare Program

Commonwealth Dept. of Primary Industries
GPO Box 858
Canberra, ACT 2601, AUSTRALIA

Periodicals Related to Forestry in Australia

Australian Forestry

Institute of Foresters of Australia
Box E73
Queen Victoria Terrace, A.C.T. 2600, AUSTRALIA

Conventional forest practices.

Environment West Australia

Environment Center
794 Hay St.
Perth 6000, West Australia, AUSTRALIA

One of Australia's leading environment magazines.

Habitat Australia

Australian Conservation Foundation
672 Glenferrie Road
Hawthorn, Victoria 3122, AUSTRALIA
Tel: 819-2888

Magazine of Conservation and Environment. Glossy. Good quality articles.

Journal of Soil Conservation New South Wales

Soil Conservation Service of New South Wales
P.O. Box 198
Chatsworth, New South Wales 2057, AUSTRALIA

Australian Directories

Green Pages Directory

Australian Conservation Foundation. (address in following section).

This directory contains 1069 listings of Peace and Environmental Organizations. Cost is A$19.50 postpaid in Australia.

Information Guide

National Tree Program Task Group. Address in following section.

Lists resources of books, articles, pamphlets, posters, films, organizations concerned with trees in Australia.

Tree Organizations in Australia

Australian Academy of Science

P.O. Box 783
Canberra City, A.C.T., 2601, AUSTRALIA

Australian Trust for Conservation Volunteers

P.O. Box 423
Ballarat, Victoria, 3350, AUSTRALIA

ATCV puts people to work planting trees and doing other earthcare work. For $9 a day, ATCV provides room, board and transport to restoration work sites. Projects throughout Australia.

Bray's Rainforest Nursery

Eland, (West of Taree), New South Wales, AUSTRALIA
Tel: (065) 504-596

One of the few nurseries specializing in native rainforest hardwood trees.

Ecological Society of Australia

P.O. Box 1564
Canberra A.C.T. 2601, AUSTRALIA

The Good Wood Group

Bob Whitworth
#2 Deserio Road
Cedar Pocket
Queensland, 4570, AUSTRALIA
Tel: 074-866147

17

They work with the Wilderness Society to encourage the use of wood from native trees planted on marginal farmland. Their farm in southeast Queensland grows native rainforest trees and takes in WWOF workers (Willing Workers on Organic Farms).

Greening Australia

GPO Box 9868
Yarralumla, ACT, 2601, AUSTRALIA
Tel: 06-281-8585

Administering Federal Government One Billion Trees Program.

International Tree Crops Institute

P.O. Box 85
Mt. Bravatt, Queensland, 4122, AUSTRALIA
Tel: 07-345-1979 Fax: 07-849-2247

The ITCI was founded in 1977 with a focus on multipurpose tree crops and agroforestry. Bi-annual publication.

Men of the Trees Victoria

P.O. Box 281
Cauberwell, Victoria, 3124, AUSTRALIA

One of the most energetic branches of Men of the Trees in the world and one of the biggest planters of trees in Victoria.

Southern Connection

Department of Plant Science, University of Tasmania
GPO Box 252C
Hobart, 7001, Tasmania, AUSTRALIA

A broad-based network of life scientists who study southern hemisphere ecosystems. Communication centers on a biannual newsletter, which aims to establish and facilitate close research links.

Subtropical Farm Forestry Association

P.O. Box 1320
Lismore, New South Wales, 2480, AUSTRALIA
Tel/Fax: 066-895374
Contact: Larry Geno

Members include growers of native and exotic cabinet timbers, eucalypt plantations, bush-foods, and ecotourist interests. Wants to exchange research results on direct seeding of rainforest species in humid subtropical environments.

Victorian Farm Trees and Land Management Groups

c/o Greg King, Victoria Farmers' Federation
Farmer House, Collins Street
Melbourne, Victoria, 3000, AUSTRALIA
Tel: 03 6509261

A network of farmers planting trees. Produces a journal, *Trunkline*.

Victorian Trust for Conservation Volunteers

P.O. Box 417
Ballarat, 3350 Victoria, AUSTRALIA
Tel: 053-32-7490 or 054-76-4217

Environmental Organizations in Australia

Australian Conservation Foundation

672 B Glenferrie Rd.
Hawthorn, Victoria, 3122, AUSTRALIA

One of the major environmental groups. They have many useful publications on forests.

Big Scrub Environmental Center

88a Keen Street
Lismore, New South Wales, AUSTRALIA
Tel: 066-21-3278

A great place for environmental networking. Sells books and publishes environmental newsletter for area.

Conservation Council of Victoria

247 Flinders Lane
Melbourne, Victoria, 3000, AUSTRALIA
Tel: 6544-833

Publishes quarterly newsmagazine entitled *Environment Victoria*. Lots of good information.

Environment Center of West Australia

P.O. Box 7375
Cloister Square, Perth, West Australia, 6850, AUSTRALIA
Tel: 9-321-5942 or 322-3045

Green Peace Australia

PO Box 51
Balmain, NSW, 2041
Tel: 02-555-7044

Natural Resources Conservation League of Victoria

P.O. Box 105
Springvale, 3171 Victoria, AUSTRALIA
Tel (03) 546-9744/Fax 547-8791

They publish *Trees and Natural Resources,* a slick conservation magazine with a 31 year history.

Queensland Conservation Council

P.O. Box 12046, Elizabeth St.
Brisbane, Queensland, 4002, AUSTRALIA
Tel: (7) 2210188

The biggest conservation group in Queensland, working on many environmental issues.

Rainforest Conservation Society of Queensland
15 Colorado Ave.
Bardon, Queensland, 4065 AUSTRALIA
Liane Newsletter.

Rainforest Information Center
PO Box 368, Lismore
New South Wales, 2480, AUSTRALIA
Tel: 066 218505.

The Rainforest Information Center (RIC) was one of the first tropical rainforest activist groups and their newsletter, *World Rainforest Report*, remains one of the best sources of information on rainforests in the world. Highly recommended. Working on regional wood certification.

Tasmania Environment Center
Greenpeace Australia
102 Bathurst St.
Hobart, Tasmania 7000, AUSTRALIA
Tel: (002) 345-566

Total Environment Center
18 Argyle Street Top Floor
Sydney, New South Wales, 2000, AUSTRALIA
Tel: 27-4714

Sydney and its environs contain about 30% of Australia's population so it is a hub of every kind of activity, including environmental. The Total Environment Center, in particular, stands out as a network hub for forest activism in Australia.

Wilderness Society
362 PH St.
Sydney, New South Wales, 2000, AUSTRALIA

Campaigns against forest destruction in Tasmania.

Conventional Forestry Organizations in Australia

Australian Forest Growers
PO Box 5
South Yarra, Victoria, 3141, AUSTRALIA
Tel: 03-525-4998

Represents private forest growers in Australia. Publishes *Australian Forest Grower.*

Australian Forestry Council
P.O. Box 858
Canberra City, ACT 2601 AUSTRALIA
Tel: 062-71-7370/Fax 062-72-4526

Australian National University
Department of Forestry
GPO Box 4
Canberra, ACT, 2601, AUSTRALIA

Center for Rainforest Studies
School of Field Studies

Yungaburra, Queensland 4872, AUSTRALIA

Conservation Commission Northern Territory
P.O. Box 38496
Winnellie, Northern Territory, 5789, AUSTRALIA

CSIRO—Division of Forest Research
P.O. Box 4008
Canberra City, 2600, ACT, AUSTRALIA
Tel: 062-81-8370/Fax 062-81-8312

Commonwealth Scientific and Industrial Research Organization.

CSIRO—Division of Forest Research
Atherton, Queensland, 4883, AUSTRALIA

CSIRO—Division of Forest Research
Hobart, Tasmania, 7000, AUSTRALIA
Tel: 002-308-169

CSIRO Library (Commonwealth Scientific and Industrial Research Organization)
Private Bag PO
Aitkenvalo, Queensland, 4814, AUSTRALIA

The most prestigious and largest government program for agriculture and forestry research. Many publications are available, some good.

Forestry Commission of New South Wales
GPO Box 2667
Sydney, New South Wales, 2001, AUSTRALIA
Tel 02-234-1552/Fax 02-290-1299

Forests Department of Western Australia
Dwellingup, Western Australia 6243, AUSTRALIA

National Association of Forest Industries Ltd.
24 Napier Close
Deakin, ACT, 2600, AUSTRALIA
Tel: 06-285-3833 Fax: 06-285-3855

Books on Australian Forest Management

Agroforestry in Australia and New Zealand
Rowan Reid and Geoff Wilson. 1986. Goddard and Dobson Pub.: 486 Station St., Box Hill, Victoria 3128. 254 pp. Out-of-print, but copies may be obtained directly from the author by calling Rowan Reid at Tel: (052) 887247.

Australia and New Zealand are both centers for research and experimentation in agroforestry. Especially pertinent for the livestock agroforester. Good presentation and lots of information.

Australia's Forests—Their role in Our Future
1981. Austr. Acad. of Science: Canberra.

Written from the viewpoint of industry and government, but it does offer one viewpoint of future forestry.

17

Bring Back the Bush: The Bradley Method of Bush Regeneration
Joan Bradley. 1988. Lansdowne-Rigby Publishers 372 Eastern Valley Rd., Willoughby, NSW 2068. 111 pp.

Bush Regeneration: Recovering Australian Landscapes
Robin A. Buchanan. 1989. TAFE Student Learning Publications: Sydney, Australia. 259 pp.

Examines regeneration projects in various plant communities throughout Australia. The most extensive publication on the subject as it is presently practiced in Australia.

Caring for Young Trees
Neil Inall and Ron Dryman, eds. Australia Broadcasting Corp., 145 Elizabeth St., Sydney, NSW 2001. 116 pp.

Ground preparation and planting, moisture supply, case histories. Goes into detail on how to make tree guards of all sorts to protect trees from livestock and wild critters—a common problem for tree planters all around the world. Includes tables for tree species recommended for different climate and rainfall regimes.

Casuarina Utilization & Management
S. J. Midgley, J. W. Turnbull and R. D. Johnson. 1983. CSIRO. 286 pp.

Proceedings of an international workshop in Canberra, 1981. Contains Casuarina reports from 10 other countries. Nursery practice, establishment, uses. Has a bibliography covering 1800 to 1981.

Casuarinas: Nitrogen Fixing Trees for Adverse Sites
Nat. Acad. Press. 1984. Washington DC, USA. Innovations in Tropical Forest Series. 118 pp.

Many references.

Eucalypts for Planting
1979. FAO: Rome. 674 pp.

Voluminous work covering most species of Eucalyptus planted commercially in Australia and elsewhere in the world. There are over 1,000 Acacia species and 450 Eucalyptus species in Australia. Eucalyptus, Acacias and Casuarinas are highly valued trees in many parts of the world. The world has more than 15 million acres of Eucalyptus plantations outside Australia. Plus, there are over 2.5 million acres of Australian Acacia and Casuarina species planted abroad.

Eucalypts for Wood Production
W. E. Hillis and A. G. Brown, eds. 1984. Academic Press: Sydney. 433 pp.

Voluminous work. Establishment, management, yields, harvest, utilization, protection. Thousands of references.

The Fight for the Forests: The Takeover of Australian Forests for Pines, Wood Chips and Intensive Forestry
Canberra: Research School of Social Sciences, Australian National University.

Germination of Australian Native Plant Seed
Peter J. Langkamp, ed. 1987. Inkata Press. 236 pp.

One of the most comprehensive books on the subject. Detailed. Many refs.

Introduction to the Successful Growing of Rainforest and Harvestable Timbers
Jack Mitchell. 1993. 16 pp. Available from Green Harvest, 52 Crystal Waters, MS 16, Maleny, QLD, 4552, Australia

Introduces the Mitchell Low Maintenance System which is designed to follow the natural regeneration cycle of an area.

Multipurpose Australian Trees and Shrubs: Lesser-Known Species for Fuelwood and Agroforestry
John W. Turnbull, ed. 1986. Australian Center for International Agriculture Research, GPO Box 1571, Canberra ACT 2601.

A useful publication which covers 100 species. Names, attributes, range, climate, soils, vegetation companions, pests, utilization, silviculture. Gives research contacts and references for each species.

Plant A Tree: A Working Guide to the Greening of Southeast Queensland
Wally Davies, ed. 1984. Ecos Educational Pub.: Nambour, Qld. 144 pp.

Very good model for other regions of Australia as well as other countries. Information on growing trees, creek revegetation, case studies, trees in the city, trees on the farm, natural plant communities, education, references and useful appendices. Lists Australian organizations planting trees and nurseries.

Prospects for Australian Hardwood Forests
J. Dargarel and G. Sheldon, eds. 1987. Monograph 19, Center for Resource and Enviromental Studies. 334 pp.

A conservation strategy from the viewpoint of the timber industry. How to stabilize industry and conserve forests. Directions to take, policies, statistics. Aimed at policymakers.

Report on Australia's Forests
The Australian Resources Assessment Commission, which reports directly to the Australian Prime Minister, published in late 1991 an encyclopedic draft report on forest resources and possible futures under different policy prescriptions.

Revegetation: Methods and Management
J. M. Temple and David Bungey. 1980. NSW Pollution Control Commission. 93 pp.

Covers many methods including transfer of brushland soil, seed, grass and brush. Short coverage of many areas, but well referenced.

Saving Australia: A Blueprint for Our Survival
Vincent Serventy. 1988. Child & Assoc. Pub., 5 Skyline Place, French Forest, NSW 2086. 176 pp.

Makes a good case for sustainable use of resources, forest preservation, etc. "Appendix 2: A National Conservation Strategy for Australia" is notable as a national strategy which can be used as a model in other countries or regions.

Total Catchment Management
Journal of Soil Conservation New South Wales. Special Edition Vol. 42 No. 1. 1986. 88 pp.

Total Catchment Management involves the coordinated use and management of land, water, vegetation and other physical resources and activities within a catchment, to ensure minimal degradation and erosion of soils and minimal impact on water yield and quality and on other features of the environment. This publication represents thinking at upper government land management levels on the subject of whole watershed management.

Tropical Rainforests of North Queensland: Their Conservation and Significance
Rainforest Conservation Soc. of Aust. 1986. Australian Heritage Pub: Series # 3. Austr. Govt. Pub. Serv. 195 pp.

The Queensland tropical rainforests are direct descents of the 140 million year old Gondwanaland forests. There is an ongoing struggle to save the last of the uncut rainforests and place them in Biosphere Reserve status.

The Use of Trees and Shrubs in the Dry Country of Australia
Norman Hall et al. 1972. Govt. Pub. Serv.: Canberra. Dept of Nat. Dev. Forestry & Timber Bureau.

Encyclopedic and very useful.

What Future for Australia's Arid Lands
John Messer and Geoff Masley, eds. 1983. Australian Conservation Foun. 206 pp. Proceedings of the Nat. Arid lands Conf. Broken Hill NSW. May, 1982

Many articles and papers covering status, current use, factors affecting, future, strategies, etc. The list of 230 participants with their addresses is a useful networking tool.

The Wood and Trees
Dr. John Cameron and Ian Penna. 1988. Australian Conservation Foundation.

This book takes a look at what sustainable forestry might look like in Australia. A commendable attempt to map out a strategy for shifting Australia's wood products industry into a sustainable path. A preliminary economic analysis of a conservation oriented forest industry strategy. Many references, facts and figures on amount of forests, rates of harvesting, plantations, how to phase into a plantation log industry

Books on Australian Forest History, Natural History, and Ecology

Australian Rainforest Plants
Vol 1, 1985. Vol 2, 1988. Both 72 pp. Terania Rainforest Nursery, The Channon, NSW 2480.

Well done books with color photographs. The text gives garden uses, culture, and brief amount on properties.

Australian Rainforests: A Review
Garry L. Werren and David Allworth. Monash Pub. in Geography. No. 28. 1982. Dept of Geography, Monash Univ., Melbourne 3168. 94 pp.

An overview of their distribution, composition, values, and dynamics. The authors also look at the threats to the rainforests and outline alternatives to logging.

Australian Soils: The Human Impact
J. S. Russell and R. F. Isbell, eds. 1986. Univ. of Queensland Press: St. Lucia. 522 pp. $50.

A well-written overview, readable, timely. Covers aboriginal impact, fire, agriculture, forestry, mining, urbanization.

Burning Bush—A Fire History of Australia
Stephen J. Pyne. Henry Holt Press. $27.95.

Fire from pre-human, aboriginal till 1983 Ash Wednesday.

The Ecology of Forests and Woodlands of South Australia
H. R. Wallace, ed. 1986. Govt. Printer, South Australia. 291 pp. $22.

Fire and the Australian Biota
A. M. Gill, R. H. Groves, and I. R. Noble, eds. 1981. Aust. Acad. of Sci. 551 pp.

Papers from a 1978 conference. Pre-European to present day.

Forest Trees of Australia
D. J. Boland, et al. 4th edition 1984. CSIRO. 687 pp.

Describes and illustrates 223 of the most important

17

native trees. 137 eucalypts and 86 non-eucalypt trees. For each species it gives range maps and photos of seedlings, leaves, veination, juvenile leaves, buds, bark, fruits and mature trees. The standard reference work. Brief ecological information.

Forest Soils and Nutrient Cycles

P. M. Attiwill and G. W. Leeper. 1987. Melbourne Univ. Press. 202 pp.

This pioneering work examines the distribution, productivity, soils and complex nutrient cycling of Australia's forests. Many references.

A History of Forestry in Australia

L. T. Carron. 1985. Aust. Nat. Univ. Press: Canberra. 355 pp.

State by state review. Mainly viewpoint of industry and government.

Native Conservation: The Role of Remnants of Native Vegetation

D. Sanders, G. Arnold, et al. 1985. Surrey Beatty and Sons, 43 Richard Rd., Cripping, Norton 2170, NSW.

Ecology, measuring, genetics, management.

Natural Legacy: Ecology in Australia

Harry F. Recher, Daniel Lunney, and Irima Dunn, eds. 2nd Ed. 1986. Pergamon Press. 443 pp.

An excellent overview. Recommended as the best ecology text. Includes forest ecosystems, biogeography, animals, invasions, human interactions. Hundreds of refs.

Nature of Australia: Portrait of the Island Continent

J. Vanderbeld. 1988. Collins Pub. 290 pp.

Based on the excellent ABC TV series. One of the best overviews of the history and ecology of Australia. Great color photos, easy to read and heaps of fascinating information. Not just a picture book.

The Vegetation of Australia

Noel C.W. Beadle. 1981. Cambridge Univ. Press. 691 pp.

First account which covers all of Australia. Detailed descriptions of plant communities. An amazing breadth of knowledge for one individual.

17

18 Restoration Forestry in Human Landscapes

Michael Guizar

18

Forestry in Human Landscapes

Michael Pilarski

IN THIS SECTION, we look at forestry in cities, suburbs, towns, villages, homesteads, and farms. Restoration forestry includes urban forestry, permaculture, agroforestry and gathering wild foods. Restoration forestry has an important role to play in sustainable agriculture, in protecting farm crops and livestock, and in conserving and building soil. Besides extensive resource guides on these subjects, this section includes articles on hedgerows, non-timber products and making paper with non-tree fibers.

One of permaculture's goals is to maximize production adjacent to human habitations. In relation to forestry, this means we bring the forest into the city and onto the farmland. Forestry can start virtually at people's doorsteps instead of being an activity relegated to the far-distant mountains. There are some cities which manage their street trees for high value timber production and bring substantial income to the town treasury. If this sort of tree awareness extended across the country there would be a large production of valuable timber which could be auctioned off to local woodworkers. Presently, a lot of valuable wood in U.S. cities ends up as firewood or landfill.

Restoration Forestry and Agriculture

Farmland offers a tremendous production possibility for forest products. For instance:

1. Conversion of marginal farmland to forests. It would cost the U.S. little in terms of total food production if the worst one-quarter of the farmland was put into forest (low productivity land which is eroded and/or eroding, much of it semiarid). As petroleum and industrial inputs increase in price, industrial mechanized agriculture on these marginal farmlands becomes less economically viable. With proper selection of species, this marginal farmland could be quite productive from a forestry standpoint.

2. Agroforestry combines trees and agricultural production in various spatial and time patterns. For instance, scattered trees in pastures, windbreaks, shelterbelts, and tree lines along fences, boundaries, riparian zones, roadways, canals, etc. These trees not only yield a significant amount of products themselves (including timber) they also can actually increase crop yields, and livestock weight gains. Shelterbelts reduced crop losses by over 40% in Denmark in the 19th century. Shelterbelts increased crop yields 100-400% in the USSR, 50-100% in China, and 23% in the Majjia Valley, Niger (statistics from *Global Forests* by Laarman and Sedjo. 1992).

3. It is possible to increase the percentage of food production which comes from tree crops as opposed to annual crops. There are hundreds and thousands of tree species which yield food. Some of them are well-known, many little-known. It is feasible to increase the tree crops share of the human diet to a much higher percentage than at present. This has benefits of reducing fuel needs for annual cropping, reducing soil erosion, providing high value foods, and increasing the world's tree cover. Some of these tree crops produce fine timber also, such as walnut, chestnut and oak.

These strategies applied on a broad scale would greatly increase the amount of wood production on lands presently not considered for forestry. This production could supply a substantial portion of a conserving society's wood needs, thus lessening need for exploitation of more distant forests. Wood production close to human habitation meets another permaculture design principle: placing needed elements as close to the point of consumption as possible to minimize transport costs.

18

Fruit and Nut Orchards as Suppliers of Wood Products

Consider the role of fruit and nut orchards in supplying wood products. There are millions of acres in tree fruits and nuts around the world. These all supply wood in the form of prunings and eventual removal of the tree.

The prunings in many cultures are used for firewood. It is more common in industrialized countries to pile and burn prunings for quick disposal. Better to slash the prunings with a heavy mower so they will break down quickly on the orchard floor and contribute organic matter. Green prunings can be run through shredders to make compost or to provide a substrate for growing edible mushrooms. Local artisans use the long, whippy water sprouts from apple and pear trees to weave baskets, wreaths and wicker furniture. This illustrates the permaculture principle of turning a waste into a resource. These are just a few examples of how fruit tree prunings can supply wood products.

Let's talk about wood products when the tree is eventually cut down. The wood from many fruit and nut trees is of good quality. Walnut wood is a famous example. American chestnut (*Castanea dentata*) wood was one of the most highly valued hardwoods in the eastern U.S. until chestnut blight wiped it out. Some fruit woods are especially tough, others take a high polish, some can be used for handles. There are large amounts of fruit wood which are milled into boards throughout the world. Apple, pear, apricot, cherry, and plum produce beautiful, dense woods. Apricot wood is very attractive with streaks of orange, apricot, and brown. Plum wood has purples. Persimmon (*Diospyros*) is the furthest north of the ebony family and its dense, hard black wood is a fine ebony. Many fruit woods lend themselves to making small articles, both ornamental and utilitarian. Wood lends itself to beauty much more than metal or plastic and is not polluting in its manufacture.

If orchardists were more encouraged by local sawmills who would take their wood, then they would probably tend to manage tree shapes to get better milling utilization. Wherever there are fruit trees, there should be tools and people equipped to deal with the valuable wood. If nothing else, fruit wood makes great firewood.

Critics may scoff at the rather small percentage of wood products that the fruit & nut wood in the world could provide. Compared to total wood demand, it isn't much, but if the acreage devoted to fruits and nuts were increased by ten times, that would correspondingly increase its contribution to the wood supply. Also consider that fruit and nut woods are high value and generally employ more people per unit volume compared to structural timber or paper pulp.

Wherever there are people, there should be fruit trees. Wherever there are fruit trees, there will be wood.

18

Permaculture: A Resource Guide

What is Permaculture?

THE TERM "PERMACULTURE" was coined in 1978 by Australian Bill Mollison as a contraction of "permanent agriculture." It can also be defined as "permanent culture."

In the broadest sense, permaculture refers to land use systems which promote stability in society, use resources in a sustainable way and preserve wildlife habitat as well as the genetic diversity of wild and domestic plants and animals.

The overall aim of permaculture design is to produce an efficient, low-maintenance, productive integration of plants, animals, structures and people; with the ultimate result of on-site stability and food self-sufficiency in the smallest practical area. The aim is also to plan for craft or other products that yield a trade or commercial potential for clients. Permaculture designs human habitats in such a way that the land grows in richness, productivity and aesthetic beauty. Permaculture is an ethical system stressing positivism and cooperation.

Permaculture involves ethics of earth care because the sustainable use of land cannot be separated from lifestyles and philosophical issues. Permaculture strongly advocates the preservation of existing wildlands and the rehabilitation of degraded ecosystems. Permaculture forests close to habitations are intensively managed, higher yielding, and use a mix of native and non-native species. Forests further out become less intensively managed and rely on native species. Stability and diversity are the keynotes. Conservation of soil, water and energy are central issues.

In permaculture systems, our aim is local production to meet local needs. Export low-volume, high-value, locally-processed items after local needs are met. This creates healthy, local economies and minimizes transportation costs.

Characteristics of permaculture

+ Permaculture is one of the most holistic, integrated systems analysis and design methodologies found in the world.

+ Permaculture can be applied to create productive ecosystems from the human-use standpoint or to help degraded ecosystems recover health and wildness. Permaculture can be applied in any ecosystem no matter how degraded.

+ Permaculture values and validates traditional knowledge and experience. Permaculture incorporates sustainable agriculture and land management techniques and strategies from around the world. Permaculture is a bridge between traditional cultures and emergent earth-tuned cultures.

+ Permaculture promotes organic agriculture which does not use pesticides to pollute the environment.

+ Permaculture aims to maximize symbiotic and synergistic relationships between site components.

+ Permaculture is urban planning as well as rural land design.

+ Permaculture design is site specific, client specific and culture specific.

Permaculture Practitioners' Relationships with Plants

Permaculture practitioners seek to know the place they live intimately: To know each plant, animal, insect and life form that make up the ecosystems in which we live; to know all the uses of each plant, when and how to collect, process and manufacture the derived products; to know the role of each species in the ecosystem. Who is the species related to? What does it eat, who eats it, where does it like to grow, how does it grow? Who are its partners? There is so much to know about the interconnected webs of life. Ethnobotany is a key subject in permaculture. Permaculture aims to integrate native plants into human landscapes to meet human needs.

In the above pursuits, permaculturists are similar to indigenous peoples. However Permaculturists find these pursuits much more difficult than indigenous peoples. For one thing, although native peoples did migrate around somewhat, they usually lived for generations in the same area. Because of this, thousands of years of plant knowledge and ecology are passed down from generation to generation. Indigenous people make the best permaculturists. At present, most permaculturists come from modern, mobile societies, and oftentimes live in a different area than where they grew up. Usually raised by parents/society which did not teach them much about native plants, animals and webs of life. Another difficulty is permaculturists not only have to learn all the native plants where they live, they also have to learn the many farm crops, garden plants, and weeds people have moved around the globe. The permaculturist has the benefit/ challenge of being able to study the flora and fauna of the world and the interactions of native and non-native species in our landscapes as we implement permaculture designs and ecosystem restoration.

The Permaculture Approach

Permaculture is not easy to define, but two of its most important characteristics are it aims to work with nature rather than against, and it is a design system for total landscapes. By total landscapes I mean all the land and water area in which humans live and find our needs, not just the purely decorative areas we normally associate with the phrase "landscape design."

There are two parts to the design process. First comes the passive, receptive part, observing and listening to the land and the people, finding out what each needs and has to offer. Second comes the active part, making suggestions and decisions about what will go where. Of the two, the first is far and away the most important. The designer who puts the most emphasis on this part of the process is more likely to come up with a design which will be indefinitely sustainable, have a low energy requirement and meet the needs of both land and people without depleting either.

This emphasis on observing and listening is fundamental to the permaculture approach. This means looking at a piece of land and asking what it is best for as it is, rather than deciding what we want to grow there and then changing the land to fit our desires. The prime example is wet land. The conven-

tional approach is to drain it in order to grow a dryland crop, whether of trees, grass or arable. A permaculture approach is to see it as an ideal place to plant willows. The natural state of the land is seen as an asset, not a problem.

—Excerpted from *Woodland in Permaculture* by Patrick Whitefield

Permaculture and Forest Preservation

What does permaculture have to do with forest preservation? Not too much yet, but the possibilities are immense. Development experts have finally realized that forest preservation is dependent on the well-being of local people. Permaculture offers the flexibility and the techniques to work with local people to create sustainable, productive farms, relieving pressure on nearby systems. Permaculture design can be applied to semi-wild buffer zones around villages and around forest preserves.

Permaculture offers perhaps the best synthesis so far, of a way for people to live in harmony with the Earth. If all people everywhere can learn to produce most of their food and resource needs locally while at the same time enriching and building up the biological productivity of their environments, then we can yet restore the earth's biological richness.

Permaculture Is An International Network

Permaculture principles and design have proven useful wherever applied; from urban cities in overdeveloped countries to subsistence villages in backcountry Nepal, India, Botswana, and Zimbabwe.

Foresters, farmers, and anyone working with land can benefit from a working knowledge of permaculture principles and methodologies. Permaculture design courses are the main educational tool of the permaculture movement. Permaculture design courses average 14 days, but some are as few as 10 and some as many as 20 days depending on venue and instructors. The main purpose of the design courses is to impart permaculture principles and methodologies, which can then be applied anywhere in the world. The international permaculture network includes over 8,000 permaculture design course graduates from dozens of countries. To find out about permaculture courses in your region, contact the nearest permaculture organization or periodical.

18

Countries where permaculture design courses have been held

This is a preliminary list compiled by Friends of the Trees Society in late 1993. Further consultation with other permaculture centers will add to this list.

Oceania

> Australia–100 +
>
> New Zealand–8

Asia

> India–14
>
> Nepal–11
>
> Vietnam–1
>
> Hong Kong–1
>
> Macao–1
>
> Indonesia–1

Americas

> USA–95
>
> Mexico–11
>
> Canada–6
>
> Ecuador–4
>
> Guatemala–3
>
> Brazil–2
>
> Belize–1
>
> Jamaica–1

Africa

> Zimbabwe–4
>
> Botswana–3
>
> South Africa–2

Europe

> England–20
>
> Germany–6
>
> France–5
>
> Denmark–5
>
> Sweden–2
>
> Norway–2
>
> Netherlands–2
>
> Hungary–1
>
> Ireland–1
>
> Spain–1
>
> Portugal–1

A total of over 300 Permaculture Design Courses.

Permaculture Organizations

These are a few of the dozens of permaculture organizations and periodicals around the world. For a full list contact the *Permaculture International Journal*.

Instituto de Permacultura da Bahia

> Condominio Aguas Finas
> Lauro De Freitas, Bahia, BRAZIL, CEP 42700-000
> Fax: 55 71 378 1520/Tel: 55 71 378 1115/1769

Marsha Hanzi has probably done more than anyone to bring permaculture to Brazil.

International Permaculture Institute

> P.O. Box 1
> Tyalgum, New South Wales, 2484, AUSTRALIA
> Tel: 61-66-79-3442/Fax: 61-66-79-3567

An international permaculture center for information, publishing and book sales. Headquarters of Tagari Publications and of permaculture's founder, Bill Mollison. Mollison practices what he preaches. After purchasing a house with a mowed lawn in 1988, Mollison had the house hidden by over 142 species of trees within 18 months. The yard has been highly productive ever since.

Eco-Logical Solutions

> 59 Crystal Waters
> MS 16, Maleny, Queensland ,4552, AUSTRALIA

Directors Max O. Lindegger and Frances Lang have taught over a thousand students in 15 different countries over the last 20 years.

This is also the address for Nascimanere and Green Harvest which offers, by mail order, a wide list of books relating to permaculture and sustainable development.

Permaculture Asia, Ltd.

> Richard Webb,
> 1/F, Lot 1969, Tai Wan New Village
> DD3, Lamma, HONG KONG
> Tel: 852-9820 703/Fax: 852-9821 400

Permaculture Association of India

> c/o Dr. Venkat
> 117 East Marredpalli
> Secunderabad 500 026, Andhra Pradesh, INDIA

"Our motto is that an ounce of practice is better than a pound of theory."

Permaculture Cayambe/Rainforest Information Center

> Quito, ECUADOR. See CIBT article in the South and Central America section for more information.

Zimbabwe Institute of Permaculture

> See Africa section

Permaculture Periodicals

Earthword Journal
580 Broadway, Suite 200
Laguna Beach, California 92651
Tel: (714) 497-1896

The first glossy permaculture magazine in North America. Geared toward professional designers, architects, and planners. The winter '93-'94 issue is on "Sustainability of Alternative and Indigenous Architecture." $20/year (4 issues).

Permaculture Activist
Rt. 1, Box 38
Primm Springs, Tennessee 38476

The best North American source of permaculture information, news, articles and calendar of events. Quarterly. $16/yr. They also sell books on permaculture and sustainable agriculture by mail order. Issue No 29-30, July 1993 was a special issue on media/networking and gives details on many permaculture and related periodicals ($7.50).

Permaculture Africa Newsletter
P.O. Box 1256,
Mahalapye, BOTSWANA

Permaculture Drylands Journal
P.O. Box 27371
Tucson, Arizona 85726

Southwestern U.S. source for permaculture information. Crucial information on water conservation and dryland plants. $25/yr.; $15/low income.

The Permaculture Edge
P.O. Box 650
Nambour, Queensland, 4560 AUSTRALIA

International quarterly journal for the permaculture movement. Mostly technical articles. Overseas rates: air A$26; surface A$20.

Permaculture India Newsletter
Published by Earthcare Books c/o Classic Books
10 Middleton St.,
Calcutta 700 071 INDIA

In addition to being the most noteworthy environmental bookstore in India, Earthcare Books has published *Ecological Visions,* an extensive directory of Permaculture and sustainable agriculture organizations in India.

Permaculture International Journal
P.O. Box 185
Lismore, New South Wales, 2480 AUSTRALIA
Tel: 066-220020 or 217654/Fax: 066-220579
e-mail peg:pcjournal

The leading periodical of the international permaculture movement. The quarterly includes useful articles, news and an international calendar of events. Once a year they publish an updated list of all the permaculture centers in the world. A$20 seamail.

In the U.S., subscriptions and back orders can be ordered from the Permaculture Activist. 4 issues are $20. Single issues are $5 ppd.

Permaculture Magazine
Little Hyden Lane, Clanfield
Hampshire, PO8 ORU, UNITED KINGDOM
Tel: 705 596500/Fax: 705 595834

The main permaculture magazine in the United Kingdom. Covers permaculture news from around Europe.

West Coast Permaculture News & Gossip
Friends of the Trees Society
P.O. Box 1064
Tonasket, Washington 98855
Tel/Fax: (509) 485-2705

Permaculture News & Gossip (PN&G) provides news on courses, events, organizations, periodicals and personal notes of interest to the West Coast permaculture community, including international news. A small publication, published sporadically. $1.00 per issue.

PN&G is edited by Michael Pilarski, a graduate of a 1982 permaculture design course, who has subsequently taught permaculture in Nepal, Belize, Canada and the U.S.

Permaculture Videos

"In Grave Danger of Falling Food"
1990.

A humorous and educational look at the world's agriculture situation and some permaculture solutions. The film stars Bill Mollison and is filmed in New Zealand and Australia.

"The Global Gardener"
1992. Available on video in the U.S. from: Living Systems Design, 369 Montezuma, Suite 225, Santa Fe, New Mexico. 87501. Tel: (505) 986-1616. $49.95 individual; $159.95 institution. + $5.05 shipping.

A series of four 30-minute films. The Global Gardener takes us on a round the world trip to visit permaculture projects with Bill Mollison. Professional, high quality films, an excellent way to introduce permaculture to people.

Permaculture Books

Earth User's Guide to Permaculture
Rosemary Morrow. 1993. Kangaroo Press: PO Box 6125, Dural Deliver Center, NSW, 2158, AUSTRALIA 152 pp.

18

Well illustrated, practical techniques. Recommended for homesteaders in countries of the South

Introduction to Permaculture

Bill Mollison. 1991. Tagari Publications.

Less formidable than the *Designers' Handbook* and full of practical information and illustrations. It incorporates and supersedes *Permaculture One* and *Permaculture Two*, published in 1978 and 1979, respectively.

Permaculture: A Designers' Handbook

Bill Mollison. 1990. Tagari Publications. P.O. Box 1, Tyalgum, NSW, 2481, Australia.

592 information-packed pages. 130 color photos and over 400 illustrations of permaculture design systems and techniques.

The most comprehensive, in-depth look at permaculture. Highly recommended for every small farmer, forester, land manager or person interested in sustainable systems. The chapter on forests and their interactions offers many insights into how permaculture can be incorporated into forestry and how forests influence climate and weather.

Permaculture: A Practical Guide for A Sustainable Future

Bill Mollison. Island Press. 1990.

The U.S. printing of the same book as the above, only under a different title, and with a different cover.

Permaculture in a Nutshell

Patrick Whitefield. Devon, United Kingdom. 75 pp. (Available in the U.S. from the *Permaculture Activist* for $13).

A concise overview of permaculture.

The Permaculture Way: Practical Steps to Create a Self-sustaining World

Graham Bell. 1992. HarperCollins. London. 239 pp.

Overview of permaculture principles, design, strategies and techniques.

TIPSY. The International Permaculture Species Yearbook

Four annual volumes, 1983-1986. Complete set is $35 for all four from: Yankee Permaculture, P.O. Box 672, Dahlonega, Georgia 30533

This set offers one of the largest collection of permaculture articles, plant species lists, original research and seed sources. Chock full of information.

Also available is the TRIP Global Green Pages. Vol. V. A directory which lists 1500 groups/resources around the world. $15.00.

Urban Permaculture: A Practical Handbook for Sustainable Living

David Watkins. 150 pp. (Available in the USA from the Permaculture Activist for US$13.)

The focus of the book is on design and techniques for the small plot in urban areas.

Woodland in Permaculture

Patrick Whitefield. 1992. 52 pp. Both of the Patrick Whitefield books are available from the author at: Hillyfield Cottage, Harbourneford, South Brent, Devon TQ10 9DT, United Kingdom.

A permaculture perspective for managing woodlands in Britain. Some of it is applicable in the northern U.S. The information is practical and based mostly on the author's experience.

Urban Forestry: A Resource Guide

Old-growth trees and forests have been forced back into the most remote areas and most difficult terrain. Let us invite old-growth forests back into the lowlands with avenues right into the cities.

Urban Forestry Defined

URBAN FORESTRY IS A SPECIALIZED BRANCH of forestry that has as its objective the cultivation and management of trees for their present and potential contribution to the physiological, sociological and economic well-being of urban society. In its broadest sense, urban forestry embraces a multimanagerial system that includes municipal watersheds, wildlife habitats, outdoor recreation opportunities, landscape design, recycling of municipal wastes, tree care in general and the production of wood fiber as a raw material.

Urban forestry is a merging of arboriculture, ornamental horticulture and forest management. It is closely related to landscape architecture and park management and must be done in concert with professionals in these fields as well as with city planners.

The Value of Urban Forests

The list of goods and services that urban forestry can provide is impressive. Trees and green spaces help keep cities cool, act as natural filters and noise absorbers, improve microclimates, and protect and improve the quality of natural resources, including soil, water, vegetation and wildlife. Trees contribute significantly to the aesthetic appeal of cities thereby helping to maintain the psychological health of their inhabitants. Beyond ecological and aesthetic benefits, urban forestry has a role in helping resource-poor populations meet basic needs, particularly, but not exclusively in developing countries.

Modifying Temperature Extremes

Trees, shrubs and other vegetation help to control temperature extremes in urban environments by modifying solar radiation. The shade of one large tree may reduce the temperature of a given building to the same extent as would 15 air conditioners at 4000 British thermal units (BTU), i.e. 4220 kJ, in a similar but unshaded building. Energy saving through tree-plant-ing around houses ranges from 10 to 50 percent for cooling and from 4 to 22 percent for heating.

Lack of Extension and Communication

Generally speaking, extension in urban forestry is very weak. Practical approaches are yet to be worked out in order to reach and involve citizens, especially the poor. Networking has proved an efficient tool in research and development in many sectors, but formal global or regional urban forestry networking activities are extremely limited. One networking structure functioning on a global level is the International Union of Forestry Research Organizations (IUFRO) Project Group on Arboriculture and Urban Forestry. In addition, a small informal network, created by the Forestry Support Program USA to link people who have forestry questions from across the world with people in the United States who may have answers to these questions, has seen an increasing number of requests. Global ReLeaf, the urban forestry program of the American Forestry Association plays an important role in information sharing and networking within the United States and, more recently, worldwide as well. While there may be similar organizations in other developed countries, such initiatives in developing countries are very rare. Other possible approaches to information exchange include: twinning arrangements between the urban forestry establishment of a city in an industrialized country and its counterpart in a developing country.

Excerpts from the article, "Urban Forestry Revisited" by G. Kuchelmeister and S. Braatz in Unasylva 173, Vol 44, 1993. pp. 3-12.

18

Urban Tree Organizations

Alliance for Community Trees
c/o Friends of Trees
P.O. Box 40851
Portland, Oregon 97240

An alliance of urban tree groups around the U.S. The Alliance enables increased lobbying of the federal government and Congress on behalf of urban trees.

American Association of Botanical Gardens and Arboreta
786 Church Road
Wayne, Pennsylvania 19087
Tel: (215) 688-1120/Fax:: (215) 293-0149

Association for Women in Landscaping
18824 93rd Ave NE
Bothell, Washington 98011

California ReLeaf
Trust for Public Land
116 New Montgomery St., Third Floor
San Francisco, California 94105
Tel: (415) 495-5660

California ReLeaf is an expanding alliance of community-based tree groups that promote citizen action and environmental stewardship through the planting and care of trees. Their quarterly newsletter *REMARKS* reports on the status of urban tree planting in California.

California Urban Forestry Program
California Department of Forestry and Fire Protection
P.O. Box 944246
Sacramento, California 94244

Jim Geiger is California's urban forester who from small beginnings thirteen years ago now directs a $1.7 million program aimed at helping community groups, cities and counties improve their forests. One of their publications available is *Guidelines for Developing and Evaluating Tree Ordinances*.

Friends of the Urban Forest
783 Buena Vista West
San Francisco, California 94117
Tel: (415) 391-7544

Friends of Trees
P.O. Box 40851
Portland, Oregon 97240

An urban tree group for the Portland metropolitan area which has gained nation-wide recognition for its programs. It has no relation to Friends of the Trees Society, except for similar names and a fond regard for trees.

Garden Clubs of America
598 Madison Ave.
New York, New York 10022
Tel: (212) 753-8287

Global Cities Project
2962 Fillmore St.
San Francisco, California 94123}
Tel: (415) 775-0791/Fax : (415) 775-4159

A national clearinghouse dedicated to building sustainable communities. They have a wide range of case studies, ordinances and handbooks available on local environmental policies and programs, water quality and water conservation. Excellent resources for anyone working with city government.

Their *Urban Forestry Handbook* (111 pp.) costs $20 to government and nonprofit organizations and $40 to others. Tells how to start many urban tree programs. They report it is their best seller with 400 to 500 copies sold.

Global ReLeaf
American Forestry Association
P.O. Box 2000
Washington, DC 20013
Tel: (202) 667-3300; 1 (800) 368-5748
Fax: (202) 667-7751

The Global ReLeaf Program is an international education, action, and policy campaign, launched in 1988, that encourages people to plant and care for trees. One of the largest urban tree planting networks in the U.S. Publishes Global Releaf Report. Contribution of $10 or more.

International Society of Arboriculture
P.O. Box 71
Urbana, Illinois 61801
Tel: (217) 328-2032

Founded in 1924, the ISA is dedicated to proper tree care and preservation, particularly in the urban setting. Members receive a monthly journal, tree care manuals, educational brochures, videos, research papers, and radio public service announcements. Membership is: Professionals $70/yr. Seniors $15/yr. Students $25/yr.

Mid-Western Urban Forestry Center
179 South Home
Franklin, Indiana 46131
Tel: (317) 736-9500

National Arbor Day Foundation
100 Arbor Ave
Nebraska City, Nebraska 68410

One of the first populist tree planting organizations in the United States with millions of trees planted over the decades. Publishes newsletter *Tree City USA Bulletin*, and makes annual awards. $10 dues.

18

National Arborist Association
P.O. Box 1094
Amherst, New Hampshire 03031
Tel: (603) 673-3311/Fax: (603) 672-2613

National Tree Trust
1455 Pennsylvania Avenue, N.W., Suite 250
Washington, D.C. 20004
Tel: (202) 628-TREE

President Bush and Congress chartered the National Tree Trust and endowed it with 20 million dollars to support private and volunteer urban and rural tree planting, as well as education programs. They publish a newsletter.

Peace Trees Cascadia
4649 Sunnyside Ave. N.
Seattle, Washington 98103
Tel: (206) 789-8905. Dwight Wilson.

Brings together youth from many countries to plant trees in rural and urban areas. Affiliated with the EarthStewards Network.

Plant Amnesty
906 NW 87th St.
Seattle, Washington 98117
Tel: (206) 783-9813. Cass Turnbull.

Plant Amnesty's goal is to end the senseless torture and mutilation of trees and shrubs caused by mal-pruning. Specifically, it seeks to effect a significant change in the way King County prunes, thus proving it can be done elsewhere in the nation and world. This urban action group educates the public and professional sectors on what constitutes bad pruning and how to perform healthy pruning. Quarterly newsletter *PlantAmnesty*. $20 annual dues.

TreePeople
12601 Mulholland Dr.
Beverly Hills, California 90201
Tel: (818) 753-4600. Andy and Katie Lipkis.

The U.S.' foremost grassroots urban tree organization. Tree People have educated nearly 1 million school children about urban forests. They also have an active, 15,000 person membership in Southern California with 350 Citizen Foresters who lead neighborhood plantings. They publish the newsletter *Seedling News* , and they've planted millions of trees!

Urban Ecology
P.O. Box 10144
Berkeley, California 94709
Tel: (510) 549-1724. Richard Register, President.

Publishes newsletter which serves as a clearinghouse for urban restoration projects worldwide. The founder/ organizer of the International Ecological City Conferences. The Conference Proceedings are excellent resources.

Urban Wildlife Coalition
137 1/2 Park Lane #5
Kirkland, Washington 98003
Tel: (206) 622-5260

UWC publishes *Outdoor News*, dedicated to informing the public of organizations, issues, and the people that affect the environment and wildlife in the Northwest. $25/membership. Subscription $10.

Community and Urban Forestry Program
Department of Natural Resources
P.O. Box 47046
Olympia, Washington 98504
Tel: (206) 753-2400/1-800-523-8733

Assists local groups around the state and facilitates state-wide networking between groups. Publishes quarterly newsletter, *TreeLink*. They offer two useful resources free on request: *An Introductory Guide to Community and Urban Forestry in Washington, Oregon and California*; and *A Technical Guide to Community and Urban Forestry in Washington, Oregon and California.*

Urban Tree Periodicals

Arboricultural Journal
A.B. Academic Pub.
P.O. Box 97
Berkhamsted, Hertfordshire HP4 2PX, ENGLAND

A quarterly journal of the Arboricultural Association.

Journal of Arboriculture
International Society of Arboriculture (address/ dues in preceding Organizations section).

A bi-monthly, technical journal. ISA also publishes a smaller, bimonthly newsletter *Arborist News*.

Urban Forests
American Forestry Association, address same as Global ReLea f in this section.

Bi-monthly newsletter. The voice of the National Urban Forest Council, established by American Forestry Assoc. in 1981. Free in the U.S., foreign $18.

Urban Forests Magazine
P.O. Box 158
Edinburgh, EH2 4PP, Scotland, UNITED KINGDOM

Quarterly. £12 overseas rate.

Urban Tree Directories And Books

City Food: Crop Selection in Third World Cities
Isabel Wade. Urban Resource Systems, 783 Buena Vista W., San Francisco, CA 94117.

A useful compendium of information on food grow-

18

ing in urban areas around the world.

Cooling Our Communities: A Guidebook On Tree Planting And Light-Colored Surfacing
(22P-2001 January 1992). United States Environmental Protection Agency, Policy, Planning And Evaluation (PM-221), Washington, D.C. 20460.

FAO Annotated Bibliography on Urban Forestry
Copies of the working version may be obtained by writing to the Forest Resources Division, FAO, Via delle Terme di Caracalla, 00100 Rome, Italy.

This international bibliography also includes selective listings of urban forestry projects, programs, conferences, symposia and workshops.

First International Ecological City Conference Report
Elmwood Institute, Planet Drum Foundation. 1990. Planet Drum Foundation, P.O. Box 31251, San Francisco, California 94131. Tel: (415) 285-6556

A Green City Program for the San Francisco Bay Area and Beyond
Peter Berg, Beryl Magilavy and Seth Zuckerman. Planet Drum. 90+ pp. $7.

Covers the wide gamut of ecological, socially responsible and sustainable topics ranging from Smart Transportation to Recycling and Reuse. Urban trees is a minor element in the book.

Greenways for America
Charles E. Little. 1990. Johns Hopkins University Press. 207 pp. $22.95.

A recent overview of greenways around and through cities.

National Urban Forestry Conferences

There have been seven national urban forestry conferences as of 1993. The written proceedings are available in some libraries. For a complete list of *Conference Proceedings*, videotapes and audio tapes available, contact the American Forestry Association at the Global ReLeaf address in this section.

Pacific Northwest Community Trees Conference
February 28-29, 1992. World Forestry Center, 4033 SW Canyon Rd., Portland, OR 97221. Tel: (503) 228-1367.

The theme of the conference was "Make Room for Trees", a forum for groups and individuals on cooperatively planting and managing trees, stewardship ethics, both rural and urban and the importance of trees and forests in the face of increasing urbanization.

Shading our Cities: A Resource Guide for Urban and Community Forests
Gary Moll and Sara Ebenreck, eds. 1989. Island

Press. 332 pp. $19.95.

A useful handbook for anyone working to get more trees into urban areas.

The Simple Act of Planting a Tree: Healing Your Neighborhoods, Your City and Your World
TreePeople with Andy and Katie Lipkis. 1990. 237 pp. $12.95.

The TreePeople of Los Angeles is the most famous urban tree group in the USA. This large resource book reflects their knowledge. It reviews organizations, books and periodicals and has a step-by-step guide for setting up an urban tree group. Recommended.

Trees of Seattle—The Complete Tree-finder's Guide to the City's 740 Varieties
Arthur Lee Jacobson. 1989. Sasquatch Books
1931 Second Ave., Seattle, WA 98101
Tel: (206) 441-5555. 432 pp. $16.95.

This attractive book is one of the best city books on trees in the U.S. A good model for other city tree books and urban tree inventories.

Tree Survey of Port Townsend
1985, 1987. Abundant Life Seed Foundation, P.O. Box 772, Port Townsend, WA 98368. $5.

This survey is a good model for anyone thinking of doing a tree inventory for their town, city or neighborhood. A report on both phases (500 city blocks) of Abundant Life's survey of the woody flora in the city of Port Townsend. Includes appendices describing preferred street species. Port Townsend, which lies at the extreme northeast corner of the Olympic Peninsula where the waters of Puget Sound meet the Straits of Juan de Fuca, has a windy, cool, maritime climate.

Unasylva
Vol. 44, #173, Winter 1993/92.

Unasylva is one the best international journals on forestry. This special issue on urban forestry contains many good articles. The focus is international with an emphasis on cities in countries of the South.

Urban and Community Forestry Program National Resource Directory
National Tree Trust, address in preceding Organizations section. 82 pp. Does not give publication date, but after 1990. To be updated periodically.

One of the most extensive resource guides on the subject, especially in regards to federal and state government agencies, cooperative extension agents, conservation agencies, large environmental groups, arboretums, and tree groups. Not much on the grass-roots.

18

Tree Festivals & Seed/Plant Exchanges

Michael Pilarski

Pierr Morgan

Annual Plant & Seed Exchanges and Spring Tree Sales

ANNUAL PLANT AND SEED EXCHANGES in every town and neighborhood are an effective grass-roots way for people to become more self-reliant and for neighborhoods to become greener. There are many variations on the theme; simple and small on up to large and elaborate; or be incorporated into tree festivals.

I have all sorts of practical experience from organizing over 100 Friends of the Trees Society's Spring Tree Sales in dozens of locations in Washington and northern Idaho. Over a twelve-year period, 150,000 trees, shrubs and vines were distributed to thousands of customers. Friends of the Trees Society provided quality trees for a low price, plus gave away thousands of trees free. It started out in 1979 as one small sale in one small town. At its height, we had three teams holding tree sales in 18 locations across northern Montana, Idaho and Washington. It was exhausting! Decentralized, locally-controlled is better! Eventually we ended up making the tree sales into public plant and seed exchanges.

Festival of the Trees—Port Townsend Bellingham Tree Extravaganza

Having a tree festival in your town or city can get trees in the ground and be lots of fun. Port Townsend's Festival of the Trees is a good example of a large and dynamic tree celebration. It has been an annual success since 1990 when Friends of the Trees Society organized the first Port Townsend Tree Extravaganza. In its second year, the name was changed to Festival of the Trees. Around 1,000 people attend each gala event. Over a dozen nurseries offer an incredible array of plant material for sale, plus the public brings lots of plant material to swap. Thousands of trees go out to new homes. Besides the plant sales and exchanges, there are educational workshops, demonstrations, environmental and tree groups, music, entertainment, bands, food booths and banners flying.

Friends of the Trees also organized the first Bellingham

Tree Extravaganza in 1990 which has continued with local organizers since, while keeping the original title. The Bellingham event hasn't achieved the size of the Port Townsend event, but it also gets a lot of trees out.

If your town has a farmer's market, then a plant exchange and/or tree festival may be timed to coincide with the opening day of the market.

Friends of the Trees' Tree Extravaganza Packet

Michael Pilarski. 1990. $10. Available from Friends of the Trees Society, P.O. Box 1064, Tonasket, WA 98855.

This packet will give you lots of ideas to apply/adapt to organizing your local tree event. It's fun, and, if you get lots of friends to help, it might even be easy. In the process of organizing the 1990 Tree Extravaganzas we prepared dozens of different documents. The packet consists of copies of these documents including: a 16-page pamphlet and plant catalog, posters, press releases, radio announcements, volunteer sign-up sheets, price lists, budgets, lists of signs, plant descriptions, tree planting guides, etc. It also includes a list of recommended wholesale nurseries.

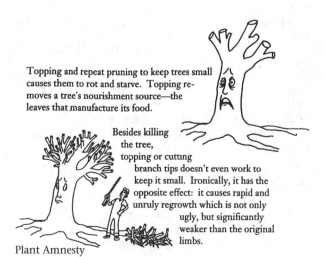

Topping and repeat pruning to keep trees small causes them to rot and starve. Topping removes a tree's nourishment source—the leaves that manufacture its food.

Besides killing the tree, topping or cutting branch tips doesn't even work to keep it small. Ironically, it has the opposite effect: it causes rapid and unruly regrowth which is not only ugly, but significantly weaker than the original limbs.

Plant Amnesty

Goods from the Woods

John C. Ryan

Extractive reserves can generate income and help protect tropical forests, but they are not a panacea.

A LOT OF GOOD NEWS has been filtered up from Brazil lately. Although vast areas of the Brazilian Amazon continue to go up in flames, deforestation rates in the region fell for the third straight year in 1990, to less than a third of the 1987 peak. Indigenous people, rubber tappers, and other forest dwellers have organized to defend their lands, gaining some government support for their claims against landowners and others who seek to clear the forest. There's also the recent conviction of the assassins of rubber tapper union leader Chico Mendes, which brings a glimmer of hope that the widespread brutality against Brazil's rural poor might be brought under control.

None of these welcome developments, though, has generated as much enthusiasm in northern nations as the idea that saving tropical forests can be a money making venture. Nonprofit groups and green-minded businesses are introducing foods, cosmetics, soaps, buttons, and other products from the world's tropical forests to stores in Europe and America. Rain Forest Crunch, marketed by Cultural Survival, a Cambridge, Massachusetts-based human rights group, is made with Brazil nuts harvested and shelled by a rubber tappers' cooperative. In coming months, the group will help bring to market new rain forest fruits and oils and even a lip balm made with beeswax from forests in Zambia.

Environmental activists encourage this new trend in consumption in the belief that increased support of sustainable uses of forests will lead governments and individuals away from destructive uses, such as logging and cattle ranching. There's an appealing logic to these efforts. The world's richest ecosystems also support millions of the poorest people; only by linking forest protection to development for the poor will either goal materialize.

Extractive reserves promise to make this linkage. These are tracts of forest set aside by governments for management by local communities. Forest dwellers get control over fruits, latexes, medicinal plants, and other valuable products, and forests are spared the ax and torch.

If these and other efforts to mesh rain forest conservation and trade are to succeed, however, a number of difficult obstacles have to be overcome, not least the near-total ignorance of the ability of ecologically complex rain forests to withstand the removal of industrial quantities of their components. Good news from Brazil to the contrary, the economic inequity that fuels violent conflict over land remains, and most forest dwellers continue to have a tenuous hold on their lands and their lives. Extractive reserves will not by themselves reverse these trends. But they have the potential to begin to transform the abusive social relations—ranging from economic exploitation to assassination—that drive the devastation of tropical forests.

The Hidden Economy

Tropical forest are critical to hundreds of millions of rural people as sources of nutrition, health care, raw materials, and cash income. Yet all the goods they provide, except for wood, are commonly considered to be minor forest products. While most governments continue to regard forests primarily as stocks of timber or as potential farmland, non-timber forest products form a major but undervalued part of Third World economies.

In villages in central Ghana, most women earn cash selling forest leaves to local food vendors for wrapping their wares. Forest dwellers of Borneo and Thailand gather nests of a cave-dwelling swiftlet for export to China, where bird's-nest soup is a prized delicacy. Traditional medicine, based largely on tropical plants, nurtures four-fifths of humanity, while rain forest plants are key ingredients in prescription drugs worth tens of billions of dollars annually.

Because most of these forest riches are used for subsistence or traded locally, they are largely overlooked by foresters and economic planners focused on national export earnings. Few statistics are kept on these riches, but the numbers that are available give some idea of the

18

importance of this economy (see table on page 27). International commerce in the most widely traded non timber forest product, rattan (palm stems used for wicker furniture and baskets), is alone worth $3 billion annually.

Whether they eventually enter international trade or are used locally, non-timber forest products are harvested using simple technologies by rural people living in or near the forest. These methods stand in sharp contrast to commercial logging, which usually employs heavy machinery and relatively few people, and is usually managed by outside interests. As a result, in some cases timber does not employ as many people as alternative forest products. For example, Indonesia's rattan industry supports more than 200,000 full-time employees, three times that of its timber industry.

A Sorry History

Fruits, resins, and many other products can be harvested without bulldozers or chainsaws, providing a promising alternative to deforestation or the degradation that almost always results from logging. But the creation of a sustainable and equitable trade based on these products will not come easily.

"A lot of the discussion of marketing efforts suggests that we can sell it all and save it at the same time and save the people too," states Christine Padoch, an anthropologist at the New York Botanical Garden who has studied local forest economies in Peru and Indonesia. "I wish that were true, but if you look at the history of these products, it's horrifying. Very few people, or forests, have benefited. Some people who are pushing marketing schemes ignore history."

The usual fate of species that gain long-term popularity in industrial markets is depletion. And the usual lot of extractors is continued poverty, as the profits from their work are siphoned off by powerful middlemen and elites. Brazil-nut gatherers, for example, receive about four cents a pound for their labors, just 2 to 3 percent of the New York wholesale price. Three-fourths of the Brazil-nut market is controlled by three companies, owned by three cousins.

The Amazon basin has seen some of the worst abuses associated with the trade in rain forest goods. The great rubber boom of 1870 to 1910 that brought thousands of rubber tappers to the area also brought with it the massive extermination of Indians and the subjugation of tappers to slave-like conditions. For many rubber tappers, conditions are nearly as miserable today. Most are chronically in debt and exploited by middlemen. As the murders of Chico Mendes and perhaps 1,500 other rural people in Brazil's interior during the past decade attest, landowners continue to use violence against anyone who threatens their economic dominance.

In the lowland jungles of Peru, where there has been little deforestation, environmental degradation has resulted from the depletion of forest species that have become popular with urban consumers. Most of the popular wild fruits in the markets of Iquitos, the Peruvian Amazon's largest city, appear to be declining in availability. The area's tall aguaje palm trees, for example, have been cut down for their highly prized fruits. As in Brazil, palms are also destroyed to harvest their hearts for export. Virtually all large fish and wildlife species in the Iquitos area also are in decline because of the city's voracious appetite for meat.

In Southeast Asia, increasing commercial demand for rattan and other rain forest products and high rates of deforestation have combined to degrade forests and their resources. Traditional systems of management—maintained by village leaders or other local authorities—have not weathered the onslaughts of timber companies and invasions of displaced peasants, and the national governments that claim control of the forests are unable to regulate their use. Local rattan shortages have been reported in Indonesia, Malaysia, and the Philippines, according to a recent study by the Netherlands branch of the International Union for the Conservation of Nature. Thailand, whose forests have been badly depleted, has gone from being a net exporter to a net importer of both timber and rattan.

This degradation worsens rural poverty, as collectors' workdays lengthen and their incomes fall. A typical collector from Palawan in the Philippines, for example, could collect 200 pieces of rattan a day in the 1960s; by the 1980s the daily take was down to 35 pieces. As in the Amazon, long chains of middlemen ensure that profits leave the forests along with raw materials.

Other regions and products tell the same tale. Sapodilla trees, tapped for the chicle used in chewing gum, have been depleted over large areas of Guatemala and Mexico. Xate leaves are destructively harvested by the dirt-poor xateros of northern Guatemala for use in floral arrangements in Europe and the United States, while most of the benefits flow to Guatemala City or outside the country. In this struggle for survival, there are few winners. "Sure the xate is dying" laments one xatero, "but the people are dying, too."

From the Amazon Up

Breaking out of this cycle of human and environmental suffering is no easy feat, but a number of groups have begun to show that it can be done. Brazil's rubber tappers are perhaps the most successful of the world's forest people to work toward this goal. Through collective action, they press the Brazilian government for rights to their land and work to reverse the inequity in land ownership that fuels deforestation in Brazil by driving the poor off the best farmland and into the forests.

Since its beginnings in the border state of Acre in the 1970s, the rubber tappers' movement has grown to encompass much of the Brazilian Amazon and has formed alliances with a wide array of supporters, from Indian groups to U.S. environmentalists. Their vision of a more equitable form of development for the Amazon has centered around extractive reserves owned by the state but managed by local communities for uses compatible with the forest. Since 1987, 14 extractive reserves covering a total of 7.5 million acres in four states have been created by the government for the use of the rubber tappers living in them. The rubber tappers hope eventually to expand these achievements and protect 250 million acres, one-fourth of the Brazilian Amazon, as extractive reserves.

Funding from groups such as Cultural Survival, which helped finance the Amazon's first cooperative Brazil nut-processing plant in Xapuri, Acre, is flowing into the Amazon to help forest extractors develop new markets, and reduce the control of middlemen over their livelihoods. The national rubber tappers' union, strengthened by its domestic and international allies, has achieved a degree of political clout virtually unmatched by any grassroots group. Support for the concepts of extractive and indigenous reserves (protected lands for Indian communities) is even written into the Brazilian constitution, due to a combination of grass roots and international pressure on Brasilia.

Despite these successes, government policies still frustrate the Indian-rubber tapper alliance. Earlier this year, Brazil's government reinstated tax breaks for cattle ranches and other destructive investments in the Amazon but refused to grant similar incentives to the Xapuri cooperative. It has failed to protect rural activists from death threats or, with a few famous exceptions, prosecute their murderers. The budget of the federal environmental agency, which is in charge of demarcating indigenous and extractive reserves, was effectively cut 80 percent in March when its funds were frozen.

Economic troubles also plague the rubber tappers. Extractors get most of their income from only two products, rubber and Brazil nuts, both of whose economic viability is fragile at best. Until 1990, when prices fell by two-thirds, rubber prices in Brazil were propped up to three times the world price with heavy taxes on imports of plantation rubber from Malaysia. In April rubber tapper leaders descended upon Brasilia to demand price increases for Amazonian rubber to help protect the forest. They also argued that they need time to decrease their reliance on rubber before price supports are phased out. Rubber tappers may also find themselves unable to com-

pete with plantations of Brazil-nut trees. These have been started in Malaysia, and a decade-old plantation near Manaus, Brazil, is expected to begin producing large quantities of nuts this year. Because they provide large crops on small areas of land, monoculture plantations threaten to undercut Brazil nut gathering as well as rubber tapping. As with other Amazonian plantations, fungus and disease will likely besiege the domesticated trees, but perhaps not until they have flooded the market with low-priced nuts.

"Domestication is a serious problem to any kind of alternative to forest destruction," warns agronomist Fernando Allegretti of the Institute for Amazon Studies, based in Curitiba, Brazil. "If the Brazil-nut plantations work out, only 30,000 hectares (74,000 acres) could provide as much as is currently being produced in the whole country."

Beyond Brazil?

Despite their problems and their unique circumstances, the Brazilian rubber tappers have become a model for other groups. Enthusiasm for extractive reserves is spreading like wildfire both inside and outside of tropical nations.

For example, a number of Peruvian Amazon peasant communities have set up lake and forest reserves on a small scale to provide fish, rubber, fruits, and other products on a sustainable basis. Communal rules regulate fishing and gathering practices to protect the reserves from outsiders and to allow depleted species to recover. Villages along the Tahuayo River, about 30 miles upstream from Iquitos, are seeking government approval for an 800,000-acre extractive reserve, to include a large preserve for the area's unique primates and other wildlife.

Last year, Guatemala established the Maya Biosphere Reserve, 3.7 million acres stretching across its northern border. Half of this area is designated as extractive reserves, reflecting the region's century-old heritage of xate and chicle extraction. Many local residents have "remarkable" expertise in forest use, according to ecologist Conrad Reining of Conservation International, a Washington-based environmental research group. But it is not clear how much control they will have over the management of their lands since they lack the political organization of the rubber tappers.

Shaman Pharmaceuticals of San Carlos, California, is working with traditional healers in indigenous communities in Ecuador, Nigeria, and other tropical nations to develop new plant-based pain killers and medicines for viral and fungal diseases. The company also is dedicated to supporting the biological and cultural diversity that has produced traditional medicines, according to Steven King, Shaman's director of ethnobotany and conservation. On a recent exploratory trip to the Ecuadorian Amazon, a doctor accompanied Shaman's botanical researchers to provide health care for Waorani and Shaur Indian communities suffering from a whooping cough epidemic and other unfamiliar diseases. Explains King, "We feel an ethical obligation to reciprocate for the use of traditional knowledge."

Taking nature to market?

While extremely varied, these local attempts to reform forest trade all seem to share at least one characteristic—the obstacles to their success are only partly problems of marketing. The chief breakthroughs needed are political reforms, such as increasing local control over natural resources, and adherence to the ecological limits imposed by tropical environments. As the history of rain forest trade shows, the market is, at best, neutral to these concerns.

Marketing can be used to improve the welfare of forest dwellers as long as the fundamental political obstacles facing these people are resolved. Amazonian Indians, for example, have full legal title to less than 30 percent of their lands. Southeast Asia's forest dwellers have been similarly dispossessed. Anthropologist Stephan Schwartzman of the Environmental Defense Fund in Washington, D.C., suggests that extractive reserves are best seen as a grass-roots bid for social change rather than a business venture. "Extractive reserves are in essence a proposal for ecologically sound and socially appropriate land reform in the Amazon," according to Schwartzman.

The question also remains: What types of markets should be pursued? Concentrating solely on exports without supporting local markets and subsistence uses could end up harming those who are supposed to benefit. Growing international demand for a food or medicine used by the rural poor, for example, could send prices up or overwhelm local production systems. So far, such concerns have received little attention.

Ecology: The Bottom Line

Extractive reserves are sometimes depicted as having no impact on forests, but there can be no doubt that removing large amounts of any living material from an ecosystem will cause changes. The key for successful development is to determine what types and levels of change are acceptable.

Forest inhabitants' knowledge of their local ecosystems far outstrips that of modern biologists, but neither group has much experience in devising sustainable systems for the commercial use of forests. Biologists know little or nothing about most of the plant and animal species of tropical forests; even the ecology of commercially important species (such as the Brazil nut) remains

little understood. No one knows if the pronounced absence of Brazil-nut seedlings and saplings noticed in many areas today is a result of over-harvesting or simply a natural cycle.

Rain forest trees form an integral part of a complex food chain. In turn, they rely on birds, insects, mammals, and even fish to disperse their pollen and seeds. According to ecologist Charles M. Peters of the New York Botanical Garden, "It is obvious that removing commercial quantities of fruits, nuts, and oil seeds will have an impact on local animal populations." The economic incentive to enrich forests with money-making species, along with increased hunting pressures, could also reduce forests' natural diversity.

Poverty and severe environmental degradation, however, are too pressing in most forested regions to await the results of long-term ecological studies. Still constant monitoring of harvests and forest health, and a willingness to adjust to the limits of the forest as they are discovered, are essential.

A forest protection movement that begins with the local people is more likely to maintain the necessary flexibility. Any outsiders, whether government agencies or environmental groups, that try to restrict the use of forests against the will of those who live in them will likely fail, as the degradation of many national parks in the tropics shows. Respecting the needs of the forests' inhabitants is crucial to ecological sustainability.

"It's not just a question of some fruit that you take from the forest," says Paulo Cipasse, a Xavante Indian leader form the Brazilian state of Mato Grosso. "The fruit has a history. The people eat it, the animals and birds eat it. You need a respect for the fruit. Perhaps the market will work out in the future, but it's very dangerous...."

Unnatural Selection

The dangers of market-oriented extractive economies can be minimized by carefully choosing the species and ecosystems to be used. For example, products that command high prices for small quantities, such as fragrances and flavors, may be easiest to produce profitably with minimal environmental impact.

Some tropical forest areas are already thick with commercially promising species. The flood plains of Peru, for example, have large stands of camu camu, a cherry-sized fruit that has vitamin C concentrations 30 times higher than oranges. Guatemala's Maya Biosphere Reserve has very high densities of xate and sapodilla plants, probably because ancient Mayans planted or refused to cut them. The denser stands of Brazil nut trees in parts of Acre and southeastern Peru that make these areas so profitable for nut gathering were also likely created by ancient resource managers.

18

Similar semi-natural forests exist in Southeast Asia. "In Kalimantan, (Indonesia) these people have been developing and creating their own forests for hundreds of years, and they just don't get the credit for it," says sociologist Nancy Peluso of the University of California at Berkeley.

These natural and pre-managed areas of relatively low species diversity are still much more diverse than forests outside the tropics. But they probably constitute a small fraction of tropical ecosystems and are not necessarily the forests most deserving of protection from deforestation. In short, if conservationists focus their attention only on profitable forms of nature conservation, then perhaps only those parts of nature that can be marketed will survive.

Limits to Extraction

Though overshadowed by the appeal of extractive reserves, inviolate biological reserves (or indigenous reserves with low population densities) are still crucial for protecting the full range of ecosystem, species, and genetic diversity. Extractive reserves cannot play this role.

Neither can non-timber forest products provide for all the needs of the rural poor. Agriculture and forest extraction usually go hand-in-hand: most forest gatherers also farm small clearings, and most small farmers rely on nearby forests for off-season food or other products. Yet relatively little attention has been paid to this connection. In Brazil, much greater effort could be put into helping poor farmers adopt extractive strategies on their land. "Nobody's dealing with small farmers in the Amazon," observes anthropologist Marianne Schmink of the University of Florida. "They're thought of as hopeless. We should be working with everyone: rubber tappers, farmers, ranchers."

Ironically, exclusive attention to the marketing of rain forest products may undermine extractive reserves' ultimate success. If the wealthy consumers and policymakers of the world come to believe that saving forests is always profitable, or that there is never a conflict between conservation and consumption, the tougher solutions to environmental degradation—those that require sacrifice rather than marketing skills could become even more difficult to pursue.

Because they can only benefit a fraction of the growing number of people that are forced to destroy forests to survive, extractive reserves are no substitute for programs to redistribute farmland, reform farming practices, and halt population growth. But they do demonstrate how fragile ecosystems can be used without causing wholesale destruction and how the rural poor can assume greater influence over their lives. These are lessons well worth learning.

Some minor forest products of major importance:

* Chicle, allspice and xate exports earn Guatemala $7 million in annual export revenues and support 6,000 families in the country's Petén region.

* Palm heart and Brazil nut exports each earned Brazil about $20 million in 1989.

* Exports of honey from forest bees in Tanzania are several times more valuable than the timber produced in the nation's forests.

* In India's Madhya Pradesh state, minor forest products (MFPs), gathered mostly by poor tribal women, are worth more than $700 million annually.

* MFPs accounted for three-fourths of the nation's net export earnings from forest products in 1986.

* Southeast Asia's rattan trade is worth more than $3 billion a year.

Sources

Tropicus, Winter 1991. S. Schwartsman, "Marketing of Extractive Products in the Brazilian Amazon," (Washington, D.C.: Environmental Defense Fund, 1990).

J. Westoby, *Introduction to World Forestry: People and Their Trees* (Oxford: Blackwell, 1989).

M. Poffenberger, *Joint Management for Forest Lands: Experiences from South Asia* (New Delhi; Ford Foundation, 1990).

R. Kaur, *Women in Forestry in India* (Washington, D.C.: World Bank, forthcoming).

J. De Beer & M. McDermott, *The Economic Value of Non-timber Forest Products in Southeast Asia* (Amsterdam: IUCN, 1989).

Note

John C. Ryan is a research associate at the Worldwatch Institute. His work focuses on forests and biological diversity.

This article was previously published in World Watch *magazine, Vol. 4, No. 4, July/August 1991.*

Growing Money Under Trees: Secondary Forest Products

Matthew Kimble

The following article outlines some of the job opportunities and economic benefits that can come from forest restoration. While the author's research is based on the example of coastal temperate rainforests, many of the ideas and principles can be applied to other forest regions.

—Editor

EVERY WINTER, billions of dollars are combed from the sky and tenaciously held in place by the forests of the Pacific Northwest. Vast, highly adapted communities of organisms collect and transform soil, rain, and sunlight into usable, profitable products. We inhabit a unique landscape where the forests and watersheds are both a home and a biotechnological factory.

Our region's temperate rainforests are full of unseen economic opportunities and have their share of innovative businesses underway. The production capital for these new ventures are the forests themselves. Intact ecosystems, watershed by watershed, are the infrastructure at the base of this economy. The more diverse and productive the ecosystems, the greater the long-term sustainable profits for forest dwellers. Our region's ecological infrastructure must be protected and restored.

Once one starts to look for ways to make money from standing, functioning forests with a healthy ancient component, the options start to multiply.

Rainforests and Estuary Fisheries

Fish are the premiere forest product of the coastal temperate rainforest. Traditionally, salmon has been the primary commercial species extracted from these rainforests. The highly productive aquatic and estuarine habitats downstream from the old forests also provide a vast array of fin fish, shell fish, and other sea edibles.

Healthy forests are the capital which allows the estuary ecosystem to work. Without large downed trees, streams lack the structures for fish to breed and grow. Without the lush hemlock, cedar, salmonberry and alder canopies shedding debris into the tributary streams, the inverte-

brates (bugs) do not have the food they need to grow, and, in turn, feed fish and the estuary.

Wild Salmon Restoration

Salmon run restoration will be necessary for continued sport and commercial harvests of native stocks. Willapa Bay in Washington provides an illustration. Chum were the most common native salmonid in the watershed. But the many forms of habitat degradation have reduced their numbers to a small percentage of their former runs. Only the hatchery strains of coho and chinook sustain the fishery. Improvements in the breeding and rearing infrastructure of the wild streams will benefit the entire ecosystem and the economy, which depends on salmon for sport and commercial fishing.

Calculating how much the economy can gain from restoration of fish habitat illuminates the profits that await. Research in the coastal streams of Oregon conclude decisively that restoration of large woody debris in damaged streams vastly increases available habitat for all salmonids. Investments in stream restoration provided a higher return to the fishery than profits from logging the area.

Oysters and Clams

Oysters and clams are valuable natural resources. In Willapa Bay, over 12,000 acres of intertidal flats are farmed for oysters. But still another 5,000 acres are infested with the burrowing ghost shrimp, and are sterile of oysters or most other living creatures. The shrimp filter all available nutrients out of the rich estuarine mud, leaving a shimmering sand.

This same ghost shrimp, which is presently sprayed with chemicals to protect producing oyster beds, is harvested in Puget Sound for sale as bait in urban markets. Salmon, crab, and even gray whales eat the shrimp. Sturgeon filter the mud and eat shrimp in large quantities. Overlapping business and restoration opportunities can dovetail to benefit the estuary. Restoring large numbers of

18

sturgeon may well prove the only way to control out-of-balance pests such as the ghost shrimp, and could allow productive shellfish beds to expand.

Sturgeon Aquaculture

Sturgeon, a long-lived, bottom-feeding fish that can attain 20 feet in length, once flourished in the estuaries of the Pacific Northwest. Now, they must be coaxed back to their former numbers. Their meat is highly edible and their eggs sell as caviar for $100 an ounce.

The potential for profitable sturgeon aquaculture is good, although many technical details remain to be worked out. It may take six to ten years before a significant profit is turned by sturgeon operations, but the efforts will improve the overall estuary ecosystem. The true return on investments in sturgeon aquaculture will be higher than simply the income from another excellent fishery or the sales of its caviar.

Foods from Restored Forests

Forest restoration can allow for the sustainable production of non-timber products. Wild agriculture can supplement the region's valuable cultivated agricultural production. Berries, mushrooms, and other high-value, marketable and easily transportable products could be extracted in sustainable quantities from cutover areas fully restored to their previous diversity and productivity. However, sustainability must be a parameter for the withdrawal of these dividends from the forest's capital.

Berry Crops

Berry plants, such as salal, Oregon grape, blackberry and elderberry, already provide commercial harvests. They are usually processed into jams or jellies and sold around the country at a considerable mark-up. With proper management, these berries could join cranberries, blueberries, and raspberries as profitable products.

In forest gaps and along streams, salmonberry, thimbleberry, and blue huckleberries often grow like thick hedges. But in cutover areas, the low, dense canopy limits berry production. Restoration of the canopy and replacement of the missing shrub layer in cutover forests will provide more berries, harvestable by humans and animals. Planted in their original profusion, these can provide profitable enterprises for pickers, processors, and marketers of berry products. Wildlife will also benefit from the increased amount and diversity of food.

Mushrooms

A wide variety of edible fungi grow in the coastal temperate rainforest. Topping the list for potential commercial harvest are Chanterelles, Matsutake, King Boletus, Morels, Oyster mushrooms, Slippery Jack, Hedgehog mushroom, Chicken of the Woods, and the cultivated Shiitake.

It is difficult to estimate the value of the wild mushroom harvest from northwestern forests, but the following statistics indicate a huge market. The 1989 export value of the prized Matsutake mushroom from a single ranger district on the Deschutes National Forest was $15 million! "Over here, we get about $50 to $60 a pound for it," said Jerry Larson, international trade manager for the Oregon Department of Agriculture. "Once it gets to Japan, it goes for $400 to $500 a pound." John Barnes of Pacific Mushrooms estimates that 2,000 to 4,000 pickers are employed full-time.

The region's production of Chanterelles is estimated to range from one to four million pounds per year. In good condition, a wholesale buyer may pay as high as $4.75 for Chanterelles, indicating an annual wholesale value of $4–16 million per year. Growing mushrooms may produce far more income than timber on certain sites. Cultivating mushrooms can bring $200 to $800 per acre. Over a comparable 50-year tree rotation, this would translate into $10,000 to $40,000 per acre!

In the short term, direct marketing to the international market will provide the most lucrative returns. Establishing locally-owned storage and distribution facilities will help keep profits in local communities. Considerable research, development and experimentation will be required to successfully restore productive mushroom areas. But the knowledge gained about production is itself a valuable—and marketable—secondary product. The fungal inoculum used to seed new areas for mushroom harvest is another valuable product. Long-term profits may also come from wholesale marketing of restoration techniques and materials, spawning a secondary industry in areas where work started soonest.

Special Forest Products

Plant-based Medicines

The Northwest's rainforests and other ecosystems provide many of the increasingly popular natural remedies derived from plants. These often come in the form of herbal teas, powders and extracts. The U.S. and global market for such natural medicines is growing rapidly. Sales of herbal medicines in 1991 accounted for hundreds of millions of dollars in the U.S. market alone.

Oregon plants now being sold as part of herbal cures include Oregon Grape root, Yarrow, Wild Rose hips, Cascara bark, Valerian root, wild sarsaparilla, Hedge nettle, Purple Cone Flower (*Echinacea*) and Kinickkinick. Sustainable production will require oversight to ensure that wild produce or herb gathering operations do not threaten the resources.

18

Chemical Prospecting

The tropical rainforests are the source of many pharmaceuticals. Already, the "green gold" of unique chemicals in plants, fungi, insects and animals of the tropical rainforests are prompting a chemical prospecting boom. Temperate rainforests are likely to contain many unique biochemicals as well. The green gold of the hills may cure cancers, kill fungal infections, or serve as a natural pesticide, herbicide or fertilizer.

Taxol, the promising new anti-cancer drug derived from our region's Pacific Yew tree, is in great demand. But due to a virtual monopoly granted by the National Cancer Institute, the huge drug company Bristol-Myers-Squibb is likely to reap the lion's share of the multi-million dollar Taxol market, leaving a small fraction to the Northwest where the resource is being harvested at unsustainable rates. Prospecting for biochemicals should require royalties to the state and/or region, protect overall diversity, and involve local and native peoples.

Ethnopharmacology

Native Americans had medical uses for virtually every major plant species in the forest. If ethnographic reports are accurate, many of these were effective cures for serious ailments. The Thompson Indians used over 160 plants; some plants may have had dozens of uses in different preparations with other plants. The Quinault tribe peeled, dried, and boiled Pacific Yew bark. "The liquid is drunk as lung medicine," reported one ethnographer, a medicinal use affirmed by recent studies showing that yew-derived Taxol is effective against lung cancer.

Floral Supplies

Collecting and selling floral supplies is an important cottage industry in the Northwest. According to the Sweet Home Ranger District, the estimated combined national sales of salal, sword ferns, huckleberry and bear grass was $43 million. Oregon provided about 40 percent of that market. Cones, moss, Oregon Grape foliage, and boughs from cedar, fir, and holly are also purchased by floral suppliers.

Many businesses obtain licenses to cut these materials from the public forests. These greenery leases are sold at auction, and harvest rights in an approximately 3,000-acre area ranged from $500 to $1,300. Like mushroom picking, much of this industry is unregulated. Further development of the industry should promote and ensure sustainable harvests.

Specialty Wood Products

Hardwoods, especially woods for furniture, carvings, and musical instruments are current rainforest exports. Many economic development projects in the Northwest focus on producing value added wood products in local communities. For example, mills should not merely mill 2 x 4's, but manufacture finished windows, doors, tables and chairs. These strategies are compatible with restoration programs and increase the economic benefits which stay in the local community. With nearby interstates and sales by phone or through catalogs, the disadvantage of distance is declining, making niche marketing profitable.

Related Forest Opportunities

Bottled Water

"Wildwater" might be the brand name of a bottled water brought from the pristine streams of the Pacific Northwestern rainforests to worldwide markets. Marketing such an extract to ecologically-minded, health-conscious consumers could make pure water a very profitable export of the region. Already several northwest springs are the source for regionally-produced bottled water.

Education and Scientific Research

Research institutes, education expeditions and other activities can produce numerous economic benefits for local communities. The money spent by visiting researchers, the employment of local residents, and the construction of local research facilities can be significant contributors to local economies. For example, the depressed timber town of Forks, Washington is the home of the new Olympic Natural Research Center, affiliated with the University of Washington. Oregon State University is expanding research in H. J. Andrew Experimental Forest in the Blue River area. The new aquarium at Newport is a popular educational facility that is drawing millions of tourist dollars.

Tourism

Already, a booming tourist industry benefits the Pacific Northwest. Tourism's economic impact in Oregon was $2.75 billion—an increase of 53 percent over the 1987 figure of $1.8 billion, making it the state's third largest industry in statewide economic impact. Although the benefits of tourism to local communities has sometimes been overstated, it is projected to be a growing source of income for the rural areas along the Oregon coast and in the Cascades.

Scenic beauty is a prime draw for many visitors. Ancient forest tours are starting to proliferate, both as profit and non-profit ventures. Wilderness trips to see big trees, waterfalls, or to climb mountains and raft rivers are staples of the back-country tourist trade. Restoration will only enhance and expand these opportunities.

18

Wildlife Reintroduction

The chance to photograph rare wildlife in their natural habitat motivates many visitors. Indeed, it is a lucrative business in Africa, where in some cases the local people profit from such tours, creating an incentive to protect habitat and reintroduce wildlife. Combined with tourism, reintroduction of beaver, eagles, owls, otter, elk, bear, and even butterflies would help balance the ecosystem and provide economic opportunities for educational tourism. The same might hold true of endangered plants, particularly photogenic flowers.

Wildlife reintroduction will be essential to fully repairing the rainforests. Numerous studies comparing streams with and without beavers found that streams with beavers have twice the salmon populations and generally are far more biologically productive. Predators are missing from vast forest areas of the Pacific Northwest. The smaller mammals include the fisher, marten, wolverine, coyote, bobcat, lynx. The larger ones include cougar, brown bear, wolf, and grizzly bear. Predatory birds, such as raptors, hawks, eagles, owls, falcons, are also missing from some areas.

Conclusion

The opportunities for Pacific Northwest rainforest residents to make a living in ways that help to restore the rainforests are as numerous as they are necessary. The rainforest can be the place where we evolve new businesses and new, sustainable lifestyles.

Our grandchildren can inherit vast, restored forests and profitable companies which take only what the ecosystem can provide, and which re-invest in the capital of nature. They can thank us for our foresight, for our willingness to risk short-term profits for their chance at a full life. They can thank us for the new array of products and services which these companies will provide to the economy. They can thank us for the chance to live healthy, productive lives in rural areas while working at jobs which support their communities and families.

We can restore the temperate rainforests of the Pacific Northwest and prosper in the process. It is the opportunity of our lifetime, the duty of our generation.

This article was excerpted from a report sponsored by Ecotrust, an organization that works with local people to build ecologically-and economically-sound communities in the rainforests of North America. For more information, contact Ecotrust, 1200 NW Front Ave., Portland, OR 97209; Tel: (503) 227-6225.

18

Hedgerows: Bridge From Farm To Forest

Matthew Hall

CLOSE YOUR EYES and I will paint you a picture: a country of small fields and woodlands connected by a matrix of hedgerows. The hedgerows line every country lane and crisscross most open countryside. They shelter fields, connect forests, and enliven the land with flowers and animals.

This is a picture of rural England; I grew up and worked in this wonderful landscape of fields, wildflowers, hedgerows, and small woodlands. Now I live in the Pacific Northwest, and the openness of the farmland and its separation from the forest makes me uneasy.

In this paper I will demonstrate how hedgerows and shelterbelts are the bridge between sustainable agriculture and sustainable forestry. First, let us look at the condition of both forest and farmland in the Pacific Northwest.

Forest

What is left of the old growth forest habitat is fragmented. Systematically, it has been cut up into isolated blocks, some large and some small. Now there is a growing awareness that in order for the wildlife that depends on old growth forest to survive there must be a system of wildlife corridors to connect these islands of undisturbed forest.

Farm

Travel down from the hills into the fertile bottom lands, river valleys, and coastal floodplain and you will see a similar isolation process. The farmland is comparatively bare of trees and scrub. Large open spaces, with only an occasional orchard or shelterbelt, dominate the valleys. Nothing ties the forested areas together across the bare expanse of farmland in between.

Here in northern coastal California, nothing connects the dune/scrub environment to the redwood forest on the first easterly ridge except a thin band of riparian habitat along the Mad River. As I walk around, I see huge plains cut up with old fences, and I see livestock shivering in the wind, snow, and rain. I see no hedgerows in this region, only places where the blackberries have managed to get a toehold into an old fence line. In this flat, fertile land, there is no shelter and precious little habitat for wildlife.

An English Background

In England, the old hedgerows are abustle with birds, insects, rare plants, and mammals. They are a joy to see throughout the year and an ecological niche where fruits, flowers, nuts, and herbs can be gathered through all seasons. Presumably, the creatures that are now characteristic of hedgerows adapted to them as the forest and scrubland were cleared for farming. Historically, hedges were planted to mark boundaries, to retain the banks of drainage ditches, and to shelter and control livestock.

For the provision of lumber, forest trees were allowed to grow up above the hedgerows. Characteristically, these trees have short, clear trunks with rounded crowns. They are commonly referred to as "standards." Dominant species of both hedge and standards vary, though usually they represent woodland and scrub plants common to the region.

At some point in the past, domestic fruit trees were added to the hedgerows, especially around dwellings. An example is the damson (*Prunus domestica*), a tart plum grown in the hedges around my parents' home in Shropshire. The fruit of these trees was supplied to the Lancashire dye trade in the last century. They yield a fast, purple dye. The small, twisted damson tree is the earliest to flower in that region, and their tart fruit makes excellent jams, pies, and wine.

Over time, every plant that could find a niche in the hedgerow's protected habitat had colonized it. This has led to the hedgerow itself becoming a recognized ecosystem. As more of England's lowland broad-leaved forest is converted to conifer plantations, the hedge has become a sanctuary for plant species that could find no place in the production forest. The hedgerow connects wooded islands in open, unfriendly ground to forest and riparian habitats. Birds and small mammals live in it, and larger creatures use it as cover to pass unseen. The most common hedgerow shrub is the hawthorn (*Crataegus monogyna*), which is also the most common shrub species in England. Associated with it are hazel (*Gorylus avellana*), holly (*Ilex aquifolium*), honeysuckle (*Lonicera* spp.), rowan (*Sorbus aucuparia*), willow (*Salix* spp. and hybrids), crabapple (*Malus sylvestris* and hybrids), birdcherry (*Prunus padus*), cherry plum (*Prunus cerasifera*), wild rose (*Rosa canina* and others), hornbeam (*Carpinus betulus*), and hops (*Humulus lupus*).

On limestone soils blackthorn (*Prunus spinosa*) tends to dominate, in association with the above species. In the East Midlands, field maple (*Acer campestre*) is dominant. In the Southeast, spindle tree (*Euonymous europeas*) is common. Common native standard trees are oak (*Quercus petrea* and *robur*), elm (*Ulmus procera* and *glabra*), ash (*Fraxinus excelsior*), beech (*Fagus sylvatica*), gean (*Prunus avium*), birch (*Betula pendula*), alder (*Alnus glutinosa*), and scotspine (*Pinus sylvestris*).

One method of determining the age of a hedgerow is to count the number of plant species in a randomly selected 60-foot section and multiply by one hundred. For instance, a sixty-foot section of hedge in Shropshire might contain hawthorn, hazel, willow, alder, holly, oak, honeysuckle, foxglove, stitchwort, cowparsley, Queen Anne's lace, and wild rose. That is twelve species multiplied by one hundred; the age of the hedge is approximately twelve hundred years.

Hedgerows in the Pacific Northwest

I am not suggesting that hedgerows and shelterbelts can be substituted for old growth habitat corridors in America. I think, however, that over time they would provide habitat for a surprising number of species. In espousing holistic and sustainable forestry practices, we should encourage farmers to plant more riparian woodlands, hedges, and shelterbelts with a high percentage of native species—in the knowledge that wildlife would make good use of these habitats.

The Pacific Northwest is blessed with numerous native species of trees and shrubs that are suitable for hedges. Suitability is dependent on the ability to resprout from dormant stem buds after cutting and mutilation. This resprouting habit is known as coppicing.

A native, livestock-proof hedge might consist of black hawthorn (*Crataegus douglasii*), western crabapple (*Malus fusca*), hazel (*Corylus cornuta*), vine maple (*Acer circinatum*), bigleaf maple (*Acer marcrophyllum*), blueblossom (*Ceanothus thyrsiflorus*), myrtle (*Umbelluloria californica*), wax myrtle (*Myrica californica*), Cascara (*Cascara sagrada*), highbush cranberry (*Viburnum edule*), serviceberry

(*Amalanchier alnifolia*), elderberry (*Sambucus* spp.), huckleberry (*Vaccinium* spp.), salal (*Gaultheria shallon*), Oregon grape (*Mahonia aquifolium*), little wood rose (*Rosa gymnocarpa*), willow (*Salix* spp.), and wild currant (*Ribas* spp.). Standards might include bigleaf maple, myrtle, madrone (*Arbutus menziesii*), oaks (*Quercus* spp.), cottonwood (*Populus* spp.), ash (*Fraxinus latifolia*), red alder (*Alnus rubra*), Douglas-fir (*Psuedotsuga menziesii*), and coastal redwood (*Sequoia sempervirons*).

A selection of the above species would provide habitat and food for wildlife, forage for bees, and wildcrafted fruit and seeds, small roundwood, and lumber for farmers. To increase the marketable products from the hedgerow, cultivated nuts and fruits can be introduced, such as walnuts, apples, pears, quince, hazel, chestnuts, plums, cherries, almonds, blueberries, cultivated currants, hops, etc.

Other benefits of hedgerows include reduced erosion, reduced wind stress on plants and animals, reduced water loss and desiccation, permanent and sustainable fencing, sustainable biomass production, a habitat for pest-controlling wildlife, privacy, and a physical barrier for disease and pests.

Trees and shrubs planted on fertile agricultural land may be expected to grow more vigorously than in their natural habitat, as they may have access to better soil and nutrient levels. At establishment, however, some species may require an initial inoculation of mycorrhiza to replace that burned out by chemical fertilizers and long-term grass/crop regimes.

Ring-porous species such as oak and ash provide stronger and straighter wood when grown quickly. This is because the springwood vessels are thin-walled, and the summerwood vessels are thick-walled. Vigorous growth increases the proportion of thick-walled vessels, thus increasing the strength of the wood. The body framework of the Morgan sports car is made from fast grown ash, which is light, strong, and bendable.

Establishing A Hedge

Establishment of native hedges does not have to expensive, even though large numbers of plants are required. Many species can be transplanted from thickets and roadsides where their removal will act as a thinning. Willow and cottonwood cuttings from two-year-old rods can be propagated in situ. Many shrubs can be propagated by cuttings and layers, and the rest will reproduce from seed. An ancient method of hedge establishment was to sow hawthorn berries into a shallow trench along the intended hedgerow.

Experiments have shown that simply fencing off an area from livestock will eventually produce a handsome hedge. Local species of plants can easily colonize the ungrazed area. If hedge planting becomes popular on a wide scale, hedge plant production would be a new source of farm income.

A thick hedge can be quickly established by planting a double staggered row of plants at eight to twelve inch spacing with six to eighteen inches between rows. A single row hedge may also be planted, this uses about one half the number of plants. Standards can be incorporated every twenty feet, then thinned to sixty feet for maturity. To create a low maintenance hedge, choose those shrubs that naturally grow to only eight to ten feet in height. Lateral growth of the hedge will probably be checked by browsing livestock or deer. With this type of hedge there would be very little shearing to do, as the hedge would maintain itself at a very desirable height. Protection from farm animals is required in the establishment years, as they will eat the new shoots of the young plants—a tasty alternative to grass.

Hedges grown for compost should be sheared annually. The sappy young growth quickly breaks down to produce a rich mulch or soil amendment, ideal for the small organic farmer. Otherwise, hedges do not need to be cut every year.

Maintaining A Hedge

Traditionally in England, a livestock-proof hedge was maintained by the process of laying. After ten or fifteen years of untrimmed growth, a hedge becomes tall and leggy, with gaps along the base where shaded foliage had died out or been suppressed. To rejuvenate the bottom, the hedge is laid with axes and regionally variable hand slashing tools, such as billhooks and slashers. First, any dead and old material is removed. The brush on the side from which the hedge is to be worked is then trimmed up to allow access to the base.

Straight stems are selected for laying; these are called pleachers. To lay them, they are cut three-fourths of the way through with an ax; the cut finishes about four to six inches above ground. The pleacher is allowed to rip over to an angle of about thirty degrees from the ground and is woven between stakes about two feet apart. It is important that the bark on the uncut side stays intact so that the pleacher stays alive. To finish off, eight- to ten-foot-long rods with one-inch butt diameters, called binders, are woven between the top of the stakes. This prevents the pleachers from springing up and adds rigidity to this living fence.

Favored species for binders are hazel or willow, although vines may also be used. The pleachers are all laid in the same direction, which depends on whether the worker is left- or right-handed.

The resulting living fence forms a thick, tight, livestock-proof hedge, as adventitious buds are stimulated into vigorous growth by such radical treatment.

The method and style of laying differs from region to region. In some places, the hedger carefully selects suitable hedgerow plants to be living stakes and binders, leaving a totally-living woven fence on completion. However, now that hedges are trimmed mechanically, often by tractor-mounted flails, laying has become somewhat of a rare rustic art form.

Value of Hedgerows

The value to wildlife varies as to the stage of growth and species content of the hedge. A recently laid hedge four feet tall and two to three feet wide offers less of a habitat than one that has been allowed to grow out for ten to fifteen years.

With sensitive management, a farm hedge can be maintained to provide maximum benefit to wildlife. For instance, a cutting regime could be designed so that sections of the hedge are cut in sequential time periods. This would create an uneven aged syndrome where there are always areas of maximum habitat. Another regime that would yield the same result would be to leave the main body of the hedge intact and simply to select out standards for timber harvest.

Over the centuries, hedgerows have demonstrated that they provide both habitat for wildlife and a livelihood for the people that tend them. I urge foresters, farmers, and homesteaders to plant hedges and shelterbelts. Increase the productivity and diversity of your land by increasing the habitat for wildlife. Replace some of the habitat lost to agriculture and development every year. Use them to divide up your cropping areas, to protect your vegetable garden, and to shelter your livestock. Grow a low-input, perennial food crop with sustainable yields of wood products and protection for your land.

For further reading on the subject of hedgerows, I recommend the following books:

Hedging: A Practical Handbook, compiled by Alan Brooks, British Trust for Conservation Volunteers, Wallingford, Oxfordshire, 1975.

Hedgerow, Eric Thomas and John T. White, Dorling Kindersley Ltd., London, 1980.

Hedges for Farm and Garden, J. L. Beddall, N.D.H., Faber and Faber Ltd., London, publication date unknown.

Farm and Estate Hedges, Ministry of Agriculture, Fisheries and Food—Fixed Equipment of the Farm Leaflet No. 11, Her Majesty's Stationery Office, London, 1960.

18

Papermaking Without Wood Pulp

Michael Pilarski

HUMANS HAVE RELIED ON HERBACEOUS PLANTS for paper stock for thousands of years. Papyrus, an Egyptian reed, gave us the word paper. Wood has been the primary paper fiber for less than a century. Paper pulp demand is one of the main reasons for the destruction of forests worldwide. Today, two out of every five trees are cut for pulp.

It takes a heavy-duty industrial process to turn wood into paper. The processes releases large amounts of dangerous pollutants, such as chlorine, dioxin, and furans, into the air and water. As forests diminish and public opinion to save forests grows there is increasing interest in alternative fiber crops.

Hundreds of annuals and herbaceous perennials can be used for paper stock, either alone or in combination with other feedstocks. Processing requires less energy and produces far less toxic wastes than wood pulp plants. In addition, facilities do not have to be so large. If our paper pulp needs could be met with herbaceous perennial and annual crops, we would lower energy consumption, save our forests, reduce toxic waste, decentralize paper production and add more crops for farmers.

If sustainable agriculture were applied on a broad scale using permaculture practices, we could increase world food supplies and do it on less land. This would free up large amounts of farmland, some of which could be used for growing paper feedstocks. The hemp plant is one of the prime candidates for paper feedstock. Hemp produces high yields and large amounts of high-quality fiber per acre, which is why it was (and still is in some countries) grown on a large scale for rope and other fiber uses. In fact, hemp makes the best grades of canvas. Varieties have been bred for high fiber production and low THC production.

Hemp, however, is just one plant out of dozens and even hundreds of species of herbaceous plants which can yield paper pulp. There are several advantages perennial herbaceous plants have over hemp (and other annual species).

For example, there is less need to till and cultivate the soil. Perennials only need to be replanted occasionally (3-10 years depending on species and management). Tillage and cultivation requires tractors, implements and fuel. Of course, they could grow produce fuel from hemp seeds since it works fine in diesel engines.

Furthermore, it takes extra care with cropping annual plants to keep the soil in good tilth with a high organic matter content. Hemp fields need to be rotated with soil-building crops to maintain soil quality. Herbaceous perennials, on the other hand, generally build soils rather then deplete them.

Some of the highest producing biomass plants come from wet lowland areas. Examples are papyrus, cattails, rushes, water hyacinth, etc. Wetlands have some of the highest nutrient loads in the landscape plus lots of water. High biomass yields from wetland species are not surprising given these conditions. Special equipment would be needed to carry out harvests in moist habitats, however.

Presently, under-utilized crop wastes could support a large paper industry without even putting new land into production. For example, large amounts of grass straw are burned every year in Washington and Oregon by seed producers. Paper production is one possibility being looked into by the grass seed industry for alternative uses of the waste straw.

There has been a notable increase in the market for hand-made paper, mainly used for arts and crafts and high-priced. Produced domestically and imported into from an increasing number of other countries, there is opportunity for larger employment in the U.S. and abroad to supply this growing market.

In the future, we might see thousands of plant species used for craft papermaking, the bulk of mass-produced paper supplied by several dozen species of herbaceous plants. Big paper plants would be replaced by many medium and small-scale producers scattered across the landscape. The trees like this scenario !

Alternatives for Wood Pulp Being Researched on the Homescale

Denise DeMarie

THE PRACTICE OF LOGGING to obtain wood pulp for paper production is one area that's ripe for change. In other countries there are successful operations using other plant fibers for paper, such as grasses (Europe and Asia), and hemp (India). Locally, I've done numerous experiments manufacturing paper using common beach grasses, corn husks, garlic skins, and other plant material. The results have consistently produced grades of paper from light cardboard to tissue. This is in my own kitchen at home! I can imagine what wonderful-quality paper could be achieved with the mechanization and standardization of commercial production.

As a former resident of Nahcotta, Washington, I was concerned that Willapa Bay would be sprayed [with herbicides] to control growth of sparteena [non-native] grass in the estuary. I then harvested some sparteena grass and made some paper out of it. Sparteena produced the best quality paper of all the plants I've experimented with thus far.

...I'm suggesting we use some vision and create new industry, re-employ wood pulp workers as grass pulp workers manufacturing paper products that exceed the limits of art and infiltrate our daily lives. I'm suggesting we pioneer innovations in the paper pulp industry that will result in more employment and ecological sustainability.

I've kept records of my experiments pertaining to types of grasses and other plants used, time harvested correlating to quality of paper produced, alternate processes used, etc. These are soon to be compiled into a format for open disclosure to the public. I invite the woodpulp paper industry to review my findings. I especially invite and encourage people to create their own businesses manufacturing sustainable, recycled paper products out of pulp sources other than wood, and to do so in an alternative way that will no longer subject themselves and their families to corporate "security."

I welcome inquires and will respond to all correspondence.

Later footnote from DeMarie

A representative from Georgia Pacific told me they're researching grass/straw fiber sources. Weyerhauser sent a representative to Spain to see how they are doing it. He reported that in Spain, grain is grown to feed the cattle—the waste (straw) from the field is made into paper, the effluent from the papermaking process is mixed with the cow manure and spread on the field for next year's grain crop. Nothing is wasted. I don't have specifics, but similar processes are apparently going on in Italy, Mexico, India and many semi-arid countries.

Grass Roots Paper
Denise DeMarie
322 NW 59th
Newport, Oregon 97365

References to Fiber Crops

The Emperor Wears No Clothes
Jack Herer. Rev. 1992 ed. $14. Available from the Ohio Hempery.

This is the most in depth look at the history and myriad uses of hemp. Paper, cloth, food, oil, canvas, rope, etc. Truly a wonder plant.

Fiber Crops
James M. Dempsey. 1975. 457 pages. $26.95. Available from agAccess
See Book Sources section.

A major reference for those interested in almost any aspect of the principal fiber crops. Flax, hemp, ramie, jute, kenay, roselle, urena, China jute and sunn hemp. All of these fiber plants can be used as sources of paper pulp.

Papyrus, Tapa, Amate & Rice Paper: Papermaking in Africa, the Pacific, Latin America, and Southeast Asia
Lilian A. Bell, 146 pp., paperback. $27.00 + $2.00 postage. Available from agAccess.

This book describes paper-making techniques in Egypt,

18

Uganda, Polynesia, the Brazilian Amazon, Indonesia, Taiwan and Southern China. Each section includes an introduction, a discussion of the trees and plants used to make paper, and tools and equipment used.

Plant Fibers for Papermaking

Lilian A. Bell. 4th Edition, 1984; 132 pages. $21.00 Available from agAccess.

The book contains information on over 75 temperate and tropical plant fibers. It includes botanical line drawings, historical uses of fiber plants, and concise information explaining how to prepare the fibers for hand papermaking. The book also includes photos of equipment, processes and artwork, photomicrographs, process drawings and information about oriental and western methods of paper casting and sheet formation. An extensive bibliography is included in addition to a botanical name index and a common name index.

Resources

Access Unlimited

P.O. Box 1900
Frazier Park, California 93225

An information center on the many uses of hemp. Their new book is reputedly one of the most comprehensive and up-to-date writings on the subject: *Eco-Hemp: Economy and Ecology with Hemp*. Lynn and Judy Osburn. 1993.

International Hemp Bulletin

Canvasmaker, Inc.
P.O. Box 14603
Portland, Oregon 97214
Tel: (503) 232-1128/Fax: (503) 232-0239

A small newsletter, but one of the few ways to keep current on the trade in hemp fiber for fabric. Some resources would be of interest to those interested in hemp for pulp or wood fiber alternative. Free subscription.

Hemp Textiles International, Inc

3200 30th ST.
Bellingham, WA 98225
Tel: 1-800-776-HEMP Fax: (206) 650-1684

Imports hemp textiles and blends into the US, has lines on Chinese sources of hemp fiberboard and paper.

K.P. Products

P.O. Box 4795
Albuquerque, NM 87196
Tel/Fax: (505) 294-0293. Tom Rymsza.

Sells kenaf paper: reams, envelopes, commercial quality.

The Ohio Hempery

14 North Court St., #328,
Athens, Ohio 45701
Tel. 1-800-BUY-HEMP or (614) 593-5826.

Mail-order supplier for hemp linen, twine, hemp seed oil, and other hemp products. Imports great quality tree-free paper made with 50% hemp and 50% cereal straw. No trees, bleaches or acids were used in its manufacture.

Tree-Free EcoPaper

121 SW Salmon, Suite 1100
Portland, Oregon 97204

Sell 50% hemp/50% cereal straw paper. Acid-free. No dioxins. No deforestation.

National Chemical Laboratory Higashi 1-1-4

Yatabe-cho,
Tsukuba-gun Ibaraki-kan-Tsukuba Gakuen 305,
JAPAN

A method of making paper out of sugar-cane waste and banana stems has been developed by researchers at Japan's National Chemical Laboratory for Industries.

The laboratory, run by Japan's Ministry of International Trade and Industry, plans to set up a commercial paper-manufacturing plant in collaboration with a private firm.

18

Agroforestry: A Resource Guide

Agroforestry, as the term is used at International Center for Research in Agroforestry (ICRAF), is a collective word for all land-use systems and practices in which woody perennials are deliberately grown on the same land management unit as crops and/or animals. This can be either in some form of spatial arrangement or in a time sequence. To qualify as agroforestry, a given land-use system or practice must permit significant economic and ecological interactions between the woody and non-woody components. Within this broad definition, a wide variety of both traditional as well as relatively new systems and practices fall under the umbrella concept of agroforestry.

—ICRAF

Agroforestry is the integration of forestry and agriculture. It can include woodlots, windbreaks, hedgerows, orchards, fodder trees, livestock and multi-purpose trees in many different assemblages. Agroforestry provides traditional forest products such as timber, poles and fuelwood as well as fodder, food, fruit, nuts and many other products. The trees also perform the functions of windbreaks, soil improvement, and habitat for beneficial insects, spiders, and insectivorous and rodent preying birds.

Agroforestry systems can vary widely between two extremes. On the one hand they can be the addition of a low density of trees to farm fields. On the other extreme they can be complex, multi-storied, symbiotic assemblages containing a diversity of plant, animal, insect, soil life, and mycorrhizal fungi. These more densely-planted, complex forms of agroforestry are similar to permaculture. Polyculture is another term used to describe diverse, intensive, multi-cropping, land-use systems.

Agroforestry systems can grade into natural forests and managed forests. Agroforestry has been under development for millennia throughout the world. In modern times the term and concepts have been mainly applied in non-overdeveloped countries in Africa, Asia and Latin America. It is only recently that agroforestry has gained credence in the U.S. and other overdeveloped countries.

A good working knowledge of agroforestry is useful to restoration foresters, especially those who manage forests intermingled with, or adjacent to, farmland.

Directory of Agroforestry Training

Training and Educational Opportunities in Agroforestry

Julie Bournes and Susan Huke. 1991. Available from: Ms. Susan Huke, International Forestry, USDA/FS, P.O. Box 96090, Washington D.C. 20090-6090. 81 pp.

A directory of 13 institutions in the USA and 23 elsewhere that provide training and educational programs in agroforestry. The entry for each institution lists contacts, program description, institutional facilities, cost, qualifications required of students, and some funding possibilities. The training courses listed contain a wide variety of subject matter and approaches relevant to agroforestry in developing countries. Course lengths vary from several weeks to one year and cater to professionals and students. The directory is to be regularly updated.

Agroforestry Organizations

Agroforestry Research Trust
17 Arden Drive, Chelston
Torquay, Devon TQ2 6DZ, UNITED KINGDOM

Finally, an agroforestry outfit focusing on temperate zone plant species. They have put together a most impressive set of plant species indexes on temperate zone agroforestry species and publish a quarterly *Agroforestry News.* £20 sterling. Highly recommended to temperate zone agroforestry enthusiasts.

Alley Farming Network for Tropical Africa (AFNETA)
c/o IITA
PMB 5320
Oyo Road, Ibadan, NIGERIA

18

Tel: 413-244 or 413-315

A network for researchers and NGO's, primarily in Nigeria, but also Togo and other African countries. They publish an agroforestry newsletter and host conferences.

American Willow Growers Network

Bonnie Gale
Rural Free Del. 1, Box 124-A
South New Berlin, New York 13843-9649, USA

A network and newsletter for growers of willows for basketry/weaving materials and other uses.

Asia-Pacific Agroforestry Network

P.O. Box 382
Bogor 16001, INDONESIA
Tel/Fax: (62-251) 32-3063

APAN is a network of government agencies, universities, and NGO's. They publish an occasional newsletter in English, free of charge.

Association for Temperate Agroforestry

Michael A. Gould
Dept. of Forestry, Michigan State University
East Lansing, Michigan 48824, USA

Promoting a network of practitioners and researchers.

Baobab Farm

P.O. Box 90202
Mombasa, KENYA
Tel: (254) 483729

A fantastic example of turning an abandoned quarry into an integrated agriculture, aquaculture, reforestation, wildlife habitat. A unique, integrated polyculture and wild animal propagation ecosystem. System includes tilapia, hippos, crocodiles, algae, rice, vegetables, prawns, nile cabbage, and 80,000 trees (80 species of palm alone).

Forestry/Fuelwood Research and Development (F/FRED) Project

See *Farm Forestry News* in periodicals section

International Center for Research in Agroforestry (ICRAF)

P.O. Box 30677
Nairobi, KENYA
Tel: (254-2) 521450/Fax: 521001

The largest international center for agroforestry research, ICRAF conducts collaborative research and training in many countries, especially in the tropics and especially in Africa. ICRAF has a wide variety of useful publications available. For a current list send for *Current Publications*. Another service is the MPTS Database software package for IBM, with information on 1000 Multi-Purpose Tree Species.

International Tree Crops Institute (ITCI)

Ryton Court, Ryton on Dunsmore
Coventry, CV83L6, UNITED KINGDOM

ITCI is an international network for information exchange on agroforestry, windbreaks and farm woodlots. I recommend ITCI for its grass-roots approach. ITCI has offices in the UK, the USA, Australia and India. ITCI publishes the *International Tree Crops Journal*, a quarterly journal of agroforestry edited by ITCI's UK Secretary, Alan Grainger. Annual subscription is US$73 or £49. The emphasis is on communication of research results and the exchange of practical experience with multi-purpose tree crops and agroforestry.

ITCI Australia: P.O. Box 283, Caulfield South 3162, VIC, Australia, Tel: (03-211) 6209/Fax: (03-211) 8502.

ITCI India, Jenal Apt. No. 1, Abhishek Colony, Racecourse Circle, Baroda, 390007, Gujarat, India.

ITCI USA, P.O. Box 4460, Davis, California 95617 USA. Tel: (916) 753-4535.

Leaf for Life

128 Owsley Ave.
Lexington, Kentucky 40502, USA
Tel: (606) 266-5337

Leaf for Life has found the trick of turning leafy greens into nutritious, good-tasting food for humans. Leaf concentrate (LC) can be made from a wide variety of highly productive leaf crops, including tree species. They have a project going in Nicaragua. They have a newsletter and publications detailing how to make LC.

Multipurpose Tree Species Research Network

MPTS Secretariat
Kasetsart University
Bangkok, THAILAND

Asian-wide program to increase knowledge of tree species that can help meet the needs of small-scale farmers.

National Paulownia Center

Peter R. Beckford
4304 Kenny Street
Beltsville, Maryland 20705-2738, USA

Mr. Beckford has distributed Paulownia seed to over 1,500 people.

Neem Association

1511 Oneco Avenue
Winter Park, Florida 32789, USA
Tel: (407) 628-2792

A clearinghouse for people interested in neem projects, programs, products and literature. Publishes *Neem Association Newsletter*.

18

Nitrogen Fixation by Tropical Agricultural Legumes

(NiFTAL)
P.O. Box 0
Paia, Hawaii, 96799, USA

NiFTAL is a University of Hawaii project involving research, outreach and training to promote nitrogen-fixing legume use among farmers in developing countries.

Nitrogen Fixing Tree Association

1010 Holumua Road
Paia, Hawaii 96779, USA
Tel: (808) 597-9568/Fax (808) 597-8516

NFTA sends lots of publications to members including *Nitrogen Fixing Tree Research Reports*. Emphasis has mainly been on the tropics and subtropics, but they are now beginning to address some cold-temperate species.

NFTA also coordinates the Agroforestry Information Service (AIS). AIS is a network, supported by the USDA Tropical Forestry Program, facilitates sharing and adoption of both traditional and innovative agroforestry ideas and technologies throughout the Pacific. They research and make available both documented and developing technologies in easily accessible and adaptable forms. These include technology fact sheets, newsletter inserts, radio broadcasts, and regular written correspondence.

Membership: developed countries US $25, institution $35. Developing countries US$5/year, institution $10. First year fee waiver to NGO's in developing countries.

North American Fruit Explorers

Rt. 1, Box 94
Chapin, Illinois 62628, USA
Tel: (217) 245-7589

Best source of information on growing unusual and hardy fruits in the USA. $15/yr. subscription to *Pomona* magazine.

Pacific Agroforestry Network (PAN)

COM Land Grant
P.O. Box 1179
Kolonia, Federated States of Micronesia 96941

English-language occasional publication *PAN Exchange*. Free of charge. Kolonia is in the Caroline Islands and still under United States control. Postage is the same as in the U.S.

PROCACAO

IICA, Apdo. 55-2200
Coronado, COSTA RICA

PROCACAO is a regional agricultural research and extension network involving three research institutions (CATIE, FHIA and Hershey), seven countries in Central America and numerous local organizations including farmers. The project focus is improved economic returns for small-scale cocoa farmers using integrated systems of annual and perennial crops. This includes foods, soil improving species, shade, forage, windbreak trees and several alternative cash crops such as spices and fruit trees.

In the U.S. we tend to think of chocolate as a junk food, but in Central America the production is consumed as very economical, nutritional and natural products. Over 130 natural colorants, diverse beverages including wines, and jellies, vinegars, cosmetics, and livestock feed are derived from cocoa. Cocoa trees are understory trees in multiple-story agro-ecosystems.

Regional Wood Energy Development in Asia (RWEDP)

FAO/RAPA, Malliwan Mansion, Phra Atit Rd.
Bangkok, 10200, THAILAND
Tel: (662) 280-0760/Fax: 280-0445

RWEDP is a regional cooperative project for the development of woodfuel resources to meet the energy needs of households and small-scale processing enterprises. It is run by the FAO and the Netherlands Government. Their main emphases are reviewing current policies, strategies and approaches in the 11 countries in the project area; documentation and dissemination of successful experiences in production, marketing and conversion of woodfuels and in participatory planning; training through national workshops and courses; preparation of field manuals, training and teaching material in forestry extension and wood energy conversion. Their quarterly *Wood Energy News* and many other publications are free.

Rodale Institute Research Center

International Information Exchange Network
611 Siegfriedale Road
Kutztown, Pennsylvania 19530
Tel: (215) 683-6383/Fax: (215) 683-8548

International Ag-Sieve is a newsletter on organic agriculture and agroforestry from Rodale's International Information Exchange Network. Rodale Institute has been the leading promoter and publisher on organic gardening and farming in the United States for over 40 years. *International Ag-Sieve* is Rodale's first international publication. Modest in size but useful. $16.00/Six issues per year (English).

Rodale staff member Rhonda Janke is doing research in agroforestry methods for temperate climates with black locust and alder. Janke can be contacted at the above address.

Springtree Agroforestry Project

Rt. 2, Box 89
Scottsville, Virginia 24590, USA
Tel: (804) 286-3466

Andy Wilson is facilitating information exchange on

the use of Honeylocust (*Gleditsia triacanthos*) in agroforestry systems for temperate zones. The project is being implemented on a 50-hectare farm in central Virginia where livestock are raised commercially.

Agroforestry Periodicals

Most of the agroforestry organizations reviewed also have newsletters.

Agroforestry Abstracts
1989. CAB International in association with ICRAF: Wallingford, Oxon OX10 8DE, ENGLAND

This quarterly journal abstracts and reviews the worlds' research and technical literature in the field of agroforestry. Thousands of abstracts a year. Subscription: US$92 Americas. £48 elsewhere.

Agroforestry Systems: an international journal
Martinus Nijhoff/Dr. W. Junk (Publishers in cooperation with ICRAF)
c/o Kluwer Academic Publishers Group Distribution Centre
P.O. Box 322
3300 AH Dordrecht, THE NETHERLANDS

An expensive professional journal which is available at most university libraries. It is worth a look once a year to select out the articles of most interest to you. Over the years, dozens of different local agroforestry systems from many parts of the world have been described. Subscription orders and requests for specimen copies can be sent to the address listed above.

Agroforestry Today
The quarterly journal of the International Center for Research in Agroforestry. Address in Organizations. Free to third world residents.

Farm Forestry News
F/Fred Network Secretariat
c/o Kasetsart University, Faculty of Forestry
P.O. Box 1038, Kasetsart Post Office
Bangkok 10903 THAILAND
Tel: (66-2) 579-1977/Fax: (66-2) 561-1041

A bit heavy on computers, but every issue has useful information and networking resources for the tropical agroforestry enthusiast. *Farm Forestry News* is overseen and published by the Winrock International Institute for Agricultural Development under a Cooperative Agreement with USAID. F/FRED also publishes *MPTS Research Notes*. Six issues per year. Free of charge.

U. S. requests for information can be addressed to:
F/FRED Project, Winrock International
1611 N. Kent St., Suite 600
Arlington, Virginia 22209

Tel: (703) 525-9430/Fax: (703) 522-8758

Inside Agroforestry
Center for Semiarid Agroforestry, Rocky Mountain Forest and Range Experiment Station
University of Nebraska-Lincoln, East Campus
Lincoln, Nebraska 68583

A quarterly newsletter to facilitate transfer technologies and information to natural resource professionals.

International Tree Crops Journal
Address and review under International Tree Crops Institute in the preceding section.

Agroforestry Conferences

First Conference on Agroforestry in North America
August 13-16, 1989. Contact: Peter Williams or Andrew Gordon, Dept. of Environmental Biology University of Guelph, Guelph, Ontario, N1G 2W1, CANADA.

Second Conference on Agroforestry in North America
August 18-21, 1991. Holiday Inn University Plaza, Springfield, MO. Proceedings are published. Contact: Dr. H. E. Garrett, The School of Natural Resources, 1-30 Agriculture Building , University of Missouri, Columbia, MO 65211

Third North American Agroforestry Conference
August 15-18, 1993. Ames, Iowa. "Opportunities for Temperate Zone Agroforestry-Worldwide" is the theme of this conference. For more information, contact: Richard C. Schultz, Department of Forestry, 251 Bessey Hall, Iowa State University, Ames, Iowa 50011-1021, USA. Tel: (515) 294-7602. Fax: (515) 294-1337.

Books on Agroforestry

Agroforestry for Soil Conservation
Anthony Young. 1989. ICRAF. 276 pp.

This volume presents the results of an ICRAF review of the potential of agroforestry for soil conservation including erosion control and maintenance of fertility.

Agroforesty in Africa, a Survey of Project Experience
Paul Kerkhof. 1990. PANOS Publications Ltd., Angel House, 9 White Lion Street, London N1 9PD, UK. 216 pp.

Much has been written about the theory of agroforestry. This study presents a first-hand report on what is happening in practice. The book presents a survey of the experience of 21 projects in 11 countries throughout Africa, based primarily on field visits, but backed up with project reports and other literature. Their combined experience provides an important insight into the potential for agroforestry, and vital clues as to how projects can be

18

better designed in future.

Agroforestry in Asia and the Pacific
W. Mellinck, Y. S. Rao and K. G. MacDicken, eds. 1991. 308 pp. FAO/RAPA Publication 1991/5, Bangkok.

A compilation of papers presented in May 1990 at a consultation on agroforestry in the Asia-Pacific Region at RAPA. The first part describes the status of agroforestry technologies in the 12 countries represented, including Laos and Vietnam where little is known about agroforestry practices. The second part discusses promotion and development of agroforestry.

Agroforestry in Dry Land Africa
D. Rochelean, Fred Weber and A. Field-Juma. 1988. ICRAF.

Describes a wide range of agroforestry practices appropriate for different sites. Practices were adapted to local needs by working with local community members. Many contacts and resources are included.

Agroforestry In Tonga: A Traditional Source for Development of Sustainable Farming Systems
W. Kunzel. 1989. South Pacific Smallholder Project (Occasional Paper 12): University of New England, Armidale, NSW, Australia.

Agroforestry Literature: A Selected Bibliography
R. Labelle, L. Majisu and H. Munyua. 1988. ICRAF. £7.95. 272 pp.

Agroforestry Systems in China
Zhu Zhaohua, ed. 1991. Chinese Academy of Forestry, and IDRC: P.O. Box 8500, Ottawa, Ont. K1G 3H9 Canada.

Agroforestry Systems in the Tropics
P. K. R. Nair. 1989. Kluwer press. £118. 672 pp.

Alley Farming in the Humid and Subhumid Tropics
B. T. Kand and L. Reynolds, eds. 1989. IDRC. $16. 251 pp.

Looks at advances in the production of annual crops between hedgerows of shrubs and trees.

Bibliography of North American Shelterbelt Research
A. E. Campbell and R. H. M. Pratt. 1974. Canada Northern Forest Research Center: Edmonton, Alberta, Canada. Information Rept. NOR-X-92. 52 pp.

Biomass Forestry in Europe: A Strategy for the Future
F. C Hummel et al. 1988. Elseveir. £82. 600 pp. Available from Natural History Book Service. See Book Source section].

Dalbergia Sisoo: An Annotated Bibliography
Kevin V. White. 1990. Winrock International, Forestry/Fuelwood Research and Development Project. 120 pp.

A fast-growing, highly-valued timber tree in east Asia. Useful abstracts.

D & D Users Manual: An Introduction to Agroforestry
Diagnosis and Design
J. B. Raintree, ed. ICRAF: Nairobi. 114 pp.

I highly recommend this book to anyone who is doing rural, extension work in the South. D&D is an excellent design methodology for small-scale and subsistence agriculture. I rate D&D right up there with permaculture. D&D is a whole systems approach which identifies key constraints to production increases and makes small adjustments to existing systems.

Economic Analysis of Agroforestry Technologies: An Annotated Bibliography
R. Swinkels and S. Scherr. 1991. ICRAF: Nairobi.

A critical analysis of the real costs and benefits of specific agroforestry technologies. It provides an essential basis for comparative analysis by permaculture practitioners.

Farming Systems With Special Reference To Agroforestry: A Literature Review and A Field Study in Babati District, Tanzania
Borje Airiksson and Agnetha Ohisson. 1990. Working Paper 129, Swedish University of Agricultural Sciences, International Rural Development Center: Box 7005, S-750 07 UPPSALA, SWEDEN

Firewood Crops: Shrub and Tree Species for Energy
Production, Vol. 2. 92 pp. Vol. 1. 1980. 237 pp. National Academy Press. 1983. National Academy of Science: Washington, DC.

Fodder Trees
L. A. Logan and J. E. Radcliffe, eds. 1985. Crop Research Division: DSIR Private Bag, Christchurch, NEW ZEALAND. 49 pp.

A summary of research in New Zealand.

Forest Farming
James Sholto Douglas and Robert A. de J. Hart. 1976. Available from Ecology Action of the MidPeninsula, 5798 Ridgewood Road, Willits, CA 95490.

One of the classics on tree crops. A widely read book which has been influential in many countries.

Forest Gardening
Robert A. de J. Hart. 1991. From Eco-logic Books, The Bakery, Somerton Rd., North Aston, Oxford OX6 4HX, UK. £7.95/212 pp.

The co-author of *Forest Farming* describes the practice and principles of forest gardening, which integrates agroforestry and permaculture to make self-reliant, tree-centered food systems. It demonstrates the potential for countering environmental devastation in the developing and developed world. A practical resource with guidelines on the design and maintenance of forest gardens and species lists for temperate, tropical, and subtropical climates.

Forest Grazing Management: Guidelines for Agro-Silvo Pastoralism
Harold F. Heady. 1985.

This is a review of the worldwide literature on agroforestry with an emphasis on grazing. Over 1000 publications were searched and about 140 cited.

Hedges
Hooper, Pollard & Moore. 1975. 245 pp.

Hedgerow ecology.

Insects of Windbreaks and Related Plantings: Distribution, Importance and Management
USDA FS Rocky Mountain For. & Range Exp. Stn. General Technical Rep. Rm. 204. Address in U.S. Government Forest Agencies section). 50 pp.

The Proceedings of a Conference held Dec. 6, 1988, Louisville, Kentucky. Nine articles on insects associated with windbreaks. The writings convey far more than just insects' relationships with windbreaks. They are ecological conversations on how windbreaks function, relationships within the windbreak, crop windbreak interactions, nutrient flows, decomposition cycles. Extensive references lead to key works on windbreaks and entomology.

Jatropha Curcas, A Multipurpose Species for Problematic Sites
Norman Jones and Joan H. Miller. The World Bank Asia Technical Department Agriculture Division. Land Resources Series—No. 1. 18 pp.

Few of you are interested in *Jatropha*. But more of you are interested in oilseed processing. This publication contains a list of organizations involved with, or with information about, oilseed processing, and an extensive reference list.

Most of this booklet is on *Jatropha curcas*, a plant native to the American tropics but which is grown in most of the tropical and subtropical regions of the world. It can also be cultivated on poor soils and in low rainfall areas. Traditionally, this plant is used for medicine, pesticides, cosmetics, and as hedges. Further testing recently indicated that its oil is a potential substitute for diesel fuel, and as a fuel wood substitute that has positive implications in forest conservation.

Johnny Walnutseed and Growing Black Walnut
J. M. Sloan. 1979. Vantage Press: NY. 141 pp.

Half of this book is a biography of Robert Willard Daubendiek who promoted black walnut plantings throughout the upper Midwest. The other half of the book is "how-to" information on planting, tending and growing black walnut.

Mayan Rainforest Farming
Bullfrog Films. 1987. Oley, PA 19547
Tel: (800) 543-FROG.

A 29-minute film.

Multipurpose Trees: Selection and Testing for Agroforestry
P. A. Huxley and S. B. Westley. 1989. ICRAF. $8. 117 pp.

Covers the steps required for the selection and testing of woody species for specific biophysical settings, agroforestry technologies, and land-use systems.

Multipurpose Tree Species for Small-farm Use
Proceedings of an international workshop in Pattaya, Thailand. 1987. Co-published by IDRC Canada and Winrock International, USA. 280 pp.

Has over 30 papers from Asian authors.

Neem: A Tree for Solving Global Problems
National Academy Press. 141 pp. $24.

Even the most cautious call neem a wonder tree. It provides a powerful pesticide that appears completely non-toxic to humans, mammals and beneficial insects. In hot dry areas that are otherwise barren it gives ample shade and firewood year round. It is easy to establish and maintain. In India, where it is native, it is used to clean gums and teeth and is known to relieve so many different pains, fevers, infections and other complaints that it has been called "the village pharmacy." It even has contraceptive properties.

Palms: An informative, practical guide to palms of the world: Their cultivation, care and landscape use
Alec Blombery and Tony Rodd. 1982. Angus & Robertson Publishers. 199 pp.

Large format with many color photos.

Paulownia in China: Cultivation and Utilization
Chinese Academy of Forestry Staff. A. N. Rao, ed. 1986. 65 pp. Published by Asian Network for Biological Sciences, c/o A. N. Rao, Botany Department, National University of Singapore, Lower Kent Ridge Road, Singapore 1511, Republic of Singapore.

An informative book with many photographs. A compilation of the Chinese experience with *Paulownia*; one of their main agroforestry trees for intercropping with cotton, wheat, corn, other grains and other food crops (hundreds of thousands of acres of *Paulownia* have been planted in recent years). The genus *Paulownia* is repre-

18

sented by nine species of timber trees which are indigenous to China. It is very adaptable, widely distributed and one of the fastest growing trees for temperate regions. A multi-purpose tree for timber, pulp, veneer, medicine, animal fodder, fertilizer, bee-food and windbreaks.

Planning for Agroforestry: With Special Reference to Low Rainfall Areas

Susan Huke and June Plecan. 1988. Save The Children, 54 Wilton Road, Westport, CT 06880. $4.

An easy-to-use handbook for development workers interested in exploring agroforestry practices with their local communities. Save the Children is a private, nonprofit, non-sectarian international development and relief organization. The agency operates programs in 43 countries, including the United States.

Poplars and Willows: In Wood Production and Land Use

FAO. 1979. 328 pp.

Covers principal species and cultivars, improvement selection, ecology, propagation, cultivation, diseases, uses, etc. A detailed view of these two important genera.

Shrubs in Tropical Forest Ecosystems

A. K. Banerjee. 1989. World Bank. $9.95. 132 pp. Available from Agribookstore.

Considers shrub's potential for solving fuelwood and fodder shortages. Covers characteristics, growth features, propagation, and management.

Tagasaste: Tree Lucerne, High Production Fodder Crop

Laurence C. Snook. $10.95. 102 pp.

Native to the arid Cape Verdes Island, Tagasaste was subsequently popularized in Australia. Tree lucerne is a fast growing shrub used on farms as a windbreak. Tagasaste is a grazeable windbreak hedge and can be harvested in winter and used instead of hay. Tagasaste (*Chamaecytisus almensis*) is a small scrubby highland nitrogen-fixing tree, which shares some of the attributes of Leucaena and could be used in tropical highlands and Mediterranean climates for fodder and fuelwood.

Tree Crops: A Permanent Agriculture

J. Russell Smith. 1950. Island Press: Covelo, CA.

One of the first, and still one of the best, books on the subject. Recommended.

Trees and Tenure: An Annotated Bibliography for Agroforesters and Others

Louise Fortmann and James Riddell. 1985. 135 pp. $8. Land Tenure Center, 1300 University Ave., U. of Wisconsin, Madison, WI 53708.

Trees for the tropics. Growing Australian multipurpose trees and shrubs in developing countries

D. J. Boland. 1989. $44 postpaid. Inkata Press, 13/170 Forster Road, Mt. Waverly, Victoria 3149, AUSTRALIA. 247 pp.

This book offers valuable information to people involved in agroforestry who have interest in the uses of Australian trees. A major part of the book is devoted to evaluation of field trials in Australia, Thailand, The People's Republic of China and East/Southeast Africa.

Research institutions in developing countries who feel they would qualify for a complimentary copy should write to the Communications Coordinator, ACIAR, GP.O. Box 1571, Canberra, ACT, 2601, AUSTRALIA.

Trees, Prairies, and People: A History of Tree Planting in the Plains States

Wilmon H. Droze. 1977. Texas Woman's University (Documents: A 13.2: T 71/291): Denton.

This book is a history of shelterbelt planting in the U.S. in the 1800's and 1900's, including the dust bowl era.

Tropical Leaf Vegetables in Human Nutrition

H.A.D.C. Oomen and G.J.H. Grubben. 1977. Communication 69. Dept of Agroforestry Research, Royal Tropical Institute, Amsterdam. 140 pp.

Refers to all the main studies on tropical leaf vegetables to that point.

Tropical Legumes: Resources for the Future

National Academy of Sciences. 1979. Washington, D.C. $12.50. 332 pp.

A must for anyone working in tropical agriculture. The book covers the history, uses and culture of leguminous root crops, pulses, fruits, forages, timber and miscellaneous plants. Major crops are covered in more detail than minor crops. For each plant there is a list of selected reading and names/addresses of tropical agricultural research centers.

The Tropical Mixed Garden in Costa Rica: A Potential Focus for Agroforestry Research

Norman W. Price. 1989. Unpublished doctorate thesis: Univ. of British Columbia, Vancouver, B.C., CANADA

Wood Energy Bibliography

RWEDP. 89 pp. (address in Organizations).

Includes charcoal and pyrolysis, improved stoves, wood energy in rural industries, bread ovens, producer gas and steam, plantations for energy systems, and briquetting. Recommended.

18

Non-Timber Forest Products: A Resource Guide

How Many Useful & Edible Plants are there in the World?

THIRTY THOUSAND SPECIES is a conservative estimate of the number of plant species utilized by people throughout the world for food, medicine, wood products, etc. How many are edible? Tanaka lists over 10,000 species as edible. How many have you tried? If you are into researching possibilities, here are reviews of the most comprehensive references.

Restoration foresters have to know far more than just tree species and their silviculture. Ideally they would know all the plants in their forests and know all their uses. Ideally they would also know the functional roles of each plant and animal species in the ecosystem. Restoration foresters should learn wildcrafting, ethnobotany, herbalism and similar skills so that they can help clients obtain income from forest lands without cutting timber.

Wildcrafting

Wildcrafting encompasses a wide range of gathering activities in forests, fields, meadows, steppes, mountains and wherever wild plants are found, even in the city. Wildcrafters collect wild fruit, nuts, berries, mushrooms, greens, roots, seeds, dried flowers, herbs, florists greens, mosses, burls, etc. Wildcrafting also includes processing of these wild materials into useful items.

Miguel Guizar

Wildcrafting puts people in touch with the plants around them. The plants provide sustenance and useful materials—they teach and provide a continual source of beauty and amazement. The more resources we obtain locally the less we draw on distant ecosystems and factories.

I have had extensive, hands-on experience with wildcrafting many kinds of seeds, cones, berries, medicinal herbs, mushrooms, dried flowers and seed heads, weaving material, poles, cedar shake bolts, and many other useful products of the forest. I can make a decent wage most of the time and sometimes good money. It is pleasant work for the most part, although success definitely calls for hard work. Many of my friends wildcraft, some commercially. It is part of our lives and livelihood.

I like wildcrafting. When I walk around in the woods and fields I see plenty of economic opportunities. I could see hundreds more wildcrafters making their living off the forests and wildlands in our local hills.

The danger lies in whether the resources are harvested sustainably or wiped out through over-harvesting. The world abounds with examples of depletion or extinction of species through overharvesting. Conscientious wildcrafting calls for maintenance and improvement of the existing stands of desired native plants, as well as helping them colonize other suitable habitats.

Books and Articles On Useful Plants

Alternative Foods: A World Guide to Lesser Known Edible Plants
J. Sholto Douglas, 1978, Pelham Books Ltd. W.C. 1 England. 177 pp.

While it does not contain as large a listing of plants as other books listed here. J. Sholto Douglas has given us a choice list of plants to consider. Over 500 species covered. Especially noteworthy dietary/nutritional information. Unfortunately the book is out of print. Try inter-library loan.

18

Cornucopia: A Source Book of Edible Plants

Stephen Facciola. 1990. 675 pp. $37.75 ppd. Kampong Publications, 1870 Sunrise Drive, Vista, CA 92084.

This fantastic volume covers about 3,000 species and many cultivars, especially tree crops and vegetables. It also gives addresses of sources of the plants.

Dictionary of Cultivated plants and Their Regions of Diversity

A. C. Zeven and J.M.J. de Wet. 1982. 263 pp. $38.25.

A quick reference to the regions of diversity of cultivated plants and related wild species. Excludes most ornamentals, forest trees and lower plants.

Dictionary of Economic Plants

J. C. Th. Uphoff. 1968. 591 pp. $50.

An extensive dictionary of economic plants from around the world. 9,500 species listed.

A Dictionary of Plants Used by Man

George Usher. 1974. Hafner Press: NY. 619 pp.

Plants used for food, dyes, medicine, etc. Very brief comments for most, but some have a paragraph or more.

The Dictionary of Useful Plants

Nelson Coon. 1977. Dover Books. 290 pp.

Discussion of the various uses of over 500 species, mainly North American natives.

Drugs and Foods from Little-Known Plants

Notes in Harvard University Herbaria. Siri Von Reis Altschul. 1973. Harvard University Press: Cambridge. 366 pp.

Notes on uses of over 5,000 plant species. Sources of information are cited.

Economic Botany, Plants in our World

Beryl Brintall Simpson and Molly Conner Ogorzaly. 640 pp. $47 ppd. Available from Fruit & Spice Park See Mail-order Book Sources section.

Complete textbook, comprehensively written. Describes the plants importance to mankind. Areas of interest include spices, herbs, perfumes, beverages, fibers, dyes, timber, medicinal and edible plants.

Edible Nuts of the World

E. Menninger. 1977. Horticulture Books, PO Box 107, Stuart, Florida 33494.

The most comprehensive nut book I have ever seen. Fascinating details about hundreds of species, including tropical. Menninger also offers many other books on tropical plants.

Edible Plants of the World

E. Lewis Sturtevant, organized by U. P. Hedrick. 1919. Dover Publishing. 686 pp.

One of the first compendiums on the subject. 2,987 species are covered and Sturtevant gives a lot of information, including exact references for the information, and native ranges of plants. This book is easily obtainable through bookstores. An affordable Dover reprint.

Flowering Plants of the World

V. H. Heywood, ed. 1978. Mayflower Books: New York. 334 pp.

A visually beautiful and useful book with detailed plant illustrations. It gives an overview of all the plant families and many of the genera. Range maps are given for each family. The major economic and cultivated plants for each family are discussed briefly.

"Adopting a more strict definition of plants that fit into Man's economic activity, the numbers can be reduced to 1,000-2,000, and of these relatively few, about 100-200, are of major importance in world trade, while only 15 provide the bulk of the world's food crops—rice, wheat, corn, sorghum, barley, sugar cane and sugar beet, potato, sweet potato, cassava, beans, soya beans and peanut, coconut and banana."

"The Economic Significance of Plants and Their Constituents as Drugs"

P.P. Principe. 1989. Economic and Medicinal Plant Research. Vol. 4. pp. 1-17.

Forestry and Nutrition: A Reference Manual

FAO. 1989. Forests, Trees and People Programme: Rome. 114 pp. Copies are available on request from Forests, Trees and People Programme. See address in international organizations section.

An exciting book for ethnobotanists, nutritionists and those interested in traditional land management. The text is rather short and focuses on a brief overview of the links between forestry and nutrition.

The main part of this book is an annotated bibliography which includes 239 references on traditional foods, little-known economic plants, and resource management. Subject and geographic indices are included.

Goods From the Woods

John C. Ryan. 1991. Forests, Trees and People Newsletter. No. 14: pp. 23-30.

Insightful analysis of the historical shortcomings and potential benefits of extractive reserves for rubber, fruits, nuts and other minor forest products. Considers social, economic, and ecological aspects.

See article in Restoration Forestry, section 18.

The Healing Forest, Medicinal and Toxic Plants of Northwest Amazonia

Richard Evans Schultes and Robert F. Raffauf. 484 pp.

An extensive work on South American ethnobotany.

18

This book includes 1,479 species and variants, representing 596 genera in 145 plant families. The Amazon represents a storehouse of as much as 16% of the plant species existing on earth today. The native peoples of the area have retained their knowledge of the medicines and poisons derived from the diverse flora. The authors emphasize the importance of ethnobotanical conservation, and call attention to the fact that from these plants might come new chemical compounds of value to medicine and industry.

The Hidden Harvest: Wild Foods and Agricultural Systems, A Literature Review and Annotated Bibliography
Ian Scoones, Mary Melnyk and Jules N. Pretty. 1993. IIED: London. 260 pp.

A literature review and annotated bibliography of 971 references to wild foods. The publications reviewed are largely inventories of the important wild foods used in various countries.

Human Food Uses: A Cross-cultural Comprehensive Annotated Bibliography
Robert L. Freedman. 1981. Greenwood Press: Westport, Conn. 552 pp. $65.

An annotated bibliography of nearly 10,000 books, articles, dissertations, and audio-visual materials devoted to cultural aspects of nutrition that influence human lives around the world. Arranged alphabetically by author. The citations, most of which are descriptively annotated, cover literature from both the social and natural sciences on food use in every region of the globe. An exhaustive key-word index is included.

An Illustrated Dictionary of Chinese Medicinal Herbs
Wee Yeow and Hsuan Keng. 184 pp. $32.95 $3.00 postage. Available from Fruit & Spice Park [see Mail-order book sources section].

A superb guide and reference book with over 270 color photographs. This useful and beautifully produced book is essential for herbalists, gardeners, botanists and any student or practitioner of the healing arts. Each plant entry includes generic name, botanical family and scientific name. Includes plant part usage and purpose within and outside of Chinese medicine, information about the origin of the plant's scientific and common names, its physical attributes, anecdotes and history.

The Major Significance of 'Minor' Forest Products: The Local Use and Value of Forests in the Western African Humid Forest Zone
J. Falconer and R. S. Koppell. 1990. Community Forestry Note #6, Forests, Trees and People Programme, FAO: Rome. 230 pp.

A fascinating book for ethnobotanists, anthropologists and anyone interested in the local use and value of forests in the West African humid zone. Covers food, medicine, fuelwood, construction, equipment, utensils and cash income. The authors discuss the changes in forest resource use and forest degradation in recent decades, assess the value of non-timber forest products to local people, and recommend forestry activists geared to meeting people's needs. Useful appendices and an annotated bibliography.

Non-Timber Products From Tropical Forests
Daniel C. Nepstad and Stephan Schwartzman, eds. Available from: Scientific Publications Department, The New York Botanical Garden, Bronx, New York, 10458-5126. 176 pp.

A volume of The Advances in Economic Botany series that brings together an interdisciplinary array of information on extractive products and extractive economies.

Non-Timber Products From Tropical Forests
FAO. 1988. 183 pp.

Plants for Man
Robert W. Sckery. 1972. Prentice-Hall.

This encyclopedic work provides an overview of most economic plants of the world. Part II covers wood products and Part III covers such topics as exudates, latex, resins, and waxes.

Tanaka's Cyclopedia of Edible Plants of the World
Tyozaburo Tanaka. 1976. Keigaku Publishing Co.: Tokyo. 924 pp.

Tanaka lists about 10,000 species, the most extensive listing I have seen. Food uses and geographic range are given for some species, but many species are listed by name only. Common and latin names are given. An extensive bibliography is most helpful for further research.

Temperate Bamboo Quarterly
30 Myers Road, Summertown, Tennessee 38483.

A journal which began publishing in 1993.

Tropical Leaf Vegetables in Human Nutrition
H.A.P.C. Oomen, Grubben, 136 pp. $22 ppd. Available from Fruit & Spice Park. See Mail-order book sources section.

Valuable information about leaf vegetables.

Uncommon Fruits Worthy of Attention
Lee Reich. 273 pp.

Rare and unusual fruits for temperate climates. A practical gardening guide as well as a book for reading and savoring. Will help garden enthusiasts from novice to expert.

18

Useful Plants of Neotropical Origin and Their Wild
*   Relatives*
   Heinz Brucher. 1989. Springer-Verlag: Berlin. 296 pp.

A state-of-the-knowledge book on useful neotropical plants including aromatic and fleshy fruits, roots and tubers, tuberous, rhizomatic and aroid plants, farinacous, protein, and oil palms, industrially used plants, aromatics, narcotics, stimulants, and spices, pasture plants, and some timber trees.

Woodland Crafts in Britain
   Herbert L. Edlin. 1974. Country Book Club. 182 pp.

An excellent look at a culture centered on wood. Edlin is a well-known tree author and here he does an admirable job of describing, with many illustrations, England's traditional wood crafts, the foundations of which were laid before the industrial revolution. He describes in detail crafts and uses of wood such as: willow weaving, coppice, hurdles, hoops, crates, tanning, cleeving, shipbuilding, thatching, fuel, charcoal, homestead uses, herbs, dyes, resins, fence stakes, gun stocks, building, fences, wooden wheels, etc. Hundreds and hundreds of products. If you like to make things out of wood you will love this book.

References on Wildcrafting

Mushroom Mania:
A New Threat to Forests?

There are growing concerns about current widescale harvesting of edible mushrooms in forests. What are the ecological effects of a 25%, 50%, or even 75% reduction in successfully sporating mushrooms in a forest? Mycorrhizal fungi and other fungi are necessary components for forest health. With careful management, forests can produce sizable mushroom harvests. However, careful research is needed to determine allowable harvesting levels, fungi carrying capacity, and fungi management. The booklet by Molina and O'Dell reviewed below is one of the best looks at this concern to date.

Biology, Ecology, and Social Aspects of Wild Edible
Mushrooms in the Forests of the Pacific Northwest:
a Preface to Managing Commercial Harvest
   Randy Molina and Thomas O'Dell. 1993. Gen. Tech. Rep. PNW-GTR-309. Portland, OR: US Department of Agriculture, Forest Service, Pacific Northwest Research Station. 42 pp. (address in the U.S. Govt. Forest Agencies section).

The primary objectives of this paper are to provide information on the biology of forest fungi, describe the major edible fungi harvested in the Pacific Northwest, integrate a perspective on the social aspects of the mushroom harvest issue, summarize the development of the commercial mushroom industry, and suggest research and monitoring protocols for developing management guidelines.

Boughs, Beargrass, Mushrooms, and Native Plants:
A Workshop on Special Forest Products of the
Pacific Northwest
   Held August 14, 1992. Portland, Oregon. Contact: Western Forestry and Conservation Association, 4033 SW Canyon Road, Portland, OR 97221.

Coltsfoot
   Box 313A
   Shipman, Virginia 22971

One of my favorite plant reads. A grass-roots, homey newsletter written "in appreciation of wild plants" with articles on wildcrafting and uses of wild plants for food, medicine and crafts. Most contributors are from the eastern United States. James Troy, Editor. 6 issues a year. Publishing since 1980. Back issues are $2.00 each, or $10 for a set of six (one year).

Native Plants of Commercial Importance:
The Nomadic Life of the Professional Forager
   Richard Alan Miller. 1988. 327 pp. $16.95

An informative book on how to supplement rural income through the harvest of native plants. Examines more than 50 crops found wild in the US. Covers permits, harvesting, drying, and marketing.

Roots-An Underground Botany and Forager's Guide:
The Useful Wild Roots, Tubers, Corms and Rhi-
zomes of North America
   Douglas B. Elliott. 1976. The Chatham Press: Old Greenwich, CT. 128 pp.

The line drawings are fine examples of botanical illustration. This easy-to-read text covers descriptions, habitats and uses of the plants. Brief instructions on harvesting. A pleasant book which imparts information gracefully.

Wild Harvest
   Leonard Wiley. 1966. Portland, Oregon. 219 pp.

Especially relevant to maritime nor'westerners. Wiley traveled all over the Pacific Northwest researching and talking to wildcrafters. Subjects covered include seeds and cone collecting, evergreen foliage for florals, hardwood logs, burls, medicinals, wildflowers, Christmas trees and wild berries. For each product he notes harvesting directions, amounts harvested annually, and buyers in the PNW. Of course the prices have changed, but the down-to-earth information is still quite useful.

Wildcrafting: Harvesting the Wilds for a Living
   Jack McQuarrie. 1975. Capra Press: Santa Barbara, Calif. 96 pp.

18

Brush-picking, fruit-tramping, worm-grunting, and other nomadic livelihoods. Forest decorations, peeling cascara bark, pollen collecting, moss-gathering and collecting seed cones. Thin on practical information, but still a useful introduction to various wildcrafting activities.

Wildcrafters News
> P.O. Box 371
> Butte Falls, Oregon 97522
> Tel: (503) 865-3777

The town of Butte Falls is wildcrafting its way to economic freedom. The Big Butte Strategic Plan is the guide of this conservation-based effort. The community has implemented 25% of their actions, with forthcoming successes in Restoration/Stewardship, Eco-manufacturing, Wildcrafting, Nature Recreation, and Community Education/Special Events.

Turning Forestry Waste Into Livelihoods

Better utilization of wood waste from forestry activities offers a tremendous resource. Bearing always in mind that there has to be lots of biomass left in the forest for healthy ecological functioning. Most logging is done for prime sawlogs or in some areas for pulpwood. In either case, there are various amounts of wood left (oftentimes huge amounts). In some cases, this "slash" is piled and burnt; in other cases it is left to rot. The latter scenario is a preferable option from the forest's nutrient point of view. We can turn some of this waste wood into assets for our communities and provide more jobs while still leaving enough behind for a healthy forest.

Hummers, Inc.
> Reagan Wells Canyon, Box 122
> Uvalde, Texas 78801
> Tel: (512) 232-6167

One example of turning waste wood into jobs and wood crafts is Hummers, Inc. of Uvalde, Texas. To quote from a 1991 letter to Friends of the Trees from Jim Lee of Hummers, Inc.:

"We selectively harvest deadfall or free-standing dead timber in the forest. By selective I mean we take some and leave some everywhere we go. In addition we recycle wood from burn piles and land clearing (sic) operations. We also use timber which has fallen due to weather conditions or disease. From this material and from this material alone we hand-fashion one at a time, each of our original designs. No two are ever the same. Due to our special process we can use up to 95% of each piece of dead timber. The case in which this is not so is when we do turned objects.... We have proven that one can be in the wood business and still have extremely minimal impact on the forest and the earth. And remember, we have almost 200 accounts!"

The Hummers have sold over $500,000 worth of wood objects in the last 15 years, supporting a number of families in the process.

Speaking of non-timber products from trees, here are some over-looked values!

A recent environmental science textbook, Living in the Environment, by G. T. Miller. 1988. presents an estimate of the dollar value of commonly overlooked benefits provided by trees. An average tree, over a span of 50 years contributes $196,250 in benefits to its community. These benefits are produced as:

1. $31,250 worth of oxygen released into the air.
2. $31,250 worth of soil additives and erosion control.
3. $31,250 for fish and wildlife protection.
4. $37,500 for recycling water and controlling air temperature and humidity through transpiration.
5. $62,500 for control and reduction of air pollution.
6. $2,500 for other minor values.

18

19 Reference Section

Children of the Green Earth

Directories and Reference Books on Forestry

MANY DIRECTORIES AND REFERENCES are reviewed throughout *Restoration Forestry*. Here are a few which did not easily fit into another category.

Beacham's Guide to Environmental Issues and Sources

1993. Beacham Pub. 3,350 pages in 5 volumes. $240.

With 40,000 citations, this is likely the most comprehensive bibliography related to worldwide environmental issues, organized by topic and by type of source. Citations include books, general interest periodicals, environmental and professional journals, law journals, reports, federal government reports, and conference proceedings. The price tag will necessitate most people using public library copies.

Directory of Directories (3rd Edition)

1985. Gale Research Co. Book Tower: Detroit, Michigan 48226. 1325 pp.

7800 directories are listed. Revised periodically.

Directory of Environmental Information Sources

4th Edition. 1992. Government Institutes. 322 pages. $74.00. Available from Island Press.

This book details hard-to-find federal and state government resources, professional, scientific, and trade organizations; newsletters, magazines, periodicals, and an expanded section on databases.

Directory of the Forest Products Industry

Forest Industries Book Department, 500 Howard Street, San Francisco, CA 94105. 1988 edition was $127, (10-day free examination). 824 pages.

Source of information about every aspect of the forest industry: logging, pulpwood, lumber, plywood and boards. Lists 3100 mills, 9000 wood harvesting operations, secondary manufacturers, and 3600 wood products wholesalers etc. Lists addresses for 18000 key personnel, agencies, and organizations.

An English-Spanish Glossary of Terminology Used in Forestry, Range, Wildlife, Fishery, Soils and Botany

Alvin Leroy Medina, Range Scientist, Rocky Mountain Forest and Range Experiment Station, 1988, USDA Forest Service, General Technical Report RM-152, 240 W. Prospect St., Fort Collins, Colorado 80526. 54 pages.

French-Language Tropical Forestry Bibliography

See European Tropical Forest Research Network in the Tropical forestry Section.

Guide to Information Sources in the Botanical Sciences

Elisabeth B. Davis. 1987. Libraries Unlimited: PO Box 263, Littleton, CO 80160. 175 pp. $32.50.

A useful book for serious plant researchers, students, librarians, and botanists. Sections include Abstracts, Indexes, Databases, Current Awareness Sources, Dictionaries and Encyclopedias, Directories and Groups, Atlases, Field Guides, Floras, Keys and Manuals.

Guide to Sources for Agricultural and Biological Research

J. Richard Blanchard and Lois Farrell. 1981. University of California Press.

International Directory of Wildland Fire

1990. 671 pp. International Association of Wildland Fire, PO Box 328, Fairfield, Washington 99012. Tel: (509) 283-2397/Fax: (509) 283-2264

Possibly the largest directory of foresters in the world to date. From Inner Mongolia to New York, this directory covers the globe. An amazing example of how a few people with a computer can create the world's most comprehensive directory in a subject area.

This directory is handy for anyone concerned with forest research since the addresses can lead you to agencies, institutions, and professional forest managers around the world. The directory lists the names, addresses and telephone numbers of 5,500 managers, 3,400 academics, 1,200 women in fire studies, 3,000 organizations, 1,250 vendors and consultants, 1,700 educational institutions, 2,200 libraries, 200 granting agencies, and 500 journals and newsletters concerning wildland fire.

The book only gives the name, address, phone number and a few keywords for each entry. The book's usefulness would be greatly increased with additional annotation, and if cross indexed by nation, state/province, and by keyword. IAWF has a limited number of 1990 printed copies which they decline to sell, but will give away free if $6.00 postage is sent.

The above review pertains to the 1990 edition printed copy. The expanded and updated directory is available as an IBM disc program for $100. With the disc version you can do all sorts of specialized searches.

Macrocosm USA: An Environmental, Political, and Social Solutions Handbook with Directories

Sandi Brockway, ed., 1992. Macrocosm USA, Inc. PO Box 969, Cambria, CA 93428. 420 pp. $24.95. A 2nd edition will be published in 1994.

A book on the global movement for progressive change. *Macrocosm USA* contains more than 200 articles and over 5,000 listings of progressive organizations, periodicals, media outlets, businesses, publishers and reference sources. Currently, this is my favorite directory to a broad spectrum of social change groups. Unfortunately it has little coverage of agriculture and forestry.

Natural Resources and Earth Science

National Technical Information Service
5285 Port Royal Rd.
Springfield, Virginia 22161
Tel: (703) 487-4650

A newsletter and bibliography. $15/year

Terminology of Forestry and Related Subjects— English and French

Jean Eugene Gorse. 1987. Int'l Bank for Reconstruction and Development, 1818 H Street., N.W., Washington, D.C. 20433. 53 pp.

This edition is a thorough revision and expansion of its predecessor, *Forestry Terms*. In addition to numerous terms in the field of forestry, greater attention is paid to the expanding areas of environmental degradation, natural resource management, household energy, erosion control, desertification control, and rural development. The Glossary consists of two sections—English-French and French-English.

Who Is Who in Service to the Earth

1993. 2nd Edition. VisionLink Education Foundation, 181 Bio Dome Drive, Waynesville, NC 28786.

Who is Who in Service to the Earth is one of the most extensive guides to progressive movements. Strong on the USA, but includes many international listings also. It contains addresses and annotations for over 8,000 projects and organizations working for a positive future. It is weak on forestry and agriculture. Thank goodness, the 2nd edition has a country index.

World Directory of Environmental Research Centers

The Oryx Press. Distributed by R. R. Bowker Co.

World Resources 1992-93: A Guide to Global Environment

A report by the World Resources Institute with the United Nations Environment and Development Programmes. 1992. Oxford University Press: London and New York. 383 pp.

Full of facts and figures for all the nations of the world including land mass, forested area, arable land, etc. One of the most complete and up-to-date sources. This guide is designed to provide information on some of the most critical problems of our time and aid those who are striving to achieve sustainable development to alleviate poverty and preserve human and wildlife.

19

Bioregional and Conflict Resolution Resources

BIOREGION=LIFE-REGION. *Bioregion* is a little-known word as yet, however many people around the Earth are co-evolving bioregional concepts and philosophy. Bioregionalists have articulated many concepts, trends and proposals which restoration foresters should be aware of. Here are some of the leading sources of information on bioregional thought.

Bioregional Series

New Society Publishers
P.O. Box 189
Gabriola Island, British Columbia
CANADA V0R 1X0
Tel: (604) 247-9737/Fax: (604) 247-7471

The nine books thus far published in their Bioregional Series presents the most comprehensive look at bioregional concepts. Each book is a compilation of writers. Of particular note to restoration forestry are:

Living with the land: Communities Restoring the Earth
Christine Meyer and Faith Moosang, eds. 144 pp. C$11.95.

Case studies of restoration from around the globe. Stimulating and encouraging reading about environmental solutions from a cooperative perspective. Recommended.

Putting Power in its Place: Create Community Control
Christopher Plant and Judith Plant, eds. 1991. 144 pp. $C11.95.

Home! A Bioregional Reader
Van Andruss, Christopher Plant, Judith Plant and Eleanor Wright, eds. 192 pp. C$17.95

North American Bioregional Congress Turtle Island Bioregional Gathering

The North American Bioregional Congress (NABC) has been held every two years since 1984. At the fifth Congress, the name was changed to Turtle Island Bioregional Gathering (TIBG). The Proceedings of these gatherings chronicle the evolution of the bioregional movement as well as directories to organizations and individuals involved.

The 6th Turtle Island Bioregional Gathering will be held August 14-21, 1994, near Louisville, Kentucky. Contact: Shepard & Tracy Hendrickson, 341 N. Hamilton, Indianapolis, IN 46201. Tel: (317) 636-3977.

Planet Drum
P.O. Box 31251
San Francisco, California 94131
Tel: (415) 285-6556

Planet Drum's founder, Peter Berg, is the originator of the term "bioregion." Planet Drum is one of the main centers for bioregional networking. Each issue of their newsletter *Raise the Stakes* includes a directory to bioregional organizations and resources.

Dispute Mediation Resources

Alternative Dispute Resolution for the Community: An Annotated Bibliography
John Lover and Andrew Pirie. 1990. University of Victoria Institute for Dispute Resolution: Victoria, British Columbia.

Literature on alternative dispute resolution (ADR) is extensive and expanding rapidly. An annotated bibliography to over two hundred key ADR publications

"How to Evaluate Fairness in Forest Dispute Settlement Processes"
A special issue of *Forest Planning Canada*, Vol. 8 No. 3 (May/June 1992). See British Columbia Forestry Periodicals for address.

Articles on consensual approaches to resolving public forest disputes from the experts on mediation, facilitation, representation, information sharing, role of public officials and much more. It includes a helpful bibliography.

Mail-Order Sources of Forestry Books

agAccess

P.O. Box 2008

Davis, California 95617

Tel: (916) 756-7177/Fax (916) 756-7188

This is the best mail-order source of books on sustainable agriculture. They also have sections on trees, specialty crops, land restoration and other subjects of interest to tree people.

Agribookstore

Winrock International

1611 North Kent Street,

Arlington Virginia 22209-2134

Tel (703) 525-9455/Fax: (703) 424-1744. Email (Dialcom) 41:TCN408.

One of the largest selections of books on development, and agriculture available. They also carry titles in forestry and related disciplines. Many are published by governments, World Bank and large NGO's such as FAO, UNEP, UNESCO, IRRI, ICRISAT, Earthscan. The quality of the information and the politics of the books carried by Agribookstore vary widely, but it is a good place to see what is available.

Banyen Books

2671 West Broadway

Vancouver, British Columbia, V6K 2G2 CANADA

Tel: (604) 732-7912/Fax (604) 737-1636

Banyen Books is one of the premier metaphysical bookstores on the West Coast. They also have an excellent catalog of environmental literature: *Planet Earth Pages: Banyen Books' Guide to Environmental Literature.* Joel Russ and Kolin Lymworth, eds. 66 pp. 1992.

An annotated bibliography of 550 books in environmental and related fields including forests and forestry in North America, tropical rain forests, gardening and agriculture, land protection and ecological restoration, new economics, urban ecology, oceans, and many other categories. All books are available by mail order from Banyen Books.

BERNAN-UNIPUB

10033-F Martin Luther King Hwy.

Lanham, Maryland 20706-4391

Tel: (301) 459-7666

A mail-order book business specializing in government and international agency publications in agriculture, forestry, and related fields.

Books of The Big Outside

Ned Ludd Books

P.O. Box 85190

Tucson, Arizona 85754-5190

Over 400 Books, Maps, Cassettes & CD's. Books for the environmental activist. Excellent selection on biodiversity. Fair section on forestry matters.

Bullfrog Films

P.O. Box 149

Oley, Pennsylvania 19547

1-800-543-FROG

One of the best selections of environmental videos, films and videodisks. Films include Adrian Cowell's "The Decade of Destruction" (World Wide Fund for Nature). "Blowpipes and Bulldozers," about the Penan people of Malaysia. "On the Edge of the Forest," filmed in a virgin forest in Western Australia with E. F. Schumacher.

CHEC Catalog of Tools for Forest Activists

Cascade Holistic Economic Consultants

14417 SE Laurie

Oak Grove, Oregon 97267

Tel/Fax: (503) 652-7049

CHEC offers one of the most extensive mail-order selection of books on sustainable forestry management and the politics of timber.

The Environmental Book Finder

991 McLean St.

Dunedin, Florida 34098

Out-of-print books found.

19

Food and Agriculture Organization of the United Nations (FAO)

Distribution and Sales Section, FAO
Via delle Terme di Caracalla
00100 Rome, ITALY

Fruit & Spice Park

24801 S.W. 187th Ave.
Homestead, Florida 33031
Tel: (305) 247-5727

Offers many titles on tropical gardening, fruit-growing, medicinal plants. Also an extensive list of children books.

The International Association of Wildland Fire

P.O. Box 328
Fairfield, Washington 99012
Tel: (509) 283-2397/Fax: (509) 283-2264

The IAWF 1993 Book Catalog is 70 pp. + supplement. It lists hundreds of books about fire ecology, fire management, suppression, history, humor, software, videos and just about anything you want to know about wildfires. There is also a liberal sprinkling of books about forestry and forests that would be of interest to restoration foresters. From the tropics to the boreal.

Island Press

1718 Connecticut Ave., NW, Suite 300
Washington, DC 20009

One of the foremost publishers of books on sustainable development and environment, including forestry.

Natural History Book Service Ltd.

2 Wills Road,
Totnes, Devon TQ9 5XN, UNITED KINGDOM
Tel: 0803 865913/Fax: 0303 865280
GreenNet Mailbox: nhbs.

NHBS carries the largest selection of natural history and environmental books I've ever seen! *The Autumn/ Winter 1990/91 Environment Catalog* is massive. Large sections on forest and forestry (about 200 titles), as well as agriculture and environment, development, aquatic resources & management, energy, climate, regional studies, etc. Their *Natural History Catalog* contained descriptions of over 3,000 books and audio-visual materials on every aspect of natural history. Also noteworthy is NHBS's catalog of books on the "Philosophy and Theory of Sustainable Development."

NHBS was founded in 1985 to provide a book information and supply service for the world environmental community. The company is now firmly established as one of the world's leading suppliers of books to those involved in the study and protection of fauna and flora and their habitats and ecosystems. They are in regular contact with over 1000 publishers in the world and are agents for dozens of international agencies.

Patricia Ledlie Booksellers, Inc.

P.O. Box 90
Buckfield, Maine 04220
Tel/Fax: (207) 336-2778

Natural Science, Conservation and Biology Books. Each catalog features a different field. #51 is on oceans, estuaries, wetlands, rivers, lakes, vernal pools and South America. #52 is on mammals, insects, and other invertebrates.

Zed Books Ltd.

57 Caledonian Rd.
London, N1 9BU UNITED KINGDOM

Publishes many books in the development and environment fields.

Zed Books (US distributor)

171 1st Ave.
Atlantic Highlands, New Jersey 07716

Sources of Tree Seed

THE WORLD TRADE IN TREE SEED is staggering. There are hundreds of companies dealing in tree seed, international, national, regional and local. The amount of seed collected by individuals and farmers which never enters any formal accounting system is also quite large. Restoration forestry prefers a multitude of local seed companies instead of a few giant centralized ones. It is usually best to utilize local seeds from native species.

Having the world's genetic diversity at our fingertips has its good points (for those who can afford it), but it also has problems and responsibilities such as meticulous care not to spread invasive plants, insect pests or plant diseases when transporting seed and other plant material.

From 1978 to 1987, Friends of the Trees ran a seed service which sold seed for several hundred species of trees, shrubs, wildflowers and herbs, native and non-native. I collected much of the seeds which the Seed Service sold, but also purchased seed from several dozen seed companies. Over the course of my seed career I looked over hundreds of seed catalogs. Here are a few of my favorite sources and other references to introduce you to the world tree seed trade.

Useful Source Books & Sources of Tree Seed

Agroforestry Seed Information Clearing House
Dept. of Agronomy
University of the Philippines at Los Baños College
Laguna 3720, PHILIPPINES

ASEAN-Canada Forest Tree Seed Center
Muak-Lek
Saraburi 18180, THAILAND
Tel: (66-36) 341-305/Fax: (66-36) 341-859

Cornucopia: A Source Book of Edible Plants
Stephen Facciola. 1990. 675 pp. $37.75 ppd. Kampong Publications, 1870 Sunrise Drive, Vista, CA 92084.

This fantastic volume attempts to catalog all the edible plants sold in the USA and sources. It is the most extensive guide on the market. It covers about 3,000 species and many cultivars, especially tree crops and vegetables. Lists names and addresses of over 1,350 nurseries, seed companies and institutions, 150 of which are from outside the USA. Each plant is cross-referenced to the extensive bibliography.

Gardening by Mail
Barbara Barton. Third Edition 1990. $16.95. Tusker Press, PO Box 1338, Sebastopol, CA 95473. (707) 829-9189.

More than 1,000 nurseries and seed companies in the United States and Canada are indexed by plant specialty and location. Plus 280 plant and horticultural societies, 500 garden supply companies, 125 horticultural libraries, and 285 horticulture and gardening magazines. While the forester might not use this reference often, horticulturists will delight in it. A fourth edition is in preparation.

A Guide to Forest Seed Handling: With Special Reference to the Tropics
FAO. 1985. 94 pp. £15. Available from Natural History Book Service. See Book Sources sections.

Hortus Northwest: A Pacific Northwest Native Plant Directory
Dale Shank (ed.), P.O. Box 955, Canby, Oregon 97103. Tel: (503) 266-7968

Lists of nurseries offering native plants in the Pacific and Rocky Mountain regions. Advertising by restoration consultants and services.

Multipurpose Trees and Shrubs: Sources of Seeds and Inoculants
Peter G. Von Carlowitz. 1991. International Center for Research in Agroforestry. See Agroforestry section for address. 334 pp.

One of the best guides to sources of tree seed from around the world. Chapter 1 lists 670 species for which seed suppliers could be identified with information on seed prices, number of seeds per kg, usual germination

19

rates and pretreatment of seeds.

Chapter 2 contains names and addresses of 96 seed suppliers from around the world and information on seed purchase and delivery procedures.

Chapter 3 constitutes an aid to species preselection through site matching. It describes 115 species by those parameters relevant to their use in agroforestry systems.

Chapter 4 contains a "Master List of Multipurpose Trees" with about 1400 species and their reported uses.

Chapter 5 takes account of the increasing importance of microsymbionts for N-fixation, providing addresses of suppliers of inoculants and pure cultures and by explaining the principles of inoculation.

Nitrogen Fixing Tree Association (NFTA)
1010 Holumua Road
Paia, Hawaii 96779.
Tel: (808) 597-9568/Fax (808) 597-8516

Vol. 9, July 1991 of *Nitrogen Fixing Tree Research Reports* contains an extensive list of seed sources of NFTs. Many countries are included but Australia and India have the largest number of listings. Government institutions often provide seed without charge in small research quantities. Private institutions may provide small quantities free or offer an exchange of seeds.

Rare Seed Locaters, Ltd.
2140 Shattuck Ave., Drawer 2479
Berkeley, California 94704

If you can't find a seed source for some rare plant you're looking for, have Mr. Singh try to find it for you.

Tree Seed Newsletter
P.O. Box 906
Starkville, Mississippi 39759
Tel: (601) 323-8162

Newsletter for people interested in tree seeds in the American tropics.

World List of Seed Sources
E. Sgaravatti, ed. 1986. FAO Seed Service, Plant Production and Protection Division. Publications Division, FAO UN, via delle Terme di Caracalla, Rome. Italy. Available in the U.S. from agAccess for $68.

Addresses of over 3,000 institutions in more than 140 countries. Mostly food crops but also seed suppliers for forest trees, industrial crops, medicinal plants, ornamentals and inoculants for legumes.

Tree Seed Sources in the USA

Callahan Seeds
6045 Foley Lane
Central Point, Oregon 97502
Tel: (503) 855-1164

One of the most extensive selections of West Coast species of trees and shrubs. Offers small packets and bulk. Catalog: long SASE.

Carter Seeds
475 Mar Vista Drive
Vista, California 92083
Tel: (619) 724-5931

A wholesale seed company with a broad selection of ornamental trees, shrubs and California wildflowers. Free catalog.

Frosty Hollow Suppliers
P.O. Box 53
Langley, Washington 98260
Tel: (206) 579-2332

They offer wild-collected seed of Northwestern native trees, shrubs and wildflowers. They will do custom collecting. They also are restoration consultants. Send SASE for seed list.

Granite Seed
1697 West 2100 North
P.O. Box 177
Lehi, Utah 84043

They offer seed of a wide range of western native plant seed including trees, shrubs and many wildflowers.

Hurov's Tropical Seeds
P.O. Box 1596
Chula Vista, California 92012

Enormous selection of tropical seeds for sale. 6,000 species of mostly wild harvested seeds. Catalog $1.

Lawyer Seeds
Rt. 2, Box 95
Plains, Montana 59859
Tel: (406) 826-3881

One of the most extensive offerings of tree seed in the USA. Wholesale, pound lots only, minimum order $50. Montana might sound like an unlikely spot but they carry tree seed from around the world including subtropical species. Also carries a large selection of hardy nursery stock. Free catalog.

Native Seed Foundation
Star Rt.
Moyie Springs, Idaho 83845
Tel: (208) 267-7938

Supplier of bulk seed for shrubs and trees native to the inter-mountain Northwest States.

Nitrogen Fixing Tree Association
Address in previous section on Seed Source Books.

NFTA provides small quantities of tree seed to Associates for field trials or demonstrations. Seed is sent free to

Associates in the USA and in countries where phytosanitary certificates are not required, but US$25 is charged for each shipment to countries that require a certificate from the United States Department of Agriculture (USDA). IF NFTA cannot supply seed, they offer suggestions for alternative seed sources.

F. W. Schumacher Co. Inc.

Sandwich, Massachusetts 02563.

"Seeds for Nurserymen and Foresters" from around the world. By the ounce, quarter pound and pound. Wide selection of U.S. and non-native trees for temperate climates.

World Seed Service

P.O. Box 1058

Redwood City, California 94064

J. L Hudson's World Seed Service is one of my favorite seed companies. They offer a large selection of vegetable, flower, tree, ornamental, and many rare, unusual, hard-to-find seeds from around the world. Lots of useful plant information. Catalog $1.

Overseas Tree Seed Sources

AgroForester Tropical Seeds

75-5260 Mamalahoa Highway

Holualoa, Hawaii 96725 USA

Tel: (808) 326-4670/Fax (808) 326-7648

email: agroforester@igc.apc.org.

A cornucopia of multipurpose species with a permaculture emphasis. Distributes seed internationally. Selected genetic material with improved growth, insect resistance, etc.

Inland & Foreign Trading Co.

Block 79A, #04-418/420, Indus Rd.

SINGAPORE 0316

Tel: 2722711.

They carry a wide selection of tree and shrub seed as well as pasture and legume seeds.

Latin American Forest Tree Seed Bank

CATIE, Turrialba, COSTA RICA

SETROPA

P.O. Box 203

1400 AE Bussum, THE NETHERLANDS

Sells seeds for Forestry and Environmental Conservation.

Tree Seed Center

CSIRO Division of Forest Research

P.O. Box 4008, Queen Victoria Terrace

Canberra, ACT 2600, AUSTRALIA

Tel: (062) 818211

The Tree Seed Centre of Australia's Commonwealth Scientific and Industrial Research Organization (CSIRO) makes available high-quality seed for research projects and pilot plantations in developing countries in Asia, the South Pacific and Africa.

Versepuy

Le Ridereau

Andard

49800 Trelaze, FRANCE

Vilmorin-Andrieux et Cie

Poste 399

La Menitré—49520 Beaufrot-En-Valleé, FRANCE

The above two French seed houses are both large, international seed houses offering a huge variety of tree seed from around the world.

19

Author Biographies

FOLLOWING ARE BRIEF BIOGRAPHIES of the 47 authors in Restoration Forestry. See the author index at the back of the book for page numbers of their articles and references to their work. The asterisk (*) denotes people who were participants of the 1990 Restoration Forestry Conference.

*Mike Amaranthus is an authority on forest ecology and soils, currently working for the U.S. Forest Service in the Siskiyou National Forest. Amaranthus is part of the ecology team from Oregon State University, Corvallis.

Kat Anderson is an ethnobotanist with a doctorate from University of California, Berkeley. Her field is the native Californian uses of plants, pre-contact management and proto-horticultural practices. Anderson has spent years of research, experimentation and communication with many Native Americans, principally in California.

*Tyhson Banighen is a forest trust consultant and the Director of Turtle Island Earth Stewards of Vancouver, British Columbia. Banighen is one of the foremost authorities on forest land trusts on the West Coast of Canada and the U.S.

Delores Broten is a resident of Cortes Island, located off the east coast of Vancouver island, British Columbia. Broten is a writer on forestry and forest issues and editor of the Watershed Sentinel.

*Robert Brothers is a long-time forest activist working with Headwaters Alliance to protect the Siskiyou forests.

*Orville Camp is the originator of "Natural Selection Ecoforestry" and one of the most well-known restoration foresters in the Pacific Northwest. Over the past 25 years, Camp has restored his own clearcut forest land and now teaches natural selection ecoforestry at his Camp Forest Farm in Selma, Oregon and elsewhere in the Pacific Northwest. Camp is the author of *The Forest Farmer's Handbook: A Guide to Natural Selection Management* .

*Ken Carloni is the owner/manager of Wild Plant Nursery in Roseburg, Oregon.

Denise DeMarie is an innovator in papermaking, using many species of grasses and herbaceous plants. DeMarie lives in coastal Oregon.

Dennis P. Dykstra is a Professor of Forest Engineering at Northern Arizona University.

*Steve Erickson is a consultant and contractor for native plant restoration in the Pacific Northwest. He is co-owner of Frosty Hollow Seed Company. As a forest activist, Erickson is a thorn in the side of the Puget Sound forest establishment.

*Tim Foss is a professional forester for the Wenatchee National Forest, currently working in the wilderness section. He is an advocate for change from within the National Forest Service and a frequent contributor to The *Inner Voice*.

Hector Franco—Fire was one of the primary tools used by the native people who tended the giant forests of the Kings Canyon and Sequoia National Park areas. The Wukchumni and other Yokuts people traditionally used fire as a forest management tool in California's San Joaquin Valley. Hector Franco preserves some of his elder's stories of the old ways of burning and tending the land with care and reverence.

Jerry F. Franklin is Bloedel Professor of Ecosystem Analysis at the College of Forest Resources, University of Washington, Seattle and the Chief Plant Ecologist for the USDA Forest Service, Pacific Northwest Region. Franklin coined the term "New Forestry" and is one of the main people developing its concepts and practices. Franklin is one of the most influential forest ecologists in the PNW.

*Matthew Hall is an English forester experienced in management of farm woodlands and arboriculture. Hall does forestry consulting, horse-logging and selection logging in the Willamette Valley, Oregon. Hall teaches courses in environmental forestry through the Aprovecho Institute of Roseburg, Oregon.

Herb Hammond is a registered professional forester

with a Masters of Forestry in silviculture and forest ecology. Hammond is the founder of the Silva Forest Foundation, which since 1977, has specialized in holistic forest use particularly for community groups and Native bands. Hammond is knowledgeable, articulate, and a well-known figure in B.C. for his stand against current industrial forestry practices. He is author of *Seeing the Forest Among the Trees: The Case for Holistic Forest Use* and co-author with his wife Susan, of *B.C. Community Guide to the Forest.*

Marco Hawk-Lowenstein coordinates the Public Forestry Foundation's southwest activities. He is fluent in written and spoken Spanish, having worked in agroforestry in Colombia and Costa Rica. He has done extensive fieldwork in community forestry and has also published numerous articles. He has worked as a forestry consultant in Oregon and New Mexico.

Rudolf Heinrich is Chief of the FAO Forest Harvesting and Transport Branch.

*Jan Iris, with his wife ***Peggy Iris**, founded Wild Iris Forestry, a small family, holistic forestry business. Jan passed away in 1992. Restoration forestry will miss Jan's talents and hands-on forestry knowledge. Peggy Iris carries on the work and the business.

*Roy Keene has worked as a logger, timber cruiser and consulting forester for 25 years. He has driven over a million miles in Regions 5 and 6 and has been on almost every Forest Service road system at least once. Keene is a Founder of, and volunteer executive director for, the Public Forestry Foundation, in Eugene, Oregon.

Matthew Kimble is a doctoral candidate in Forest Biology and Conservation at the Department of Forest Biology, University of Washington, Seattle.

Rosemary LaVernier is a writer and resident of North Idaho.

Dennis Martinez is an indigenous forest restorationist and a West Coast authority on restoration ecology. Martinez is the Northwestern U.S. Regional Representative for the Society for Ecosystem Restoration, a member of the American Indian Cultural Affairs Center in Talent, Oregon, and restoration consultant to the InterTribal Sinkyone Wilderness Council.

Chris Maser is a freelance consultant on sustainable forestry. Maser worked as a research scientist for the U.S. Department of the Interior Bureau of Land Management for 17 years, spending the last seven years studying the old-growth forest of western Oregon. Maser has published over 170 research papers. An articulate, moving speaker and writer, Maser is the author of *The Redesigned Forest, The Forest Primeval,* and *Global Imperative: Harmonizing Culture and Nature.*

Mark McCalmon is Chief Forester for the City of Seattle's watershed forest holdings. McCalman is developing innovative forest harvesting practices, combined with selection management and preservation areas.

Jefferson Mecham is a forester who works in the fields of permaculture and international development. Mecham is currently directing a large-scale permaculture project in Ecuador.

Dr. Leon Minckler is a retired Forest Service employee with 33 years of experience at four southeastern forest experiment stations, researching silvicultural treatments and ecology of hardwoods. Minckler is a well-known proponent of selection management in eastern forests, and the author of *Woodland Ecology.*

Merilio Morell is a Forestry Officer in Policy and Institutions Branch of the FAO Forestry Department, Rome, Italy.

Gary Paul Nabhan is one of the most knowledgeable and respected researchers and writers on ethnobotany and native land management in the southwest states and adjacent Mexico. Nabhan is a co-founder of Native Seeds/SEARCH, an organization preserving cultivated plant diversity of Native Americans. Nabhan is research Director at the Desert Botanical Garden in Tucson. His writings include *The Desert Smells Like Rain*, and *Gathering the Desert.*

Reed Noss is one of the most influential thinkers and writers on biodiversity and large-scale wilderness restoration in the U.S.

Julio Ocaña-Vidal is Director of the governing committee of Associacíon Amazonia, based in Lima, Peru.

*David Perry is Professor of Ecosystem Studies in the Department of Forestry at Oregon State University. He is well-known for his contributions to the development of New Forestry. Perry is a major authority regarding forest ecology and biodiversity in old-growth forests. He has authored, co-authored and edited many publications.

*Michael Pilarski is a grassroots, international networker for the forests with his roots in the interior Pacific Northwest. Pilarski founded Friends of the Trees Society in 1978, and is the editor of *Restoration Forestry.*

Alfredo Quarto is the Founder/Director of the Mangrove Action Project. From his home on the Olympic Peninsula in Washington State, Quarto travels to mangrove communities around the world to work for their preservation and sustainable use.

Marie Reeder is a freelance writer who lives in a commercial forest area of southwestern Oregon. In the past she has served as coordinator of Southern Oregon NCAP (National Coalition Against Pesticides), board member of

19

Headwaters, and Public Education Director for 1000 Friends of Oregon.

Gordon Robinson has been a forester for over half a century and worked in many parts of the U.S. Robinson is the author of *Excellent Forestry* and has been an influential voice for restoration forestry for decades.

John C. Ryan is a research associate at the Worldwatch Institute. His work focuses on forests and biological diversity.

Gary Schneider is one of the most active people in the Environmental Coalition of Prince Edward Island. Schneider is the editor of the *ECOPEI Newsletter* and is developing the Macphail Woods Ecological Forestry Project on a 140-acre property in Orwell.

Timothy D. Schowalter is with the Entomology Department at Oregon State University at Corvallis.

Michael G. Smith has formal training in engineering and ecology. He has worked with experimental building, sustainable development, forest management, permaculture and conservation in North and Central America.

Walton R. Smith is a retired career forester in the U.S. Forest Service. He has been a long time proponent of selective harvesting, which he has been using on his Waldee Forest in North Carolina for over 40 years.

Torolf Torgerson is a research ecologist from the U.S. Forest Service Pacific Northwest Research Station in La Grande, Oregon. Torgerson has made many contributions to our understanding of the roles insects, ants and birds play in forest functioning in eastside PNW forests.

Nancy Turner is a Professor in the Environmental Studies Department at the University of Victoria, British Columbia, and one of B.C.'s foremost ethnobotanists. She has spent many years working closely with individuals from many tribes in British Columbia.

*Mark Wigg is a forest economist and consultant in Oregon.

*Merv Wilkinson is an outspoken British Columbia forestland owner, who is well known for his success with uneven-aged management of mature Douglas-fir forests. Merv has lived and worked for more than 50 years at Wildwood, his 55-hectare forest near Ladysmith on Vancouver Island. Wilkinson's work is featured in the book *Wildwood* and in the video, *Thinking Like a Forest*.

George Wuerthner is a conservationist, writer and photographer in Livingston, Montana.

Robert Zahner was a professor of forestry at Clemson University specializing in the ecology of southern Appalachian hardwoods until his retirement in 1988.

19

Friends of the Trees Society's Services and Publications

Friends of the Trees Society

Inspiring, empowering, and informing people in their efforts to plant more trees and heal the planet.

Christine Howe

FRIENDS OF THE TREES SOCIETY is dedicated to world reforestation. Founded in 1978, the Society has helped thousands of people from many countries in their efforts for the trees and the Earth. Friends of the Trees Society (FTS) has sponsored plant exchanges, seed companies, tree sales, tree festivals; published newsletters and books; and organized numerous workshops, seminars, conferences and events. Networking has been a major focus

Everyone can plant trees. Do your part to help re-green the planet. Write and tell us what you are doing for the trees. Suggest ways for us to cooperate. How can Friends of the Trees serve you?

The Society's current projects and publications include the following.

Travelers' Earth Repair Network

The Travelers' Earth Repair Network (TERN) is a Friends of the Trees Society service started in 1990. TERN links travelers with individuals and organizations in countries around the world who are involved with sustainable forestry, sustainable agriculture, permaculture, restoration and related activities.

Currently, there are over 2,000 addresses in our TERN database from over 100 countries. TERN provides the traveler with a detailed list of contacts in the designated region(s) of travel. The TERN network includes over 150 TERN Hosts who offer living arrangements and opportunity for hands-on involvement to travelers. Many TERN Hosts in the USA and Canada are organic farmers who take apprentices.

Using TERN is an excellent way to travel, gain valuable experience, and help the Earth, all at the same time! If you are interested in being a TERN Host or Traveler send for application forms. We are happy to hear from people in all countries.

Travelers fee : $50, students $35. Hosts listed free

Permaculture Design Courses

Permaculture is the design of sustainable human habitats. Friends of the Trees Society has been involved in permaculture education since 1981. FTS director, Michael Pilarski, has taught design courses in the US, Canada, Belize, and Nepal. Permaculture design courses (average two weeks long) are the main educational tool of the permaculture movement and are especially useful to anyone interested in sustainable systems design. Some areas covered in the courses are permaculture principles and methodology, integrated systems design, ethnobotany, agroforestry, restoration forestry, small-scale energy systems, organic agriculture, water control, urban food production, village development and many other topics. Let us know if you are interested in sponsoring a permaculture design course in you state or country. Contact Friends of the Trees for dates of our next round of seminars and courses.

International Green Front Report

Michael Pilarski, editor. 1988. Friends of the Trees Society. 196 pages. $8.00 postpaid in the U.S. & Canada. Overseas US$9 surface mail.

The *International Green Front Report* is Friends of the Trees Society's first international resource guide. 500 organizations and 350 books/periodicals are reviewed. The *Green Front Report* covers a wide subject area concerned with trees, plants, and sustainable agriculture. Some particularly noteworthy sections include "World Reforestation," "Sustainable Land Use in Arid and Semi-arid Lands," "Fruits and Nuts," "Plant Societies," and "Plant Species Indexes."

"Among the 1,300 documents received by the SATIS secretariat this year, this is the most outstanding... This book is an essential part of every information center known to SATIS."

19

Kiwifruit Enthusiasts Journal, Vol. 6

 Michael Pilarski and Bob Glanzman, editors. 1993.
 Friends of the Trees Society. 196 pages. $17 postpaid
 in the U.S. & Canada. Overseas US$19 surface mail.

In 1984, Friends of the Trees published the first issue of
the *Actinidia Enthusiasts Newsletter*. *Actinidia* is the botanical name for kiwifruit and its hardy relatives. Each issue
became larger and more international. In the 6th Issue we
changed the name to *Kiwifruit Enthusiasts Journal* (*KEJ*).
KEJ is the world's leading source of information on
growing hardy kiwifruit (primarily *Actinidia arguta, A.
kolomikta, A. polygama, A. purpurea* and *A. melanandra*), as
well as much information on growing kiwifruit (*Actinidia
deliciosa* and *A. chinensis*) . *KEJ* #6 includes articles by
leading experts and researchers from around the world
(over 100 contributors); the latest on hardy kiwifruit and
kiwifruit varieties; practical details on planting, trellising,
pruning, training, fertilizing, organic growing, and propagation; reports on *Actinidia* growing in New Zealand, the
USA, British Columbia, Chile, Russia, the Ukraine and
other countries; and, the most complete guide to sources
of plants in the USA & Canada.

 Send orders and correspondence to:
 Friends of the Trees Society
 P.O. Box 1064
 Tonasket, Washington 98855
 Tel/Fax: (509) 485-2705

19

20 Indices

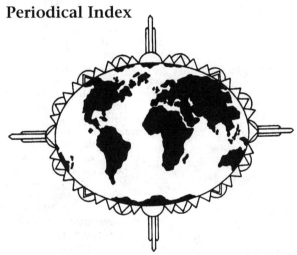

Index

General Index

Book Index

Film and Video Index

Organization Index

Periodical Index

Notes

Notes